Introduction

to Linear Optimization

ATHENA SCIENTIFIC SERIES
IN OPTIMIZATION AND NEURAL COMPUTATION

1. Dynamic Programming and Optimal Control, Vols. I and II, by Dimitri P. Bertsekas, 1995.

2. Nonlinear Programming, by Dimitri P. Bertsekas, 1995.

3. Neuro-Dynamic Programming, by Dimitri P. Bertsekas and John N. Tsitsiklis, 1996.

4. Constrained Optimization and Lagrange Multiplier Methods, by Dimitri P. Bertsekas, 1996.

5. Stochastic Optimal Control: The Discrete-Time Case, by Dimitri P. Bertsekas and Steven E. Shreve, 1996.

6. Introduction to Linear Optimization, by Dimitris Bertsimas and John N. Tsitsiklis, 1997.

Introduction
to Linear Optimization

Dimitris Bertsimas
John N. Tsitsiklis

Massachusetts Institute of Technology

 Athena Scientific, Belmont, Massachusetts

Athena Scientific
Post Office Box 391
Belmont, Mass. 02178-9998
U.S.A.

Email: athenasc@world.std.com
WWW information and orders: http://world.std.com/~athenasc/

Cover Design: *Ann Gallager*

Publisher's Cataloging-in-Publication Data

Bertsimas, Dimitris, Tsitsiklis, John N.
Introduction to Linear Optimization
Includes bibliographical references and index
1. Linear programming. 2. Mathematical optimization.
3. Integer programming. I. Title.
T57.74.B465 1997   519.7   96-78786

ISBN 1-886529-19-1

To Georgia,
and to George Michael, who left us so early
To Alexandra and Melina

Contents

Preface

The purpose of this book is to provide a unified, insightful, and modern treatment of linear optimization, that is, linear programming, network flow problems, and discrete linear optimization. We discuss both classical topics, as well as the state of the art. We give special attention to theory, but also cover applications and present case studies. Our main objective is to help the reader become a sophisticated practitioner of (linear) optimization, or a researcher. More specifically, we wish to develop the ability to formulate fairly complex optimization problems, provide an appreciation of the main classes of problems that are practically solvable, describe the available solution methods, and build an understanding of the qualitative properties of the solutions they provide.

Our general philosophy is that insight matters most. For the subject matter of this book, this necessarily requires a geometric view. On the other hand, problems are solved by algorithms, and these can only be described algebraically. Hence, our focus is on the beautiful interplay between algebra and geometry. We build understanding using figures and geometric arguments, and then translate ideas into algebraic formulas and algorithms. Given enough time, we expect that the reader will develop the ability to pass from one domain to the other without much effort.

Another of our objectives is to be comprehensive, but economical. We have made an effort to cover and highlight all of the principal ideas in this field. However, we have not tried to be encyclopedic, or to discuss every possible detail relevant to a particular algorithm. Our premise is that once mature understanding of the basic principles is in place, further details can be acquired by the reader with little additional effort.

Our last objective is to bring the reader up to date with respect to the state of the art. This is especially true in our treatment of interior point methods, large scale optimization, and the presentation of case studies that stretch the limits of currently available algorithms and computers.

The success of any optimization methodology hinges on its ability to deal with large and important problems. In that sense, the last chapter, on the art of linear optimization, is a critical part of this book. It will, we hope, convince the reader that progress on challenging problems requires both problem specific insight, as well as a deeper understanding of the underlying theory.

In any book dealing with linear programming, there are some important choices to be made regarding the treatment of the simplex method. Traditionally, the simplex method is developed in terms of the full simplex tableau, which tends to become the central topic. We have found that the full simplex tableau is a useful device for working out numerical examples. But other than that, we have tried not to overemphasize its importance.

Let us also mention another departure from many other textbooks. Introductory treatments often focus on standard form problems, which is sufficient for the purposes of the simplex method. On the other hand, this approach often leaves the reader wondering whether certain properties are generally true, and can hinder the deeper understanding of the subject. We depart from this tradition: we consider the general form of linear programming problems and define key concepts (e.g., extreme points) within this context. (Of course, when it comes to algorithms, we often have to specialize to the standard form.) In the same spirit, we separate the structural understanding of linear programming from the particulars of the simplex method. For example, we include a derivation of duality theory that does not rely on the simplex method.

Finally, this book contains a treatment of several important topics that are not commonly covered. These include a discussion of the column geometry and of the insights it provides into the efficiency of the simplex method, the connection between duality and the pricing of financial assets, a unified view of delayed column generation and cutting plane methods, stochastic programming and Benders decomposition, the auction algorithm for the assignment problem, certain theoretical implications of the ellipsoid algorithm, a thorough treatment of interior point methods, and a whole chapter on the practice of linear optimization. There are also several noteworthy topics that are covered in the exercises, such as Leontief systems, strict complementarity, options pricing, von Neumann's algorithm, submodular function minimization, and bounds for a number of integer programming problems.

Here is a chapter by chapter description of the book.

Chapter 1: Introduces the linear programming problem, together with a number of examples, and provides some background material on linear algebra.

Chapter 2: Deals with the basic geometric properties of polyhedra, focusing on the definition and the existence of extreme points, and emphasizing the interplay betwen the geometric and the algebraic viewpoints.

Chapter 3: Contains more or less the classical material associated with the simplex method, as well as a discussion of the column geometry. It starts with a high-level and geometrically motivated derivation of the simplex method. It then introduces the revised simplex method, and concludes with the simplex tableau. The usual topics of Phase I and anticycling are also covered.

Chapter 4: It is a comprehensive treatment of linear programming duality. The duality theorem is first obtained as a corollary of the simplex method. A more abstract derivation is also provided, based on the separating hyperplane theorem, which is developed from first principles. It ends with a deeper look into the geometry of polyhedra.

Chapter 5: Discusses sensitivity analysis, that is, the dependence of solutions and the optimal cost on the problem data, including parametric programming. It also develops a characterization of dual optimal solutions as subgradients of a suitably defined optimal cost function.

Chapter 6: Presents the complementary ideas of delayed column generation and cutting planes. These methods are first developed at a high level, and are then made concrete by discussing the cutting stock problem, Dantzig-Wolfe decomposition, stochastic programming, and Benders decomposition.

Chapter 7: Provides a comprehensive review of the principal results and methods for the different variants of the network flow problem. It contains representatives from all major types of algorithms: primal descent (the simplex method), dual ascent (the primal-dual method), and approximate dual ascent (the auction algorithm). The focus is on the major algorithmic ideas, rather than on the refinements that can lead to better complexity estimates.

Chapter 8: Includes a discussion of complexity, a development of the ellipsoid method, and a proof of the polynomiality of linear programming. It also discusses the equivalence of separation and optimization, and provides examples where the ellipsoid algorithm can be used to derive polynomial time results for problems involving an exponential number of constraints.

Chapter 9: Contains an overview of all major classes of interior point methods, including affine scaling, potential reduction, and path following (both primal and primal-dual) methods. It includes a discussion of the underlying geometric ideas and computational issues, as well as convergence proofs and complexity analysis.

Chapter 10: Introduces integer programming formulations of discrete optimization problems. It provides a number of examples, as well as some intuition as to what constitutes a "strong" formulation.

Chapter 11: Covers the major classes of integer programming algorithms, including exact methods (branch and bound, cutting planes, dynamic programming), approximation algorithms, and heuristic methods (local search and simulated annealing). It also introduces a duality theory for integer programming.

Chapter 12: Deals with the art in linear optimization, i.e., the process of modeling, exploiting problem structure, and fine tuning of optimization algorithms. We discuss the relative performance of interior point methods and different variants of the simplex method, in a realistic large scale setting. We also give some indication of the size of problems that can be currently solved.

An important theme that runs through several chapters is the modeling, complexity, and algorithms for problems with an exponential number constraints. We discuss modeling in Section 10.3, complexity in Section 8.5, algorithmic approaches in Chapter 6 and 8.5, and we conclude with a case study in Section 12.5.

There is a fair number of exercises that are given at the end of each chapter. Most of them are intended to deepen the understanding of the subject, or to explore extensions of the theory in the text, as opposed to routine drills. However, several numerical exercises are also included. Starred exercises are supposed to be fairly hard. A solutions manual for qualified instructors can be obtained from the authors.

We have made a special effort to keep the text as modular as possible, allowing the reader to omit certain topics without loss of continuity. For example, much of the material in Chapters 5 and 6 is rarely used in the rest of the book. Furthermore, in Chapter 7 (on network flow problems), a reader who has gone through the problem formulation (Sections 7.1-7.2) can immediately move to any later section in that chapter. Also, the interior point algorithms of Chapter 9 are not used later, with the exception of some of the applications in Chapter 12. Even within the core chapters (Chapters 1-4), there are many sections that can be skipped during a first reading. Some sections have been marked with a star indicating that they contain somewhat more advanced material that is not usually covered in an introductory course.

The book was developed while we took turns teaching a first-year graduate course at M.I.T., for students in engineering and operations research. The only prerequisite is a working knowledge of linear algebra. In fact, it is only a small subset of linear algebra that is needed (e.g., the concepts of subspaces, linear independence, and the rank of a matrix). However, these elementary tools are sometimes used in subtle ways, and some mathematical maturity on the part of the reader can lead to a better appreciation of the subject.

The book can be used to teach several different types of courses. The first two suggestions below are one-semester variants that we have tried at M.I.T., but there are also other meaningful alternatives, depending on the students' background and the course's objectives.

(a) Cover most of Chapters 1-7, and if time permits, cover a small number of topics from Chapters 9-12.

(b) An alternative could be the same as above, except that interior point algorithms (Chapter 9) are fully covered, replacing network flow problems (Chapter 7).

(c) A broad overview course can be constructed by concentrating on the easier material in most of the chapters. The core of such a course could consist of Chapter 1, Sections 2.1-2.4, 3.1-3.5, 4.1-4.3, 5.1, 7.1-7.3, 9.1, 10.1, some of the easier material in Chapter 11, and an application from Chapter 12.

(d) Finally, the book is also suitable for a half-course on integer programming, based on parts of Chapters 1 and 8, as well as Chapters 10-12.

There is a truly large literature on linear optimization, and we make no attempt to provide a comprehensive bibliography. To a great extent, the sources that we cite are either original references of historical interest, or recent texts where additional information can be found. For those topics, however, that touch upon current research, we also provide pointers to recent journal articles.

We would like to express our thanks to a number of individuals. We are grateful to our colleagues Dimitri Bertsekas and Rob Freund, for many discussions on the subjects in this book, as well as for reading parts of the manuscript. Several of our students, colleagues, and friends have contributed by reading parts of the manuscript, providing critical comments, and working on the exercises: Jim Christodouleas, Thalia Chryssikou, Austin Frakt, David Gamarnik, Leon Hsu, Spyros Kontogiorgis, Peter Marbach, Gina Mourtzinou, Yannis Paschalidis, Georgia Perakis, Lakis Polymenakos, Jay Sethuraman, Sarah Stock, Paul Tseng, and Ben Van Roy. But mostly, we are grateful to our families for their patience, love, and support in the course of this long project.

Dimitris Bertsimas
John N. Tsitsiklis
Cambridge, January 1997

Chapter 1

Introduction

Contents

In this chapter, we introduce *linear programming*, the problem of minimizing a linear cost function subject to linear equality and inequality constraints. We consider a few equivalent forms and then present a number of examples to illustrate the applicability of linear programming to a wide variety of contexts. We also solve a few simple examples and obtain some basic geometric intuition on the nature of the problem. The chapter ends with a review of linear algebra and of the conventions used in describing the computational requirements (operation count) of algorithms.

1.1   Variants of the linear programming problem

In this section, we pose the linear programming problem, discuss a few special forms that it takes, and establish some standard notation that we will be using. Rather than starting abstractly, we first state a concrete example, which is meant to facilitate understanding of the formal definition that will follow. The example we give is devoid of any interpretation. Later on, in Section 1.2, we will have ample opportunity to develop examples that arise in practical settings.

Example 1.1 The following is a linear programming problem:

$$
\begin{array}{rrcrcrcrcl}
\text{minimize} & 2x_1 & - & x_2 & + & 4x_3 & & & & \\
\text{subject to} & x_1 & + & x_2 & & & + & x_4 & \leq & 2 \\
& & & 3x_2 & - & x_3 & & & = & 5 \\
& & & & & x_3 & + & x_4 & \geq & 3 \\
& x_1 & & & & & & & \geq & 0 \\
& & & & & x_3 & & & \leq & 0.
\end{array}
$$

Here x_1, x_2, x_3, and x_4 are variables whose values are to be chosen to minimize the linear cost function $2x_1 - x_2 + 4x_3$, subject to a set of linear equality and inequality constraints. Some of these constraints, such as $x_1 \geq 0$ and $x_3 \leq 0$, amount to simple restrictions on the sign of certain variables. The remaining constraints are of the form $\mathbf{a}'\mathbf{x} \leq b$, $\mathbf{a}'\mathbf{x} = b$, or $\mathbf{a}'\mathbf{x} \geq b$, where $\mathbf{a} = (a_1, a_2, a_3, a_4)$ is a given vector[1], $\mathbf{x} = (x_1, x_2, x_3, x_4)$ is the vector of decision variables, $\mathbf{a}'\mathbf{x}$ is their inner product $\sum_{i=1}^{4} a_i x_i$, and b is a given scalar. For example, in the first constraint, we have $\mathbf{a} = (1, 1, 0, 1)$ and $b = 2$.

We now generalize. In a *general* linear programming problem, we are given a cost vector $\mathbf{c} = (c_1, \ldots, c_n)$ and we seek to minimize a linear cost function $\mathbf{c}'\mathbf{x} = \sum_{i=1}^{n} c_i x_i$ over all n-dimensional vectors $\mathbf{x} = (x_1, \ldots, x_n)$,

---

[1] As discussed further in Section 1.5, all vectors are assumed to be column vectors, and are treated as such in matrix-vector products. Row vectors are indicated as transposes of (column) vectors. However, whenever we refer to a vector $\mathbf{x}$ inside the text, we use the more economical notation $\mathbf{x} = (x_1, \ldots, x_n)$, even though $\mathbf{x}$ is a column vector. The reader who is unfamiliar with our notation may wish to consult Section 1.5 before continuing.

subject to a set of linear equality and inequality constraints. In particular, let M_1, M_2, M_3 be some finite index sets, and suppose that for every i in any one of these sets, we are given an n-dimensional vector $\mathbf{a}_i$ and a scalar b_i, that will be used to form the ith constraint. Let also N_1 and N_2 be subsets of $\{1, \ldots, n\}$ that indicate which variables x_j are constrained to be nonnegative or nonpositive, respectively. We then consider the problem

$$
\begin{aligned}
\text{minimize} \quad & \mathbf{c'x} \\
\text{subject to} \quad & \mathbf{a}_i'\mathbf{x} \geq b_i, \quad i \in M_1, \\
& \mathbf{a}_i'\mathbf{x} \leq b_i, \quad i \in M_2, \\
& \mathbf{a}_i'\mathbf{x} = b_i, \quad i \in M_3, \\
& x_j \geq 0, \quad j \in N_1, \\
& x_j \leq 0, \quad j \in N_2.
\end{aligned}
\tag{1.1}
$$

The variables $x_1, \ldots, x_n$ are called *decision variables*, and a vector $\mathbf{x}$ satisfying all of the constraints is called a *feasible solution* or *feasible vector*. The set of all feasible solutions is called the *feasible set* or *feasible region*. If j is in neither N_1 nor N_2, there are no restrictions on the sign of x_j, in which case we say that x_j is a *free* or *unrestricted* variable. The function $\mathbf{c'x}$ is called the *objective function* or *cost function*. A feasible solution $\mathbf{x}^*$ that minimizes the objective function (that is, $\mathbf{c'x}^* \leq \mathbf{c'x}$, for all feasible $\mathbf{x}$) is called an *optimal feasible solution* or, simply, an *optimal solution*. The value of $\mathbf{c'x}^*$ is then called the *optimal cost*. On the other hand, if for every real number K we can find a feasible solution $\mathbf{x}$ whose cost is less than K, we say that the optimal cost is $-\infty$ or that the cost is *unbounded below*. (Sometimes, we will abuse terminology and say that the problem is *unbounded*.) We finally note that there is no need to study maximization problems separately, because maximizing $\mathbf{c'x}$ is equivalent to minimizing the linear cost function $-\mathbf{c'x}$.

An equality constraint $\mathbf{a}_i'\mathbf{x} = b_i$ is equivalent to the two constraints $\mathbf{a}_i'\mathbf{x} \leq b_i$ and $\mathbf{a}_i'\mathbf{x} \geq b_i$. In addition, any constraint of the form $\mathbf{a}_i'\mathbf{x} \leq b_i$ can be rewritten as $(-\mathbf{a}_i)'\mathbf{x} \geq -b_i$. Finally, constraints of the form $x_j \geq 0$ or $x_j \leq 0$ are special cases of constraints of the form $\mathbf{a}_i'\mathbf{x} \geq b_i$, where $\mathbf{a}_i$ is a unit vector and $b_i = 0$. We conclude that the feasible set in a general linear programming problem can be expressed exclusively in terms of inequality constraints of the form $\mathbf{a}_i'\mathbf{x} \geq b_i$. Suppose that there is a total of m such constraints, indexed by $i = 1, \ldots, m$, let $\mathbf{b} = (b_1, \ldots, b_m)$, and let $\mathbf{A}$ be the $m \times n$ matrix whose rows are the row vectors $\mathbf{a}_1', \ldots, \mathbf{a}_m'$, that is,

$$
\mathbf{A} = \begin{bmatrix} - & \mathbf{a}_1' & - \\ & \vdots & \\ - & \mathbf{a}_m' & - \end{bmatrix}.
$$

Then, the constraints $\mathbf{a}_i'\mathbf{x} \geq b_i$, $i = 1, \ldots, m$, can be expressed compactly in the form $\mathbf{Ax} \geq \mathbf{b}$, and the linear programming problem can be written as

$$\text{minimize} \quad \mathbf{c}'\mathbf{x}$$
$$\text{subject to} \quad \mathbf{A}\mathbf{x} \geq \mathbf{b}. \tag{1.2}$$

Inequalities such as $\mathbf{A}\mathbf{x} \geq \mathbf{b}$ will always be interpreted componentwise; that is, for every i, the ith component of the vector $\mathbf{A}\mathbf{x}$, which is $\mathbf{a}_i'\mathbf{x}$, is greater than or equal to the ith component b_i of the vector $\mathbf{b}$.

Example 1.2 The linear programming problem in Example 1.1 can be rewritten as

$$
\begin{array}{rrrrrr}
\text{minimize} & 2x_1 & - & x_2 & + 4x_3 \\
\text{subject to} & -x_1 & - & x_2 & & - x_4 & \geq & -2 \\
& & & 3x_2 & - x_3 & & \geq & 5 \\
& & - & 3x_2 & + x_3 & & \geq & -5 \\
& & & & x_3 & + x_4 & \geq & 3 \\
& x_1 & & & & & \geq & 0 \\
& & & & - x_3 & & \geq & 0,
\end{array}
$$

which is of the same form as the problem (1.2), with $\mathbf{c} = (2, -1, 4, 0)$,

$$
\mathbf{A} = \begin{bmatrix}
-1 & -1 & 0 & -1 \\
0 & 3 & -1 & 0 \\
0 & -3 & 1 & 0 \\
0 & 0 & 1 & 1 \\
1 & 0 & 0 & 0 \\
0 & 0 & -1 & 0
\end{bmatrix},
$$

and $\mathbf{b} = (-2, 5, -5, 3, 0, 0)$.

Standard form problems

A linear programming problem of the form

$$\text{minimize} \quad \mathbf{c}'\mathbf{x}$$
$$\text{subject to} \quad \mathbf{A}\mathbf{x} = \mathbf{b} \tag{1.3}$$
$$\mathbf{x} \geq \mathbf{0},$$

is said to be in *standard form*. We provide an interpretation of problems in standard form. Suppose that $\mathbf{x}$ has dimension n and let $\mathbf{A}_1, \ldots, \mathbf{A}_n$ be the columns of $\mathbf{A}$. Then, the constraint $\mathbf{A}\mathbf{x} = \mathbf{b}$ can be written in the form

$$\sum_{i=1}^{n} \mathbf{A}_i x_i = \mathbf{b}.$$

Intuitively, there are n available resource vectors $\mathbf{A}_1, \ldots, \mathbf{A}_n$, and a target vector $\mathbf{b}$. We wish to "synthesize" the target vector $\mathbf{b}$ by using a non-negative amount x_i of each resource vector $\mathbf{A}_i$, while minimizing the cost $\sum_{i=1}^{n} c_i x_i$, where c_i is the unit cost of the ith resource. The following is a more concrete example.

Example 1.3 (The diet problem) Suppose that there are n different foods and m different nutrients, and that we are given the following table with the nutritional content of a unit of each food:

	food 1	$\cdots$	food n
nutrient 1	a_{11}	$\cdots$	a_{1n}
$\vdots$	$\vdots$		$\vdots$
nutrient m	a_{m1}	$\cdots$	a_{mn}

Let $\mathbf{A}$ be the $m \times n$ matrix with entries a_{ij}. Note that the jth column $\mathbf{A}_j$ of this matrix represents the nutritional content of the jth food. Let $\mathbf{b}$ be a vector with the requirements of an ideal diet or, equivalently, a specification of the nutritional contents of an "ideal food." We then interpret the standard form problem as the problem of mixing nonnegative quantities x_i of the available foods, to synthesize the ideal food at minimal cost. In a variant of this problem, the vector $\mathbf{b}$ specifies the *minimal* requirements of an adequate diet; in that case, the constraints $\mathbf{Ax} = \mathbf{b}$ are replaced by $\mathbf{Ax} \geq \mathbf{b}$, and the problem is not in standard form.

Reduction to standard form

As argued earlier, any linear programming problem, including the standard form problem (1.3), is a special case of the general form (1.1). We now argue that the converse is also true and that a general linear programming problem can be transformed into an equivalent problem in standard form. Here, when we say that the two problems are equivalent, we mean that given a feasible solution to one problem, we can construct a feasible solution to the other, with the same cost. In particular, the two problems have the same optimal cost and given an optimal solution to one problem, we can construct an optimal solution to the other. The problem transformation we have in mind involves two steps:

(a) *Elimination of free variables:* Given an unrestricted variable x_j in a problem in general form, we replace it by $x_j^+ - x_j^-$, where x_j^+ and x_j^- are new variables on which we impose the sign constraints $x_j^+ \geq 0$ and $x_j^- \geq 0$. The underlying idea is that any real number can be written as the difference of two nonnegative numbers.

(b) *Elimination of inequality constraints:* Given an inequality constraint of the form

$$\sum_{j=1}^{n} a_{ij} x_j \leq b_i,$$

we introduce a new variable s_i and the standard form constraints

$$\sum_{j=1}^{n} a_{ij} x_j + s_i = b_i,$$

$$s_i \geq 0.$$

Such a variable s_i is called a *slack* variable. Similarly, an inequality constraint $\sum_{j=1}^{n} a_{ij} x_j \geq b_i$ can be put in standard form by introducing a *surplus* variable s_i and the constraints $\sum_{j=1}^{n} a_{ij} x_j - s_i = b_i$, $s_i \geq 0$.

We conclude that a general problem can be brought into standard form and, therefore, we only need to develop methods that are capable of solving standard form problems.

Example 1.4 The problem

$$
\begin{aligned}
\text{minimize} \quad & 2x_1 + 4x_2 \\
\text{subject to} \quad & x_1 + x_2 \geq 3 \\
& 3x_1 + 2x_2 = 14 \\
& x_1 \qquad\qquad \geq 0,
\end{aligned}
$$

is equivalent to the standard form problem

$$
\begin{aligned}
\text{minimize} \quad & 2x_1 + 4x_2^+ - 4x_2^- \\
\text{subject to} \quad & x_1 + x_2^+ - x_2^- - x_3 = 3 \\
& 3x_1 + 2x_2^+ - 2x_2^- = 14 \\
& x_1, x_2^+, x_2^-, x_3 \geq 0.
\end{aligned}
$$

For example, given the feasible solution $(x_1, x_2) = (6, -2)$ to the original problem, we obtain the feasible solution $(x_1, x_2^+, x_2^-, x_3) = (6, 0, 2, 1)$ to the standard form problem, which has the same cost. Conversely, given the feasible solution $(x_1, x_2^+, x_2^-, x_3) = (8, 1, 6, 0)$ to the standard form problem, we obtain the feasible solution $(x_1, x_2) = (8, -5)$ to the original problem with the same cost.

In the sequel, we will often use the general form $\mathbf{Ax} \geq \mathbf{b}$ to develop the theory of linear programming. However, when it comes to algorithms, and especially the simplex and interior point methods, we will be focusing on the standard form $\mathbf{Ax} = \mathbf{b}$, $\mathbf{x} \geq \mathbf{0}$, which is computationally more convenient.

1.2 Examples of linear programming problems

In this section, we discuss a number of examples of linear programming problems. One of our purposes is to indicate the vast range of situations to which linear programming can be applied. Another purpose is to develop some familiarity with the art of constructing mathematical formulations of loosely defined optimization problems.

A production problem

A firm produces n different goods using m different raw materials. Let b_i, $i = 1,\ldots,m$, be the available amount of the ith raw material. The jth good, $j = 1,\ldots,n$, requires a_{ij} units of the ith material and results in a revenue of c_j per unit produced. The firm faces the problem of deciding how much of each good to produce in order to maximize its total revenue.

In this example, the choice of the decision variables is simple. Let x_j, $j = 1,\ldots,n$, be the amount of the jth good. Then, the problem facing the firm can be formulated as follows:

$$
\begin{array}{lll}
\text{maximize} & c_1 x_1 + \cdots + c_n x_n & \\
\text{subject to} & a_{i1} x_1 + \cdots + a_{in} x_n \leq b_i, & i = 1,\ldots,m, \\
& x_j \geq 0, & j = 1,\ldots,n.
\end{array}
$$

Production planning by a computer manufacturer

The example that we consider here is a problem that Digital Equipment Corporation (DEC) had faced in the fourth quarter of 1988. It illustrates the complexities and uncertainties of real world applications, as well as the usefulness of mathematical modeling for making important strategic decisions.

In the second quarter of 1988, DEC introduced a new family of (single CPU) computer systems and workstations: GP-1, GP-2, and GP-3, which are general purpose computer systems with different memory, disk storage, and expansion capabilities, as well as WS-1 and WS-2, which are workstations. In Table 1.1, we list the models, the list prices, the average disk usage per system, and the memory usage. For example, GP-1 uses four 256K memory boards, and 3 out of every 10 units are produced with a disk drive.

System	Price	# disk drives	# 256K boards
GP-1	$60,000	0.3	4
GP-2	$40,000	1.7	2
GP-3	$30,000	0	2
WS-1	$30,000	1.4	2
WS-2	$15,000	0	1

Table 1.1: Features of the five different DEC systems.

Shipments of this new family of products started in the third quarter and ramped slowly during the fourth quarter. The following difficulties were anticipated for the next quarter:

(a) The in-house supplier of CPUs could provide at most 7,000 units, due to debugging problems.

(b) The supply of disk drives was uncertain and was estimated by the manufacturer to be in the range of 3,000 to 7,000 units.

(c) The supply of 256K memory boards was also limited in the range of 8,000 to 16,000 units.

On the demand side, the marketing department established that the maximum demand for the first quarter of 1989 would be 1,800 for GP-1 systems, 300 for GP-3 systems, 3,800 systems for the whole GP family, and 3,200 systems for the WS family. Included in these projections were 500 orders for GP-2, 500 orders for WS-1, and 400 orders for WS-2 that had already been received and had to be fulfilled in the next quarter.

In the previous quarters, in order to address the disk drive shortage, DEC had produced GP-1, GP-3, and WS-2 with no disk drive (although 3 out of 10 customers for GP-1 systems wanted a disk drive), and GP-2, WS-1 with one disk drive. We refer to this way of configuring the systems as the constrained mode of production.

In addition, DEC could address the shortage of 256K memory boards by using two alternative boards, instead of four 256K memory boards, in the GP-1 system. DEC could provide 4,000 alternative boards for the next quarter.

It was clear to the manufacturing staff that the problem had become complex, as revenue, profitability, and customer satisfaction were at risk. The following decisions needed to be made:

(a) The production plan for the first quarter of 1989.

(b) Concerning disk drive usage, should DEC continue to manufacture products in the constrained mode, or should it plan to satisfy customer preferences?

(c) Concerning memory boards, should DEC use alternative memory boards for its GP-1 systems?

(d) A final decision that had to be made was related to tradeoffs between shortages of disk drives and of 256K memory boards. The manufacturing staff would like to concentrate their efforts on either decreasing the shortage of disks or decreasing the shortage of 256K memory boards. Hence, they would like to know which alternative would have a larger effect on revenue.

In order to model the problem that DEC faced, we introduce variables x_1, x_2, x_3, x_4, x_5, that represent the number (in thousands) of GP-1, GP-2, GP-3, WS-1, and WS-2 systems, respectively, to be produced in the next quarter. Strictly speaking, since $1000x_i$ stands for number of units, it must be an integer. This can be accomplished by truncating each x_i after the third decimal point; given the size of the demand and the size of the variables x_i, this has a negligible effect and the integrality constraint on $1000x_i$ can be ignored.

DEC had to make two distinct decisions: whether to use the constrained mode of production regarding disk drive usage, and whether to use alternative memory boards for the GP-1 system. As a result, there are four different combinations of possible choices.

We first develop a model for the case where alternative memory boards are not used and the constrained mode of production of disk drives is selected. The problem can be formulated as follows:

$$\text{maximize} \quad 60x_1 + 40x_2 + 30x_3 + 30x_4 + 15x_5 \quad \text{(total revenue)}$$

subject to the following constraints:

$$
\begin{array}{lll}
x_1 + x_2 + x_3 + x_4 + x_5 \le 7 & \text{(CPU availability)} \\
4x_1 + 2x_2 + 2x_3 + 2x_4 + x_5 \le 8 & \text{(256K availability)} \\
x_2 + x_4 \le 3 & \text{(disk drive availability)} \\
x_1 \le 1.8 & \text{(max demand for GP-1)} \\
x_3 \le 0.3 & \text{(max demand for GP-3)} \\
x_1 + x_2 + x_3 \le 3.8 & \text{(max demand for GP)} \\
x_4 + x_5 \le 3.2 & \text{(max demand for WS)} \\
x_2 \ge 0.5 & \text{(min demand for GP-2)} \\
x_4 \ge 0.5 & \text{(min demand for WS-1)} \\
x_5 \ge 0.4 & \text{(min demand for WS-2)} \\
x_1, x_2, x_3, x_4, x_5 \ge 0.
\end{array}
$$

Notice that the objective function is in millions of dollars. In some respects, this is a pessimistic formulation, because the 256K memory and disk drive availability were set to 8 and 3, respectively, which is the lowest value in the range that was estimated. It is actually of interest to determine the solution to this problem as the 256K memory availability ranges from 8 to 16, and the disk drive availability ranges from 3 to 7, because this provides valuable information on the sensitivity of the optimal solution on availability. In another respect, the formulation is optimistic because, for example, it assumes that the revenue from GP-1 systems is $60x_1$ for any $x_1 \le 1.8$, even though a demand for 1,800 GP-1 systems is not guaranteed.

In order to accommodate the other three choices that DEC had, some of the problem constraints have to be modified, as follows. If we use the unconstrained mode of production for disk drives, the constraint $x_2 + x_4 \le 3$ is replaced by

$$0.3x_1 + 1.7x_2 + 1.4x_4 \le 3.$$

Furthermore, if we wish to use alternative memory boards in GP-1 systems, we replace the constraint $4x_1 + 2x_2 + 2x_3 + 2x_4 + x_5 \le 8$ by the two constraints

$$2x_1 \leq 4,$$
$$2x_2 + 2x_3 + 2x_4 + x_5 \leq 8.$$

The four combinations of choices lead to four different linear programming problems, each of which needs to be solved for a variety of parameter values because, as discussed earlier, the right-hand side of some of the constraints is only known to lie within a certain range. Methods for solving linear programming problems, when certain parameters are allowed to vary, will be studied in Chapter 5, where this case study is revisited.

Multiperiod planning of electric power capacity

A state wants to plan its electricity capacity for the next T years. The state has a forecast of d_t megawatts, presumed accurate, of the demand for electricity during year $t = 1, \ldots, T$. The existing capacity, which is in oil-fired plants, that will not be retired and will be available during year t, is e_t. There are two alternatives for expanding electric capacity: coal-fired or nuclear power plants. There is a capital cost of c_t per megawatt of coal-fired capacity that becomes operational at the beginning of year t. The corresponding capital cost for nuclear power plants is n_t. For various political and safety reasons, it has been decided that no more than 20% of the total capacity should ever be nuclear. Coal plants last for 20 years, while nuclear plants last for 15 years. A least cost capacity expansion plan is desired.

The first step in formulating this problem as a linear programming problem is to define the decision variables. Let x_t and y_t be the amount of coal (respectively, nuclear) capacity brought on line at the beginning of year t. Let w_t and z_t be the total coal (respectively, nuclear) capacity available in year t. The cost of a capacity expansion plan is therefore,

$$\sum_{t=1}^{T}(c_t x_t + n_t y_t).$$

Since coal-fired plants last for 20 years, we have

$$w_t = \sum_{s=\max\{1, t-19\}}^{t} x_s, \qquad t = 1, \ldots, T.$$

Similarly, for nuclear power plants,

$$z_t = \sum_{s=\max\{1, t-14\}}^{t} y_s, \qquad t = 1, \ldots, T.$$

Since the available capacity must meet the forecasted demand, we require

$$w_t + z_t + e_t \geq d_t, \qquad t = 1, \ldots, T.$$

Finally, since no more than 20% of the total capacity should ever be nuclear, we have

$$\frac{z_t}{w_t + z_t + e_t} \leq 0.2,$$

which can be written as

$$0.8 z_t - 0.2 w_t \leq 0.2 e_t.$$

Summarizing, the capacity expansion problem is as follows:

$$\text{minimize} \quad \sum_{t=1}^{T} (c_t x_t + n_t y_t)$$

$$\text{subject to} \quad w_t - \sum_{s = \max\{1, t-19\}}^{t} x_s = 0, \qquad t = 1, \ldots, T,$$

$$z_t - \sum_{s = \max\{1, t-14\}}^{t} y_s = 0, \qquad t = 1, \ldots, T,$$

$$w_t + z_t \geq d_t - e_t, \qquad t = 1, \ldots, T,$$

$$0.8 z_t - 0.2 w_t \leq 0.2 e_t, \qquad t = 1, \ldots, T,$$

$$x_t, y_t, w_t, z_t \geq 0, \qquad t = 1, \ldots, T.$$

We note that this formulation is not entirely realistic, because it disregards certain economies of scale that may favor larger plants. However, it can provide a ballpark estimate of the true cost.

A scheduling problem

In the previous examples, the choice of the decision variables was fairly straightforward. We now discuss an example where this choice is less obvious.

A hospital wants to make a weekly night shift (12pm-8am) schedule for its nurses. The demand for nurses for the night shift on day j is an integer d_j, $j = 1, \ldots, 7$. Every nurse works 5 days in a row on the night shift. The problem is to find the minimal number of nurses the hospital needs to hire.

One could try using a decision variable y_j equal to the number of nurses that work on day j. With this definition, however, we would not be able to capture the constraint that every nurse works 5 days in a row. For this reason, we choose the decision variables differently, and define x_j as the number of nurses starting their week on day j. (For example, a nurse whose week starts on day 5 will work days $5, 6, 7, 1, 2$.) We then have the following problem formulation:

$$
\begin{array}{llll}
\text{minimize} & x_1 + x_2 + x_3 + x_4 + x_5 + x_6 + x_7 \\
\text{subject to} & x_1 \quad\quad\quad + x_4 + x_5 + x_6 + x_7 \geq d_1 \\
& x_1 + x_2 \quad\quad\quad + x_5 + x_6 + x_7 \geq d_2 \\
& x_1 + x_2 + x_3 \quad\quad\quad + x_6 + x_7 \geq d_3 \\
& x_1 + x_2 + x_3 + x_4 \quad\quad\quad + x_7 \geq d_4 \\
& x_1 + x_2 + x_3 + x_4 + x_5 \quad\quad\quad \geq d_5 \\
& \quad\quad x_2 + x_3 + x_4 + x_5 + x_6 \quad\quad\quad \geq d_6 \\
& \quad\quad\quad\quad x_3 + x_4 + x_5 + x_6 + x_7 \geq d_7 \\
& x_j \geq 0, \quad x_j \text{ integer.}
\end{array}
$$

This would be a linear programming problem, except for the constraint that each x_j must be an integer, and we actually have a linear *integer programming* problem. One way of dealing with this issue is to ignore ("relax") the integrality constraints and obtain the so-called *linear programming relaxation* of the original problem. Because the linear programming problem has fewer constraints, and therefore more options, the optimal cost will be less than or equal to the optimal cost of the original problem. If the optimal solution to the linear programming relaxation happens to be integer, then it is also an optimal solution to the original problem. If it is not integer, we can round each x_j upwards, thus obtaining a feasible, but not necessarily optimal, solution to the original problem. It turns out that for this particular problem, an optimal solution can be found without too much effort. However, this is the exception rather than the rule: finding optimal solutions to general integer programming problems is typically difficult; some methods will be discussed in Chapter 11.

Choosing paths in a communication network

Consider a communication network consisting of n nodes. Nodes are connected by communication links. A link allowing one-way transmission from node i to node j is described by an ordered pair (i, j). Let $\mathcal{A}$ be the set of all links. We assume that each link $(i, j) \in \mathcal{A}$ can carry up to u_{ij} bits per second. There is a positive charge c_{ij} per bit transmitted along that link. Each node k generates data, at the rate of $b^{k\ell}$ bits per second, that have to be transmitted to node ℓ, either through a direct link (k, ℓ) or by tracing a sequence of links. The problem is to choose paths along which all data reach their intended destinations, while minimizing the total cost. We allow the data with the same origin and destination to be split and be transmitted along different paths.

In order to formulate this problem as a linear programming problem, we introduce variables $x_{ij}^{k\ell}$ indicating the amount of data with origin k and destination ℓ that traverse link (i, j). Let

$$b_i^{k\ell} = \begin{cases} b^{k\ell}, & \text{if } i = k, \\ -b^{k\ell}, & \text{if } i = \ell, \\ 0, & \text{otherwise.} \end{cases}$$

Thus, $b_i^{k\ell}$ is the net inflow at node i, from outside the network, of data with origin k and destination ℓ. We then have the following formulation:

$$\text{minimize} \quad \sum_{(i,j)\in\mathcal{A}} \sum_{k=1}^{n} \sum_{\ell=1}^{n} c_{ij} x_{ij}^{k\ell}$$

$$\text{subject to} \quad \sum_{\{j|(i,j)\in\mathcal{A}\}} x_{ij}^{k\ell} - \sum_{\{j|(j,i)\in\mathcal{A}\}} x_{ji}^{k\ell} = b_i^{k\ell}, \qquad i, k, \ell = 1, \ldots, n,$$

$$\sum_{k=1}^{n} \sum_{\ell=1}^{n} x_{ij}^{k\ell} \leq u_{ij}, \qquad\qquad (i, j) \in \mathcal{A},$$

$$x_{ij}^{k\ell} \geq 0, \qquad\qquad (i, j) \in \mathcal{A}, \quad k, \ell = 1, \ldots, n.$$

The first constraint is a flow conservation constraint at node i for data with origin k and destination ℓ. The expression

$$\sum_{\{j|(i,j)\in\mathcal{A}\}} x_{ij}^{k\ell}$$

represents the amount of data with origin and destination k and ℓ, respectively, that leave node i along some link. The expression

$$\sum_{\{j|(j,i)\in\mathcal{A}\}} x_{ji}^{k\ell}$$

represents the amount of data with the same origin and destination that enter node i through some link. Finally, $b_i^{k\ell}$ is the net amount of such data that enter node i from outside the network. The second constraint expresses the requirement that the total traffic through a link (i, j) cannot exceed the link's capacity.

This problem is known as the *multicommodity flow* problem, with the traffic corresponding to each origin-destination pair viewed as a different commodity. A mathematically similar problem arises when we consider a transportation company that wishes to transport several commodities from their origins to their destinations through a network. There is a version of this problem, known as the minimum cost *network flow* problem, in which we do not distinguish between different commodities. Instead, we are given the amount b_i of external supply or demand at each node i, and the objective is to transport material from the supply nodes to the demand nodes, at minimum cost. The network flow problem, which is the subject of Chapter 7, contains as special cases some important problems such as the shortest path problem, the maximum flow problem, and the assignment problem.

Pattern classification

We are given m examples of objects and for each one, say the ith one, a description of its features in terms of an n-dimensional vector $\mathbf{a}_i$. Objects belong to one of two classes, and for each example we are told the class that it belongs to.

More concretely, suppose that each object is an image of an apple or an orange (these are our two classes). In this context, we can use a three-dimensional feature vector $\mathbf{a}_i$ to summarize the contents of the ith image. The three components of $\mathbf{a}_i$ (the features) could be the ellipticity of the object, the length of its stem, and its color, as measured in some scale. We are interested in designing a *classifier* which, given a new object (other than the originally available examples), will figure out whether it is an image of an apple or of an orange.

A *linear classifier* is defined in terms of an n-dimensional vector $\mathbf{x}$ and a scalar x_{n+1}, and operates as follows. Given a new object with feature vector $\mathbf{a}$, the classifier declares it to be an object of the first class if

$$\mathbf{a}'\mathbf{x} \geq x_{n+1},$$

and of the second class if

$$\mathbf{a}'\mathbf{x} < x_{n+1}.$$

In words, a linear classifier makes decisions on the basis of a linear combination of the different features. Our objective is to use the available examples in order to design a "good" linear classifier.

There are many ways of approaching this problem, but a reasonable starting point could be the requirement that the classifier must give the correct answer for each one of the available examples. Let S be the set of examples of the first class. We are then looking for some $\mathbf{x}$ and x_{n+1} that satisfy the constraints

$$\mathbf{a}_i'\mathbf{x} \geq x_{n+1}, \qquad i \in S,$$
$$\mathbf{a}_i'\mathbf{x} < x_{n+1}, \qquad i \notin S.$$

Note that the second set of constraints involves a strict inequality and is not quite of the form arising in linear programming. This issue can be bypassed by observing that if some choice of $\mathbf{x}$ and x_{n+1} satisfies all of the above constraints, then there exists some other choice (obtained by multiplying $\mathbf{x}$ and x_{n+1} by a suitably large positive scalar) that satisfies

$$\mathbf{a}_i'\mathbf{x} \geq x_{n+1}, \qquad i \in S,$$
$$\mathbf{a}_i'\mathbf{x} \leq x_{n+1} - 1, \qquad i \notin S.$$

We conclude that the search for a linear classifier consistent with all available examples is a problem of finding a feasible solution to a linear programming problem.

1.3   Piecewise linear convex objective functions

All of the examples in the preceding section involved a *linear* objective function. However, there is an important class of optimization problems with a nonlinear objective function that can be cast as linear programming problems; these are examined next.

We first need some definitions:

Definition 1.1

(a)   A function $f : \Re^n \mapsto \Re$ is called **convex** if for every $\mathbf{x}, \mathbf{y} \in \Re^n$, and every $\lambda \in [0, 1]$, we have

$$f\big(\lambda \mathbf{x} + (1 - \lambda)\mathbf{y}\big) \leq \lambda f(\mathbf{x}) + (1 - \lambda)f(\mathbf{y}).$$

(b)   A function $f : \Re^n \mapsto \Re$ is called **concave** if for every $\mathbf{x}, \mathbf{y} \in \Re^n$, and every $\lambda \in [0, 1]$, we have

$$f\big(\lambda \mathbf{x} + (1 - \lambda)\mathbf{y}\big) \geq \lambda f(\mathbf{x}) + (1 - \lambda)f(\mathbf{y}).$$

Note that if $\mathbf{x}$ and $\mathbf{y}$ are vectors in $\Re^n$ and if λ ranges in $[0, 1]$, then points of the form $\lambda \mathbf{x} + (1 - \lambda)\mathbf{y}$ belong to the line segment joining $\mathbf{x}$ and $\mathbf{y}$. The definition of a convex function refers to the values of f, as its argument traces this segment. If f were linear, the inequality in part (a) of the definition would hold with equality. The inequality therefore means that when we restrict attention to such a segment, the graph of the function lies no higher than the graph of a corresponding linear function; see Figure 1.1(a).

It is easily seen that a function f is convex if and only if the function $-f$ is concave. Note that a function of the form $f(\mathbf{x}) = a_0 + \sum_{i=1}^{n} a_i x_i$, where $a_0, \ldots, a_n$ are scalars, called an *affine* function, is both convex and concave. (It turns out that affine functions are the only functions that are both convex and concave.) Convex (as well as concave) functions play a central role in optimization.

We say that a vector $\mathbf{x}$ is a *local minimum* of f if $f(\mathbf{x}) \leq f(\mathbf{y})$ for all $\mathbf{y}$ in the vicinity of $\mathbf{x}$. We also say that $\mathbf{x}$ is a *global minimum* if $f(\mathbf{x}) \leq f(\mathbf{y})$ for all $\mathbf{y}$. A convex function cannot have local minima that fail to be global minima (see Figure 1.1), and this property is of great help in designing efficient optimization algorithms.

Let $\mathbf{c}_1, \ldots, \mathbf{c}_m$ be vectors in $\Re^n$, let $d_1, \ldots, d_m$ be scalars, and consider the function $f : \Re^n \mapsto \Re$ defined by

$$f(\mathbf{x}) = \max_{i=1,\ldots,m} (\mathbf{c}_i'\mathbf{x} + d_i)$$

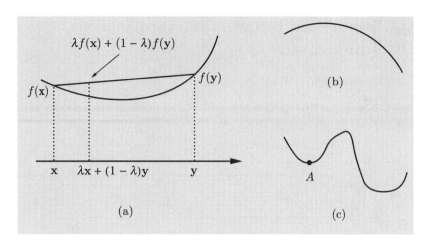

Figure 1.1: (a) Illustration of the definition of a convex function. (b) A concave function. (c) A function that is neither convex nor concave; note that A is a local, but not global, minimum.

[see Figure 1.2(a)]. Such a function is convex, as a consequence of the following result.

Theorem 1.1 *Let $f_1, \ldots, f_m : \Re^n \mapsto \Re$ be convex functions. Then, the function f defined by $f(\mathbf{x}) = \max_{i=1,\ldots,m} f_i(\mathbf{x})$ is also convex.*

Proof. Let $\mathbf{x}, \mathbf{y} \in \Re^n$ and let $\lambda \in [0, 1]$. We have

$$
\begin{aligned}
f\big(\lambda\mathbf{x} + (1 - \lambda)\mathbf{y}\big) &= \max_{i=1,\ldots,m} f_i\big(\lambda\mathbf{x} + (1 - \lambda)\mathbf{y}\big) \\
&\leq \max_{i=1,\ldots,m} \big(\lambda f_i(\mathbf{x}) + (1 - \lambda)f_i(\mathbf{y})\big) \\
&\leq \max_{i=1,\ldots,m} \lambda f_i(\mathbf{x}) + \max_{i=1,\ldots,m} (1 - \lambda)f_i(\mathbf{y}) \\
&= \lambda f(\mathbf{x}) + (1 - \lambda)f(\mathbf{y}). \qquad \square
\end{aligned}
$$

A function of the form $\max_{i=1,\ldots,m}(\mathbf{c}_i'\mathbf{x}+d_i)$ is called a *piecewise linear convex* function. A simple example is the absolute value function defined by $f(x) = |x| = \max\{x, -x\}$. As illustrated in Figure 1.2(b), a piecewise linear convex function can be used to approximate a general convex function.

We now consider a generalization of linear programming, where the objective function is piecewise linear and convex rather than linear:

$$
\begin{aligned}
\text{minimize} \quad & \max_{i=1,\ldots,m} (\mathbf{c}_i'\mathbf{x} + d_i) \\
\text{subject to} \quad & \mathbf{A}\mathbf{x} \geq \mathbf{b}.
\end{aligned}
$$

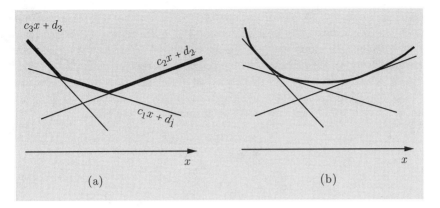

$c_3 x + d_3$

$c_2 x + d_2$

$c_1 x + d_1$

x

x

(a)

(b)

Figure 1.2: (a) A piecewise linear convex function of a single variable. (b) An approximation of a convex function by a piecewise linear convex function.

Note that $\max_{i=1,\dots,m}(\mathbf{c}_i'\mathbf{x} + d_i)$ is equal to the smallest number z that satisfies $z \geq \mathbf{c}_i'\mathbf{x} + d_i$ for all i. For this reason, the optimization problem under consideration is equivalent to the linear programming problem

$$\begin{aligned}
\text{minimize} \quad & z \\
\text{subject to} \quad & z \geq \mathbf{c}_i'\mathbf{x} + d_i, \qquad i = 1, \dots, m, \\
& \mathbf{A}\mathbf{x} \geq \mathbf{b},
\end{aligned}$$

where the decision variables are z and $\mathbf{x}$.

To summarize, linear programming can be used to solve problems with piecewise linear convex cost functions, and the latter class of functions can be used as an approximation of more general convex cost functions. On the other hand, such a piecewise linear approximation is not always a good idea because it can turn a smooth function into a nonsmooth one (piecewise linear functions have discontinuous derivatives).

We finally note that if we are given a constraint of the form $f(\mathbf{x}) \leq h$, where f is the piecewise linear convex function $f(\mathbf{x}) = \max_{i=1,\dots,m}(\mathbf{f}_i'\mathbf{x}+g_i)$, such a constraint can be rewritten as

$$\mathbf{f}_i'\mathbf{x} + g_i \leq h, \qquad i = 1, \dots, m,$$

and linear programming is again applicable.

Problems involving absolute values

Consider a problem of the form

$$\begin{aligned}
\text{minimize} \quad & \sum_{i=1}^{n} c_i |x_i| \\
\text{subject to} \quad & \mathbf{A}\mathbf{x} \geq \mathbf{b},
\end{aligned}$$

where $\mathbf{x} = (x_1, \ldots, x_n)$, and where the cost coefficients c_i are assumed to be nonnegative. The cost criterion, being the sum of the piecewise linear convex functions $c_i|x_i|$ is easily shown to be piecewise linear and convex (Exercise 1.2). However, expressing this cost criterion in the form $\max_j(\mathbf{c}_j'\mathbf{x} + d_j)$ is a bit involved, and a more direct route is preferable. We observe that $|x_i|$ is the smallest number z_i that satisfies $x_i \leq z_i$ and $-x_i \leq z_i$, and we obtain the linear programming formulation

$$\text{minimize} \quad \sum_{i=1}^{n} c_i z_i$$
$$\text{subject to} \quad \mathbf{Ax} \geq \mathbf{b}$$
$$x_i \leq z_i, \qquad i = 1, \ldots, n,$$
$$-x_i \leq z_i, \qquad i = 1, \ldots, n.$$

An alternative method for dealing with absolute values is to introduce new variables x_i^+, x_i^-, constrained to be nonnegative, and let $x_i = x_i^+ - x_i^-$. (Our intention is to have $x_i = x_i^+$ or $x_i = -x_i^-$, depending on whether x_i is positive or negative.) We then replace every occurrence of $|x_i|$ with $x_i^+ + x_i^-$ and obtain the alternative formulation

$$\text{minimize} \quad \sum_{i=1}^{n} c_i(x_i^+ + x_i^-)$$
$$\text{subject to} \quad \mathbf{Ax^+} - \mathbf{Ax^-} \geq \mathbf{b}$$
$$\mathbf{x^+}, \mathbf{x^-} \geq \mathbf{0},$$

where $\mathbf{x^+} = (x_1^+, \ldots, x_n^+)$ and $\mathbf{x^-} = (x_1^-, \ldots, x_n^-)$.

The relations $x_i = x_i^+ - x_i^-$, $x_i^+ \geq 0$, $x_i^- \geq 0$, are not enough to guarantee that $|x_i| = x_i^+ + x_i^-$, and the validity of this reformulation may not be entirely obvious. Let us assume for simplicity that $c_i > 0$ for all i. At an optimal solution to the reformulated problem, and for each i, we must have either $x_i^+ = 0$ or $x_i^- = 0$, because otherwise we could reduce both x_i^+ and x_i^- by the same amount and preserve feasibility, while reducing the cost, in contradiction of optimality. Having guaranteed that either $x_i^+ = 0$ or $x_i^- = 0$, the desired relation $|x_i| = x_i^+ + x_i^-$ now follows.

The formal correctness of the two reformulations that have been presented here, and in a somewhat more general setting, is the subject of Exercise 1.5. We also note that the nonnegativity assumption on the cost coefficients c_i is crucial because, otherwise, the cost criterion is nonconvex.

Example 1.5 Consider the problem

$$\text{minimize} \quad 2|x_1| + x_2$$
$$\text{subject to} \quad x_1 + x_2 \geq 4.$$

Our first reformulation yields

$$
\begin{aligned}
\text{minimize} \quad & 2z_1 + x_2 \\
\text{subject to} \quad & x_1 + x_2 \geq 4 \\
& x_1 \leq z_1 \\
& -x_1 \leq z_1,
\end{aligned}
$$

while the second yields

$$
\begin{aligned}
\text{minimize} \quad & 2x_1^+ + 2x_1^- + x_2 \\
\text{subject to} \quad & x_1^+ - x_1^- + x_2 \geq 4 \\
& x_1^+ \geq 0 \\
& x_1^- \geq 0.
\end{aligned}
$$

We now continue with some applications involving piecewise linear convex objective functions.

Data fitting

We are given m data points of the form $(\mathbf{a}_i, b_i)$, $i = 1, \ldots, m$, where $\mathbf{a}_i \in \Re^n$ and $b_i \in \Re$, and wish to build a model that predicts the value of the variable b from knowledge of the vector $\mathbf{a}$. In such a situation, one often uses a linear model of the form $b = \mathbf{a}'\mathbf{x}$, where $\mathbf{x}$ is a parameter vector to be determined. Given a particular parameter vector $\mathbf{x}$, the *residual*, or prediction error, at the ith data point is defined as $|b_i - \mathbf{a}_i'\mathbf{x}|$. Given a choice between alternative models, one should choose a model that "explains" the available data as best as possible, i.e., a model that results in small residuals.

One possibility is to minimize the largest residual. This is the problem of minimizing

$$
\max_i |b_i - \mathbf{a}_i'\mathbf{x}|,
$$

with respect to $\mathbf{x}$, subject to no constraints. Note that we are dealing here with a piecewise linear convex cost criterion. The following is an equivalent linear programming formulation:

$$
\begin{aligned}
\text{minimize} \quad & z \\
\text{subject to} \quad & b_i - \mathbf{a}_i'\mathbf{x} \leq z, \qquad i = 1, \ldots, m, \\
& -b_i + \mathbf{a}_i'\mathbf{x} \leq z, \qquad i = 1, \ldots, m,
\end{aligned}
$$

the decision variables being z and $\mathbf{x}$.

In an alternative formulation, we could adopt the cost criterion

$$
\sum_{i=1}^m |b_i - \mathbf{a}_i'\mathbf{x}|.
$$

Since $|b_i - \mathbf{a}_i'\mathbf{x}|$ is the smallest number z_i that satisfies $b_i - \mathbf{a}_i'\mathbf{x} \leq z_i$ and $-b_i + \mathbf{a}_i'\mathbf{x} \leq z_i$, we obtain the formulation

$$
\begin{aligned}
\text{minimize} \quad & z_1 + \cdots + z_m \\
\text{subject to} \quad & b_i - \mathbf{a}_i'\mathbf{x} \leq z_i, && i = 1, \ldots, m, \\
& -b_i + \mathbf{a}_i'\mathbf{x} \leq z_i, && i = 1, \ldots, m.
\end{aligned}
$$

In practice, one may wish to use the quadratic cost criterion $\sum_{i=1}^{m}(b_i - \mathbf{a}_i'\mathbf{x})^2$, in order to obtain a "least squares fit." This is a problem which is easier than linear programming; it can be solved using calculus methods, but its discussion is outside the scope of this book.

Optimal control of linear systems

Consider a dynamical system that evolves according to a model of the form

$$
\begin{aligned}
\mathbf{x}(t+1) &= \mathbf{A}\mathbf{x}(t) + \mathbf{B}\mathbf{u}(t), \\
y(t) &= \mathbf{c}'\mathbf{x}(t).
\end{aligned}
$$

Here $\mathbf{x}(t)$ is the state of the system at time t, $y(t)$ is the system output, assumed scalar, and $\mathbf{u}(t)$ is a control vector that we are free to choose subject to linear constraints of the form $\mathbf{D}\mathbf{u}(t) \leq \mathbf{d}$ [these might include saturation constraints, i.e., hard bounds on the magnitude of each component of $\mathbf{u}(t)$]. To mention some possible applications, this could be a model of an airplane, an engine, an electrical circuit, a mechanical system, a manufacturing system, or even a model of economic growth. We are also given the initial state $\mathbf{x}(0)$. In one possible problem, we are to choose the values of the control variables $\mathbf{u}(0), \ldots, \mathbf{u}(T-1)$ to drive the state $\mathbf{x}(T)$ to a target state, assumed for simplicity to be zero. In addition to zeroing the state, it is often desirable to keep the magnitude of the output small at all intermediate times, and we may wish to minimize

$$
\max_{t=1,\ldots,T-1} |y(t)|.
$$

We then obtain the following linear programming problem:

$$
\begin{aligned}
\text{minimize} \quad & z \\
\text{subject to} \quad & -z \leq y(t) \leq z, && t = 1, \ldots, T-1, \\
& \mathbf{x}(t+1) = \mathbf{A}\mathbf{x}(t) + \mathbf{B}\mathbf{u}(t), && t = 0, \ldots, T-1, \\
& y(t) = \mathbf{c}'\mathbf{x}(t), && t = 1, \ldots, T-1, \\
& \mathbf{D}\mathbf{u}(t) \leq \mathbf{d}, && t = 0, \ldots, T-1, \\
& \mathbf{x}(T) = \mathbf{0}, \\
& \mathbf{x}(0) = \text{given}.
\end{aligned}
$$

Additional linear constraints on the state vectors $\mathbf{x}(t)$, or a more general piecewise linear convex cost function of the state and the control, can also be incorporated.

Rocket control

Consider a rocket that travels along a straight path. Let x_t, v_t, and a_t be the position, velocity, and acceleration, respectively, of the rocket at time t. By discretizing time and by taking the time increment to be unity, we obtain an approximate discrete-time model of the form

$$x_{t+1} = x_t + v_t,$$
$$v_{t+1} = v_t + a_t.$$

We assume that the acceleration a_t is under our control, as it is determined by the rocket thrust. In a rough model, the magnitude $|a_t|$ of the acceleration can be assumed to be proportional to the rate of fuel consumption at time t.

Suppose that the rocket is initially at rest at the origin, that is, $x_0 = 0$ and $v_0 = 0$. We wish the rocket to take off and "land softly" at unit distance from the origin after T time units, that is, $x_T = 1$ and $v_T = 0$. Furthermore, we wish to accomplish this in an economical fashion. One possibility is to minimize the total fuel $\sum_{t=0}^{T-1} |a_t|$ spent subject to the preceding constraints. Alternatively, we may wish to minimize the maximum thrust required, which is $\max_t |a_t|$. Under either alternative, the problem can be formulated as a linear programming problem (Exercise 1.6).

1.4   Graphical representation and solution

In this section, we consider a few simple examples that provide useful geometric insights into the nature of linear programming problems. Our first example involves the graphical solution of a linear programming problem with two variables.

Example 1.6 Consider the problem

$$
\begin{array}{rl}
\text{minimize} & -x_1 - x_2 \\
\text{subject to} & x_1 + 2x_2 \le 3 \\
& 2x_1 + x_2 \le 3 \\
& x_1, x_2 \ge 0.
\end{array}
$$

The feasible set is the shaded region in Figure 1.3. In order to find an optimal solution, we proceed as follows. For any given scalar z, we consider the set of all points whose cost $\mathbf{c}'\mathbf{x}$ is equal to z; this is the line described by the equation $-x_1 - x_2 = z$. Note that this line is perpendicular to the vector $\mathbf{c} = (-1, -1)$. Different values of z lead to different lines, all of them parallel to each other. In

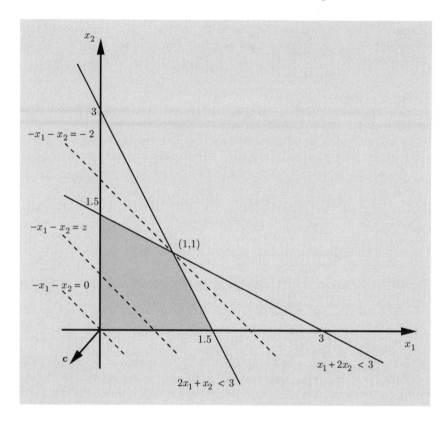

Figure 1.3: Graphical solution of the problem in Example 1.6.

particular, increasing z corresponds to moving the line $z = -x_1 - x_2$ along the direction of the vector **c**. Since we are interested in minimizing z, we would like to move the line as much as possible in the direction of $-\mathbf{c}$, as long as we do not leave the feasible region. The best we can do is $z = -2$ (see Figure 1.3), and the vector $\mathbf{x} = (1,1)$ is an optimal solution. Note that this is a corner of the feasible set. (The concept of a "corner" will be defined formally in Chapter 2.)

For a problem in three dimensions, the same approach can be used except that the set of points with the same value of $\mathbf{c}'\mathbf{x}$ is a plane, instead of a line. This plane is again perpendicular to the vector **c**, and the objective is to slide this plane as much as possible in the direction of $-\mathbf{c}$, as long as we do not leave the feasible set.

Example 1.7 Suppose that the feasible set is the unit cube, described by the constraints $0 \le x_i \le 1$, $i = 1, 2, 3$, and that $\mathbf{c} = (-1, -1, -1)$. Then, the vector $\mathbf{x} = (1, 1, 1)$ is an optimal solution. Once more, the optimal solution happens to be a corner of the feasible set (Figure 1.4).

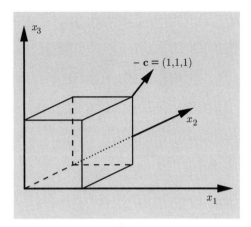

Figure 1.4: The three-dimensional linear programming problem in Example 1.7.

In both of the preceding examples, the feasible set is bounded (does not extend to infinity), and the problem has a unique optimal solution. This is not always the case and we have some additional possibilities that are illustrated by the example that follows.

Example 1.8 Consider the feasible set in $\Re^2$ defined by the constraints

$$\begin{aligned}
-x_1 + x_2 &\leq 1 \\
x_1 &\geq 0 \\
x_2 &\geq 0,
\end{aligned}$$

which is shown in Figure 1.5.

(a) For the cost vector $\mathbf{c} = (1, 1)$, it is clear that $\mathbf{x} = (0, 0)$ is the unique optimal solution.

(b) For the cost vector $\mathbf{c} = (1, 0)$, there are multiple optimal solutions, namely, every vector $\mathbf{x}$ of the form $\mathbf{x} = (0, x_2)$, with $0 \leq x_2 \leq 1$, is optimal. Note that the set of optimal solutions is bounded.

(c) For the cost vector $\mathbf{c} = (0, 1)$, there are multiple optimal solutions, namely, every vector $\mathbf{x}$ of the form $\mathbf{x} = (x_1, 0)$, with $x_1 \geq 0$, is optimal. In this case, the set of optimal solutions is unbounded (contains vectors of arbitrarily large magnitude).

(d) Consider the cost vector $\mathbf{c} = (-1, -1)$. For any feasible solution (x_1, x_2), we can always produce another feasible solution with less cost, by increasing the value of x_1. Therefore, no feasible solution is optimal. Furthermore, by considering vectors (x_1, x_2) with ever increasing values of x_1 and x_2, we can obtain a sequence of feasible solutions whose cost converges to $-\infty$. We therefore say that the optimal cost is $-\infty$.

(e) If we impose an additional constraint of the form $x_1 + x_2 \leq -2$, it is evident that no feasible solution exists.

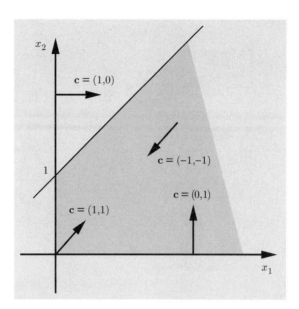

Figure 1.5: The feasible set in Example 1.8. For each choice of
c, an optimal solution is obtained by moving as much as possible
in the direction of −**c**.

To summarize the insights obtained from Example 1.8, we have the
following possibilities:

(a) There exists a unique optimal solution.

(b) There exist multiple optimal solutions; in this case, the set of optimal
     solutions can be either bounded or unbounded.

(c) The optimal cost is −∞, and no feasible solution is optimal.

(d) The feasible set is empty.

In principle, there is an additional possibility: an optimal solution
does not exist even though the problem is feasible and the optimal cost is
not −∞; this is the case, for example, in the problem of minimizing $1/x$
subject to $x > 0$ (for every feasible solution, there exists another with less
cost, but the optimal cost is not −∞). We will see later in this book that
this possibility never arises in linear programming.

In the examples that we have considered, if the problem has at least
one optimal solution, then an optimal solution can be found among the
corners of the feasible set. In Chapter 2, we will show that this is a general
feature of linear programming problems, as long as the feasible set has at
least one corner.

Visualizing standard form problems

We now discuss a method that allows us to visualize standard form problems even if the dimension n of the vector $\mathbf{x}$ is greater than three. The reason for wishing to do so is that when $n \leq 3$, the feasible set of a standard form problem does not have much variety and does not provide enough insight into the general case. (In contrast, if the feasible set is described by constraints of the form $\mathbf{Ax} \geq \mathbf{b}$, enough variety is obtained even if $\mathbf{x}$ has dimension three.)

Suppose that we have a standard form problem, and that the matrix $\mathbf{A}$ has dimensions $m \times n$. In particular, the decision vector $\mathbf{x}$ is of dimension n and we have m equality constraints. We assume that $m \leq n$ and that the constraints $\mathbf{Ax} = \mathbf{b}$ force $\mathbf{x}$ to lie on an $(n - m)$-dimensional set. (Intuitively, each constraint removes one of the "degrees of freedom" of $\mathbf{x}$.) If we "stand" on that $(n - m)$-dimensional set and ignore the m dimensions orthogonal to it, the feasible set is only constrained by the linear inequality constraints $x_i \geq 0$, $i = 1, \ldots, n$. In particular, if $n - m = 2$, the feasible set can be drawn as a two-dimensional set defined by n linear inequality constraints.

To illustrate this approach, consider the feasible set in $\Re^3$ defined by the constraints $x_1 + x_2 + x_3 = 1$ and $x_1, x_2, x_3 \geq 0$ [Figure 1.6(a)], and note that $n = 3$ and $m = 1$. If we stand on the plane defined by the constraint $x_1 + x_2 + x_3 = 1$, then the feasible set has the appearance of a triangle in two-dimensional space. Furthermore, each edge of the triangle corresponds to one of the constraints $x_1, x_2, x_3 \geq 0$; see Figure 1.6(b).

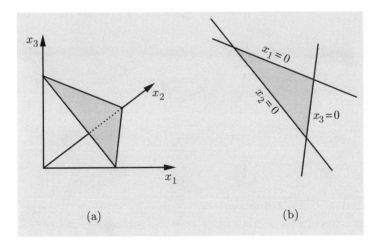

(a)   (b)

Figure 1.6: (a) An n-dimensional view of the feasible set. (b) An $(n - m)$-dimensional view of the same set.

1.5   Linear algebra background and notation

This section provides a summary of the main notational conventions that we will be employing. It also contains a brief review of those results from linear algebra that are used in the sequel.

Set theoretic notation

If S is a set and x is an element of S, we write $x \in S$. A set can be specified in the form $S = \{x \mid x \text{ satisfies } P\}$, as the set of all elements having property P. The cardinality of a finite set S is denoted by $|S|$. The union of two sets S and T is denoted by $S \cup T$, and their intersection by $S \cap T$. We use $S \backslash T$ to denote the set of all elements of S that do not belong to T. The notation $S \subset T$ means that S is a subset of T, i.e., every element of S is also an element of T; in particular, S could be equal to T. If in addition $S \neq T$, we say that S is a *proper* subset of T. We use $\emptyset$ to denote the empty set. The symbols $\exists$ and $\forall$ have the meanings "there exists" and "for all," respectively.

We use $\Re$ to denote the set of real numbers. For any real numbers a and b, we define the closed and open intervals $[a, b]$ and (a, b), respectively, by

$$[a, b] = \{x \in \Re \mid a \leq x \leq b\},$$

and

$$(a, b) = \{x \in \Re \mid a < x < b\}.$$

Vectors and matrices

A *matrix* of dimensions $m \times n$ is an array of real numbers a_{ij}:

$$\mathbf{A} = \begin{bmatrix} a_{11} & a_{12} & \cdots & a_{1n} \\ a_{21} & a_{22} & \cdots & a_{2n} \\ \vdots & \vdots & & \vdots \\ a_{m1} & a_{m2} & \cdots & a_{mn} \end{bmatrix}.$$

Matrices will be always denoted by upper case boldface characters. If $\mathbf{A}$ is a matrix, we use the notation a_{ij} or $[\mathbf{A}]_{ij}$ to refer to its (i, j)th entry. A *row vector* is a matrix with $m = 1$ and a *column vector* is a matrix with $n = 1$. The word *vector* will always mean *column vector* unless the contrary is explicitly stated. Vectors will be usually denoted by lower case boldface characters. We use the notation $\Re^n$ to indicate the set of all n-dimensional vectors. For any vector $\mathbf{x} \in \Re^n$, we use $x_1, x_2, \ldots, x_n$ to indicate its components. Thus,

$$\mathbf{x} = \begin{bmatrix} x_1 \\ x_2 \\ \vdots \\ x_n \end{bmatrix}.$$

The more economical notation $\mathbf{x} = (x_1, x_2, \ldots, x_n)$ will also be used even if we are referring to column vectors. We use $\mathbf{0}$ to denote the vector with all components equal to zero. The ith *unit vector* $\mathbf{e}_i$ is the vector with all components equal to zero except for the ith component which is equal to one.

The *transpose* $\mathbf{A}'$ of an $m \times n$ matrix $\mathbf{A}$ is the $n \times m$ matrix

$$\mathbf{A}' = \begin{bmatrix} a_{11} & a_{21} & \cdots & a_{m1} \\ a_{12} & a_{22} & \cdots & a_{m2} \\ \vdots & \vdots & & \vdots \\ a_{1n} & a_{2n} & \cdots & a_{mn} \end{bmatrix};$$

that is, $[\mathbf{A}']_{ij} = [\mathbf{A}]_{ji}$. Similarly, if $\mathbf{x}$ is a vector in $\Re^n$, its transpose $\mathbf{x}'$ is the row vector with the same entries.

If $\mathbf{x}$ and $\mathbf{y}$ are two vectors in $\Re^n$, then

$$\mathbf{x}'\mathbf{y} = \mathbf{y}'\mathbf{x} = \sum_{i=1}^{n} x_i y_i.$$

This quantity is called the *inner product* of $\mathbf{x}$ and $\mathbf{y}$. Two vectors are called *orthogonal* if their inner product is zero. Note that $\mathbf{x}'\mathbf{x} \geq 0$ for every vector $\mathbf{x}$, with equality holding if and only if $\mathbf{x} = \mathbf{0}$. The expression $\sqrt{\mathbf{x}'\mathbf{x}}$ is the *Euclidean norm* of $\mathbf{x}$ and is denoted by $\|\mathbf{x}\|$. The *Schwartz inequality* asserts that for any two vectors of the same dimension, we have

$$|\mathbf{x}'\mathbf{y}| \leq \|\mathbf{x}\| \cdot \|\mathbf{y}\|,$$

with equality holding if and only if one of the two vectors is a scalar multiple of the other.

If $\mathbf{A}$ is an $m \times n$ matrix, we use $\mathbf{A}_j$ to denote its jth column, that is, $\mathbf{A}_j = (a_{1j}, a_{2j}, \ldots, a_{mj})$. (This is our only exception to the rule of using lower case characters to represent vectors.) We also use $\mathbf{a}_i$ to denote the vector formed by the entries of the ith row, that is, $\mathbf{a}_i = (a_{i1}, a_{i2}, \ldots, a_{in})$. Thus,

$$\mathbf{A} = \begin{bmatrix} | & | & & | \\ \mathbf{A}_1 & \mathbf{A}_2 & \cdots & \mathbf{A}_n \\ | & | & & | \end{bmatrix} = \begin{bmatrix} - & \mathbf{a}_1' & - \\ & \vdots & \\ - & \mathbf{a}_m' & - \end{bmatrix}.$$

Given two matrices $\mathbf{A}$, $\mathbf{B}$ of dimensions $m \times n$ and $n \times k$, respectively, their *product* $\mathbf{AB}$ is a matrix of dimensions $m \times k$ whose entries are given by

$$[\mathbf{AB}]_{ij} = \sum_{\ell=1}^{n} [\mathbf{A}]_{i\ell} [\mathbf{B}]_{\ell j} = \mathbf{a}_i' \mathbf{B}_j,$$

where $\mathbf{a}_i'$ is the ith row of $\mathbf{A}$, and $\mathbf{B}_j$ is the jth column of $\mathbf{B}$. Matrix multiplication is associative, i.e., $(\mathbf{AB})\mathbf{C} = \mathbf{A}(\mathbf{BC})$, but, in general, it is not commutative, that is, the equality $\mathbf{AB} = \mathbf{BA}$ is not always true. We also have $(\mathbf{AB})' = \mathbf{B}'\mathbf{A}'$.

Let $\mathbf{A}$ be an $m \times n$ matrix with columns $\mathbf{A}_i$. We then have $\mathbf{A}\mathbf{e}_i = \mathbf{A}_i$. Any vector $\mathbf{x} \in \Re^n$ can be written in the form $\mathbf{x} = \sum_{i=1}^{n} x_i \mathbf{e}_i$, which leads to

$$\mathbf{A}\mathbf{x} = \mathbf{A} \sum_{i=1}^{n} \mathbf{e}_i x_i = \sum_{i=1}^{n} \mathbf{A}\mathbf{e}_i x_i = \sum_{i=1}^{n} \mathbf{A}_i x_i.$$

A different representation of the matrix-vector product $\mathbf{A}\mathbf{x}$ is provided by the formula

$$\mathbf{A}\mathbf{x} = \begin{bmatrix} \mathbf{a}_1' \mathbf{x} \\ \mathbf{a}_2' \mathbf{x} \\ \vdots \\ \mathbf{a}_m' \mathbf{x} \end{bmatrix},$$

where $\mathbf{a}_1', \ldots, \mathbf{a}_m'$ are the rows of $\mathbf{A}$.

A matrix is called *square* if the number m of its rows is equal to the number n of its columns. We use $\mathbf{I}$ to denote the *identity* matrix, which is a square matrix whose diagonal entries are equal to one and its off-diagonal entries are equal to zero. The identity matrix satisfies $\mathbf{IA} = \mathbf{A}$ and $\mathbf{BI} = \mathbf{B}$ for any matrices $\mathbf{A}$, $\mathbf{B}$ of dimensions compatible with those of $\mathbf{I}$.

If $\mathbf{x}$ is a vector, the notation $\mathbf{x} \geq \mathbf{0}$ and $\mathbf{x} > \mathbf{0}$ means that every component of $\mathbf{x}$ is nonnegative (respectively, positive). If $\mathbf{A}$ is a matrix, the inequalities $\mathbf{A} \geq \mathbf{0}$ and $\mathbf{A} > \mathbf{0}$ have a similar meaning.

Matrix inversion

Let $\mathbf{A}$ be a square matrix. If there exists a square matrix $\mathbf{B}$ of the same dimensions satisfying $\mathbf{AB} = \mathbf{BA} = \mathbf{I}$, we say that $\mathbf{A}$ is *invertible* or *nonsingular*. Such a matrix $\mathbf{B}$, called the *inverse* of $\mathbf{A}$, is unique and is denoted by $\mathbf{A}^{-1}$. We note that $(\mathbf{A}')^{-1} = (\mathbf{A}^{-1})'$. Also, if $\mathbf{A}$ and $\mathbf{B}$ are invertible matrices of the same dimensions, then $\mathbf{AB}$ is also invertible and $(\mathbf{AB})^{-1} = \mathbf{B}^{-1}\mathbf{A}^{-1}$.

Given a finite collection of vectors $\mathbf{x}^1, \ldots, \mathbf{x}^K \in \Re^n$, we say that they are *linearly dependent* if there exist real numbers $a_1, \ldots, a_K$, not all of them zero, such that $\sum_{k=1}^{K} a_k \mathbf{x}^k = \mathbf{0}$; otherwise, they are called *linearly independent*. An equivalent definition of linear independence requires that none of the vectors $\mathbf{x}^1, \dots, \mathbf{x}^K$ is a linear combination of the remaining vectors (Exercise 1.18). We have the following result.

Theorem 1.2 *Let* $\mathbf{A}$ *be a square matrix. Then, the following statements are equivalent:*

  (a) *The matrix* $\mathbf{A}$ *is invertible.*

  (b) *The matrix* $\mathbf{A}'$ *is invertible.*

  (c) *The determinant of* $\mathbf{A}$ *is nonzero.*

  (d) *The rows of* $\mathbf{A}$ *are linearly independent.*

  (e) *The columns of* $\mathbf{A}$ *are linearly independent.*

  (f) *For every vector* $\mathbf{b}$, *the linear system* $\mathbf{A}\mathbf{x} = \mathbf{b}$ *has a unique solution.*

  (g) *There exists some vector* $\mathbf{b}$ *such that the linear system* $\mathbf{A}\mathbf{x} = \mathbf{b}$ *has a unique solution.*

Assuming that $\mathbf{A}$ is an invertible square matrix, an explicit formula for the solution $\mathbf{x} = \mathbf{A}^{-1}\mathbf{b}$ of the system $\mathbf{A}\mathbf{x} = \mathbf{b}$, is given by *Cramer's rule*. Specifically, the jth component of $\mathbf{x}$ is given by

$$x_j = \frac{\det(\mathbf{A}^j)}{\det(\mathbf{A})},$$

where $\mathbf{A}^j$ is the same matrix as $\mathbf{A}$, except that its jth column is replaced by $\mathbf{b}$. Here, as well as later, the notation $\det(\mathbf{A})$ is used to denote the *determinant* of a square matrix $\mathbf{A}$.

Subspaces and bases

A nonempty subset S of $\Re^n$ is called a *subspace* of $\Re^n$ if $a\mathbf{x} + b\mathbf{y} \in S$ for every $\mathbf{x}, \mathbf{y} \in S$ and every $a, b \in \Re$. If, in addition, $S \neq \Re^n$, we say that S is a *proper* subspace. Note that every subspace must contain the zero vector.

The *span* of a finite number of vectors $\mathbf{x}^1, \dots, \mathbf{x}^K$ in $\Re^n$ is the subspace of $\Re^n$ defined as the set of all vectors $\mathbf{y}$ of the form $\mathbf{y} = \sum_{k=1}^{K} a_k \mathbf{x}^k$, where each a_k is a real number. Any such vector $\mathbf{y}$ is called a *linear combination* of $\mathbf{x}^1, \dots, \mathbf{x}^K$.

Given a subspace S of $\Re^n$, with $S \neq \{\mathbf{0}\}$, a *basis* of S is a collection of vectors that are linearly independent and whose span is equal to S. Every basis of a given subspace has the same number of vectors and this number is called the *dimension* of the subspace. In particular, the dimension of $\Re^n$ is equal to n and every proper subspace of $\Re^n$ has dimension smaller than n. Note that one-dimensional subspaces are lines through the origin; two-dimensional subspaces are planes through the origin. Finally, the set $\{\mathbf{0}\}$ is a subspace and its dimension is defined to be zero.

If S is a proper subspace of $\Re^n$, then there exists a nonzero vector $\mathbf{a}$ which is orthogonal to S, that is, $\mathbf{a}'\mathbf{x} = 0$ for every $\mathbf{x} \in S$. More generally, if S has dimension $m < n$, there exist $n - m$ linearly independent vectors that are orthogonal to S.

The result that follows provides some important facts regarding bases and linear independence.

Theorem 1.3 *Suppose that the span S of the vectors $\mathbf{x}^1, \ldots, \mathbf{x}^K$ has dimension m. Then:*

(a) *There exists a basis of S consisting of m of the vectors $\mathbf{x}^1, \ldots, \mathbf{x}^K$.*

(b) *If $k \leq m$ and $\mathbf{x}^1, \ldots, \mathbf{x}^k$ are linearly independent, we can form a basis of S by starting with $\mathbf{x}^1, \ldots, \mathbf{x}^k$, and choosing $m - k$ of the vectors $\mathbf{x}^{k+1}, \ldots, \mathbf{x}^K$.*

Proof.   We only prove part (b), because (a) is the special case of part (b) with $k = 0$. If every vector $\mathbf{x}^{k+1}, \ldots, \mathbf{x}^K$ can be expressed as a linear combination of $\mathbf{x}^1, \ldots, \mathbf{x}^k$, then every vector in the span of $\mathbf{x}^1, \ldots, \mathbf{x}^K$ is also a linear combination of $\mathbf{x}^1, \ldots, \mathbf{x}^k$, and the latter vectors form a basis. (In particular, $m = k$.) Otherwise, at least one of the vectors $\mathbf{x}^{k+1}, \ldots, \mathbf{x}^K$ is linearly independent from $\mathbf{x}^1, \ldots, \mathbf{x}^k$. By picking one such vector, we now have $k + 1$ of the vectors $\mathbf{x}^1, \ldots, \mathbf{x}^K$ that are linearly independent. By repeating this process $m - k$ times, we end up with the desired basis of S. $\qquad\square$

Let $\mathbf{A}$ be a matrix of dimensions $m \times n$. The *column space* of $\mathbf{A}$ is the subspace of $\Re^m$ spanned by the columns of $\mathbf{A}$. The *row space* of $\mathbf{A}$ is the subspace of $\Re^n$ spanned by the rows of $\mathbf{A}$. The dimension of the column space is always equal to the dimension of the row space, and this number is called the *rank* of $\mathbf{A}$. Clearly, $\mathrm{rank}(\mathbf{A}) \leq \min\{m, n\}$. The matrix $\mathbf{A}$ is said to have *full rank* if $\mathrm{rank}(\mathbf{A}) = \min\{m, n\}$. Finally, the set $\{\mathbf{x} \in \Re^n \mid \mathbf{A}\mathbf{x} = \mathbf{0}\}$ is called the *nullspace* of $\mathbf{A}$; it is a subspace of $\Re^n$ and its dimension is equal to $n - \mathrm{rank}(\mathbf{A})$.

Affine subspaces

Let S_0 be a subspace of $\Re^n$ and let $\mathbf{x}^0$ be some vector. If we add $\mathbf{x}^0$ to every element of S_0, this amounts to translating S_0 by $\mathbf{x}^0$. The resulting set S can be defined formally by

$$S = S_0 + \mathbf{x}^0 = \{\mathbf{x} + \mathbf{x}^0 \mid \mathbf{x} \in S_0\}.$$

In general, S is not a subspace, because it does not necessarily contain the zero vector, and it is called an *affine subspace*. The *dimension* of S is defined to be equal to the dimension of the underlying subspace S_0.

As an example, let $\mathbf{x}^0, \mathbf{x}^1, \ldots, \mathbf{x}^k$ be some vectors in $\Re^n$, and consider the set S of all vectors of the form

$$\mathbf{x}^0 + \lambda_1 \mathbf{x}^1 + \cdots + \lambda_k \mathbf{x}^k,$$

where $\lambda_1, \ldots, \lambda_k$ are arbitrary scalars. For this case, S_0 can be identified with the span of the vectors $\mathbf{x}^1, \ldots, \mathbf{x}^k$, and S is an affine subspace. If the vectors $\mathbf{x}^1, \ldots, \mathbf{x}^k$ are linearly independent, their span has dimension k, and the affine subspace S also has dimension k.

For a second example, we are given an $m \times n$ matrix $\mathbf{A}$ and a vector $\mathbf{b} \in \Re^m$, and we consider the set

$$S = \{\mathbf{x} \in \Re^n \mid \mathbf{A}\mathbf{x} = \mathbf{b}\},$$

which we assume to be nonempty. Let us fix some $\mathbf{x}^0$ such that $\mathbf{A}\mathbf{x}^0 = \mathbf{b}$. An arbitrary vector $\mathbf{x}$ belongs to S if and only if $\mathbf{A}\mathbf{x} = \mathbf{b} = \mathbf{A}\mathbf{x}^0$, or $\mathbf{A}(\mathbf{x} - \mathbf{x}^0) = \mathbf{0}$. Hence, $\mathbf{x} \in S$ if and only if $\mathbf{x} - \mathbf{x}^0$ belongs to the subspace $S_0 = \{\mathbf{y} \mid \mathbf{A}\mathbf{y} = \mathbf{0}\}$. We conclude that $S = \{\mathbf{y} + \mathbf{x}^0 \mid \mathbf{y} \in S_0\}$, and S is an affine subspace of $\Re^n$. If $\mathbf{A}$ has m linearly independent rows, its nullspace S_0 has dimension $n - m$. Hence, the affine subspace S also has dimension $n - m$. Intuitively, if $\mathbf{a}'_i$ are the rows of $\mathbf{A}$, each one of the constraints $\mathbf{a}'_i \mathbf{x} = b_i$ removes one degree of freedom from $\mathbf{x}$, thus reducing the dimension from n to $n - m$; see Figure 1.7 for an illustration.

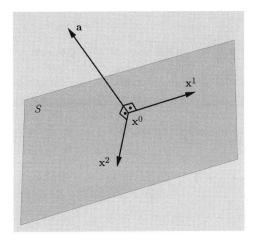

Figure 1.7: Consider a set S in $\Re^3$ defined by a single equality constraint $\mathbf{a}'\mathbf{x} = b$. Let $\mathbf{x}^0$ be an element of S. The vector $\mathbf{a}$ is perpendicular to S. If $\mathbf{x}^1$ and $\mathbf{x}^2$ are linearly independent vectors that are orthogonal to $\mathbf{a}$, then every $\mathbf{x} \in S$ is of the form $\mathbf{x} = \mathbf{x}^0 + \lambda_1 \mathbf{x}^1 + \lambda_2 \mathbf{x}^2$. In particular, S is a two-dimensional affine subspace.

1.6   Algorithms and operation counts

Optimization problems such as linear programming and, more generally, all computational problems are solved by *algorithms*. Loosely speaking, an algorithm is a finite set of instructions of the type used in common programming languages (arithmetic operations, conditional statements, read and write statements, etc.). Although the running time of an algorithm may depend substantially on clever programming or on the computer hardware available, we are interested in comparing algorithms without having to examine the details of a particular implementation. As a first approximation, this can be accomplished by counting the number of arithmetic operations (additions, multiplications, divisions, comparisons) required by an algorithm. This approach is often adequate even though it ignores the fact that adding or multiplying large integers or high-precision floating point numbers is more demanding than adding or multiplying single-digit integers. A more refined approach will be discussed briefly in Chapter 8.

Example 1.9

(a) Let $\mathbf{a}$ and $\mathbf{b}$ be vectors in $\Re^n$. The natural algorithm for computing $\mathbf{a}'\mathbf{b}$ requires n multiplications and $n-1$ additions, for a total of $2n-1$ arithmetic operations.

(b) Let $\mathbf{A}$ and $\mathbf{B}$ be matrices of dimensions $n \times n$. The traditional way of computing $\mathbf{AB}$ forms the inner product of a row of $\mathbf{A}$ and a column of $\mathbf{B}$ to obtain an entry of $\mathbf{AB}$. Since there are n^2 entries to be evaluated, a total of $(2n-1)n^2$ arithmetic operations are involved.

In Example 1.9, an exact operation count was possible. However, for more complicated problems and algorithms, an exact count is usually very difficult. For this reason, we will settle for an estimate of the rate of growth of the number of arithmetic operations, as a function of the problem parameters. Thus, in Example 1.9, we might be content to say that the number of operations in the computation of an inner product increases linearly with n, and the number of operations in matrix multiplication increases cubically with n. This leads us to the order of magnitude notation that we define next.

Definition 1.2 *Let f and g be functions that map positive numbers to positive numbers.*

(a) *We write $f(n) = O\big(g(n)\big)$ if there exist positive numbers n_0 and c such that $f(n) \leq cg(n)$ for all $n \geq n_0$.*

(b) *We write $f(n) = \Omega\big(g(n)\big)$ if there exist positive numbers n_0 and c such that $f(n) \geq cg(n)$ for all $n \geq n_0$.*

(c) *We write $f(n) = \Theta\big(g(n)\big)$ if both $f(n) = O\big(g(n)\big)$ and $f(n) = \Omega\big(g(n)\big)$ hold.*

For example, we have $3n^3 + n^2 + 10 = \Theta(n^3)$, $n \log n = O(n^2)$, and $n \log n = \Omega(n)$.

While the running time of the algorithms considered in Example 1.9 is predictable, the running time of more complicated algorithms often depends on the numerical values of the input data. In such cases, instead of trying to estimate the running time for each possible choice of the input, it is customary to estimate the running time for the *worst possible input data* of a given "size." For example, if we have an algorithm for linear programming, we might be interested in estimating its worst-case running time over all problems with a given number of variables and constraints. This emphasis on the worst case is somewhat conservative and, in practice, the "average" running time of an algorithm might be more relevant. However, the average running time is much more difficult to estimate, or even to define, and for this reason, the worst-case approach is widely used.

Example 1.10 (Operation count of linear system solvers and matrix inversion) Consider the problem of solving a system of n linear equations in n unknowns. The classical method that eliminates one variable at a time (Gaussian elimination) is known to require $O(n^3)$ arithmetic operations in order to either compute a solution or to decide that no solution exists. Practical methods for matrix inversion also require $O(n^3)$ arithmetic operations. These facts will be of use later on.

Is the $O(n^3)$ running time of Gaussian elimination good or bad? Some perspective into this question is provided by the following observation: each time that technological advances lead to computer hardware that is faster by a factor of 8 (presumably every few years), we can solve problems of twice the size than earlier possible. A similar argument applies to algorithms whose running time is $O(n^k)$ for some positive integer k. Such algorithms are said to run in *polynomial time*.

Algorithms also exist whose running time is $\Omega(2^{cn})$, where n is a parameter representing problem size and c is a constant; these are said to take at least *exponential time*. For such algorithms and if $c = 1$, each time that computer hardware becomes faster by a factor of 2, we can increase the value of n that we can handle only by 1. It is then reasonable to expect that no matter how much technology improves, problems with truly large values of n will always be difficult to handle.

Example 1.11 Suppose that we have a choice of two algorithms. The running time of the first is $10^n/100$ (exponential) and the running time of the second is $10n^3$ (polynomial). For very small n, e.g., for $n = 3$, the exponential time algorithm is preferable. To gain some perspective as to what happens for larger n, suppose that we have access to a workstation that can execute 10^7 arithmetic operations per second and that we are willing to let it run for 1000 seconds. Let us figure out what size problems can each algorithm handle within this time frame. The equation $10^n/100 = 10^7 \times 1000$ yields $n = 12$, whereas the equation

$10n^3 = 10^7 \times 1000$ yields $n = 1000$, indicating that the polynomial time algorithm allows us to solve much larger problems.

The point of view emerging from the above discussion is that, as a first cut, it is useful to juxtapose polynomial and exponential time algorithms, the former being viewed as relatively fast and efficient, and the latter as relatively slow. This point of view is justified in many – but not all – contexts and we will be returning to it later in this book.

1.7   Exercises

Exercise 1.1* Suppose that a function $f : \Re^n \mapsto \Re$ is both concave and convex. Prove that f is an affine function.

Exercise 1.2 Suppose that $f_1, \ldots, f_m$ are convex functions from $\Re^n$ into $\Re$ and let $f(\mathbf{x}) = \sum_{i=1}^m f_i(\mathbf{x})$.

(a) Show that if each f_i is convex, so is f.

(b) Show that if each f_i is piecewise linear and convex, so is f.

Exercise 1.3 Consider the problem of minimizing a cost function of the form $\mathbf{c}'\mathbf{x} + f(\mathbf{d}'\mathbf{x})$, subject to the linear constraints $\mathbf{Ax} \geq \mathbf{b}$. Here, $\mathbf{d}$ is a given vector and the function $f : \Re \mapsto \Re$ is as specified in Figure 1.8. Provide a linear programming formulation of this problem.

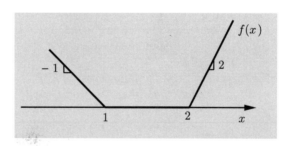

Figure 1.8: The function f of Exercise 1.3.

Exercise 1.4 Consider the problem

$$\begin{aligned} \text{minimize} \quad & 2x_1 + 3|x_2 - 10| \\ \text{subject to} \quad & |x_1 + 2| + |x_2| \leq 5, \end{aligned}$$

and reformulate it as a linear programming problem.

Exercise 1.5 Consider a linear optimization problem, with absolute values, of the following form:

$$\text{minimize} \quad \mathbf{c}'\mathbf{x} + \mathbf{d}'\mathbf{y}$$
$$\text{subject to} \quad \mathbf{Ax} + \mathbf{By} \le \mathbf{b}$$
$$y_i = |x_i|, \qquad \forall\, i.$$

Assume that all entries of $\mathbf{B}$ and $\mathbf{d}$ are nonnegative.

(a) Provide two different linear programming formulations, along the lines discussed in Section 1.3.

(b) Show that the original problem and the two reformulations are equivalent in the sense that either all three are infeasible, or all three have the same optimal cost.

(c) Provide an example to show that if $\mathbf{B}$ has negative entries, the problem may have a local minimum that is not a global minimum. (It will be seen in Chapter 2 that this is never the case in linear programming problems. Hence, in the presence of such negative entries, a linear programming reformulation is implausible.)

Exercise 1.6 Provide linear programming formulations of the two variants of the rocket control problem discussed at the end of Section 1.3.

Exercise 1.7 (**The moment problem**) Suppose that Z is a random variable taking values in the set $0, 1, \ldots, K$, with probabilities $p_0, p_1, \ldots, p_K$, respectively. We are given the values of the first two moments $E[Z] = \sum_{k=0}^{K} k p_k$ and $E[Z^2] = \sum_{k=0}^{K} k^2 p_k$ of Z and we would like to obtain upper and lower bounds on the value of the fourth moment $E[Z^4] = \sum_{k=0}^{K} k^4 p_k$ of Z. Show how linear programming can be used to approach this problem.

Exercise 1.8 (**Road lighting**) Consider a road divided into n segments that is illuminated by m lamps. Let p_j be the power of the jth lamp. The illumination I_i of the ith segment is assumed to be $\sum_{j=1}^{m} a_{ij} p_j$, where a_{ij} are known coefficients. Let I_i^* be the desired illumination of road i.

We are interested in choosing the lamp powers p_j so that the illuminations I_i are close to the desired illuminations I_i^*. Provide a reasonable linear programming formulation of this problem. Note that the wording of the problem is loose and there is more than one possible formulation.

Exercise 1.9 Consider a school district with I neighborhoods, J schools, and G grades at each school. Each school j has a capacity of C_{jg} for grade g. In each neighborhood i, the student population of grade i is S_{ig}. Finally, the distance of school j from neighborhood i is d_{ij}. Formulate a linear programming problem whose objective is to assign all students to schools, while minimizing the total distance traveled by all students. (You may ignore the fact that numbers of students must be integer.)

Exercise 1.10 (**Production and inventory planning**) A company must deliver d_i units of its product at the end of the ith month. Material produced during a month can be delivered either at the end of the same month or can be stored as inventory and delivered at the end of a subsequent month; however, there is a storage cost of c_1 dollars per month for each unit of product held in inventory. The year begins with zero inventory. If the company produces x_i units in month i and x_{i+1} units in month $i+1$, it incurs a cost of $c_2|x_{i+1} - x_i|$ dollars, reflecting the cost of switching to a new production level. Formulate a linear programming problem whose objective is to minimize the total cost of the production and inventory schedule over a period of twelve months. Assume that inventory left at the end of the year has no value and does not incur any storage costs.

Exercise 1.11 (Optimal currency conversion) Suppose that there are N available currencies, and assume that one unit of currency i can be exchanged for r_{ij} units of currency j. (Naturally, we assume that $r_{ij} > 0$.) There also certain regulations that impose a limit u_i on the total amount of currency i that can be exchanged on any given day. Suppose that we start with B units of currency 1 and that we would like to maximize the number of units of currency N that we end up with at the end of the day, through a sequence of currency transactions. Provide a linear programming formulation of this problem. Assume that for any sequence $i_1, \ldots, i_k$ of currencies, we have $r_{i_1 i_2} r_{i_2 i_3} \cdots r_{i_{k-1} i_k} r_{i_k i_1} \leq 1$, which means that wealth cannot be multiplied by going through a cycle of currencies.

Exercise 1.12 (Chebychev center) Consider a set P described by linear inequality constraints, that is, $P = \{\mathbf{x} \in \Re^n \mid \mathbf{a}_i'\mathbf{x} \leq b_i, \ i = 1, \ldots, m\}$. A ball with center $\mathbf{y}$ and radius r is defined as the set of all points within (Euclidean) distance r from $\mathbf{y}$. We are interested in finding a ball with the largest possible radius, which is entirely contained within the set P. (The center of such a ball is called the *Chebychev center* of P.) Provide a linear programming formulation of this problem.

Exercise 1.13 (Linear fractional programming) Consider the problem

$$
\begin{aligned}
\text{minimize} \quad & \frac{\mathbf{c}'\mathbf{x} + d}{\mathbf{f}'\mathbf{x} + g} \\
\text{subject to} \quad & \mathbf{Ax} \leq \mathbf{b} \\
& \mathbf{f}'\mathbf{x} + g > 0.
\end{aligned}
$$

Suppose that we have some prior knowledge that the optimal cost belongs to an interval $[K, L]$. Provide a procedure, that uses linear programming as a subroutine, and that allows us to compute the optimal cost within any desired accuracy. *Hint:* Consider the problem of deciding whether the optimal cost is less than or equal to a certain number.

Exercise 1.14 A company produces and sells two different products. The demand for each product is unlimited, but the company is constrained by cash availability and machine capacity.

    Each unit of the first and second product requires 3 and 4 machine hours, respectively. There are 20,000 machine hours available in the current production period. The production costs are \$3 and \$2 per unit of the first and second product, respectively. The selling prices of the first and second product are \$6 and \$5.40 per unit, respectively. The available cash is \$4,000; furthermore, 45%

of the sales revenues from the first product and 30% of the sales revenues from the second product will be made available to finance operations during the current period.

(a) Formulate a linear programming problem that aims at maximizing net income subject to the cash availability and machine capacity limitations.

(b) Solve the problem graphically to obtain an optimal solution.

(c) Suppose that the company could increase its available machine hours by 2,000, after spending $400 for certain repairs. Should the investment be made?

Exercise 1.15 A company produces two kinds of products. A product of the first type requires 1/4 hours of assembly labor, 1/8 hours of testing, and $1.2 worth of raw materials. A product of the second type requires 1/3 hours of assembly, 1/3 hours of testing, and $0.9 worth of raw materials. Given the current personnel of the company, there can be at most 90 hours of assembly labor and 80 hours of testing, each day. Products of the first and second type have a market value of $9 and $8, respectively.

(a) Formulate a linear programming problem that can be used to maximize the daily profit of the company.

(b) Consider the following two modifications to the original problem:

  (i) Suppose that up to 50 hours of overtime assembly labor can be scheduled, at a cost of $7 per hour.

  (ii) Suppose that the raw material supplier provides a 10% discount if the daily bill is above $300.

  Which of the above two elements can be easily incorporated into the linear programming formulation and how? If one or both are not easy to incorporate, indicate how you might nevertheless solve the problem.

Exercise 1.16 A manager of an oil refinery has 8 million barrels of crude oil A and 5 million barrels of crude oil B allocated for production during the coming month. These resources can be used to make either gasoline, which sells for $38 per barrel, or home heating oil, which sells for $33 per barrel. There are three production processes with the following characteristics:

	Process 1	Process 2	Process 3
Input crude A	3	1	5
Input crude B	5	1	3
Output gasoline	4	1	3
Output heating oil	3	1	4
Cost	$51	$11	$40

All quantities are in barrels. For example, with the first process, 3 barrels of crude A and 5 barrels of crude B are used to produce 4 barrels of gasoline and

3 barrels of heating oil. The costs in this table refer to variable and allocated overhead costs, and there are no separate cost items for the cost of the crudes. Formulate a linear programming problem that would help the manager maximize net revenue over the next month.

Exercise 1.17 (Investment under taxation) An investor has a portfolio of n different stocks. He has bought s_i shares of stock i at price p_i, $i = 1, \ldots, n$. The current price of one share of stock i is q_i. The investor expects that the price of one share of stock i in one year will be r_i. If he sells shares, the investor pays transaction costs at the rate of 1% of the amount transacted. In addition, the investor pays taxes at the rate of 30% on capital gains. For example, suppose that the investor sells 1,000 shares of a stock at $50 per share. He has bought these shares at $30 per share. He receives $50,000. However, he owes $0.30\times(50{,}000 - 30{,}000) = \$6{,}000$ on capital gain taxes and $0.01\times(50{,}000) = \$500$ on transaction costs. So, by selling 1,000 shares of this stock he nets $50{,}000 - 6{,}000 - 500 = \$43{,}500$. Formulate the problem of selecting how many shares the investor needs to sell in order to raise an amount of money K, net of capital gains and transaction costs, while maximizing the expected value of his portfolio next year.

Exercise 1.18 Show that the vectors in a given finite collection are linearly independent if and only if none of the vectors can be expressed as a linear combination of the others.

Exercise 1.19 Suppose that we are given a set of vectors in $\Re^n$ that form a basis, and let $\mathbf{y}$ be an arbitrary vector in $\Re^n$. We wish to express $\mathbf{y}$ as a linear combination of the basis vectors. How can this be accomplished?

Exercise 1.20

(a) Let $S = \{\mathbf{A}\mathbf{x} \mid \mathbf{x} \in \Re^n\}$, where $\mathbf{A}$ is a given matrix. Show that S is a subspace of $\Re^n$.

(b) Assume that S is a proper subspace of $\Re^n$. Show that there exists a matrix $\mathbf{B}$ such that $S = \{\mathbf{y} \in \Re^n \mid \mathbf{B}\mathbf{y} = \mathbf{0}\}$. *Hint:* Use vectors that are orthogonal to S to form the matrix $\mathbf{B}$.

(c) Suppose that V is an m-dimensional affine subspace of $\Re^n$, with $m < n$. Show that there exist linearly independent vectors $\mathbf{a}_1, \ldots, \mathbf{a}_{n-m}$, and scalars $b_1, \ldots, b_{n-m}$, such that

$$V = \left\{\mathbf{y} \mid \mathbf{a}_i'\mathbf{y} = b_i, \ i = 1, \ldots, n - m\right\}.$$

1.8   History, notes, and sources

The word "programming" has been used traditionally by planners to describe the process of operations planning and resource allocation. In the 1940s, it was realized that this process could often be aided by solving optimization problems involving linear constraints and linear objectives. The term "linear programming" then emerged. The initial impetus came in the aftermath of World War II, within the context of military planning problems. In 1947, Dantzig proposed an algorithm, the *simplex method*, which made the solution of linear programming problems practical. There followed a period of intense activity during which many important problems in transportation, economics, military operations, scheduling, etc., were cast in this framework. Since then, computer technology has advanced rapidly, the range of applications has expanded, new powerful methods have been discovered, and the underlying mathematical understanding has become deeper and more comprehensive. Today, linear programming is a routinely used tool that can be found in some spreadsheet software packages.

Dantzig's development of the simplex method has been a defining moment in the history of the field, because it came at a time of growing practical needs and of advances in computing technology. But, as is the case with most "scientific revolutions," the history of the field is much richer. Early work goes back to Fourier, who in 1824 developed an algorithm for solving systems of linear inequalities. Fourier's method is far less efficient than the simplex method, but this issue was not relevant at the time. In 1910, de la Vallée Poussin developed a method, similar to the simplex method, for minimizing $\max_i |b_i - \mathbf{a}'_i\mathbf{x}|$, a problem that we discussed in Section 1.3.

In the late 1930s, the Soviet mathematician Kantorovich became interested in problems of optimal resource allocation in a centrally planned economy, for which he gave linear programming formulations. He also provided a solution method, but his work did not become widely known at the time. Around the same time, several models arising in classical, Walrasian, economics were studied and refined, and led to formulations closely related to linear programming. Koopmans, an economist, played an important role and eventually (in 1975) shared the Nobel Prize in economic science with Kantorovich.

On the theoretical front, the mathematical structures that underlie linear programming were independently studied, in the period 1870-1930, by many prominent mathematicians, such as Farkas, Minkowski, Carathéodory, and others. Also, in 1928, von Neumann developed an important result in game theory that would later prove to have strong connections with the deeper structure of linear programming.

Subsequent to Dantzig's work, there has been much and important research in areas such as large scale optimization, network optimization, interior point methods, integer programming, and complexity theory. We defer the discussion of this research to the notes and sources sections of later chapters. For a more detailed account of the history of linear programming, the reader is referred to Schrijver (1986), Orden (1993), and the volume edited by Lenstra, Rinnooy Kan, and Schrijver (1991) (see especially the article by Dantzig in that volume).

There are several texts that cover the general subject of linear programming, starting with a comprehensive one by Dantzig (1963). Some more recent texts are Papadimitriou and Steiglitz (1982), Chvátal (1983), Murty (1983), Luenberger (1984), Bazaraa, Jarvis, and Sherali (1990). Finally, Schrijver (1986) is a comprehensive, but more advanced reference on the subject.

1.1.   The formulation of the diet problem is due to Stigler (1945).

1.2.   The case study on DEC's production planning was developed by Freund and Shannahan (1992). Methods for dealing with the nurse scheduling and other cyclic problems are studied by Bartholdi, Orlin, and Ratliff (1980). More information on pattern classification can be found in Duda and Hart (1973), or Haykin (1994).

1.3.   A deep and comprehensive treatment of convex functions and their properties is provided by Rockafellar (1970). Linear programming arises in control problems, in ways that are more sophisticated than what is described here; see, e.g., Dahleh and Diaz-Bobillo (1995).

1.5.   For an introduction to linear algebra, see Strang (1988).

1.6.   For a more detailed treatment of algorithms and their computational requirements, see Lewis and Papadimitriou (1981), Papadimitriou and Steiglitz (1982), or Cormen, Leiserson, and Rivest (1990).

1.7.   Exercise 1.8 is adapted from Boyd and Vandenberghe (1995). Exercises 1.9 and 1.14 are adapted from Bradley, Hax, and Magnanti (1977). Exercise 1.11 is adapted from Ahuja, Magnanti, and Orlin (1993).

Chapter 2

The geometry of linear programming

Contents

In this chapter, we define a polyhedron as a set described by a finite number of linear equality and inequality constraints. In particular, the feasible set in a linear programming problem is a polyhedron. We study the basic geometric properties of polyhedra in some detail, with emphasis on their "corner points" (vertices). As it turns out, common geometric intuition derived from the familiar three-dimensional polyhedra is essentially correct when applied to higher-dimensional polyhedra. Another interesting aspect of the development in this chapter is that certain concepts (e.g., the concept of a vertex) can be defined either geometrically or algebraically. While the geometric view may be more natural, the algebraic approach is essential for carrying out computations. Much of the richness of the subject lies in the interplay between the geometric and the algebraic points of view.

Our development starts with a characterization of the corner points of feasible sets in the general form $\{x \mid Ax \geq b\}$. Later on, we focus on the case where the feasible set is in the standard form $\{x \mid Ax = b,\ x \geq 0\}$, and we derive a simple algebraic characterization of the corner points. The latter characterization will play a central role in the development of the simplex method in Chapter 3.

The main results of this chapter state that a nonempty polyhedron has at least one corner point if and only if it does not contain a line, and if this is the case, the search for optimal solutions to linear programming problems can be restricted to corner points. These results are proved for the most general case of linear programming problems using geometric arguments. The same results will also be proved in the next chapter, for the case of standard form problems, as a corollary of our development of the simplex method. Thus, the reader who wishes to focus on standard form problems may skip the proofs in Sections 2.5 and 2.6. Finally, Sections 2.7 and 2.8 can also be skipped during a first reading; any results in these sections that are needed later on will be rederived in Chapter 4, using different techniques.

2.1 Polyhedra and convex sets

In this section, we introduce some important concepts that will be used to study the geometry of linear programming, including a discussion of convexity.

Hyperplanes, halfspaces, and polyhedra

We start with the formal definition of a polyhedron.

Definition 2.1 *A **polyhedron** is a set that can be described in the form $\{x \in \Re^n \mid Ax \geq b\}$, where A is an $m \times n$ matrix and b is a vector in $\Re^m$.*

As discussed in Section 1.1, the feasible set of any linear programming problem can be described by inequality constraints of the form $\mathbf{A}\mathbf{x} \geq \mathbf{b}$, and is therefore a polyhedron. In particular, a set of the form $\{\mathbf{x} \in \Re^n \mid \mathbf{A}\mathbf{x} = \mathbf{b}, \ \mathbf{x} \geq \mathbf{0}\}$ is also a polyhedron and will be referred to as a *polyhedron in standard form*.

A polyhedron can either "extend to infinity," or can be confined in a finite region. The definition that follows refers to this distinction.

Definition 2.2 *A set $S \subset \Re^n$ is* **bounded** *if there exists a constant K such that the absolute value of every component of every element of S is less than or equal to K.*

The next definition deals with polyhedra determined by a single linear constraint.

Definition 2.3 *Let $\mathbf{a}$ be a nonzero vector in $\Re^n$ and let b be a scalar.*
(a)   *The set $\{\mathbf{x} \in \Re^n \mid \mathbf{a}'\mathbf{x} = b\}$ is called a* **hyperplane**.
(b)   *The set $\{\mathbf{x} \in \Re^n \mid \mathbf{a}'\mathbf{x} \geq b\}$ is called a* **halfspace**.

Note that a hyperplane is the boundary of a corresponding halfspace. In addition, the vector $\mathbf{a}$ in the definition of the hyperplane is perpendicular to the hyperplane itself. [To see this, note that if $\mathbf{x}$ and $\mathbf{y}$ belong to the same hyperplane, then $\mathbf{a}'\mathbf{x} = \mathbf{a}'\mathbf{y}$. Hence, $\mathbf{a}'(\mathbf{x} - \mathbf{y}) = 0$ and therefore $\mathbf{a}$ is orthogonal to any direction vector confined to the hyperplane.] Finally, note that a polyhedron is equal to the intersection of a finite number of halfspaces; see Figure 2.1.

Convex Sets

We now define the important notion of a convex set.

Definition 2.4 *A set $S \subset \Re^n$ is* **convex** *if for any $\mathbf{x}, \mathbf{y} \in S$, and any $\lambda \in [0, 1]$, we have $\lambda \mathbf{x} + (1 - \lambda)\mathbf{y} \in S$.*

Note that if $\lambda \in [0, 1]$, then $\lambda \mathbf{x} + (1 - \lambda)\mathbf{y}$ is a weighted average of the vectors $\mathbf{x}, \mathbf{y}$, and therefore belongs to the line segment joining $\mathbf{x}$ and $\mathbf{y}$. Thus, a set is convex if the segment joining any two of its elements is contained in the set; see Figure 2.2.

Our next definition refers to weighted averages of a finite number of vectors; see Figure 2.3.

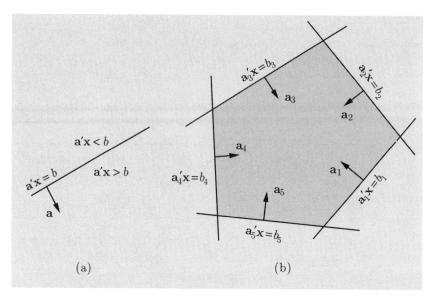

Figure 2.1: (a) A hyperplane and two halfspaces. (b) The poly-hedron $\{\mathbf{x} \mid \mathbf{a}_i'\mathbf{x} \geq b_i, \ i = 1, \ldots, 5\}$ is the intersection of five halfs-paces. Note that each vector $\mathbf{a}_i$ is perpendicular to the hyperplane $\{\mathbf{x} \mid \mathbf{a}_i'\mathbf{x} = b_i\}$.

Definition 2.5 *Let* $\mathbf{x}^1, \ldots, \mathbf{x}^k$ *be vectors in* $\Re^n$ *and let* $\lambda_1, \ldots, \lambda_k$ *be nonnegative scalars whose sum is unity.*

(a) *The vector* $\sum_{i=1}^{k} \lambda_i \mathbf{x}^i$ *is said to be a* **convex combination** *of the vectors* $\mathbf{x}^1, \ldots, \mathbf{x}^k$.

(b) *The* **convex hull** *of the vectors* $\mathbf{x}^1, \ldots, \mathbf{x}^k$ *is the set of all convex combinations of these vectors.*

The result that follows establishes some important facts related to convexity.

Theorem 2.1

(a) *The intersection of convex sets is convex.*

(b) *Every polyhedron is a convex set.*

(c) *A convex combination of a finite number of elements of a convex set also belongs to that set.*

(d) *The convex hull of a finite number of vectors is a convex set.*

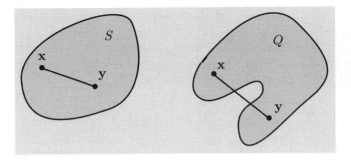

Figure 2.2: The set S is convex, but the set Q is not, because the segment joining $\mathbf{x}$ and $\mathbf{y}$ is not contained in Q.

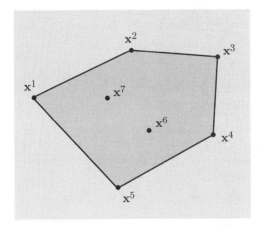

Figure 2.3: The convex hull of seven points in $\Re^2$.

Proof.

(a) Let S_i, $i \in I$, be convex sets where I is some index set, and suppose that $\mathbf{x}$ and $\mathbf{y}$ belong to the intersection $\cap_{i \in I} S_i$. Let $\lambda \in [0,1]$. Since each S_i is convex and contains $\mathbf{x}, \mathbf{y}$, we have $\lambda \mathbf{x} + (1-\lambda)\mathbf{y} \in S_i$, which proves that $\lambda \mathbf{x} + (1-\lambda)\mathbf{y}$ also belongs to the intersection of the sets S_i. Therefore, $\cap_{i \in I} S_i$ is convex.

(b) Let $\mathbf{a}$ be a vector and let b a scalar. Suppose that $\mathbf{x}$ and $\mathbf{y}$ satisfy $\mathbf{a}'\mathbf{x} \geq b$ and $\mathbf{a}'\mathbf{y} \geq b$, respectively, and therefore belong to the same halfspace. Let $\lambda \in [0,1]$. Then, $\mathbf{a}'(\lambda \mathbf{x} + (1-\lambda)\mathbf{y}) \geq \lambda b + (1-\lambda)b = b$, which proves that $\lambda \mathbf{x} + (1-\lambda)\mathbf{y}$ also belongs to the same halfspace. Therefore a halfspace is convex. Since a polyhedron is the intersection of a finite number of halfspaces, the result follows from part (a).

(c) A convex combination of two elements of a convex set lies in that set, by the definition of convexity. Let us assume, as an induction hypothesis, that a convex combination of k elements of a convex set belongs to that set. Consider $k+1$ elements $\mathbf{x}^1, \ldots, \mathbf{x}^{k+1}$ of a convex set S and let $\lambda_1, \ldots, \lambda_{k+1}$ be nonnegative scalars that sum to 1. We assume, without loss of generality, that $\lambda_{k+1} \neq 1$. We then have

$$\sum_{i=1}^{k+1} \lambda_i \mathbf{x}^i = \lambda_{k+1} \mathbf{x}^{k+1} + (1 - \lambda_{k+1}) \sum_{i=1}^{k} \frac{\lambda_i}{1 - \lambda_{k+1}} \mathbf{x}^i. \qquad (2.1)$$

The coefficients $\lambda_i / (1 - \lambda_{k+1})$, $i = 1, \ldots, k$, are nonnegative and sum to unity; using the induction hypothesis, $\sum_{i=1}^{k} \lambda_i \mathbf{x}^i / (1 - \lambda_{k+1}) \in S$. Then, the fact that S is convex and Eq. (2.1) imply that $\sum_{i=1}^{k+1} \lambda_i \mathbf{x}^i \in S$, and the induction step is complete.

(d) Let S be the convex hull of the vectors $\mathbf{x}^1, \ldots, \mathbf{x}^k$ and let $\mathbf{y} = \sum_{i=1}^{k} \zeta_i \mathbf{x}^i$, $\mathbf{z} = \sum_{i=1}^{k} \theta_i \mathbf{x}^i$ be two elements of S, where $\zeta_i \geq 0$, $\theta_i \geq 0$, and $\sum_{i=1}^{k} \zeta_i = \sum_{i=1}^{k} \theta_i = 1$. Let $\lambda \in [0, 1]$. Then,

$$\lambda \mathbf{y} + (1 - \lambda) \mathbf{z} = \lambda \sum_{i=1}^{k} \zeta_i \mathbf{x}^i + (1 - \lambda) \sum_{i=1}^{k} \theta_i \mathbf{x}^i = \sum_{i=1}^{k} \big(\lambda \zeta_i + (1 - \lambda) \theta_i \big) \mathbf{x}^i.$$

We note that the coefficients $\lambda \zeta_i + (1 - \lambda) \theta_i$, $i = 1, \ldots, k$, are nonnegative and sum to unity. This shows that $\lambda \mathbf{y} + (1 - \lambda) \mathbf{z}$ is a convex combination of $\mathbf{x}^1, \ldots, \mathbf{x}^k$ and, therefore, belongs to S. This establishes the convexity of S. $\square$

2.2 Extreme points, vertices, and basic feasible solutions

We observed in Section 1.4 that an optimal solution to a linear programming problem tends to occur at a "corner" of the polyhedron over which we are optimizing. In this section, we suggest three different ways of defining the concept of a "corner" and then show that all three definitions are equivalent.

Our first definition defines an *extreme point* of a polyhedron as a point that cannot be expressed as a convex combination of two other elements of the polyhedron, and is illustrated in Figure 2.4. Notice that this definition is entirely geometric and does not refer to a specific representation of a polyhedron in terms of linear constraints.

Definition 2.6 *Let P be a polyhedron. A vector $\mathbf{x} \in P$ is an extreme point of P if we cannot find two vectors $\mathbf{y}, \mathbf{z} \in P$, both different from $\mathbf{x}$, and a scalar $\lambda \in [0, 1]$, such that $\mathbf{x} = \lambda \mathbf{y} + (1 - \lambda) \mathbf{z}$.*

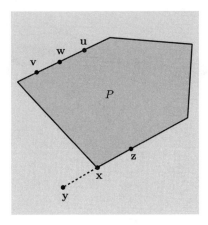

Figure 2.4: The vector **w** is not an extreme point because it is a convex combination of **v** and **u**. The vector **x** is an extreme point: if $\mathbf{x} = \lambda\mathbf{y} + (1 - \lambda)\mathbf{z}$ and $\lambda \in [0, 1]$, then either $\mathbf{y} \notin P$, or $\mathbf{z} \notin P$, or $\mathbf{x} = \mathbf{y}$, or $\mathbf{x} = \mathbf{z}$.

An alternative geometric definition defines a *vertex* of a polyhedron P as the unique optimal solution to some linear programming problem with feasible set P.

Definition 2.7 *Let P be a polyhedron. A vector $\mathbf{x} \in P$ is a* **vertex** *of P if there exists some $\mathbf{c}$ such that $\mathbf{c}'\mathbf{x} < \mathbf{c}'\mathbf{y}$ for all $\mathbf{y}$ satisfying $\mathbf{y} \in P$ and $\mathbf{y} \neq \mathbf{x}$.*

In other words, $\mathbf{x}$ is a vertex of P if and only if P is on one side of a hyperplane (the hyperplane $\{\mathbf{y} \mid \mathbf{c}'\mathbf{y} = \mathbf{c}'\mathbf{x}\}$) which meets P only at the point $\mathbf{x}$; see Figure 2.5.

The two geometric definitions that we have given so far are not easy to work with from an algorithmic point of view. We would like to have a definition that relies on a representation of a polyhedron in terms of linear constraints and which reduces to an algebraic test. In order to provide such a definition, we need some more terminology.

Consider a polyhedron $P \subset \Re^n$ defined in terms of the linear equality and inequality constraints

$$\mathbf{a}_i'\mathbf{x} \geq b_i, \qquad i \in M_1,$$
$$\mathbf{a}_i'\mathbf{x} \leq b_i, \qquad i \in M_2,$$
$$\mathbf{a}_i'\mathbf{x} = b_i, \qquad i \in M_3,$$

where M_1, M_2, and M_3 are finite index sets, each $\mathbf{a}_i$ is a vector in $\Re^n$, and

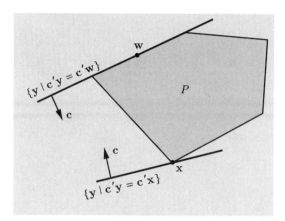

Figure 2.5: The line at the bottom touches P at a single point and $\mathbf{x}$ is a vertex. On the other hand, $\mathbf{w}$ is not a vertex because there is no hyperplane that meets P only at $\mathbf{w}$.

each b_i is a scalar. The definition that follows is illustrated in Figure 2.6.

Definition 2.8 *If a vector $\mathbf{x}^*$ satisfies $\mathbf{a}_i'\mathbf{x}^* = b_i$ for some i in M_1, M_2, or M_3, we say that the corresponding constraint is **active** or **binding** at $\mathbf{x}^*$.*

If there are n constraints that are active at a vector $\mathbf{x}^*$, then $\mathbf{x}^*$ satisfies a certain system of n linear equations in n unknowns. This system has a unique solution if and only if these n equations are "linearly independent." The result that follows gives a precise meaning to this statement, together with a slight generalization.

Theorem 2.2 *Let $\mathbf{x}^*$ be an element of $\Re^n$ and let $I = \{i \mid \mathbf{a}_i'\mathbf{x}^* = b_i\}$ be the set of indices of constraints that are active at $\mathbf{x}^*$. Then, the following are equivalent:*

  (a) *There exist n vectors in the set $\{\mathbf{a}_i \mid i \in I\}$, which are linearly independent.*

  (b) *The span of the vectors $\mathbf{a}_i$, $i \in I$, is all of $\Re^n$, that is, every element of $\Re^n$ can be expressed as a linear combination of the vectors $\mathbf{a}_i$, $i \in I$.*

  (c) *The system of equations $\mathbf{a}_i'\mathbf{x} = b_i$, $i \in I$, has a unique solution.*

Proof. Suppose that the vectors $\mathbf{a}_i$, $i \in I$, span $\Re^n$. Then, the span of these vectors has dimension n. By Theorem 1.3(a) in Section 1.5, n of

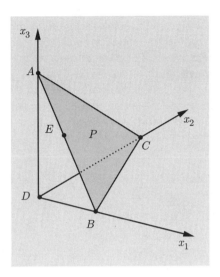

Figure 2.6: Let $P = \big\{(x_1, x_2, x_3) \mid x_1 + x_2 + x_3 = 1,\ x_1, x_2, x_3 \geq 0\big\}$. There are three constraints that are active at each one of the points A, B, C and D. There are only two constraints that are active at point E, namely $x_1 + x_2 + x_3 = 1$ and $x_2 = 0$.

these vectors form a basis of $\Re^n$, and are therefore linearly independent. Conversely, suppose that n of the vectors $\mathbf{a}_i$, $i \in I$, are linearly independent. Then, the subspace spanned by these n vectors is n-dimensional and must be equal to $\Re^n$. Hence, every element of $\Re^n$ is a linear combination of the vectors $\mathbf{a}_i$, $i \in I$. This establishes the equivalence of (a) and (b).

If the system of equations $\mathbf{a}_i'\mathbf{x} = b_i$, $i \in I$, has multiple solutions, say $\mathbf{x}^1$ and $\mathbf{x}^2$, then the nonzero vector $\mathbf{d} = \mathbf{x}^1 - \mathbf{x}^2$ satisfies $\mathbf{a}_i'\mathbf{d} = 0$ for all $i \in I$. Since $\mathbf{d}$ is orthogonal to every vector $\mathbf{a}_i$, $i \in I$, $\mathbf{d}$ is not a linear combination of these vectors and it follows that the vectors $\mathbf{a}_i$, $i \in I$, do not span $\Re^n$. Conversely, if the vectors $\mathbf{a}_i$, $i \in I$, do not span $\Re^n$, choose a nonzero vector $\mathbf{d}$ which is orthogonal to the subspace spanned by these vectors. If $\mathbf{x}$ satisfies $\mathbf{a}_i'\mathbf{x} = b_i$ for all $i \in I$, we also have $\mathbf{a}_i'(\mathbf{x} + \mathbf{d}) = b_i$ for all $i \in I$, thus obtaining multiple solutions. We have therefore established that (b) and (c) are equivalent. $\square$

With a slight abuse of language, we will often say that certain *constraints* are *linearly independent*, meaning that the corresponding vectors $\mathbf{a}_i$ are linearly independent. With this terminology, statement (a) in Theorem 2.2 requires that there exist n linearly independent constraints that are active at $\mathbf{x}^*$.

We are now ready to provide an algebraic definition of a corner point, as a feasible solution at which there are n linearly independent active constraints. Note that since we are interested in a feasible solution, all equality constraints must be active. This suggests the following way of looking for corner points: first impose the equality constraints and then require that enough additional constraints be active, so that we get a total of n linearly independent active constraints. Once we have n linearly independent active constraints, a unique vector $\mathbf{x}^*$ is determined (Theorem 2.2). However, this procedure has no guarantee of leading to a feasible vector $\mathbf{x}^*$, because some of the inactive constraints could be violated; in the latter case we say that we have a basic (but not basic feasible) solution.

Definition 2.9 *Consider a polyhedron P defined by linear equality and inequality constraints, and let $\mathbf{x}^*$ be an element of $\Re^n$.*

(a) *The vector $\mathbf{x}^*$ is a **basic solution** if:*

   (i) *All equality constraints are active;*

   (ii) *Out of the constraints that are active at $\mathbf{x}^*$, there are n of them that are linearly independent.*

(b) *If $\mathbf{x}^*$ is a basic solution that satisfies all of the constraints, we say that it is a **basic feasible solution**.*

In reference to Figure 2.6, we note that points A, B, and C are basic feasible solutions. Point D is not a basic solution because it fails to satisfy the equality constraint. Point E is feasible, but not basic. If the equality constraint $x_1 + x_2 + x_3 = 1$ were to be replaced by the constraints $x_1 + x_2 + x_3 \leq 1$ and $x_1 + x_2 + x_3 \geq 1$, then D would be a basic solution, according to our definition. This shows that whether a point is a basic solution or not may depend on the way that a polyhedron is represented. Definition 2.9 is also illustrated in Figure 2.7.

Note that if the number m of constraints used to define a polyhedron $P \subset \Re^n$ is less than n, the number of active constraints at any given point must also be less than n, and there are no basic or basic feasible solutions.

We have given so far three different definitions that are meant to capture the same concept; two of them are geometric (extreme point, vertex) and the third is algebraic (basic feasible solution). Fortunately, all three definitions are equivalent as we prove next and, for this reason, the three terms can be used interchangeably.

Theorem 2.3 *Let P be a nonempty polyhedron and let $\mathbf{x}^* \in P$. Then, the following are equivalent:*

(a) *$\mathbf{x}^*$ is a vertex;*

(b) *$\mathbf{x}^*$ is an extreme point;*

(c) *$\mathbf{x}^*$ is a basic feasible solution.*

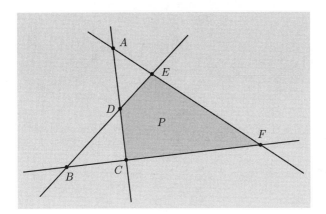

Figure 2.7: The points A, B, C, D, E, F are all basic solutions because at each one of them, there are two linearly independent constraints that are active. Points C, D, E, F are basic feasible solutions.

Proof. For the purposes of this proof and without loss of generality, we assume that P is represented in terms of constraints of the form $\mathbf{a}_i'\mathbf{x} \geq b_i$ and $\mathbf{a}_i'\mathbf{x} = b_i$.

Vertex ⇒ Extreme point

Suppose that $\mathbf{x}^* \in P$ is a vertex. Then, by Definition 2.7, there exists some $\mathbf{c} \in \Re^n$ such that $\mathbf{c}'\mathbf{x}^* < \mathbf{c}'\mathbf{y}$ for every $\mathbf{y}$ satisfying $\mathbf{y} \in P$ and $\mathbf{y} \neq \mathbf{x}^*$. If $\mathbf{y} \in P$, $\mathbf{z} \in P$, $\mathbf{y} \neq \mathbf{x}^*$, $\mathbf{z} \neq \mathbf{x}^*$, and $0 \leq \lambda \leq 1$, then $\mathbf{c}'\mathbf{x}^* < \mathbf{c}'\mathbf{y}$ and $\mathbf{c}'\mathbf{x}^* < \mathbf{c}'\mathbf{z}$, which implies that $\mathbf{c}'\mathbf{x}^* < \mathbf{c}'(\lambda\mathbf{y} + (1 - \lambda)\mathbf{z})$ and, therefore, $\mathbf{x}^* \neq \lambda\mathbf{y}+(1-\lambda)\mathbf{z}$. Thus, $\mathbf{x}^*$ cannot be expressed as a convex combination of two other elements of P and is, therefore, an extreme point (cf. Definition 2.6).

Extreme point ⇒ Basic feasible solution

Suppose that $\mathbf{x}^* \in P$ is not a basic feasible solution. We will show that $\mathbf{x}^*$ is not an extreme point of P. Let $I = \{i \mid \mathbf{a}_i'\mathbf{x}^* = b_i\}$. Since $\mathbf{x}^*$ is not a basic feasible solution, there do not exist n linearly independent vectors in the family $\mathbf{a}_i$, $i \in I$. Thus, the vectors $\mathbf{a}_i$, $i \in I$, lie in a proper subspace of $\Re^n$, and there exists some nonzero vector $\mathbf{d} \in \Re^n$ such that $\mathbf{a}_i'\mathbf{d} = 0$, for all $i \in I$. Let ϵ be a small positive number and consider the vectors $\mathbf{y} = \mathbf{x}^* + \epsilon\mathbf{d}$ and $\mathbf{z} = \mathbf{x}^* - \epsilon\mathbf{d}$. Notice that $\mathbf{a}_i'\mathbf{y} = \mathbf{a}_i'\mathbf{x}^* = b_i$, for $i \in I$. Furthermore, for $i \notin I$, we have $\mathbf{a}_i'\mathbf{x}^* > b_i$ and, provided that ϵ is small, we will also have $\mathbf{a}_i'\mathbf{y} > b_i$. (It suffices to choose ϵ so that $\epsilon|\mathbf{a}_i'\mathbf{d}| < \mathbf{a}_i'\mathbf{x}^* - b_i$ for all $i \notin I$.) Thus, when ϵ is small enough, $\mathbf{y} \in P$ and, by a similar argument, $\mathbf{z} \in P$. We finally notice that $\mathbf{x}^* = (\mathbf{y} + \mathbf{z})/2$, which implies that $\mathbf{x}^*$ is not an extreme point.

Basic feasible solution ⇒ Vertex

Let $\mathbf{x}^*$ be a basic feasible solution and let $I = \{i \mid \mathbf{a}_i'\mathbf{x}^* = b_i\}$. Let $\mathbf{c} = \sum_{i \in I} \mathbf{a}_i$. We then have

$$\mathbf{c}'\mathbf{x}^* = \sum_{i \in I} \mathbf{a}_i'\mathbf{x}^* = \sum_{i \in I} b_i.$$

Furthermore, for any $\mathbf{x} \in P$ and any i, we have $\mathbf{a}_i'\mathbf{x} \geq b_i$, and

$$\mathbf{c}'\mathbf{x} = \sum_{i \in I} \mathbf{a}_i'\mathbf{x} \geq \sum_{i \in I} b_i. \tag{2.2}$$

This shows that $\mathbf{x}^*$ is an optimal solution to the problem of minimizing $\mathbf{c}'\mathbf{x}$ over the set P. Furthermore, equality holds in (2.2) if and only if $\mathbf{a}_i'\mathbf{x} = b_i$ for all $i \in I$. Since $\mathbf{x}^*$ is a basic feasible solution, there are n linearly independent constraints that are active at $\mathbf{x}^*$, and $\mathbf{x}^*$ is the unique solution to the system of equations $\mathbf{a}_i'\mathbf{x} = b_i$, $i \in I$ (Theorem 2.2). It follows that $\mathbf{x}^*$ is the unique minimizer of $\mathbf{c}'\mathbf{x}$ over the set P and, therefore, $\mathbf{x}^*$ is a vertex of P.   □

Since a vector is a basic feasible solution if and only if it is an extreme point, and since the definition of an extreme point does not refer to any particular representation of a polyhedron, we conclude that the property of being a basic feasible solution is also independent of the representation used. (This is in contrast to the definition of a basic solution, which is representation dependent, as pointed out in the discussion that followed Definition 2.9.)

We finally note the following important fact.

Corollary 2.1 *Given a finite number of linear inequality constraints, there can only be a finite number of basic or basic feasible solutions.*

Proof. Consider a system of m linear inequality constraints imposed on a vector $\mathbf{x} \in \Re^n$. At any basic solution, there are n linearly independent active constraints. Since any n linearly independent active constraints define a unique point, it follows that different basic solutions correspond to different sets of n linearly independent active constraints. Therefore, the number of basic solutions is bounded above by the number of ways that we can choose n constraints out of a total of m, which is finite.   □

Although the number of basic and, therefore, basic feasible solutions is guaranteed to be finite, it can be very large. For example, the unit cube $\{\mathbf{x} \in \Re^n \mid 0 \leq x_i \leq 1,\ i = 1, \ldots, n\}$ is defined in terms of $2n$ constraints, but has 2^n basic feasible solutions.

Adjacent basic solutions

Two distinct basic solutions to a set of linear constraints in $\Re^n$ are said to be *adjacent* if we can find $n - 1$ linearly independent constraints that are active at both of them. In reference to Figure 2.7, D and E are adjacent to B; also, A and C are adjacent to D. If two adjacent basic solutions are also feasible, then the line segment that joins them is called an *edge* of the feasible set (see also Exercise 2.15).

2.3   Polyhedra in standard form

The definition of a basic solution (Definition 2.9) refers to general polyhedra. We will now specialize to polyhedra in standard form. The definitions and the results in this section are central to the development of the simplex method in the next chapter.

Let $P = \{\mathbf{x} \in \Re^n \mid \mathbf{Ax} = \mathbf{b},\ \mathbf{x} \geq \mathbf{0}\}$ be a polyhedron in standard form, and let the dimensions of $\mathbf{A}$ be $m \times n$, where m is the number of equality constraints. In most of our discussion of standard form problems, we will make the assumption that the m rows of the matrix $\mathbf{A}$ are linearly independent. (Since the rows are n-dimensional, this requires that $m \leq n$.) At the end of this section, we show that when P is nonempty, linearly dependent rows of $\mathbf{A}$ correspond to redundant constraints that can be discarded; therefore, our linear independence assumption can be made without loss of generality.

Recall that at any basic solution, there must be n linearly independent constraints that are active. Furthermore, every basic solution must satisfy the equality constraints $\mathbf{Ax} = \mathbf{b}$, which provides us with m active constraints; these are linearly independent because of our assumption on the rows of $\mathbf{A}$. In order to obtain a total of n active constraints, we need to choose $n - m$ of the variables x_i and set them to zero, which makes the corresponding nonnegativity constraints $x_i \geq 0$ active. However, for the resulting set of n active constraints to be linearly independent, the choice of these $n - m$ variables is not entirely arbitrary, as shown by the following result.

Theorem 2.4 *Consider the constraints $\mathbf{Ax} = \mathbf{b}$ and $\mathbf{x} \geq \mathbf{0}$ and assume that the $m \times n$ matrix $\mathbf{A}$ has linearly independent rows. A vector $\mathbf{x} \in \Re^n$ is a basic solution if and only if we have $\mathbf{Ax} = \mathbf{b}$, and there exist indices $B(1), \ldots, B(m)$ such that:*

(a) *The columns $\mathbf{A}_{B(1)}, \ldots, \mathbf{A}_{B(m)}$ are linearly independent;*

(b) *If $i \neq B(1), \ldots, B(m)$, then $x_i = 0$.*

Proof. Consider some $\mathbf{x} \in \Re^n$ and suppose that there are indices $B(1), \ldots,$

$B(m)$ that satisfy (a) and (b) in the statement of the theorem. The active constraints $x_i = 0$, $i \neq B(1), \ldots, B(m)$, and $\mathbf{A}\mathbf{x} = \mathbf{b}$ imply that

$$\sum_{i=1}^{m} \mathbf{A}_{B(i)} x_{B(i)} = \sum_{i=1}^{n} \mathbf{A}_i x_i = \mathbf{A}\mathbf{x} = \mathbf{b}.$$

Since the columns $\mathbf{A}_{B(i)}$, $i = 1, \ldots, m$, are linearly independent, $x_{B(1)}, \ldots,$ $x_{B(m)}$ are uniquely determined. Thus, the system of equations formed by the active constraints has a unique solution. By Theorem 2.2, there are n linearly independent active constraints, and this implies that $\mathbf{x}$ is a basic solution.

For the converse, we assume that $\mathbf{x}$ is a basic solution and we will show that conditions (a) and (b) in the statement of the theorem are satisfied. Let $x_{B(1)}, \ldots, x_{B(k)}$ be the components of $\mathbf{x}$ that are nonzero. Since $\mathbf{x}$ is a basic solution, the system of equations formed by the active constraints $\sum_{i=1}^{n} \mathbf{A}_i x_i = \mathbf{b}$ and $x_i = 0$, $i \neq B(1), \ldots, B(k)$, have a unique solution (cf. Theorem 2.2); equivalently, the equation $\sum_{i=1}^{k} \mathbf{A}_{B(i)} x_{B(i)} = \mathbf{b}$ has a unique solution. It follows that the columns $\mathbf{A}_{B(1)}, \ldots, \mathbf{A}_{B(k)}$ are linearly independent. [If they were not, we could find scalars $\lambda_1, \ldots, \lambda_k$, not all of them zero, such that $\sum_{i=1}^{k} \mathbf{A}_{B(i)} \lambda_i = 0$. This would imply that $\sum_{i=1}^{k} \mathbf{A}_{B(i)}(x_{B(i)} + \lambda_i) = \mathbf{b}$, contradicting the uniqueness of the solution.]

We have shown that the columns $\mathbf{A}_{B(1)}, \ldots, \mathbf{A}_{B(k)}$ are linearly independent and this implies that $k \leq m$. Since $\mathbf{A}$ has m linearly independent rows, it also has m linearly independent columns, which span $\Re^m$. It follows [cf. Theorem 1.3(b) in Section 1.5] that we can find $m-k$ additional columns $\mathbf{A}_{B(k+1)}, \ldots, \mathbf{A}_{B(m)}$ so that the columns $\mathbf{A}_{B(i)}$, $i = 1, \ldots, m$, are linearly independent. In addition, if $i \neq B(1), \ldots, B(m)$, then $i \neq B(1), \ldots, B(k)$ (because $k \leq m$), and $x_i = 0$. Therefore, both conditions (a) and (b) in the statement of the theorem are satisfied. $\qquad\square$

In view of Theorem 2.4, all basic solutions to a standard form polyhedron can be constructed according to the following procedure.

Procedure for constructing basic solutions
1. Choose m linearly independent columns $\mathbf{A}_{B(1)}, \ldots, \mathbf{A}_{B(m)}$.
2. Let $x_i = 0$ for all $i \neq B(1), \ldots, B(m)$.
3. Solve the system of m equations $\mathbf{A}\mathbf{x} = \mathbf{b}$ for the unknowns $x_{B(1)}, \ldots, x_{B(m)}$.

If a basic solution constructed according to this procedure is nonnegative, then it is feasible, and it is a basic feasible solution. Conversely, since every basic feasible solution is a basic solution, it can be obtained from this procedure. If $\mathbf{x}$ is a basic solution, the variables $x_{B(1)}, \ldots, x_{B(m)}$ are called *basic variables*; the remaining variables are called *nonbasic*. The columns $\mathbf{A}_{B(1)}, \ldots, \mathbf{A}_{B(m)}$ are called the *basic columns* and, since they are linearly independent, they form a *basis* of $\Re^m$. We will sometimes talk about two bases being *distinct* or *different*; our convention is that distinct bases involve different sets $\{B(1), \ldots, B(m)\}$ of *basic indices*; if two bases involve the same set of indices in a different order, they will be viewed as one and the same basis.

By arranging the m basic columns next to each other, we obtain an $m \times m$ matrix $\mathbf{B}$, called a *basis matrix*. (Note that this matrix is invertible because the basic columns are required to be linearly independent.) We can similarly define a vector $\mathbf{x}_B$ with the values of the basic variables. Thus,

$$
\mathbf{B} = \left[\begin{array}{cccc} | & | & & | \\ \mathbf{A}_{B(1)} & \mathbf{A}_{B(2)} & \cdots & \mathbf{A}_{B(m)} \\ | & | & & | \end{array} \right], \qquad \mathbf{x}_B = \left[\begin{array}{c} x_{B(1)} \\ \vdots \\ x_{B(m)} \end{array} \right].
$$

The basic variables are determined by solving the equation $\mathbf{B}\mathbf{x}_B = \mathbf{b}$ whose unique solution is given by

$$
\mathbf{x}_B = \mathbf{B}^{-1}\mathbf{b}.
$$

Example 2.1 Let the constraint $\mathbf{A}\mathbf{x} = \mathbf{b}$ be of the form

$$
\left[\begin{array}{ccccccc} 1 & 1 & 2 & 1 & 0 & 0 & 0 \\ 0 & 1 & 6 & 0 & 1 & 0 & 0 \\ 1 & 0 & 0 & 0 & 0 & 1 & 0 \\ 0 & 1 & 0 & 0 & 0 & 0 & 1 \end{array} \right] \mathbf{x} = \left[\begin{array}{c} 8 \\ 12 \\ 4 \\ 6 \end{array} \right].
$$

Let us choose $\mathbf{A}_4, \mathbf{A}_5, \mathbf{A}_6, \mathbf{A}_7$ as our basic columns. Note that they are linearly independent and the corresponding basis matrix is the identity. We then obtain the basic solution $\mathbf{x} = (0, 0, 0, 8, 12, 4, 6)$ which is nonnegative and, therefore, is a basic feasible solution. Another basis is obtained by choosing the columns $\mathbf{A}_3, \mathbf{A}_5, \mathbf{A}_6, \mathbf{A}_7$ (note that they are linearly independent). The corresponding basic solution is $\mathbf{x} = (0, 0, 4, 0, -12, 4, 6)$, which is not feasible because $x_5 = -12 < 0$.

Suppose now that there was an eighth column $\mathbf{A}_8$, identical to $\mathbf{A}_7$. Then, the two sets of columns $\{\mathbf{A}_3, \mathbf{A}_5, \mathbf{A}_6, \mathbf{A}_7\}$ and $\{\mathbf{A}_3, \mathbf{A}_5, \mathbf{A}_6, \mathbf{A}_8\}$ coincide. On the other hand the corresponding sets of basic indices, which are $\{3, 5, 6, 7\}$ and $\{3, 5, 6, 8\}$, are different and we have two different bases, according to our conventions.

For an intuitive view of basic solutions, recall our interpretation of the constraint $\mathbf{A}\mathbf{x} = \mathbf{b}$, or $\sum_{i=1}^{n} \mathbf{A}_i x_i = \mathbf{b}$, as a requirement to synthesize the vector $\mathbf{b} \in \Re^m$ using the resource vectors $\mathbf{A}_i$ (Section 1.1). In a basic solution, we use only m of the resource vectors, those associated with the basic variables. Furthermore, in a basic feasible solution, this is accomplished using a nonnegative amount of each basic vector; see Figure 2.8.

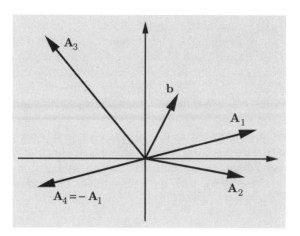

Figure 2.8: Consider a standard form problem with $n = 4$ and $m = 2$, and let the vectors $\mathbf{b}, \mathbf{A}_1, \ldots, \mathbf{A}_4$ be as shown. The vectors $\mathbf{A}_1, \mathbf{A}_2$ form a basis; the corresponding basic solution is infeasible because a negative value of x_2 is needed to synthesize $\mathbf{b}$ from $\mathbf{A}_1$, $\mathbf{A}_2$. The vectors $\mathbf{A}_1, \mathbf{A}_3$ form another basis; the corresponding basic solution is feasible. Finally, the vectors $\mathbf{A}_1, \mathbf{A}_4$ do not form a basis because they are linearly dependent.

Correspondence of bases and basic solutions

We now elaborate on the correspondence between basic solutions and bases. Different basic solutions must correspond to different bases, because a basis uniquely determines a basic solution. However, two different bases may lead to the same basic solution. (For an extreme example, if we have $\mathbf{b} = \mathbf{0}$, then every basis matrix leads to the same basic solution, namely, the zero vector.) This phenomenon has some important algorithmic implications, and is closely related to degeneracy, which is the subject of the next section.

Adjacent basic solutions and adjacent bases

Recall that two distinct basic solutions are said to be adjacent if there are $n - 1$ linearly independent constraints that are active at both of them. For standard form problems, we also say that two bases are *adjacent* if they share all but one basic column. Then, it is not hard to check that adjacent basic solutions can always be obtained from two adjacent bases. Conversely, if two adjacent bases lead to distinct basic solutions, then the latter are adjacent.

Example 2.2 In reference to Example 2.1, the bases $\{\mathbf{A}_4, \mathbf{A}_5, \mathbf{A}_6, \mathbf{A}_7\}$ and $\{\mathbf{A}_3, \mathbf{A}_5, \mathbf{A}_6, \mathbf{A}_7\}$ are adjacent because all but one columns are the same. The corresponding basic solutions $\mathbf{x} = (0, 0, 0, 8, 12, 4, 6)$ and $\mathbf{x} = (0, 0, 4, 0, -12, 4, 6)$

are adjacent: we have $n = 7$ and a total of six common linearly independent active constraints; these are $x_1 \geq 0$, $x_2 \geq 0$, and the four equality constraints.

The full row rank assumption on A

We close this section by showing that the full row rank assumption on the matrix $\mathbf{A}$ results in no loss of generality.

Theorem 2.5 *Let $P = \{\mathbf{x} \mid \mathbf{A}\mathbf{x} = \mathbf{b}, \ \mathbf{x} \geq \mathbf{0}\}$ be a nonempty polyhedron, where $\mathbf{A}$ is a matrix of dimensions $m \times n$, with rows $\mathbf{a}_1', \ldots, \mathbf{a}_m'$. Suppose that $\mathrm{rank}(\mathbf{A}) = k < m$ and that the rows $\mathbf{a}_{i_1}', \ldots, \mathbf{a}_{i_k}'$ are linearly independent. Consider the polyhedron*

$$Q = \left\{ \mathbf{x} \mid \mathbf{a}_{i_1}'\mathbf{x} = b_{i_1}, \ldots, \mathbf{a}_{i_k}'\mathbf{x} = b_{i_k}, \ \mathbf{x} \geq \mathbf{0} \right\}.$$

Then $Q = P$.

Proof. We provide the proof for the case where $i_1 = 1, \ldots, i_k = k$, that is, the first k rows of $\mathbf{A}$ are linearly independent. The general case can be reduced to this one by rearranging the rows of $\mathbf{A}$.

Clearly $P \subset Q$ since any element of P automatically satisfies the constraints defining Q. We will now show that $Q \subset P$.

Since $\mathrm{rank}(\mathbf{A}) = k$, the row space of $\mathbf{A}$ has dimension k and the rows $\mathbf{a}_1', \ldots, \mathbf{a}_k'$ form a basis of the row space. Therefore, every row $\mathbf{a}_i'$ of $\mathbf{A}$ can be expressed in the form $\mathbf{a}_i' = \sum_{j=1}^k \lambda_{ij}\mathbf{a}_j'$, for some scalars λ_{ij}. Let $\mathbf{x}$ be an element of P and note that

$$b_i = \mathbf{a}_i'\mathbf{x} = \sum_{j=1}^k \lambda_{ij}\mathbf{a}_j'\mathbf{x} = \sum_{j=1}^k \lambda_{ij}b_j, \qquad i = 1, \ldots, m.$$

Consider now an element $\mathbf{y}$ of Q. We will show that it belongs to P. Indeed, for any i,

$$\mathbf{a}_i'\mathbf{y} = \sum_{j=1}^k \lambda_{ij}\mathbf{a}_j'\mathbf{y} = \sum_{j=1}^k \lambda_{ij}b_j = b_i,$$

which establishes that $\mathbf{y} \in P$ and $Q \subset P$. $\qquad\square$

Notice that the polyhedron Q in Theorem 2.5 is in standard form; namely, $Q = \{\mathbf{x} \mid \mathbf{D}\mathbf{x} = \mathbf{f}, \ \mathbf{x} \geq \mathbf{0}\}$ where $\mathbf{D}$ is a $k \times n$ submatrix of $\mathbf{A}$, with rank equal to k, and $\mathbf{f}$ is a k-dimensional subvector of $\mathbf{b}$. We conclude that as long as the feasible set is nonempty, a linear programming problem in standard form can be reduced to an equivalent standard form problem (with the same feasible set) in which the equality constraints are linearly independent.

Example 2.3 Consider the (nonempty) polyhedron defined by the constraints

$$
\begin{aligned}
2x_1 + x_2 + x_3 &= 2 \\
x_1 + x_2 \phantom{{}+ x_3} &= 1 \\
x_1 \phantom{{}+ x_2} + x_3 &= 1 \\
x_1, x_2, x_3 &\geq 0.
\end{aligned}
$$

The corresponding matrix $\mathbf{A}$ has rank two. This is because the last two rows $(1, 1, 0)$ and $(1, 0, 1)$ are linearly independent, but the first row is equal to the sum of the other two. Thus, the first constraint is redundant and after it is eliminated, we still have the same polyhedron.

2.4   Degeneracy

According to our definition, at a basic solution, we must have n linearly independent active constraints. This allows for the possibility that the number of active constraints is greater than n. (Of course, in n dimensions, no more than n of them can be linearly independent.) In this case, we say that we have a *degenerate* basic solution. In other words, at a degenerate basic solution, the number of active constraints is greater than the minimum necessary.

Definition 2.10 *A basic solution* $\mathbf{x} \in \Re^n$ *is said to be* **degenerate** *if more than n of the constraints are active at* $\mathbf{x}$.

In two dimensions, a degenerate basic solution is at the intersection of three or more lines; in three dimensions, a degenerate basic solution is at the intersection of four or more planes; see Figure 2.9 for an illustration. It turns out that the presence of degeneracy can strongly affect the behavior of linear programming algorithms and for this reason, we will now develop some more intuition.

Example 2.4 Consider the polyhedron P defined by the constraints

$$
\begin{aligned}
x_1 + x_2 + 2x_3 &\leq 8 \\
x_2 + 6x_3 &\leq 12 \\
x_1 &\leq 4 \\
x_2 &\leq 6 \\
x_1, x_2, x_3 &\geq 0.
\end{aligned}
$$

The vector $\mathbf{x} = (2, 6, 0)$ is a nondegenerate basic feasible solution, because there are exactly three active and linearly independent constraints, namely, $x_1 + x_2 + 2x_3 \leq 8$, $x_2 \leq 6$, and $x_3 \geq 0$. The vector $\mathbf{x} = (4, 0, 2)$ is a degenerate basic feasible solution, because there are four active constraints, three of them linearly independent, namely, $x_1 + x_2 + 2x_3 \leq 8$, $x_2 + 6x_3 \leq 12$, $x_1 \leq 4$, and $x_2 \geq 0$.

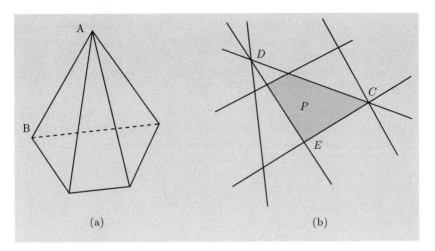

Figure 2.9: The points A and C are degenerate basic feasible solutions. The points B and E are nondegenerate basic feasible solutions. The point D is a degenerate basic solution.

Degeneracy in standard form polyhedra

At a basic solution of a polyhedron in standard form, the m equality constraints are always active. Therefore, having more than n active constraints is the same as having more than $n - m$ variables at zero level. This leads us to the next definition which is a special case of Definition 2.10.

Definition 2.11 *Consider the standard form polyhedron $P = \{\mathbf{x} \in \Re^n \mid \mathbf{Ax} = \mathbf{b}, \ \mathbf{x} \geq \mathbf{0}\}$ and let $\mathbf{x}$ be a basic solution. Let m be the number of rows of $\mathbf{A}$. The vector $\mathbf{x}$ is a **degenerate** basic solution if more than $n - m$ of the components of $\mathbf{x}$ are zero.*

Example 2.5 Consider once more the polyhedron of Example 2.4. By introducing the slack variables $x_4, \ldots, x_7$, we can transform it into the standard form $P = \{\mathbf{x} = (x_1, \ldots, x_7) \mid \mathbf{Ax} = \mathbf{b}, \ \mathbf{x} \geq \mathbf{0}\}$, where

$$
\mathbf{A} = \begin{bmatrix} 1 & 1 & 2 & 1 & 0 & 0 & 0 \\ 0 & 1 & 6 & 0 & 1 & 0 & 0 \\ 1 & 0 & 0 & 0 & 0 & 1 & 0 \\ 0 & 1 & 0 & 0 & 0 & 0 & 1 \end{bmatrix}, \qquad \mathbf{b} = \begin{bmatrix} 8 \\ 12 \\ 4 \\ 6 \end{bmatrix}.
$$

Consider the basis consisting of the linearly independent columns $\mathbf{A}_1$, $\mathbf{A}_2$, $\mathbf{A}_3$, $\mathbf{A}_7$. To calculate the corresponding basic solution, we first set the nonbasic variables x_4, x_5, and x_6 to zero, and then solve the system $\mathbf{Ax} = \mathbf{b}$ for the remaining variables, to obtain $\mathbf{x} = (4, 0, 2, 0, 0, 0, 6)$. This is a degenerate basic feasible solution, because we have a total of four variables that are zero, whereas

$n - m = 7 - 4 = 3$. Thus, while we initially set only the three nonbasic variables to zero, the solution to the system $\mathbf{Ax} = \mathbf{b}$ turned out to satisfy one more of the constraints (namely, the constraint $x_2 \geq 0$) with equality. Consider now the basis consisting of the linearly independent columns $\mathbf{A}_1$, $\mathbf{A}_3$, $\mathbf{A}_4$, and $\mathbf{A}_7$. The corresponding basic feasible solution is again $\mathbf{x} = (4, 0, 2, 0, 0, 0, 6)$.

The preceding example suggests that we can think of degeneracy in the following terms. We pick a basic solution by picking n linearly independent constraints to be satisfied with equality, and we realize that certain other constraints are also satisfied with equality. If the entries of $\mathbf{A}$ or $\mathbf{b}$ were chosen at random, this would almost never happen. Also, Figure 2.10 illustrates that if the coefficients of the active constraints are slightly perturbed, degeneracy can disappear (cf. Exercise 2.18). In practical problems, however, the entries of $\mathbf{A}$ and $\mathbf{b}$ often have a special (nonrandom) structure, and degeneracy is more common than the preceding argument would seem to suggest.

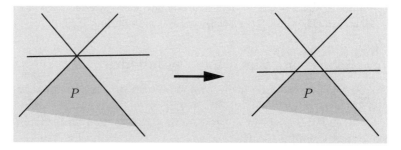

Figure 2.10: Small changes in the constraining inequalities can remove degeneracy.

In order to visualize degeneracy in standard form polyhedra, we assume that $n - m = 2$ and we draw the feasible set as a subset of the two-dimensional set defined by the equality constraints $\mathbf{Ax} = \mathbf{b}$; see Figure 2.11. At a nondegenerate basic solution, exactly $n-m$ of the constraints $x_i \geq 0$ are active; the corresponding variables are nonbasic. In the case of a degenerate basic solution, more than $n - m$ of the constraints $x_i \geq 0$ are active, and there are usually several ways of choosing which $n-m$ variables to call nonbasic; in that case, there are several bases corresponding to that same basic solution. (This discussion refers to the typical case. However, there are examples of degenerate basic solutions to which there corresponds only one basis.)

Degeneracy is not a purely geometric property

We close this section by pointing out that degeneracy of basic feasible solutions is not, in general, a geometric (representation independent) property,

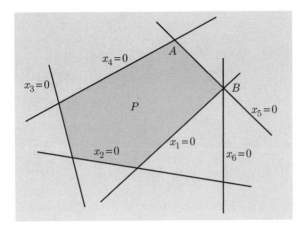

Figure 2.11: An $(n - m)$-dimensional illustration of degeneracy. Here, $n = 6$ and $m = 4$. The basic feasible solution A is nondegenerate and the basic variables are x_1, x_2, x_3, x_6. The basic feasible solution B is degenerate. We can choose x_1, x_6 as the nonbasic variables. Other possibilities are to choose x_1, x_5, or to choose x_5, x_6. Thus, there are three possible bases, for the same basic feasible solution B.

but rather it may depend on the particular representation of a polyhedron. To illustrate this point, consider the standard form polyhedron (cf. Figure 2.12)

$$P = \Big\{ (x_1, x_2, x_3) \mid x_1 - x_2 = 0, \ x_1 + x_2 + 2x_3 = 2, \ x_1, x_2, x_3 \geq 0 \Big\}.$$

We have $n = 3$, $m = 2$ and $n - m = 1$. The vector $(1, 1, 0)$ is nondegenerate because only one variable is zero. The vector $(0,0,1)$ is degenerate because two variables are zero. However, the same polyhedron can also be described

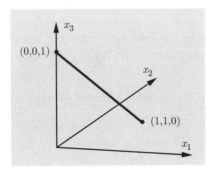

Figure 2.12: An example of degeneracy in a standard form problem.

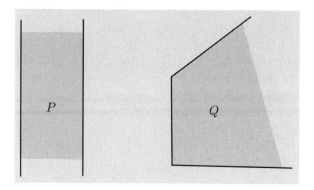

Figure 2.13: The polyhedron P contains a line and does not have an extreme point, while Q does not contain a line and has extreme points.

in the (nonstandard) form

$$P = \Big\{ (x_1, x_2, x_3) \mid x_1 - x_2 = 0, \ x_1 + x_2 + 2x_3 = 2, \ x_1 \geq 0, \ x_3 \geq 0 \Big\}.$$

The vector $(0,0,1)$ is now a nondegenerate basic feasible solution, because there are only three active constraints.

For another example, consider a nondegenerate basic feasible solution $\mathbf{x}^*$ of a standard form polyhedron $P = \{\mathbf{x} \mid \mathbf{A}\mathbf{x} = \mathbf{b}, \ \mathbf{x} \geq \mathbf{0}\}$, where $\mathbf{A}$ is of dimensions $m \times n$. In particular, exactly $n - m$ of the variables x_i^* are equal to zero. Let us now represent P in the form $P = \{\mathbf{x} \mid \mathbf{A}\mathbf{x} \geq \mathbf{b}, \ -\mathbf{A}\mathbf{x} \geq -\mathbf{b}, \ \mathbf{x} \geq \mathbf{0}\}$. Then, at the basic feasible solution $\mathbf{x}^*$, we have $n - m$ variables set to zero and an additional $2m$ inequality constraints are satisfied with equality. We therefore have $n + m$ active constraints and $\mathbf{x}^*$ is degenerate. Hence, under the second representation, every basic feasible solution is degenerate.

We have established that a degenerate basic feasible solution under one representation could be nondegenerate under another representation. Still, it can be shown that if a basic feasible solution is degenerate under one particular standard form representation, then it is degenerate under every standard form representation of the same polyhedron (Exercise 2.19).

2.5   Existence of extreme points

We obtain in this section necessary and sufficient conditions for a polyhedron to have at least one extreme point. We first observe that not every polyhedron has this property. For example, if $n > 1$, a halfspace in $\Re^n$ is a polyhedron without extreme points. Also, as argued in Section 2.2 (cf. the discussion after Definition 2.9), if the matrix $\mathbf{A}$ has fewer than n rows, then the polyhedron $\{\mathbf{x} \in \Re^n \mid \mathbf{A}\mathbf{x} \geq \mathbf{b}\}$ does not have a basic feasible solution.

It turns out that the existence of an extreme point depends on whether a polyhedron contains an infinite line or not; see Figure 2.13. We need the following definition.

Definition 2.12 *A polyhedron $P \subset \Re^n$* **contains a line** *if there exists a vector $\mathbf{x} \in P$ and a nonzero vector $\mathbf{d} \in \Re^n$ such that $\mathbf{x} + \lambda \mathbf{d} \in P$ for all scalars λ.*

We then have the following result.

Theorem 2.6 *Suppose that the polyhedron $P = \{\mathbf{x} \in \Re^n \mid \mathbf{a}_i' \mathbf{x} \geq b_i, \; i = 1, \ldots, m\}$ is nonempty. Then, the following are equivalent:*

(a) *The polyhedron P has at least one extreme point.*

(b) *The polyhedron P does not contain a line.*

(c) *There exist n vectors out of the family $\mathbf{a}_1, \ldots, \mathbf{a}_m$, which are linearly independent.*

Proof.

(b) $\Rightarrow$ (a)

We first prove that if P does not contain a line, then it has a basic feasible solution and, therefore, an extreme point. A geometric interpretation of this proof is provided in Figure 2.14.

Let $\mathbf{x}$ be an element of P and let $I = \{i \mid \mathbf{a}_i' \mathbf{x} = b_i\}$. If n of the vectors $\mathbf{a}_i$, $i \in I$, corresponding to the active constraints are linearly independent, then $\mathbf{x}$ is, by definition, a basic feasible solution and, therefore, a basic feasible solution exists. If this is not the case, then all of the vectors $\mathbf{a}_i$, $i \in I$, lie in a proper subspace of $\Re^n$ and there exists a nonzero vector $\mathbf{d} \in \Re^n$ such that $\mathbf{a}_i' \mathbf{d} = 0$, for every $i \in I$. Let us consider the line consisting of all points of the form $\mathbf{y} = \mathbf{x} + \lambda \mathbf{d}$, where λ is an arbitrary scalar. For $i \in I$, we have $\mathbf{a}_i' \mathbf{y} = \mathbf{a}_i' \mathbf{x} + \lambda \mathbf{a}_i' \mathbf{d} = \mathbf{a}_i' \mathbf{x} = b_i$. Thus, those constraints that were active at $\mathbf{x}$ remain active at all points on the line. However, since the polyhedron is assumed to contain no lines, it follows that as we vary λ, some constraint will be eventually violated. At the point where some constraint is about to be violated, a new constraint must become active, and we conclude that there exists some λ^* and some $j \notin I$ such that $\mathbf{a}_j'(\mathbf{x} + \lambda^* \mathbf{d}) = b_j$.

We claim that $\mathbf{a}_j$ is not a linear combination of the vectors $\mathbf{a}_i$, $i \in I$. Indeed, we have $\mathbf{a}_j' \mathbf{x} \neq b_j$ (because $j \notin I$) and $\mathbf{a}_j'(\mathbf{x} + \lambda^* \mathbf{d}) = b_j$ (by the definition of λ^*). Thus, $\mathbf{a}_j' \mathbf{d} \neq 0$. On the other hand, $\mathbf{a}_i' \mathbf{d} = 0$ for every $i \in I$ (by the definition of $\mathbf{d}$) and therefore, $\mathbf{d}$ is orthogonal to any linear combination of the vectors $\mathbf{a}_i$, $i \in I$. Since $\mathbf{d}$ is not orthogonal to $\mathbf{a}_j$, we

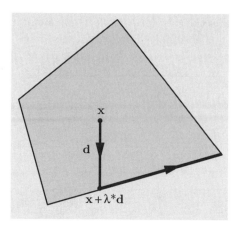

Figure 2.14: Starting from an arbitrary point of a polyhedron, we choose a direction along which all currently active constraints remain active. We then move along that direction until a new constraint is about to be violated. At that point, the number of linearly independent active constraints has increased by at least one. We repeat this procedure until we end up with n linearly independent active constraints, at which point we have a basic feasible solution.

conclude that $\mathbf{a}_j$ is a not a linear combination of the vectors $\mathbf{a}_i$, $i \in I$. Thus, by moving from $\mathbf{x}$ to $\mathbf{x} + \lambda^*\mathbf{d}$, the number of linearly independent active constraints has been increased by at least one. By repeating the same argument, as many times as needed, we eventually end up with a point at which there are n linearly independent active constraints. Such a point is, by definition, a basic solution; it is also feasible since we have stayed within the feasible set.

(a) $\Rightarrow$ (c)

If P has an extreme point $\mathbf{x}$, then $\mathbf{x}$ is also a basic feasible solution (cf. Theorem 2.3), and there exist n constraints that are active at $\mathbf{x}$, with the corresponding vectors $\mathbf{a}_i$ being linearly independent.

(c) $\Rightarrow$ (b)

Suppose that n of the vectors $\mathbf{a}_i$ are linearly independent and, without loss of generality, let us assume that $\mathbf{a}_1, \ldots, \mathbf{a}_n$ are linearly independent. Suppose that P contains a line $\mathbf{x} + \lambda\mathbf{d}$, where $\mathbf{d}$ is a nonzero vector. We then have $\mathbf{a}_i'(\mathbf{x} + \lambda\mathbf{d}) \geq b_i$ for all i and all λ. We conclude that $\mathbf{a}_i'\mathbf{d} = 0$ for all i. (If $\mathbf{a}_i'\mathbf{d} < 0$, we can violate the constraint by picking λ very large; a symmetric argument applies if $\mathbf{a}_i'\mathbf{d} > 0$.) Since the vectors $\mathbf{a}_i$, $i = 1, \ldots, n$, are linearly independent, this implies that $\mathbf{d} = \mathbf{0}$. This is a contradiction and establishes that P does not contain a line. $\Box$

Notice that a bounded polyhedron does not contain a line. Similarly, the positive orthant $\{\mathbf{x} \mid \mathbf{x} \geq \mathbf{0}\}$ does not contain a line. Since a polyhedron in standard form is contained in the positive orthant, it does not contain a line either. These observations establish the following important corollary of Theorem 2.6.

> **Corollary 2.2** *Every nonempty bounded polyhedron and every nonempty polyhedron in standard form has at least one basic feasible solution.*

2.6   Optimality of extreme points

Having established the conditions for the existence of extreme points, we will now confirm the intuition developed in Chapter 1: as long as a linear programming problem has an optimal solution and as long as the feasible set has at least one extreme point, we can always find an optimal solution within the set of extreme points of the feasible set. Later in this section, we prove a somewhat stronger result, at the expense of a more complicated proof.

> **Theorem 2.7** *Consider the linear programming problem of minimizing $\mathbf{c}'\mathbf{x}$ over a polyhedron P. Suppose that P has at least one extreme point and that there exists an optimal solution. Then, there exists an optimal solution which is an extreme point of P.*

Proof. (See Figure 2.15 for an illustration.) Let Q be the set of all optimal solutions, which we have assumed to be nonempty. Let P be of the form $P = \{\mathbf{x} \in \Re^n \mid \mathbf{Ax} \geq \mathbf{b}\}$ and let v be the optimal value of the cost $\mathbf{c}'\mathbf{x}$. Then, $Q = \{\mathbf{x} \in \Re^n \mid \mathbf{Ax} \geq \mathbf{b}, \ \mathbf{c}'\mathbf{x} = v\}$, which is also a polyhedron. Since

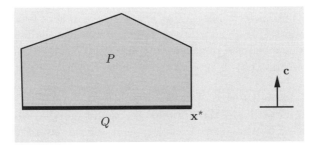

Figure 2.15: Illustration of the proof of Theorem 2.7. Here, Q is the set of optimal solutions and an extreme point $\mathbf{x}^*$ of Q is also an extreme point of P.

$Q \subset P$, and since P contains no lines (cf. Theorem 2.6), Q contains no lines either. Therefore, Q has an extreme point.

Let $\mathbf{x}^*$ be an extreme point of Q. We will show that $\mathbf{x}^*$ is also an extreme point of P. Suppose, in order to derive a contradiction, that $\mathbf{x}^*$ is not an extreme point of P. Then, there exist $\mathbf{y} \in P$, $\mathbf{z} \in P$, such that $\mathbf{y} \neq \mathbf{x}^*$, $\mathbf{z} \neq \mathbf{x}^*$, and some $\lambda \in [0,1]$ such that $\mathbf{x}^* = \lambda\mathbf{y} + (1-\lambda)\mathbf{z}$. It follows that $v = \mathbf{c}'\mathbf{x}^* = \lambda\mathbf{c}'\mathbf{y} + (1 - \lambda)\mathbf{c}'\mathbf{z}$. Furthermore, since v is the optimal cost, $\mathbf{c}'\mathbf{y} \geq v$ and $\mathbf{c}'\mathbf{z} \geq v$. This implies that $\mathbf{c}'\mathbf{y} = \mathbf{c}'\mathbf{z} = v$ and therefore $\mathbf{z} \in Q$ and $\mathbf{y} \in Q$. But this contradicts the fact that $\mathbf{x}^*$ is an extreme point of Q. The contradiction establishes that $\mathbf{x}^*$ is an extreme point of P. In addition, since $\mathbf{x}^*$ belongs to Q, it is optimal. $\qquad\square$

The above theorem applies to polyhedra in standard form, as well as to bounded polyhedra, since they do not contain a line.

Our next result is stronger than Theorem 2.7. It shows that the existence of an optimal solution can be taken for granted, as long as the optimal cost is finite.

Theorem 2.8 *Consider the linear programming problem of minimizing $\mathbf{c}'\mathbf{x}$ over a polyhedron P. Suppose that P has at least one extreme point. Then, either the optimal cost is equal to $-\infty$, or there exists an extreme point which is optimal.*

Proof. The proof is essentially a repetition of the proof of Theorem 2.6. The difference is that as we move towards a basic feasible solution, we will also make sure that the costs do not increase. We will use the following terminology: an element $\mathbf{x}$ of P has *rank k* if we can find k, but not more than k, linearly independent constraints that are active at $\mathbf{x}$.

Let us assume that the optimal cost is finite. Let $P = \{\mathbf{x} \in \Re^n \mid \mathbf{A}\mathbf{x} \geq \mathbf{b}\}$ and consider some $\mathbf{x} \in P$ of rank $k < n$. We will show that there exists some $\mathbf{y} \in P$ which has greater rank and satisfies $\mathbf{c}'\mathbf{y} \leq \mathbf{c}'\mathbf{x}$. Let $I = \{i \mid \mathbf{a}_i'\mathbf{x} = b_i\}$, where $\mathbf{a}_i'$ is the ith row of $\mathbf{A}$. Since $k < n$, the vectors $\mathbf{a}_i$, $i \in I$, lie in a proper subspace of $\Re^n$, and we can choose some nonzero $\mathbf{d} \in \Re^n$ orthogonal to every $\mathbf{a}_i$, $i \in I$. Furthermore, by possibly taking the negative of $\mathbf{d}$, we can assume that $\mathbf{c}'\mathbf{d} \leq 0$.

Suppose that $\mathbf{c}'\mathbf{d} < 0$. Let us consider the half-line $\mathbf{y} = \mathbf{x} + \lambda\mathbf{d}$, where λ is a positive scalar. As in the proof of Theorem 2.6, all points on this half-line satisfy the relations $\mathbf{a}_i'\mathbf{y} = b_i$, $i \in I$. If the entire half-line were contained in P, the optimal cost would be $-\infty$, which we have assumed not to be the case. Therefore, the half-line eventually exits P. When this is about to happen, we have some $\lambda^* > 0$ and $j \notin I$ such that $\mathbf{a}_j'(\mathbf{x} + \lambda^*\mathbf{d}) = b_j$. We let $\mathbf{y} = \mathbf{x} + \lambda^*\mathbf{d}$ and note that $\mathbf{c}'\mathbf{y} < \mathbf{c}'\mathbf{x}$. As in the proof of Theorem 2.6, $\mathbf{a}_j$ is linearly independent from $\mathbf{a}_i$, $i \in I$, and the rank of $\mathbf{y}$ is at least $k + 1$.

Suppose now that $\mathbf{c'd} = 0$. We consider the line $\mathbf{y} = \mathbf{x} + \lambda\mathbf{d}$, where λ is an arbitrary scalar. Since P contains no lines, the line must eventually exit P and when that is about to happen, we are again at a vector $\mathbf{y}$ of rank greater than that of $\mathbf{x}$. Furthermore, since $\mathbf{c'd} = 0$, we have $\mathbf{c'y} = \mathbf{c'x}$.

In either case, we have found a new point $\mathbf{y}$ such that $\mathbf{c'y} \leq \mathbf{c'x}$, and whose rank is greater than that of $\mathbf{x}$. By repeating this process as many times as needed, we end up with a vector $\mathbf{w}$ of rank n (thus, $\mathbf{w}$ is a basic feasible solution) such that $\mathbf{c'w} \leq \mathbf{c'x}$.

Let $\mathbf{w}^1, \ldots, \mathbf{w}^r$ be the basic feasible solutions in P and let $\mathbf{w}^*$ be a basic feasible solution such that $\mathbf{c'w}^* \leq \mathbf{c'w}^i$ for all i. We have already shown that for every $\mathbf{x}$ there exists some i such that $\mathbf{c'w}^i \leq \mathbf{c'x}$. It follows that $\mathbf{c'w}^* \leq \mathbf{c'x}$ for all $\mathbf{x} \in P$, and the basic feasible solution $\mathbf{w}^*$ is optimal. $\qquad\square$

For a general linear programming problem, if the feasible set has no extreme points, then Theorem 2.8 does not apply directly. On the other hand, any linear programming problem can be transformed into an equivalent problem in standard form to which Theorem 2.8 does apply. This establishes the following corollary.

Corollary 2.3 *Consider the linear programming problem of minimizing $\mathbf{c'x}$ over a nonempty polyhedron. Then, either the optimal cost is equal to $-\infty$ or there exists an optimal solution.*

The result in Corollary 2.3 should be contrasted with what may happen in optimization problems with a nonlinear cost function. For example, in the problem of minimizing $1/x$ subject to $x \geq 1$, the optimal cost is not $-\infty$, but an optimal solution does not exist.

2.7   Representation of bounded polyhedra*

So far, we have been representing polyhedra in terms of their defining inequalities. In this section, we provide an alternative, by showing that a bounded polyhedron can also be represented as the convex hull of its extreme points. The proof that we give here is elementary and constructive, and its main idea is summarized in Figure 2.16. There is a similar representation of unbounded polyhedra involving extreme points and "extreme rays" (edges that extend to infinity). This representation can be developed using the tools that we already have, at the expense of a more complicated proof. A more elegant argument, based on duality theory, will be presented in Section 4.9 and will also result in an alternative proof of Theorem 2.9 below.

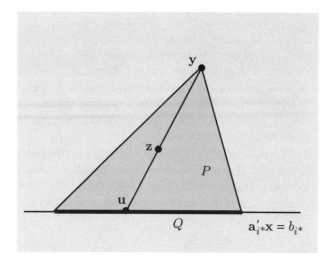

Figure 2.16: Given the vector **z**, we express it as a convex combination of **y** and **u**. The vector **u** belongs to the polyhedron Q whose dimension is lower than that of P. Using induction on dimension, we can express the vector **u** as a convex combination of extreme points of Q. These are also extreme points of P.

Theorem 2.9 *A nonempty and bounded polyhedron is the convex hull of its extreme points.*

Proof. Every convex combination of extreme points is an element of the polyhedron, since polyhedra are convex sets. Thus, we only need to prove the converse result and show that every element of a bounded polyhedron can be represented as a convex combination of extreme points.

We define the *dimension* of a polyhedron $P \subset \Re^n$ as the smallest integer k such that P is contained in some k-dimensional affine subspace of $\Re^n$. (Recall from Section 1.5, that a k-dimensional affine subspace is a translation of a k-dimensional subspace.) Our proof proceeds by induction on the dimension of the polyhedron P. If P is zero-dimensional, it consists of a single point. This point is an extreme point of P and the result is true.

Let us assume that the result is true for all polyhedra of dimension less than k. Let $P = \{\mathbf{x} \in \Re^n \mid \mathbf{a}_i'\mathbf{x} \geq b_i, \ i = 1, \ldots, m\}$ be a nonempty bounded k-dimensional polyhedron. Then, P is contained in a k-dimensional affine subspace S of $\Re^n$, which can be assumed to be of the form

$$S = \{\mathbf{x}^0 + \lambda_1 \mathbf{x}^1 + \cdots + \lambda_k \mathbf{x}^k \mid \lambda_1, \ldots, \lambda_k \in \Re\},$$

where $\mathbf{x}^1, \ldots, \mathbf{x}^k$ are some vectors in $\Re^n$. Let $\mathbf{f}_1, \ldots, \mathbf{f}_{n-k}$ be $n - k$ linearly independent vectors that are orthogonal to $\mathbf{x}^1, \ldots, \mathbf{x}^k$. Let $g_i = \mathbf{f}_i'\mathbf{x}^0$, for

$i = 1, \ldots, n - k$. Then, every element $\mathbf{x}$ of S satisfies

$$\mathbf{f}'_i \mathbf{x} = g_i, \qquad i = 1, \ldots, n - k. \tag{2.3}$$

Since $P \subset S$, the same must be true for every element of P.

Let $\mathbf{z}$ be an element of P. If $\mathbf{z}$ is an extreme point of P, then $\mathbf{z}$ is a trivial convex combination of the extreme points of P and there is nothing more to be proved. If $\mathbf{z}$ is not an extreme point of P, let us choose an arbitrary extreme point $\mathbf{y}$ of P and form the half-line consisting of all points of the form $\mathbf{z} + \lambda(\mathbf{z} - \mathbf{y})$, where λ is a nonnegative scalar. Since P is bounded, this half-line must eventually exit P and violate one of the constraints, say the constraint $\mathbf{a}'_{i*} \mathbf{x} \geq b_{i*}$. By considering what happens when this constraint is just about to be violated, we find some $\lambda^* \geq 0$ and $\mathbf{u} \in P$, such that

$$\mathbf{u} = \mathbf{z} + \lambda^*(\mathbf{z} - \mathbf{y}),$$

and

$$\mathbf{a}'_{i*} \mathbf{u} = b_{i*}.$$

Since the constraint $\mathbf{a}'_{i*} \mathbf{x} \geq b_{i*}$ is violated if λ grows beyond λ^*, it follows that $\mathbf{a}'_{i*}(\mathbf{z} - \mathbf{y}) < 0$.

Let Q be the polyhedron defined by

$$\begin{aligned} Q &= \{\mathbf{x} \in P \mid \mathbf{a}'_{i*} \mathbf{x} = b_{i*}\} \\ &= \{\mathbf{x} \in \Re^n \mid \mathbf{a}'_i \mathbf{x} \geq b_i, \ i = 1, \ldots, m, \ \mathbf{a}'_{i*} \mathbf{x} = b_{i*}\}. \end{aligned}$$

Since $\mathbf{z}, \mathbf{y} \in P$, we have $\mathbf{f}'_i \mathbf{z} = g_i = \mathbf{f}'_i \mathbf{y}$ which shows that $\mathbf{z} - \mathbf{y}$ is orthogonal to each vector $\mathbf{f}_i$, for $i = 1, \ldots, n-k$. On the other hand, we have shown that $\mathbf{a}'_{i*}(\mathbf{z} - \mathbf{y}) < 0$, which implies that the vector $\mathbf{a}_{i*}$ is not a linear combination of, and is therefore linearly independent from, the vectors $\mathbf{f}_i$. Note that

$$Q \subset \{\mathbf{x} \in \Re^n \mid \mathbf{a}'_{i*} \mathbf{x} = b_i, \ \mathbf{f}'_i \mathbf{x} = g_i, \ i = 1, \ldots, n - k\},$$

since Eq. (2.3) holds for every element of P. The set on the right is defined by $n - k + 1$ linearly independent equality constraints. Hence, it is an affine subspace of dimension $k - 1$ (see the discussion at the end of Section 1.5). Therefore, Q has dimension at most $k - 1$.

By applying the induction hypothesis to Q and $\mathbf{u}$, we see that $\mathbf{u}$ can be expressed as a convex combination

$$\mathbf{u} = \sum_i \lambda_i \mathbf{v}^i$$

of the extreme points $\mathbf{v}^i$ of Q, where λ_i are nonnegative scalars that sum to one. Note that at an extreme point $\mathbf{v}$ of Q, we must have $\mathbf{a}'_i \mathbf{v} = b_i$ for n linearly independent vectors $\mathbf{a}_i$; therefore, $\mathbf{v}$ must also be an extreme point of P. Using the definition of λ^*, we also have

$$\mathbf{z} = \frac{\mathbf{u} + \lambda^* \mathbf{y}}{1 + \lambda^*}.$$

Therefore,

$$\mathbf{z} = \frac{\lambda^* \mathbf{y}}{1 + \lambda^*} + \sum_i \frac{\lambda_i}{1 + \lambda^*} \mathbf{v}^i,$$

which shows that $\mathbf{z}$ is a convex combination of the extreme points of P. □

Example 2.6 Consider the polyhedron

$$P = \big\{(x_1, x_2, x_3) \mid x_1 + x_2 + x_3 \leq 1, \ x_1, x_2, x_3 \geq 0\big\}.$$

It has four extreme points, namely, $\mathbf{x}^1 = (1, 0, 0)$, $\mathbf{x}^2 = (0, 1, 0)$, $\mathbf{x}^3 = (0, 0, 1)$, and $\mathbf{x}^4 = (0, 0, 0)$. The vector $\mathbf{x} = (1/3, 1/3, 1/4)$ belongs to P. It can be represented as

$$\mathbf{x} = \frac{1}{3}\mathbf{x}^1 + \frac{1}{3}\mathbf{x}^2 + \frac{1}{4}\mathbf{x}^3 + \frac{1}{12}\mathbf{x}^4.$$

There is a converse to Theorem 2.9 asserting that the convex hull of a finite number of points is a polyhedron. This result is proved in the next section and again in Section 4.9.

2.8   Projections of polyhedra: Fourier-Motzkin elimination*

In this section, we present perhaps the oldest method for solving linear programming problems. This method is not practical because it requires a very large number of steps, but it has some interesting theoretical corollaries.

The key to this method is the concept of a *projection*, defined as follows: if $\mathbf{x} = (x_1, \ldots, x_n)$ is a vector in $\Re^n$ and $k \leq n$, the projection mapping $\pi_k : \Re^n \mapsto \Re^k$ projects $\mathbf{x}$ onto its first k coordinates:

$$\pi_k(\mathbf{x}) = \pi_k(x_1, \ldots, x_n) = (x_1, \ldots, x_k).$$

We also define the projection $\Pi_k(S)$ of a set $S \subset \Re^n$ by letting

$$\Pi_k(S) = \big\{\pi_k(\mathbf{x}) \mid \mathbf{x} \in S\big\};$$

see Figure 2.17 for an illustration. Note that S is nonempty if and only if $\Pi_k(S)$ is nonempty. An equivalent definition is

$$\Pi_k(S) = \Big\{(x_1, \ldots, x_k) \mid \text{there exist } x_{k+1}, \ldots, x_n \text{ s.t. } (x_1, \ldots, x_n) \in S\Big\}.$$

Suppose now that we wish to decide whether a given polyhedron $P \subset \Re^n$ is nonempty. If we can somehow eliminate the variable x_n and construct the set $\Pi_{n-1}(P) \subset \Re^{n-1}$, we can instead consider the presumably easier problem of deciding whether $\Pi_{n-1}(P)$ is nonempty. If we keep eliminating variables one by one, we eventually arrive at the set $\Pi_1(P)$ that

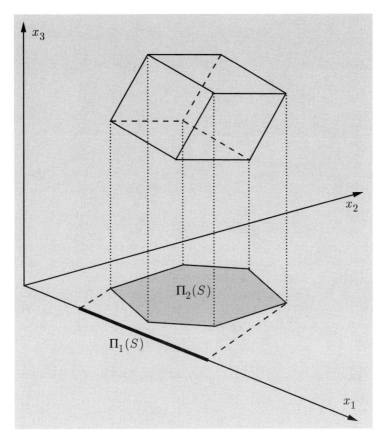

Figure 2.17: The projections $\Pi_1(S)$ and $\Pi_2(S)$ of a rotated three-dimensional cube.

involves a single variable, and whose emptiness is easy to check. The main disadvantage of this method is that while each step reduces the dimension by one, a large number of constraints is usually added. Exercise 2.20 deals with a family of examples in which the number of constraints increases exponentially with the problem dimension.

We now describe the elimination method. We are given a polyhedron P in terms of linear inequality constraints of the form

$$\sum_{j=1}^{n} a_{ij}x_j \geq b_i, \qquad i = 1, \ldots, m.$$

We wish to eliminate x_n and construct the projection $\Pi_{n-1}(P)$.

Elimination algorithm

1. Rewrite each constraint $\sum_{j=1}^{n} a_{ij}x_j \geq b_i$ in the form

$$a_{in}x_n \geq -\sum_{j=1}^{n-1} a_{ij}x_j + b_i, \qquad i = 1, \ldots, m;$$

if $a_{in} \neq 0$, divide both sides by a_{in}. By letting $\overline{\mathbf{x}} = (x_1, \ldots, x_{n-1})$, we obtain an equivalent representation of P involving the following constraints:

$$
\begin{array}{lll}
x_n \geq d_i + \mathbf{f}_i'\overline{\mathbf{x}}, & \text{if } a_{in} > 0, & (2.4) \\
d_j + \mathbf{f}_j'\overline{\mathbf{x}} \geq x_n, & \text{if } a_{jn} < 0, & (2.5) \\
0 \geq d_k + \mathbf{f}_k'\overline{\mathbf{x}}, & \text{if } a_{kn} = 0. & (2.6)
\end{array}
$$

Here, each d_i, d_j, d_k is a scalar, and each $\mathbf{f}_i, \mathbf{f}_j, \mathbf{f}_k$ is a vector in $\Re^{n-1}$.

2. Let Q be the polyhedron in $\Re^{n-1}$ defined by the constraints

$$
\begin{array}{lll}
d_j + \mathbf{f}_j'\overline{\mathbf{x}} \geq d_i + \mathbf{f}_i'\overline{\mathbf{x}}, & \text{if } a_{in} > 0 \text{ and } a_{jn} < 0, & (2.7) \\
0 \geq d_k + \mathbf{f}_k'\overline{\mathbf{x}}, & \text{if } a_{kn} = 0. & (2.8)
\end{array}
$$

Example 2.7 Consider the polyhedron defined by the constraints

$$
\begin{array}{rl}
x_1 + x_2 & \geq 1 \\
x_1 + x_2 + 2x_3 & \geq 2 \\
2x_1 + 3x_3 & \geq 3 \\
x_1 - 4x_3 & \geq 4 \\
-2x_1 + x_2 - x_3 & \geq 5.
\end{array}
$$

We rewrite these constraints in the form

$$
\begin{array}{rl}
0 & \geq 1 - x_1 - x_2 \\
x_3 & \geq 1 - (x_1/2) - (x_2/2) \\
x_3 & \geq 1 - (2x_1/3) \\
-1 + (x_1/4) & \geq x_3 \\
-5 - 2x_1 + x_2 & \geq x_3.
\end{array}
$$

Then, the set Q is defined by the constraints

$$
\begin{array}{rl}
0 & \geq 1 - x_1 - x_2 \\
-1 + x_1/4 & \geq 1 - (x_1/2) - (x_2/2)
\end{array}
$$

$$-1 + x_1/4 \geq 1 - (2x_1/3)$$
$$-5 - 2x_1 + x_2 \geq 1 - (x_1/2) - (x_2/2)$$
$$-5 - 2x_1 + x_2 \geq 1 - (2x_1/3).$$

Theorem 2.10 *The polyhedron Q constructed by the elimination algorithm is equal to the projection $\Pi_{n-1}(P)$ of P.*

Proof. If $\overline{\mathbf{x}} \in \Pi_{n-1}(P)$, there exists some x_n such that $(\overline{\mathbf{x}}, x_n) \in P$. In particular, the vector $\mathbf{x} = (\overline{\mathbf{x}}, x_n)$ satisfies Eqs. (2.4)-(2.6), from which it follows immediately that $\overline{\mathbf{x}}$ satisfies Eqs. (2.7)-(2.8), and $\overline{\mathbf{x}} \in Q$. This shows that $\Pi_{n-1}(P) \subset Q$.

We will now prove that $Q \subset \Pi_{n-1}(P)$. Let $\overline{\mathbf{x}} \in Q$. It follows from Eq. (2.7) that

$$\min_{\{j | a_{jn} < 0\}} \left(d_j + \mathbf{f}_j' \overline{\mathbf{x}} \right) \geq \max_{\{i | a_{in} > 0\}} \left(d_i + \mathbf{f}_i' \overline{\mathbf{x}} \right).$$

Let x_n be any number between the two sides of the above inequality. It then follows that $(\overline{\mathbf{x}}, x_n)$ satisfies Eqs. (2.4)-(2.6) and, therefore, belongs to the polyhedron P. $\square$

Notice that for any vector $\mathbf{x} = (x_1, \dots, x_n)$, we have

$$\pi_{n-2}\big(\pi_{n-1}(\mathbf{x})\big) = (x_1, \dots, x_{n-2}) = \pi_{n-2}(\mathbf{x}).$$

Accordingly, for any polyhedron P, we also have

$$\Pi_{n-2}\big(\Pi_{n-1}(P)\big) = \Pi_{n-2}(P).$$

By generalizing this observation, we see that if we apply the elimination algorithm k times, we end up with the set $\Pi_{n-k}(P)$; if we apply it $n-1$ times, we end up with $\Pi_1(P)$. Unfortunately, each application of the elimination algorithm can increase the number of constraints substantially, leading to a polyhedron $\Pi_1(P)$ described by a very large number of constraints. Of course, since $\Pi_1(P)$ is one-dimensional, almost all of these constraints will be redundant, but this is of no help: in order to decide which ones are redundant, we must, in general, enumerate them.

The elimination algorithm has an important theoretical consequence: since the projection $\Pi_k(P)$ can be generated by repeated application of the elimination algorithm, and since the elimination algorithm always produces a polyhedron, it follows that a projection $\Pi_k(P)$ of a polyhedron is also a polyhedron. This fact might be considered obvious, but a proof simpler than the one we gave is not apparent. We now restate it in somewhat different language.

Corollary 2.4 *Let $P \subset \Re^{n+k}$ be a polyhedron. Then, the set*

$$\left\{\mathbf{x} \in \Re^n \mid \text{there exists } \mathbf{y} \in \Re^k \text{ such that } (\mathbf{x}, \mathbf{y}) \in P\right\}$$

is also a polyhedron.

A variation of Corollary 2.4 states that the image of a polyhedron under a linear mapping is also a polyhedron.

Corollary 2.5 *Let $P \subset \Re^n$ be a polyhedron and let $\mathbf{A}$ be an $m \times n$ matrix. Then, the set $Q = \{\mathbf{A}\mathbf{x} \mid \mathbf{x} \in P\}$ is also a polyhedron.*

Proof. We have $Q = \{\mathbf{y} \in \Re^m \mid \text{there exists } \mathbf{x} \in \Re^n \text{ such that } \mathbf{A}\mathbf{x} = \mathbf{y},\ \mathbf{x} \in P\}$. Therefore, Q is the projection of the polyhedron $\{(\mathbf{x}, \mathbf{y}) \in \Re^{n+m} \mid \mathbf{A}\mathbf{x} = \mathbf{y},\ \mathbf{x} \in P\}$ onto the $\mathbf{y}$ coordinates. $\qquad\square$

Corollary 2.6 *The convex hull of a finite number of vectors is a polyhedron.*

Proof. The convex hull

$$\left\{\sum_{i=1}^{k} \lambda_i \mathbf{x}^i \;\middle|\; \sum_{i=1}^{k} \lambda_i = 1,\ \lambda_i \geq 0\right\}$$

of a finite number of vectors $\mathbf{x}^1, \ldots, \mathbf{x}^k$ is the image of the polyhedron

$$\left\{(\lambda_1, \ldots, \lambda_k) \;\middle|\; \sum_{i=1}^{k} \lambda_i = 1,\ \lambda_i \geq 0\right\}$$

under the linear mapping that maps $(\lambda_1, \ldots, \lambda_k)$ to $\sum_{i=1}^{k} \lambda_i \mathbf{x}^i$ and is, therefore, a polyhedron. $\qquad\square$

We finally indicate how the elimination algorithm can be used to solve linear programming problems. Consider the problem of minimizing $\mathbf{c}'\mathbf{x}$ subject to $\mathbf{x}$ belonging to a polyhedron P. We define a new variable x_0 and introduce the constraint $x_0 = \mathbf{c}'\mathbf{x}$. If we use the elimination algorithm n times to eliminate the variables $x_1, \ldots, x_n$, we are left with the set

$$Q = \left\{x_0 \mid \text{there exists } \mathbf{x} \in P \text{ such that } x_0 = \mathbf{c}'\mathbf{x}\right\},$$

and the optimal cost is equal to the smallest element of Q. An optimal solution $\mathbf{x}$ can be recovered by backtracking (Exercise 2.21).

2.9   Summary

We summarize our main conclusions so far regarding the solutions to linear programming problems.

(a) If the feasible set is nonempty and bounded, there exists an optimal solution. Furthermore, there exists an optimal solution which is an extreme point.

(b) If the feasible set is unbounded, there are the following possibilities:

   (i) There exists an optimal solution which is an extreme point.

   (ii) There exists an optimal solution, but no optimal solution is an extreme point. (This can only happen if the feasible set has no extreme points; it never happens when the problem is in standard form.)

   (iii) The optimal cost is $-\infty$.

Suppose now that the optimal cost is finite and that the feasible set contains at least one extreme point. Since there are only finitely many extreme points, the problem can be solved in a finite number of steps, by enumerating all extreme points and evaluating the cost of each one. This is hardly a practical algorithm because the number of extreme points can increase exponentially with the number of variables and constraints. In the next chapter, we will exploit the geometry of the feasible set and develop the *simplex method*, a systematic procedure that moves from one extreme point to another, without having to enumerate all extreme points.

An interesting aspect of the material in this chapter is the distinction between geometric (representation independent) properties of a polyhedron and those properties that depend on a particular representation. In that respect, we have established the following:

(a) Whether or not a point is an extreme point (equivalently, vertex, or basic feasible solution) is a geometric property.

(b) Whether or not a point is a basic solution may depend on the way that a polyhedron is represented.

(c) Whether or not a basic or basic feasible solution is degenerate may depend on the way that a polyhedron is represented.

2.10   Exercises

Exercise 2.1 For each one of the following sets, determine whether it is a polyhedron.

(a) The set of all $(x, y) \in \Re^2$ satisfying the constraints

$$x \cos \theta + y \sin \theta \leq 1, \qquad \forall\, \theta \in [0, \pi/2],$$
$$x \geq 0,$$
$$y \geq 0.$$

(b) The set of all $x \in \Re$ satisfying the constraint $x^2 - 8x + 15 \leq 0$.

(c) The empty set.

Exercise 2.2 Let $f : \Re^n \mapsto \Re$ be a convex function and let c be some constant. Show that the set $S = \{\mathbf{x} \in \Re^n \mid f(\mathbf{x}) \leq c\}$ is convex.

Exercise 2.3 (Basic feasible solutions in standard form polyhedra with upper bounds) Consider a polyhedron defined by the constraints $\mathbf{Ax} = \mathbf{b}$ and $\mathbf{0} \leq \mathbf{x} \leq \mathbf{u}$, and assume that the matrix $\mathbf{A}$ has linearly independent rows. Provide a procedure analogous to the one in Section 2.3 for constructing basic solutions, and prove an analog of Theorem 2.4.

Exercise 2.4 We know that every linear programming problem can be converted to an equivalent problem in standard form. We also know that nonempty polyhedra in standard form have at least one extreme point. We are then tempted to conclude that every nonempty polyhedron has at least one extreme point. Explain what is wrong with this argument.

Exercise 2.5 (Extreme points of isomorphic polyhedra) A mapping f is called *affine* if it is of the form $f(\mathbf{x}) = \mathbf{Ax} + \mathbf{b}$, where $\mathbf{A}$ is a matrix and $\mathbf{b}$ is a vector. Let P and Q be polyhedra in $\Re^n$ and $\Re^m$, respectively. We say that P and Q are *isomorphic* if there exist affine mappings $f : P \mapsto Q$ and $g : Q \mapsto P$ such that $g(f(\mathbf{x})) = \mathbf{x}$ for all $\mathbf{x} \in P$, and $f(g(\mathbf{y})) = \mathbf{y}$ for all $\mathbf{y} \in Q$. (Intuitively, isomorphic polyhedra have the same shape.)

(a) If P and Q are isomorphic, show that there exists a one-to-one correspondence between their extreme points. In particular, if f and g are as above, show that $\mathbf{x}$ is an extreme point of P if and only if $f(\mathbf{x})$ is an extreme point of Q.

(b) **(Introducing slack variables leads to an isomorphic polyhedron)** Let $P = \{\mathbf{x} \in \Re^n \mid \mathbf{Ax} \geq \mathbf{b}, \ \mathbf{x} \geq \mathbf{0}\}$, where $\mathbf{A}$ is a matrix of dimensions $k \times n$. Let $Q = \{(\mathbf{x}, \mathbf{z}) \in \Re^{n+k} \mid \mathbf{Ax} - \mathbf{z} = \mathbf{b}, \ \mathbf{x} \geq \mathbf{0}, \ \mathbf{z} \geq \mathbf{0}\}$. Show that P and Q are isomorphic.

Exercise 2.6 (Carathéodory's theorem) Let $\mathbf{A}_1, \ldots, \mathbf{A}_n$ be a collection of vectors in $\Re^m$.

(a) Let
$$C = \left\{ \sum_{i=1}^{n} \lambda_i \mathbf{A}_i \ \middle| \ \lambda_1, \ldots, \lambda_n \geq 0 \right\}.$$

Show that any element of C can be expressed in the form $\sum_{i=1}^{n} \lambda_i \mathbf{A}_i$, with $\lambda_i \geq 0$, and with at most m of the coefficients λ_i being nonzero. *Hint:* Consider the polyhedron
$$\Lambda = \left\{ (\lambda_1, \ldots, \lambda_n) \in \Re^n \ \middle| \ \sum_{i=1}^{n} \lambda_i \mathbf{A}_i = \mathbf{y}, \ \lambda_1, \ldots, \lambda_n \geq 0 \right\}.$$

(b) Let P be the convex hull of the vectors $\mathbf{A}_i$:
$$P = \left\{ \sum_{i=1}^{n} \lambda_i \mathbf{A}_i \ \middle| \ \sum_{i=1}^{n} \lambda_i = 1, \ \lambda_1, \ldots, \lambda_n \geq 0 \right\}.$$

Show that any element of P can be expressed in the form $\sum_{i=1}^{n} \lambda_i \mathbf{A}_i$, where $\sum_{i=1}^{n} \lambda_i = 1$ and $\lambda_i \geq 0$ for all i, with at most $m+1$ of the coefficients λ_i being nonzero.

Exercise 2.7 Suppose that $\{\mathbf{x} \in \Re^n \mid \mathbf{a}_i'\mathbf{x} \geq b_i, \ i = 1,\ldots,m\}$ and $\{\mathbf{x} \in \Re^n \mid \mathbf{g}_i'\mathbf{x} \geq h_i, \ i = 1,\ldots,k\}$ are two representations of the same nonempty polyhedron. Suppose that the vectors $\mathbf{a}_1,\ldots,\mathbf{a}_m$ span $\Re^n$. Show that the same must be true for the vectors $\mathbf{g}_1,\ldots,\mathbf{g}_k$.

Exercise 2.8 Consider the standard form polyhedron $\{\mathbf{x} \mid \mathbf{A}\mathbf{x} = \mathbf{b}, \ \mathbf{x} \geq \mathbf{0}\}$, and assume that the rows of the matrix $\mathbf{A}$ are linearly independent. Let $\mathbf{x}$ be a basic solution, and let $J = \{i \mid x_i \neq 0\}$. Show that a basis is associated with the basic solution $\mathbf{x}$ if and only if every column $\mathbf{A}_i$, $i \in J$, is in the basis.

Exercise 2.9 Consider the standard form polyhedron $\{\mathbf{x} \mid \mathbf{A}\mathbf{x} = \mathbf{b}, \ \mathbf{x} \geq \mathbf{0}\}$, and assume that the rows of the matrix $\mathbf{A}$ are linearly independent.

(a) Suppose that two different bases lead to the same basic solution. Show that the basic solution is degenerate.

(b) Consider a degenerate basic solution. Is it true that it corresponds to two or more distinct bases? Prove or give a counterexample.

(c) Suppose that a basic solution is degenerate. Is it true that there exists an adjacent basic solution which is degenerate? Prove or give a counterexample.

Exercise 2.10 Consider the standard form polyhedron $P = \{\mathbf{x} \mid \mathbf{A}\mathbf{x} = \mathbf{b}, \ \mathbf{x} \geq \mathbf{0}\}$. Suppose that the matrix $\mathbf{A}$ has dimensions $m \times n$ and that its rows are linearly independent. For each one of the following statements, state whether it is true or false. If true, provide a proof, else, provide a counterexample.

(a) If $n = m+1$, then P has at most two basic feasible solutions.

(b) The set of all optimal solutions is bounded.

(c) At every optimal solution, no more than m variables can be positive.

(d) If there is more than one optimal solution, then there are uncountably many optimal solutions.

(e) If there are several optimal solutions, then there exist at least two basic feasible solutions that are optimal.

(f) Consider the problem of minimizing $\max\{\mathbf{c}'\mathbf{x}, \mathbf{d}'\mathbf{x}\}$ over the set P. If this problem has an optimal solution, it must have an optimal solution which is an extreme point of P.

Exercise 2.11 Let $P = \{\mathbf{x} \in \Re^n \mid \mathbf{A}\mathbf{x} \geq \mathbf{b}\}$. Suppose that at a particular basic feasible solution, there are k active constraints, with $k > n$. Is it true that there exist exactly $\binom{k}{n}$ bases that lead to this basic feasible solution? Here $\binom{k}{n} = k!/\big(n!(k-n)!\big)$ is the number of ways that we can choose n out of k given items.

Exercise 2.12 Consider a nonempty polyhedron P and suppose that for each variable x_i we have either the constraint $x_i \geq 0$ or the constraint $x_i \leq 0$. Is it true that P has at least one basic feasible solution?

Exercise 2.13 Consider the standard form polyhedron $P = \{x \mid Ax = b, \, x \geq 0\}$. Suppose that the matrix A, of dimensions $m \times n$, has linearly independent rows, and that all basic feasible solutions are nondegenerate. Let x be an element of P that has exactly m positive components.

(a) Show that x is a basic feasible solution.

(b) Show that the result of part (a) is false if the nondegeneracy assumption is removed.

Exercise 2.14 Let P be a bounded polyhedron in $\Re^n$, let a be a vector in $\Re^n$, and let b be some scalar. We define

$$Q = \big\{ x \in P \mid a'x = b \big\}.$$

Show that every extreme point of Q is either an extreme point of P or a convex combination of two adjacent extreme points of P.

Exercise 2.15 (Edges joining adjacent vertices) Consider the polyhedron $P = \{x \in \Re^n \mid a_i'x \geq b_i, \, i = 1, \ldots, m\}$. Suppose that u and v are distinct basic feasible solutions that satisfy $a_i'u = a_i'v = b_i, \, i = 1, \ldots, n-1$, and that the vectors $a_1, \ldots, a_{n-1}$ are linearly independent. (In particular, u and v are adjacent.) Let $L = \{\lambda u + (1-\lambda)v \mid 0 \leq \lambda \leq 1\}$ be the segment that joins u and v. Prove that $L = \{z \in P \mid a_i'z = b_i, \, i = 1, \ldots, n-1\}$.

Exercise 2.16 Consider the set $\{x \in \Re^n \mid x_1 = \cdots = x_{n-1} = 0, \, 0 \leq x_n \leq 1\}$. Could this be the feasible set of a problem in standard form?

Exercise 2.17 Consider the polyhedron $\{x \in \Re^n \mid Ax \leq b, \, x \geq 0\}$ and a nondegenerate basic feasible solution x^*. We introduce slack variables z and construct a corresponding polyhedron $\{(x, z) \mid Ax + z = b, \, x \geq 0, \, z \geq 0\}$ in standard form. Show that $(x^*, b - Ax^*)$ is a nondegenerate basic feasible solution for the new polyhedron.

Exercise 2.18 Consider a polyhedron $P = \{x \mid Ax \geq b\}$. Given any $\epsilon > 0$, show that there exists some $\bar{b}$ with the following two properties:

(a) The absolute value of every component of $b - \bar{b}$ is bounded by ϵ.

(b) Every basic feasible solution in the polyhedron $P = \{x \mid Ax \geq \bar{b}\}$ is nondegenerate.

Exercise 2.19* Let $P \subset \Re^n$ be a polyhedron in standard form whose definition involves m linearly independent equality constraints. Its dimension is defined as the smallest integer k such that P is contained in some k-dimensional affine subspace of $\Re^n$.

(a) Explain why the dimension of P is at most $n - m$.

(b) Suppose that P has a nondegenerate basic feasible solution. Show that the dimension of P is equal to $n - m$.

(c) Suppose that x is a degenerate basic feasible solution. Show that x is degenerate under every standard form representation of the same polyhedron (in the same space $\Re^n$). *Hint:* Using parts (a) and (b), compare the number of equality constraints in two representations of P under which x is degenerate and nondegenerate, respectively. Then, count active constraints.

Exercise 2.20 * Consider the Fourier-Motzkin elimination algorithm.

(a) Suppose that the number m of constraints defining a polyhedron P is even. Show, by means of an example, that the elimination algorithm may produce a description of the polyhedron $\Pi_{n-1}(P)$ involving as many as $m^2/4$ linear constraints, but no more than that.

(b) Show that the elimination algorithm produces a description of the one-dimensional polyhedron $\Pi_1(P)$ involving no more than $m^{2^{n-1}}/2^{2^n-2}$ constraints.

(c) Let $n = 2^p + p + 2$, where p is a nonnegative integer. Consider a polyhedron in $\Re^n$ defined by the $8\binom{n}{3}$ constraints

$$\pm x_i \pm x_j \pm x_k \le 1, \qquad 1 \le i < j < k \le n,$$

where all possible combinations are present. Show that after p eliminations, we have at least

$$2^{2^p+2}$$

constraints. (Note that this number increases exponentially with n.)

Exercise 2.21 Suppose that Fourier-Motzkin elimination is used in the manner described at the end of Section 2.8 to find the optimal cost in a linear programming problem. Show how this approach can be augmented to obtain an optimal solution as well.

Exercise 2.22 Let P and Q be polyhedra in $\Re^n$. Let $P + Q = \{x + y \mid x \in P, \; y \in Q\}$.

(a) Show that $P + Q$ is a polyhedron.

(b) Show that every extreme point of $P + Q$ is the sum of an extreme point of P and an extreme point of Q.

2.11   Notes and sources

The relation between algebra and geometry goes far back in the history of mathematics, but was limited to two and three-dimensional spaces. The insight that the same relation goes through in higher dimensions only came in the middle of the nineteenth century.

2.2. Our algebraic definition of basic (feasible) solutions for general polyhedra, in terms of the number of linearly independent active constraints, is not common. Nevertheless, we consider it to be quite central, because it provides the main bridge between the algebraic and geometric viewpoint, it allows for a unified treatment, and shows that there is not much that is special about standard form problems.

2.8. Fourier-Motzkin elimination is due to Fourier (1827), Dines (1918), and Motzkin (1936).

Chapter 3

The simplex method

Contents

We saw in Chapter 2, that if a linear programming problem in standard form has an optimal solution, then there exists a basic feasible solution that is optimal. The simplex method is based on this fact and searches for an optimal solution by moving from one basic feasible solution to another, along the edges of the feasible set, always in a cost reducing direction. Eventually, a basic feasible solution is reached at which none of the available edges leads to a cost reduction; such a basic feasible solution is optimal and the algorithm terminates. In this chapter, we provide a detailed development of the simplex method and discuss a few different implementations, including the simplex tableau and the revised simplex method. We also address some difficulties that may arise in the presence of degeneracy. We provide an interpretation of the simplex method in terms of column geometry, and we conclude with a discussion of its running time, as a function of the dimension of the problem being solved.

Throughout this chapter, we consider the standard form problem

$$
\begin{array}{ll}
\text{minimize} & \mathbf{c'x} \\
\text{subject to} & \mathbf{Ax} = \mathbf{b} \\
& \mathbf{x} \geq \mathbf{0},
\end{array}
$$

and we let P be the corresponding feasible set. We assume that the dimensions of the matrix $\mathbf{A}$ are $m \times n$ and that its rows are linearly independent. We continue using our previous notation: $\mathbf{A}_i$ is the ith column of the matrix $\mathbf{A}$, and $\mathbf{a}'_i$ is its ith row.

3.1   Optimality conditions

Many optimization algorithms are structured as follows: given a feasible solution, we search its neighborhood to find a nearby feasible solution with lower cost. If no nearby feasible solution leads to a cost improvement, the algorithm terminates and we have a *locally optimal* solution. For general optimization problems, a locally optimal solution need not be (globally) optimal. Fortunately, in linear programming, local optimality implies global optimality; this is because we are minimizing a convex function over a convex set (cf. Exercise 3.1). In this section, we concentrate on the problem of searching for a direction of cost decrease in a neighborhood of a given basic feasible solution, and on the associated optimality conditions.

Suppose that we are at a point $\mathbf{x} \in P$ and that we contemplate moving away from $\mathbf{x}$, in the direction of a vector $\mathbf{d} \in \Re^n$. Clearly, we should only consider those choices of $\mathbf{d}$ that do not immediately take us outside the feasible set. This leads to the following definition, illustrated in Figure 3.1.

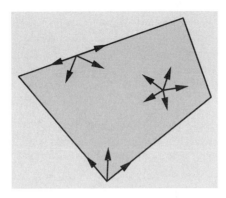

Figure 3.1: Feasible directions at different points of a polyhedron.

Definition 3.1 *Let* **x** *be an element of a polyhedron* P. *A vector* $\mathbf{d} \in \Re^n$ *is said to be a* **feasible direction** *at* **x**, *if there exists a positive scalar* θ *for which* $\mathbf{x} + \theta\mathbf{d} \in P$.

Let **x** be a basic feasible solution to the standard form problem, let $B(1), \ldots, B(m)$ be the indices of the basic variables, and let $\mathbf{B} = [\mathbf{A}_{B(1)} \cdots \mathbf{A}_{B(m)}]$ be the corresponding basis matrix. In particular, we have $x_i = 0$ for every nonbasic variable, while the vector $\mathbf{x}_B = (x_{B(1)}, \ldots, x_{B(m)})$ of basic variables is given by

$$\mathbf{x}_B = \mathbf{B}^{-1}\mathbf{b}.$$

We consider the possibility of moving away from **x**, to a new vector $\mathbf{x} + \theta\mathbf{d}$, by selecting a nonbasic variable x_j (which is initially at zero level), and increasing it to a positive value θ, while keeping the remaining nonbasic variables at zero. Algebraically, $d_j = 1$, and $d_i = 0$ for every nonbasic index i other than j. At the same time, the vector $\mathbf{x}_B$ of basic variables changes to $\mathbf{x}_B + \theta\mathbf{d}_B$, where $\mathbf{d}_B = (d_{B(1)}, d_{B(2)}, \ldots, d_{B(m)})$ is the vector with those components of **d** that correspond to the basic variables.

Given that we are only interested in feasible solutions, we require $\mathbf{A}(\mathbf{x} + \theta\mathbf{d}) = \mathbf{b}$, and since **x** is feasible, we also have $\mathbf{A}\mathbf{x} = \mathbf{b}$. Thus, for the equality constraints to be satisfied for $\theta > 0$, we need $\mathbf{A}\mathbf{d} = \mathbf{0}$. Recall now that $d_j = 1$, and that $d_i = 0$ for all other nonbasic indices i. Then,

$$\mathbf{0} = \mathbf{A}\mathbf{d} = \sum_{i=1}^{n} \mathbf{A}_i d_i = \sum_{i=1}^{m} \mathbf{A}_{B(i)} d_{B(i)} + \mathbf{A}_j = \mathbf{B}\mathbf{d}_B + \mathbf{A}_j.$$

Since the basis matrix **B** is invertible, we obtain

$$\mathbf{d}_B = -\mathbf{B}^{-1}\mathbf{A}_j. \tag{3.1}$$

The direction vector $\mathbf{d}$ that we have just constructed will be referred to as the jth *basic direction*. We have so far guaranteed that the equality constraints are respected as we move away from $\mathbf{x}$ along the basic direction $\mathbf{d}$. How about the nonnegativity constraints? We recall that the variable x_j is increased, and all other nonbasic variables stay at zero level. Thus, we need only worry about the basic variables. We distinguish two cases:

(a) Suppose that $\mathbf{x}$ is a nondegenerate basic feasible solution. Then, $\mathbf{x}_B > \mathbf{0}$, from which it follows that $\mathbf{x}_B + \theta \mathbf{d}_B \geq \mathbf{0}$, and feasibility is maintained, when θ is sufficiently small. In particular, $\mathbf{d}$ is a feasible direction.

(b) Suppose now that $\mathbf{x}$ is degenerate. Then, $\mathbf{d}$ is not always a feasible direction. Indeed, it is possible that a basic variable $x_{B(i)}$ is zero, while the corresponding component $d_{B(i)}$ of $\mathbf{d}_B = -\mathbf{B}^{-1}\mathbf{A}_j$ is negative. In that case, if we follow the jth basic direction, the nonnegativity constraint for $x_{B(i)}$ is immediately violated, and we are led to infeasible solutions; see Figure 3.2.

We now study the effects on the cost function if we move along a basic direction. If $\mathbf{d}$ is the jth basic direction, then the rate $\mathbf{c}'\mathbf{d}$ of cost change along the direction $\mathbf{d}$ is given by $\mathbf{c}_B'\mathbf{d}_B + c_j$, where $\mathbf{c}_B = (c_{B(1)}, \ldots, c_{B(m)})$. Using Eq. (3.1), this is the same as $c_j - \mathbf{c}_B'\mathbf{B}^{-1}\mathbf{A}_j$. This quantity is important enough to warrant a definition. For an intuitive interpretation, c_j is the cost per unit increase in the variable x_j, and the term $-\mathbf{c}_B'\mathbf{B}^{-1}\mathbf{A}_j$ is the cost of the compensating change in the basic variables necessitated by the constraint $\mathbf{A}\mathbf{x} = \mathbf{b}$.

Definition 3.2 *Let $\mathbf{x}$ be a basic solution, let $\mathbf{B}$ be an associated basis matrix, and let $\mathbf{c}_B$ be the vector of costs of the basic variables. For each j, we define the reduced cost $\bar{c}_j$ of the variable x_j according to the formula*

$$\bar{c}_j = c_j - \mathbf{c}_B'\mathbf{B}^{-1}\mathbf{A}_j.$$

Example 3.1 Consider the linear programming problem

$$
\begin{array}{lrcrcrcr}
\text{minimize} & c_1 x_1 &+& c_2 x_2 &+& c_3 x_3 &+& c_4 x_4 \\
\text{subject to} & x_1 &+& x_2 &+& x_3 &+& x_4 &= 2 \\
& 2x_1 & & &+& 3x_3 &+& 4x_4 &= 2 \\
& \multicolumn{8}{l}{x_1, x_2, x_3, x_4 \geq 0.}
\end{array}
$$

The first two columns of the matrix $\mathbf{A}$ are $\mathbf{A}_1 = (1, 2)$ and $\mathbf{A}_2 = (1, 0)$. Since they are linearly independent, we can choose x_1 and x_2 as our basic variables. The corresponding basis matrix is

$$\mathbf{B} = \begin{bmatrix} 1 & 1 \\ 2 & 0 \end{bmatrix}.$$

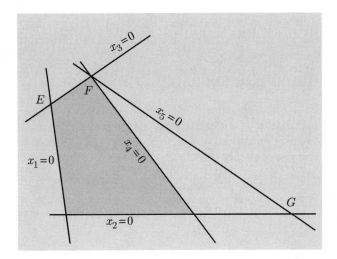

Figure 3.2: Let $n = 5$, $n-m = 2$. As discussed in Section 1.4, we can visualize the feasible set by standing on the two-dimensional set defined by the constraint $\mathbf{Ax} = \mathbf{b}$, in which case, the edges of the feasible set are associated with the nonnegativity constraints $x_i \geq 0$. At the nondegenerate basic feasible solution E, the variables x_1 and x_3 are at zero level (nonbasic) and x_2, x_4, x_5 are positive basic variables. The first basic direction is obtained by increasing x_1, while keeping the other nonbasic variable x_3 at zero level. This is the direction corresponding to the edge EF. Consider now the degenerate basic feasible solution F and let x_3, x_5 be the nonbasic variables. Note that x_4 is a basic variable at zero level. A basic direction is obtained by increasing x_3, while keeping the other nonbasic variable x_5 at zero level. This is the direction corresponding to the line FG and it takes us outside the feasible set. Thus, this basic direction is not a feasible direction.

We set $x_3 = x_4 = 0$, and solve for x_1, x_2, to obtain $x_1 = 1$ and $x_2 = 1$. We have thus obtained a nondegenerate basic feasible solution.

A basic direction corresponding to an increase in the nonbasic variable x_3, is constructed as follows. We have $d_3 = 1$ and $d_4 = 0$. The direction of change of the basic variables is obtained using Eq. (3.1):

$$\begin{bmatrix} d_1 \\ d_2 \end{bmatrix} = \begin{bmatrix} d_{B(1)} \\ d_{B(2)} \end{bmatrix} = \mathbf{d}_B = -\mathbf{B}^{-1}\mathbf{A}_3 = -\begin{bmatrix} 0 & 1/2 \\ 1 & -1/2 \end{bmatrix}\begin{bmatrix} 1 \\ 3 \end{bmatrix} = \begin{bmatrix} -3/2 \\ 1/2 \end{bmatrix}.$$

The cost of moving along this basic direction is $\mathbf{c}'\mathbf{d} = -3c_1/2 + c_2/2 + c_3$. This is the same as the reduced cost of the variable x_3.

Consider now Definition 3.2 for the case of a basic variable. Since $\mathbf{B}$ is the matrix $[\mathbf{A}_{B(1)} \cdots \mathbf{A}_{B(m)}]$, we have $\mathbf{B}^{-1}[\mathbf{A}_{B(1)} \cdots \mathbf{A}_{B(m)}] = \mathbf{I}$, where

$\mathbf{I}$ is the $m \times m$ identity matrix. In particular, $\mathbf{B}^{-1}\mathbf{A}_{B(i)}$ is the ith column of the identity matrix, which is the ith unit vector $\mathbf{e}_i$. Therefore, for every basic variable $x_{B(i)}$, we have

$$\bar{c}_{B(i)} = c_{B(i)} - \mathbf{c}_B'\mathbf{B}^{-1}\mathbf{A}_{B(i)} = c_{B(i)} - \mathbf{c}_B'\mathbf{e}_i = c_{B(i)} - c_{B(i)} = 0,$$

and we see that the reduced cost of every basic variable is zero.

Our next result provides us with optimality conditions. Given our interpretation of the reduced costs as rates of cost change along certain directions, this result is intuitive.

Theorem 3.1 *Consider a basic feasible solution* $\mathbf{x}$ *associated with a basis matrix* $\mathbf{B}$, *and let* $\bar{\mathbf{c}}$ *be the corresponding vector of reduced costs.*

(a) *If* $\bar{\mathbf{c}} \geq \mathbf{0}$, *then* $\mathbf{x}$ *is optimal.*

(b) *If* $\mathbf{x}$ *is optimal and nondegenerate, then* $\bar{\mathbf{c}} \geq \mathbf{0}$.

Proof.

(a) We assume that $\bar{\mathbf{c}} \geq \mathbf{0}$, we let $\mathbf{y}$ be an arbitrary feasible solution, and we define $\mathbf{d} = \mathbf{y} - \mathbf{x}$. Feasibility implies that $\mathbf{Ax} = \mathbf{Ay} = \mathbf{b}$ and, therefore, $\mathbf{Ad} = \mathbf{0}$. The latter equality can be rewritten in the form

$$\mathbf{Bd}_B + \sum_{i \in N} \mathbf{A}_i d_i = \mathbf{0},$$

where N is the set of indices corresponding to the nonbasic variables under the given basis. Since $\mathbf{B}$ is invertible, we obtain

$$\mathbf{d}_B = -\sum_{i \in N} \mathbf{B}^{-1}\mathbf{A}_i d_i,$$

and

$$\mathbf{c}'\mathbf{d} = \mathbf{c}_B'\mathbf{d}_B + \sum_{i \in N} c_i d_i = \sum_{i \in N}(c_i - \mathbf{c}_B'\mathbf{B}^{-1}\mathbf{A}_i)d_i = \sum_{i \in N} \bar{c}_i d_i.$$

For any nonbasic index $i \in N$, we must have $x_i = 0$ and, since $\mathbf{y}$ is feasible, $y_i \geq 0$. Thus, $d_i \geq 0$ and $\bar{c}_i d_i \geq 0$, for all $i \in N$. We conclude that $\mathbf{c}'(\mathbf{y} - \mathbf{x}) = \mathbf{c}'\mathbf{d} \geq 0$, and since $\mathbf{y}$ was an arbitrary feasible solution, $\mathbf{x}$ is optimal.

(b) Suppose that $\mathbf{x}$ is a nondegenerate basic feasible solution and that $\bar{c}_j < 0$ for some j. Since the reduced cost of a basic variable is always zero, x_j must be a nonbasic variable and $\bar{c}_j$ is the rate of cost change along the jth basic direction. Since $\mathbf{x}$ is nondegenerate, the jth basic direction is a feasible direction of cost decrease, as discussed earlier. By moving in that direction, we obtain feasible solutions whose cost is less than that of $\mathbf{x}$, and $\mathbf{x}$ is not optimal.   □

Note that Theorem 3.1 allows the possibility that $\mathbf{x}$ is a (degenerate) optimal basic feasible solution, but that $\bar{c}_j < 0$ for some nonbasic index j. There is an analog of Theorem 3.1 that provides conditions under which a basic feasible solution $\mathbf{x}$ is a unique optimal solution; see Exercise 3.6. A related view of the optimality conditions is developed in Exercises 3.2 and 3.3.

According to Theorem 3.1, in order to decide whether a nondegenerate basic feasible solution is optimal, we need only check whether all reduced costs are nonnegative, which is the same as examining the $n - m$ basic directions. If $\mathbf{x}$ is a degenerate basic feasible solution, an equally simple computational test for determining whether $\mathbf{x}$ is optimal is not available (see Exercises 3.7 and 3.8). Fortunately, the simplex method, as developed in subsequent sections, manages to get around this difficulty in an effective manner.

Note that in order to use Theorem 3.1 and assert that a certain basic solution is optimal, we need to satisfy two conditions: feasibility, and nonnegativity of the reduced costs. This leads us to the following definition.

Definition 3.3 *A basis matrix* $\mathbf{B}$ *is said to be* **optimal** *if:*

(a) $\mathbf{B}^{-1}\mathbf{b} \geq \mathbf{0}$, *and*

(b) $\bar{\mathbf{c}}' = \mathbf{c}' - \mathbf{c}_B'\mathbf{B}^{-1}\mathbf{A} \geq \mathbf{0}'$.

Clearly, if an optimal basis is found, the corresponding basic solution is feasible, satisfies the optimality conditions, and is therefore optimal. On the other hand, in the degenerate case, having an optimal basic feasible solution does not necessarily mean that the reduced costs are nonnegative.

3.2   Development of the simplex method

We will now complete the development of the simplex method. Our main task is to work out the details of how to move to a better basic feasible solution, whenever a profitable basic direction is discovered.

Let us assume that every basic feasible solution is nondegenerate. This assumption will remain in effect until it is explicitly relaxed later in this section. Suppose that we are at a basic feasible solution $\mathbf{x}$ and that we have computed the reduced costs $\bar{c}_j$ of the nonbasic variables. If all of them are nonnegative, Theorem 3.1 shows that we have an optimal solution, and we stop. If on the other hand, the reduced cost $\bar{c}_j$ of a nonbasic variable x_j is negative, the jth basic direction $\mathbf{d}$ is a feasible direction of cost decrease. [This is the direction obtained by letting $d_j = 1$, $d_i = 0$ for $i \neq B(1), \ldots, B(m), j$, and $\mathbf{d}_B = -\mathbf{B}^{-1}\mathbf{A}_j$.] While moving along this direction $\mathbf{d}$, the nonbasic variable x_j becomes positive and all other nonbasic variables remain at zero. We describe this situation by saying that x_j (or $\mathbf{A}_j$) *enters* or *is brought into the basis*.

Once we start moving away from $\mathbf{x}$ along the direction $\mathbf{d}$, we are tracing points of the form $\mathbf{x} + \theta\mathbf{d}$, where $\theta \geq 0$. Since costs decrease along the direction $\mathbf{d}$, it is desirable to move as far as possible. This takes us to the point $\mathbf{x} + \theta^*\mathbf{d}$, where

$$\theta^* = \max\left\{\theta \geq 0 \mid \mathbf{x} + \theta\mathbf{d} \in P\right\}.$$

The resulting cost change is $\theta^*\mathbf{c}'\mathbf{d}$, which is the same as $\theta^*\bar{c}_j$.

We now derive a formula for θ^*. Given that $\mathbf{Ad} = \mathbf{0}$, we have $\mathbf{A}(\mathbf{x} + \theta\mathbf{d}) = \mathbf{Ax} = \mathbf{b}$ for all θ, and the equality constraints will never be violated. Thus, $\mathbf{x} + \theta\mathbf{d}$ can become infeasible only if one of its components becomes negative. We distinguish two cases:

(a) If $\mathbf{d} \geq \mathbf{0}$, then $\mathbf{x} + \theta\mathbf{d} \geq \mathbf{0}$ for all $\theta \geq 0$, the vector $\mathbf{x} + \theta\mathbf{d}$ never becomes infeasible, and we let $\theta^* = \infty$.

(b) If $d_i < 0$ for some i, the constraint $x_i + \theta d_i \geq 0$ becomes $\theta \leq -x_i/d_i$. This constraint on θ must be satisfied for every i with $d_i < 0$. Thus, the largest possible value of θ is

$$\theta^* = \min_{\{i\mid d_i < 0\}}\left(-\frac{x_i}{d_i}\right).$$

Recall that if x_i is a nonbasic variable, then either x_i is the entering variable and $d_i = 1$, or else $d_i = 0$. In either case, d_i is nonnegative. Thus, we only need to consider the basic variables and we have the equivalent formula

$$\theta^* = \min_{\{i=1,\ldots,m\mid d_{B(i)}<0\}}\left(-\frac{x_{B(i)}}{d_{B(i)}}\right). \tag{3.2}$$

Note that $\theta^* > 0$, because $x_{B(i)} > 0$ for all i, as a consequence of nondegeneracy.

Example 3.2 This is a continuation of Example 3.1 from the previous section, dealing with the linear programming problem

$$\begin{array}{rlll} \text{minimize} & c_1x_1 + c_2x_2 + c_3x_3 + c_4x_4 \\ \text{subject to} & x_1 + x_2 + x_3 + x_4 = 2 \\ & 2x_1 + 3x_3 + 4x_4 = 2 \\ & x_1, x_2, x_3, x_4 \geq 0. \end{array}$$

Let us again consider the basic feasible solution $\mathbf{x} = (1, 1, 0, 0)$ and recall that the reduced cost $\bar{c}_3$ of the nonbasic variable x_3 was found to be $-3c_1/2 + c_2/2 + c_3$. Suppose that $\mathbf{c} = (2, 0, 0, 0)$, in which case, we have $\bar{c}_3 = -3$. Since $\bar{c}_3$ is negative, we form the corresponding basic direction, which is $\mathbf{d} = (-3/2, 1/2, 1, 0)$, and consider vectors of the form $\mathbf{x} + \theta\mathbf{d}$, with $\theta \geq 0$. As θ increases, the only component of $\mathbf{x}$ that decreases is the first one (because $d_1 < 0$). The largest possible value of θ is given by $\theta^* = -(x_1/d_1) = 2/3$. This takes us to the point $\mathbf{y} = \mathbf{x} + 2\mathbf{d}/3 = (0, 4/3, 2/3, 0)$. Note that the columns $\mathbf{A}_2$ and $\mathbf{A}_3$ corresponding to the nonzero variables at the new vector $\mathbf{y}$ are $(1, 0)$ and $(1, 3)$, respectively, and are linearly independent. Therefore, they form a basis and the vector $\mathbf{y}$ is a new basic feasible solution. In particular, the variable x_3 has entered the basis and the variable x_1 has exited the basis.

Once θ^* is chosen, and assuming it is finite, we move to the new feasible solution $\mathbf{y} = \mathbf{x} + \theta^* \mathbf{d}$. Since $x_j = 0$ and $d_j = 1$, we have $y_j = \theta^* > 0$. Let ℓ be a minimizing index in Eq. (3.2), that is,

$$-\frac{x_{B(\ell)}}{d_{B(\ell)}} = \min_{\{i=1,\dots,m \mid d_{B(i)} < 0\}} \left(-\frac{x_{B(i)}}{d_{B(i)}} \right) = \theta^*;$$

in particular,

$$d_{B(\ell)} < 0,$$

and

$$x_{B(\ell)} + \theta^* d_{B(\ell)} = 0.$$

We observe that the basic variable $x_{B(\ell)}$ has become zero, whereas the nonbasic variable x_j has now become positive, which suggests that x_j should replace $x_{B(\ell)}$ in the basis. Accordingly, we take the old basis matrix $\mathbf{B}$ and replace $\mathbf{A}_{B(\ell)}$ with $\mathbf{A}_j$, thus obtaining the matrix

$$\overline{\mathbf{B}} = \begin{bmatrix} | & & | & | & | & & | \\ \mathbf{A}_{B(1)} & \cdots & \mathbf{A}_{B(\ell-1)} & \mathbf{A}_j & \mathbf{A}_{B(\ell+1)} & \cdots & \mathbf{A}_{B(m)} \\ | & & | & | & | & & | \end{bmatrix}. \quad (3.3)$$

Equivalently, we are replacing the set $\{B(1), \dots, B(m)\}$ of basic indices by a new set $\{\overline{B}(1), \dots, \overline{B}(m)\}$ of indices given by

$$\overline{B}(i) = \begin{cases} B(i), & i \neq \ell, \\ j, & i = \ell. \end{cases} \quad (3.4)$$

Theorem 3.2

(a) The columns $\mathbf{A}_{B(i)}$, $i \neq \ell$, and $\mathbf{A}_j$ are linearly independent and, therefore, $\overline{\mathbf{B}}$ is a basis matrix.

(b) The vector $\mathbf{y} = \mathbf{x} + \theta^* \mathbf{d}$ is a basic feasible solution associated with the basis matrix $\overline{\mathbf{B}}$.

Proof.

(a) If the vectors $\mathbf{A}_{\overline{B}(i)}$, $i = 1, \dots, m$, are linearly dependent, then there exist coefficients $\lambda_1, \dots, \lambda_m$, not all of them zero, such that

$$\sum_{i=1}^{m} \lambda_i \mathbf{A}_{\overline{B}(i)} = \mathbf{0},$$

which implies that

$$\sum_{i=1}^{m} \lambda_i \mathbf{B}^{-1} \mathbf{A}_{\overline{B}(i)} = \mathbf{0},$$

and the vectors $\mathbf{B}^{-1}\mathbf{A}_{\overline{B}(i)}$ are also linearly dependent. To show that this is not the case, we will prove that the vectors $\mathbf{B}^{-1}\mathbf{A}_{B(i)}$, $i \neq \ell$, and $\mathbf{B}^{-1}\mathbf{A}_j$ are linearly independent. We have $\mathbf{B}^{-1}\mathbf{B} = \mathbf{I}$. Since $\mathbf{A}_{B(i)}$ is the ith column of $\mathbf{B}$, it follows that the vectors $\mathbf{B}^{-1}\mathbf{A}_{B(i)}$, $i \neq \ell$, are all the unit vectors except for the ℓth unit vector. In particular, they are linearly independent and their ℓth component is zero. On the other hand, $\mathbf{B}^{-1}\mathbf{A}_j$ is equal to $-\mathbf{d}_B$. Its ℓth entry, $-d_{B(\ell)}$, is nonzero by the definition of ℓ. Thus, $\mathbf{B}^{-1}\mathbf{A}_j$ is linearly independent from the unit vectors $\mathbf{B}^{-1}\mathbf{A}_{B(i)}$, $i \neq \ell$.

(b) We have $\mathbf{y} \geq \mathbf{0}$, $\mathbf{Ay} = \mathbf{b}$, and $y_i = 0$ for $i \neq \overline{B}(1), \ldots, \overline{B}(m)$. Furthermore, the columns $\mathbf{A}_{\overline{B}(1)}, \ldots, \mathbf{A}_{\overline{B}(m)}$ have just been shown to be linearly independent. It follows that $\mathbf{y}$ is a basic feasible solution associated with the basis matrix $\overline{\mathbf{B}}$.   □

Since θ^* is positive, the new basic feasible solution $\mathbf{x} + \theta^* \mathbf{d}$ is distinct from $\mathbf{x}$; since $\mathbf{d}$ is a direction of cost decrease, the cost of this new basic feasible solution is strictly smaller. We have therefore accomplished our objective of moving to a new basic feasible solution with lower cost. We can now summarize a typical iteration of the simplex method, also known as a *pivot* (see Section 3.6 for a discussion of the origins of this term). For our purposes, it is convenient to define a vector $\mathbf{u} = (u_1, \ldots, u_m)$ by letting

$$\mathbf{u} = -\mathbf{d}_B = \mathbf{B}^{-1}\mathbf{A}_j,$$

where $\mathbf{A}_j$ is the column that enters the basis; in particular, $u_i = -d_{B(i)}$, for $i = 1, \ldots, m$.

An iteration of the simplex method

1. In a typical iteration, we start with a basis consisting of the basic columns $\mathbf{A}_{B(1)}, \ldots, \mathbf{A}_{B(m)}$, and an associated basic feasible solution $\mathbf{x}$.

2. Compute the reduced costs $\bar{c}_j = c_j - \mathbf{c}_B' \mathbf{B}^{-1} \mathbf{A}_j$ for all nonbasic indices j. If they are all nonnegative, the current basic feasible solution is optimal, and the algorithm terminates; else, choose some j for which $\bar{c}_j < 0$.

3. Compute $\mathbf{u} = \mathbf{B}^{-1}\mathbf{A}_j$. If no component of $\mathbf{u}$ is positive, we have $\theta^* = \infty$, the optimal cost is $-\infty$, and the algorithm terminates.

4. If some component of **u** is positive, let

$$\theta^* = \min_{\{i=1,\ldots,m \mid u_i > 0\}} \frac{x_{B(i)}}{u_i}.$$

5. Let ℓ be such that $\theta^* = x_{B(\ell)}/u_\ell$. Form a new basis by replacing $\mathbf{A}_{B(\ell)}$ with $\mathbf{A}_j$. If **y** is the new basic feasible solution, the values of the new basic variables are $y_j = \theta^*$ and $y_{B(i)} = x_{B(i)} - \theta^* u_i$, $i \neq \ell$.

The simplex method is initialized with an arbitrary basic feasible solution, which, for feasible standard form problems, is guaranteed to exist. The following theorem states that, in the nondegenerate case, the simplex method works correctly and terminates after a finite number of iterations.

Theorem 3.3 *Assume that the feasible set is nonempty and that every basic feasible solution is nondegenerate. Then, the simplex method terminates after a finite number of iterations. At termination, there are the following two possibilities:*

(a) *We have an optimal basis* **B** *and an associated basic feasible solution which is optimal.*

(b) *We have found a vector* **d** *satisfying* $\mathbf{Ad} = \mathbf{0}$, $\mathbf{d} \geq \mathbf{0}$, *and* $\mathbf{c'd} < 0$, *and the optimal cost is* $-\infty$.

Proof. If the algorithm terminates due to the stopping criterion in Step 2, then the optimality conditions in Theorem 3.1 have been met, **B** is an optimal basis, and the current basic feasible solution is optimal.

If the algorithm terminates because the criterion in Step 3 has been met, then we are at a basic feasible solution **x** and we have discovered a nonbasic variable x_j such that $\bar{c}_j < 0$ and such that the corresponding basic direction **d** satisfies $\mathbf{Ad} = \mathbf{0}$ and $\mathbf{d} \geq \mathbf{0}$. In particular, $\mathbf{x} + \theta \mathbf{d} \in P$ for all $\theta > 0$. Since $\mathbf{c'd} = \bar{c}_j < 0$, by taking θ arbitrarily large, the cost can be made arbitrarily negative, and the optimal cost is $-\infty$.

At each iteration, the algorithm moves by a positive amount θ^* along a direction **d** that satisfies $\mathbf{c'd} < 0$. Therefore, the cost of every successive basic feasible solution visited by the algorithm is strictly less than the cost of the previous one, and no basic feasible solution can be visited twice. Since there is a finite number of basic feasible solutions, the algorithm must eventually terminate. $\qquad\square$

Theorem 3.3 provides an independent proof of some of the results of Chapter 2 for nondegenerate standard form problems. In particular, it shows that for feasible and nondegenerate problems, either the optimal cost is $-\infty$, or there exists a basic feasible solution which is optimal (cf. Theorem 2.8 in Section 2.6). While the proof given here might appear more elementary, its extension to the degenerate case is not as simple.

The simplex method for degenerate problems

We have been working so far under the assumption that all basic feasible solutions are nondegenerate. Suppose now that the exact same algorithm is used in the presence of degeneracy. Then, the following new possibilities may be encountered in the course of the algorithm.

(a) If the current basic feasible solution $\mathbf{x}$ is degenerate, θ^* can be equal to zero, in which case, the new basic feasible solution $\mathbf{y}$ is the same as $\mathbf{x}$. This happens if some basic variable $x_{B(\ell)}$ is equal to zero and the corresponding component $d_{B(\ell)}$ of the direction vector $\mathbf{d}$ is negative. Nevertheless, we can still define a new basis $\overline{\mathbf{B}}$, by replacing $\mathbf{A}_{B(\ell)}$ with $\mathbf{A}_j$ [cf. Eqs. (3.3)-(3.4)], and Theorem 3.2 is still valid.

(b) Even if θ^* is positive, it may happen that more than one of the original basic variables becomes zero at the new point $\mathbf{x} + \theta^*\mathbf{d}$. Since only one of them exits the basis, the others remain in the basis at zero level, and the new basic feasible solution is degenerate.

Basis changes while staying at the same basic feasible solution are not in vain. As illustrated in Figure 3.3, a sequence of such basis changes may lead to the eventual discovery of a cost reducing feasible direction. On the other hand, a sequence of basis changes might lead back to the initial basis, in which case the algorithm may loop indefinitely. This undesirable phenomenon is called *cycling*. An example of cycling is given in Section 3.3, after we develop some bookkeeping tools for carrying out the mechanics of the algorithm. It is sometimes maintained that cycling is an exceptionally rare phenomenon. However, for many highly structured linear programming problems, most basic feasible solutions are degenerate, and cycling is a real possibility. Cycling can be avoided by judiciously choosing the variables that will enter or exit the basis (see Section 3.4). We now discuss the freedom available in this respect.

Pivot Selection

The simplex algorithm, as we described it, has certain degrees of freedom: in Step 2, we are free to choose any j whose reduced cost $\bar{c}_j$ is negative; also, in Step 5, there may be several indices ℓ that attain the minimum in the definition of θ^*, and we are free to choose any one of them. Rules for making such choices are called *pivoting rules*.

Regarding the choice of the entering column, the following rules are some natural candidates:

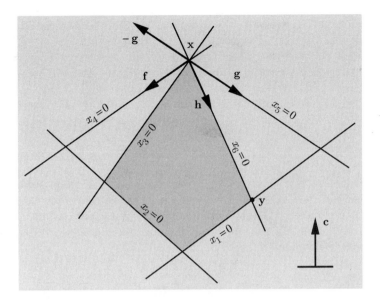

Figure 3.3: We visualize a problem in standard form, with $n - m = 2$, by standing on the two-dimensional plane defined by the equality constraints $\mathbf{Ax} = \mathbf{b}$. The basic feasible solution $\mathbf{x}$ is degenerate. If x_4 and x_5 are the nonbasic variables, then the two corresponding basic directions are the vectors $\mathbf{g}$ and $\mathbf{f}$. For either of these two basic directions, we have $\theta^* = 0$. However, if we perform a change of basis, with x_4 entering the basis and x_6 exiting, the new nonbasic variables are x_5 and x_6, and the two basic directions are $\mathbf{h}$ and $-\mathbf{g}$. (The direction $-\mathbf{g}$ is the one followed if x_6 is increased while x_5 is kept at zero.) In particular, we can now follow direction $\mathbf{h}$ to reach a new basic feasible solution $\mathbf{y}$ with lower cost.

(a) *Choose a column $\mathbf{A}_j$, with $\bar{c}_j < 0$, whose reduced cost is the most negative.* Since the reduced cost is the rate of change of the cost function, this rule chooses a direction along which costs decrease at the fastest rate. However, the actual cost decrease depends on how far we move along the chosen direction. This suggests the next rule.

(b) *Choose a column with $\bar{c}_j < 0$ for which the corresponding cost decrease $\theta^* |\bar{c}_j|$ is largest.* This rule offers the possibility of reaching optimality after a smaller number of iterations. On the other hand, the computational burden at each iteration is larger, because we need to compute θ^* for each column with $\bar{c}_j < 0$. The available empirical evidence suggests that the overall running time does not improve.

For large problems, even the rule that chooses the most negative $\bar{c}_j$ can be computationally expensive, because it requires the computation of the reduced cost of every variable. In practice, simpler rules are sometimes used, such as the *smallest subscript* rule, that chooses the smallest j for which $\bar{c}_j$ is negative. Under this rule, once a negative reduced cost is discovered, there is no reason to compute the remaining reduced costs. Other criteria that have been found to improve the overall running time are the *Devex* (Harris, 1973) and the *steepest edge* rule (Goldfarb and Reid, 1977). Finally, there are methods based on *candidate lists* whereby one examines the reduced costs of nonbasic variables by picking them one at a time from a prioritized list. There are different ways of maintaining such prioritized lists, depending on the rule used for adding, removing, or reordering elements of the list.

Regarding the choice of the exiting column, the simplest option is again the *smallest subscript* rule: out of all variables eligible to exit the basis, choose one with the smallest subscript. It turns out that by following the smallest subscript rule for both the entering and the exiting column, cycling can be avoided (cf. Section 3.4).

3.3   Implementations of the simplex method

In this section, we discuss some ways of carrying out the mechanics of the simplex method. It should be clear from the statement of the algorithm that the vectors $\mathbf{B}^{-1}\mathbf{A}_j$ play a key role. If these vectors are available, the reduced costs, the direction of motion, and the stepsize θ^* are easily computed. Thus, the main difference between alternative implementations lies in the way that the vectors $\mathbf{B}^{-1}\mathbf{A}_j$ are computed and on the amount of related information that is carried from one iteration to the next.

When comparing different implementations, it is important to keep the following facts in mind (cf. Section 1.6). If $\mathbf{B}$ is a given $m \times m$ matrix and $\mathbf{b} \in \Re^m$ is a given vector, computing the inverse of $\mathbf{B}$ or solving a linear system of the form $\mathbf{B}\mathbf{x} = \mathbf{b}$ takes $O(m^3)$ arithmetic operations. Computing a matrix-vector product $\mathbf{B}\mathbf{b}$ takes $O(m^2)$ operations. Finally, computing an inner product $\mathbf{p}'\mathbf{b}$ of two m-dimensional vectors takes $O(m)$ arithmetic operations.

Naive implementation

We start by describing the most straightforward implementation in which no auxiliary information is carried from one iteration to the next. At the beginning of a typical iteration, we have the indices $B(1), \ldots, B(m)$ of the current basic variables. We form the basis matrix $\mathbf{B}$ and compute $\mathbf{p}' = \mathbf{c}'_B\mathbf{B}^{-1}$, by solving the linear system $\mathbf{p}'\mathbf{B} = \mathbf{c}'_B$ for the unknown vector $\mathbf{p}$. (This vector $\mathbf{p}$ is called the vector of *simplex multipliers* associated with the basis $\mathbf{B}$.) The reduced cost $\bar{c}_j = c_j - \mathbf{c}'_B\mathbf{B}^{-1}\mathbf{A}_j$ of any variable x_j is then obtained according to the formula

$$\bar{c}_j = c_j - \mathbf{p}'\mathbf{A}_j.$$

Depending on the pivoting rule employed, we may have to compute all of the reduced costs or we may compute them one at a time until a variable with a negative reduced cost is encountered. Once a column $\mathbf{A}_j$ is selected to enter the basis, we solve the linear system $\mathbf{Bu} = \mathbf{A}_j$ in order to determine the vector $\mathbf{u} = \mathbf{B}^{-1}\mathbf{A}_j$. At this point, we can form the direction along which we will be moving away from the current basic feasible solution. We finally determine θ^* and the variable that will exit the basis, and construct the new basic feasible solution.

We note that we need $O(m^3)$ arithmetic operations to solve the systems $\mathbf{p}'\mathbf{B} = \mathbf{c}'_B$ and $\mathbf{Bu} = \mathbf{A}_j$. In addition, computing the reduced costs of all variables requires $O(mn)$ arithmetic operations, because we need to form the inner product of the vector $\mathbf{p}$ with each one of the nonbasic columns $\mathbf{A}_j$. Thus, the total computational effort per iteration is $O(m^3 + mn)$. We will see shortly that alternative implementations require only $O(m^2 + mn)$ arithmetic operations. Therefore, the implementation described here is rather inefficient, in general. On the other hand, for certain problems with a special structure, the linear systems $\mathbf{p}'\mathbf{B} = \mathbf{c}'_B$ and $\mathbf{Bu} = \mathbf{A}_j$ can be solved very fast, in which case this implementation can be of practical interest. We will revisit this point in Chapter 7, when we apply the simplex method to network flow problems.

Revised simplex method

Much of the computational burden in the naive implementation is due to the need for solving two linear systems of equations. In an alternative implementation, the matrix $\mathbf{B}^{-1}$ is made available at the beginning of each iteration, and the vectors $\mathbf{c}'_B\mathbf{B}^{-1}$ and $\mathbf{B}^{-1}\mathbf{A}_j$ are computed by a matrix-vector multiplication. For this approach to be practical, we need an efficient method for updating the matrix $\mathbf{B}^{-1}$ each time that we effect a change of basis. This is discussed next.

Let

$$\mathbf{B} = \left[\mathbf{A}_{B(1)} \cdots \mathbf{A}_{B(m)}\right]$$

be the basis matrix at the beginning of an iteration and let

$$\overline{\mathbf{B}} = \left[\mathbf{A}_{B(1)} \cdots \mathbf{A}_{B(\ell-1)} \quad \mathbf{A}_j \quad \mathbf{A}_{B(\ell+1)} \cdots \mathbf{A}_{B(m)}\right]$$

be the basis matrix at the beginning of the next iteration. These two basis matrices have the same columns except that the ℓth column $\mathbf{A}_{B(\ell)}$ (the one that exits the basis) has been replaced by $\mathbf{A}_j$. It is then reasonable to expect that $\mathbf{B}^{-1}$ contains information that can be exploited in the computation of $\overline{\mathbf{B}}^{-1}$. After we develop some needed tools and terminology, we will see that this is indeed the case. An alternative explanation and line of development is outlined in Exercise 3.13.

> **Definition 3.4** *Given a matrix, not necessarily square, the operation of adding a constant multiple of one row to the same or to another row is called an* **elementary row operation.**

The example that follows indicates that performing an elementary row operation on a matrix $\mathbf{C}$ is equivalent to forming the matrix $\mathbf{QC}$, where $\mathbf{Q}$ is a suitably constructed square matrix.

Example 3.3 Let

$$
\mathbf{Q} = \begin{bmatrix} 1 & 0 & 2 \\ 0 & 1 & 0 \\ 0 & 0 & 1 \end{bmatrix}, \qquad \mathbf{C} = \begin{bmatrix} 1 & 2 \\ 3 & 4 \\ 5 & 6 \end{bmatrix},
$$

and note that

$$
\mathbf{QC} = \begin{bmatrix} 11 & 14 \\ 3 & 4 \\ 5 & 6 \end{bmatrix}.
$$

In particular, multiplication from the left by the matrix $\mathbf{Q}$ has the effect of multiplying the third row of $\mathbf{C}$ by two and adding it to the first row.

Generalizing Example 3.3, we see that multiplying the jth row by β and adding it to the ith row (for $i \neq j$) is the same as left-multiplying by the matrix $\mathbf{Q} = \mathbf{I} + \mathbf{D}_{ij}$, where $\mathbf{D}_{ij}$ is a matrix with all entries equal to zero, except for the (i,j)th entry which is equal to β. The determinant of such a matrix $\mathbf{Q}$ is equal to 1 and, therefore, $\mathbf{Q}$ is invertible.

Suppose now that we apply a *sequence* of K elementary row operations and that the kth such operation corresponds to left-multiplication by a certain invertible matrix $\mathbf{Q}_k$. Then, the sequence of these elementary row operations is the same as left-multiplication by the invertible matrix $\mathbf{Q}_K \mathbf{Q}_{K-1} \cdots \mathbf{Q}_2 \mathbf{Q}_1$. We conclude that performing a *sequence* of elementary row operations on a given matrix is equivalent to left-multiplying that matrix by a certain invertible matrix.

Since $\mathbf{B}^{-1}\mathbf{B} = \mathbf{I}$, we see that $\mathbf{B}^{-1}\mathbf{A}_{B(i)}$ is the ith unit vector $\mathbf{e}_i$. Using this observation, we have

$$
\mathbf{B}^{-1}\overline{\mathbf{B}} = \begin{bmatrix} | & & | & | & | & & | \\ \mathbf{e}_1 & \cdots & \mathbf{e}_{\ell-1} & \mathbf{u} & \mathbf{e}_{\ell+1} & \cdots & \mathbf{e}_m \\ | & & | & | & | & & | \end{bmatrix}
$$

$$
= \begin{bmatrix} 1 & & u_1 & & \\ & \ddots & \vdots & & \\ & & u_\ell & & \\ & & \vdots & \ddots & \\ & & u_m & & 1 \end{bmatrix},
$$

where $\mathbf{u} = \mathbf{B}^{-1}\mathbf{A}_j$. Let us apply a sequence of elementary row operations that will change the above matrix to the identity matrix. In particular, consider the following sequence of elementary row operations.

(a) For each $i \neq \ell$, we add the ℓth row times $-u_i/u_\ell$ to the ith row. (Recall that $u_\ell > 0$.) This replaces u_i by zero.

(b) We divide the ℓth row by u_ℓ. This replaces u_ℓ by one.

In words, we are adding to each row a multiple of the ℓth row to replace the ℓth column $\mathbf{u}$ by the ℓth unit vector $\mathbf{e}_\ell$. This sequence of elementary row operations is equivalent to left-multiplying $\mathbf{B}^{-1}\overline{\mathbf{B}}$ by a certain invertible matrix $\mathbf{Q}$. Since the result is the identity, we have $\mathbf{Q}\mathbf{B}^{-1}\overline{\mathbf{B}} = \mathbf{I}$, which yields $\mathbf{Q}\mathbf{B}^{-1} = \overline{\mathbf{B}}^{-1}$. The last equation shows that if we apply the same sequence of row operations to the matrix $\mathbf{B}^{-1}$ (equivalently, left-multiply by $\mathbf{Q}$), we obtain $\overline{\mathbf{B}}^{-1}$. We conclude that all it takes to generate $\overline{\mathbf{B}}^{-1}$, is to start with $\mathbf{B}^{-1}$ and apply the sequence of elementary row operations described above.

Example 3.4 Let

$$\mathbf{B}^{-1} = \begin{bmatrix} 1 & 2 & 3 \\ -2 & 3 & 1 \\ 4 & -3 & -2 \end{bmatrix}, \qquad \mathbf{u} = \begin{bmatrix} -4 \\ 2 \\ 2 \end{bmatrix},$$

and suppose that $\ell = 3$. Thus, our objective is to transform the vector $\mathbf{u}$ to the unit vector $\mathbf{e}_3 = (0, 0, 1)$. We multiply the third row by 2 and add it to the first row. We subtract the third row from the second row. Finally, we divide the third row by 2. We obtain

$$\overline{\mathbf{B}}^{-1} = \begin{bmatrix} 9 & -4 & -1 \\ -6 & 6 & 3 \\ 2 & -1.5 & -1 \end{bmatrix}.$$

When the matrix $\mathbf{B}^{-1}$ is updated in the manner we have described, we obtain an implementation of the simplex method known as the *revised simplex method*, which we summarize below.

An iteration of the revised simplex method

1. In a typical iteration, we start with a basis consisting of the basic columns $\mathbf{A}_{B(1)}, \ldots, \mathbf{A}_{B(m)}$, an associated basic feasible solution $\mathbf{x}$, and the inverse $\mathbf{B}^{-1}$ of the basis matrix.

2. Compute the row vector $\mathbf{p}' = \mathbf{c}_B'\mathbf{B}^{-1}$ and then compute the reduced costs $\bar{c}_j = c_j - \mathbf{p}'\mathbf{A}_j$. If they are all nonnegative, the current basic feasible solution is optimal, and the algorithm terminates; else, choose some j for which $\bar{c}_j < 0$.

3. Compute $\mathbf{u} = \mathbf{B}^{-1}\mathbf{A}_j$. If no component of $\mathbf{u}$ is positive, the optimal cost is $-\infty$, and the algorithm terminates.

4. If some component of $\mathbf{u}$ is positive, let

$$\theta^* = \min_{\{i=1,\ldots,m\,|\,u_i>0\}} \frac{x_{B(i)}}{u_i}.$$

5. Let ℓ be such that $\theta^* = x_{B(\ell)}/u_\ell$. Form a new basis by replacing $\mathbf{A}_{B(\ell)}$ with $\mathbf{A}_j$. If $\mathbf{y}$ is the new basic feasible solution, the values of the new basic variables are $y_j = \theta^*$ and $y_{B(i)} = x_{B(i)} - \theta^* u_i$, $i \neq \ell$.

6. Form the $m \times (m+1)$ matrix $[\mathbf{B}^{-1} \mid \mathbf{u}]$. Add to each one of its rows a multiple of the ℓth row to make the last column equal to the unit vector $\mathbf{e}_\ell$. The first m columns of the result is the matrix $\overline{\mathbf{B}}^{-1}$.

The full tableau implementation

We finally describe the implementation of simplex method in terms of the so-called *full tableau*. Here, instead of maintaining and updating the matrix $\mathbf{B}^{-1}$, we maintain and update the $m \times (n+1)$ matrix

$$\mathbf{B}^{-1}\Big[\mathbf{b} \mid \mathbf{A}\Big]$$

with columns $\mathbf{B}^{-1}\mathbf{b}$ and $\mathbf{B}^{-1}\mathbf{A}_1,\ldots,\mathbf{B}^{-1}\mathbf{A}_n$. This matrix is called the *simplex tableau*. Note that the column $\mathbf{B}^{-1}\mathbf{b}$, called the *zeroth column*, contains the values of the basic variables. The column $\mathbf{B}^{-1}\mathbf{A}_i$ is called the *i*th column of the tableau. The column $\mathbf{u} = \mathbf{B}^{-1}\mathbf{A}_j$ corresponding to the variable that enters the basis is called the *pivot column*. If the ℓth basic variable exits the basis, the ℓth row of the tableau is called the *pivot row*. Finally, the element belonging to both the pivot row and the pivot column is called the *pivot element*. Note that the pivot element is u_ℓ and is always positive (unless $\mathbf{u} \leq \mathbf{0}$, in which case the algorithm has met the termination condition in Step 3).

The information contained in the rows of the tableau admits the following interpretation. The equality constraints are initially given to us in the form $\mathbf{b} = \mathbf{A}\mathbf{x}$. Given the current basis matrix $\mathbf{B}$, these equality constraints can also be expressed in the equivalent form

$$\mathbf{B}^{-1}\mathbf{b} = \mathbf{B}^{-1}\mathbf{A}\mathbf{x},$$

which is precisely the information in the tableau. In other words, the rows of the tableau provide us with the coefficients of the equality constraints $\mathbf{B}^{-1}\mathbf{b} = \mathbf{B}^{-1}\mathbf{A}\mathbf{x}$.

At the end of each iteration, we need to update the tableau $\mathbf{B}^{-1}[\mathbf{b} \mid \mathbf{A}]$ and compute $\overline{\mathbf{B}}^{-1}[\mathbf{b} \mid \mathbf{A}]$. This can be accomplished by left-multiplying the simplex tableau with a matrix $\mathbf{Q}$ satisfying $\mathbf{Q}\mathbf{B}^{-1} = \overline{\mathbf{B}}^{-1}$. As explained earlier, this is the same as performing those elementary row operations that turn $\mathbf{B}^{-1}$ to $\overline{\mathbf{B}}^{-1}$; that is, we add to each row a multiple of the pivot row to set all entries of the pivot column to zero, with the exception of the pivot element which is set to one.

Regarding the determination of the exiting column $\mathbf{A}_{B(\ell)}$ and the stepsize θ^*, Steps 4 and 5 in the summary of the simplex method amount to the following: $x_{B(i)}/u_i$ is the ratio of the ith entry in the zeroth column of the tableau to the ith entry in the pivot column of the tableau. We only consider those i for which u_i is positive. The smallest ratio is equal to θ^* and determines ℓ.

It is customary to augment the simplex tableau by including a top row, to be referred to as the *zeroth row*. The entry at the top left corner contains the value $-\mathbf{c}'_B\mathbf{x}_B$, which is the negative of the current cost. (The reason for the minus sign is that it allows for a simple update rule, as will be seen shortly.) The rest of the zeroth row is the row vector of reduced costs, that is, the vector $\overline{\mathbf{c}}' = \mathbf{c}' - \mathbf{c}'_B\mathbf{B}^{-1}\mathbf{A}$. Thus, the structure of the tableau is:

$-\mathbf{c}'_B\mathbf{B}^{-1}\mathbf{b}$	$\mathbf{c}' - \mathbf{c}'_B\mathbf{B}^{-1}\mathbf{A}$
$\mathbf{B}^{-1}\mathbf{b}$	$\mathbf{B}^{-1}\mathbf{A}$

or, in more detail,

$-\mathbf{c}'_B\mathbf{x}_B$	$\overline{c}_1$	$\ldots$	$\overline{c}_n$
$x_{B(1)}$			
$\vdots$	$\mathbf{B}^{-1}\mathbf{A}_1$	$\ldots$	$\mathbf{B}^{-1}\mathbf{A}_n$
$x_{B(m)}$			

The rule for updating the zeroth row turns out to be identical to the rule used for the other rows of the tableau: add a multiple of the pivot row to the zeroth row to set the reduced cost of the entering variable to zero. We will now verify that this update rule produces the correct results for the zeroth row.

At the beginning of a typical iteration, the zeroth row is of the form

$$[0 \mid \mathbf{c}'] - \mathbf{g}'[\mathbf{b} \mid \mathbf{A}],$$

where $\mathbf{g}' = \mathbf{c}'_B\mathbf{B}^{-1}$. Hence, the zeroth row is equal to $[0 \mid \mathbf{c}']$ plus a linear combination of the rows of $[\mathbf{b} \mid \mathbf{A}]$. Let column j be the pivot column, and row ℓ be the pivot row. Note that the pivot row is of the form $\mathbf{h}'[\mathbf{b} \mid \mathbf{A}]$, where the vector $\mathbf{h}'$ is the ℓth row of $\mathbf{B}^{-1}$. Hence, after a multiple of the pivot row is added to the zeroth row, that row is again equal to $[0 \mid \mathbf{c}']$ plus a (different) linear combination of the rows of $[\mathbf{b} \mid \mathbf{A}]$, and is of the form

$$[0 \mid \mathbf{c}'] - \mathbf{p}'[\mathbf{b} \mid \mathbf{A}],$$

for some vector $\mathbf{p}$. Recall that our update rule is such that the pivot column entry of the zeroth row becomes zero, that is,

$$c_{\overline{B}(\ell)} - \mathbf{p}'\mathbf{A}_{\overline{B}(\ell)} = c_j - \mathbf{p}'\mathbf{A}_j = 0.$$

Consider now the $\overline{B}(i)$th column for $i \neq \ell$. (This is a column corresponding to a basic variable that stays in the basis.) The zeroth row entry of that column is zero, before the change of basis, since it is the reduced cost of a basic variable. Because $\mathbf{B}^{-1}\mathbf{A}_{B(i)}$ is the ith unit vector and $i \neq \ell$, the entry in the pivot row for that column is also equal to zero. Hence, adding a multiple of the pivot row to the zeroth row of the tableau does not affect the zeroth row entry of that column, which is left at zero. We conclude that the vector $\mathbf{p}$ satisfies $c_{\overline{B}(i)} - \mathbf{p}'\mathbf{A}_{\overline{B}(i)} = 0$ for every column $\mathbf{A}_{\overline{B}(i)}$ in the new basis. This implies that $\mathbf{c}'_{\overline{B}} - \mathbf{p}'\overline{\mathbf{B}} = \mathbf{0}$, and $\mathbf{p}' = \mathbf{c}'_{\overline{B}}\overline{\mathbf{B}}^{-1}$. Hence, with our update rule, the updated zeroth row of the tableau is equal to

$$[0 \mid \mathbf{c}'] - \mathbf{c}'_{\overline{B}}\overline{\mathbf{B}}^{-1}[\mathbf{b} \mid \mathbf{A}],$$

as desired.

We can now summarize the mechanics of the full tableau implementation.

An iteration of the full tableau implementation

1. A typical iteration starts with the tableau associated with a basis matrix $\mathbf{B}$ and the corresponding basic feasible solution $\mathbf{x}$.

2. Examine the reduced costs in the zeroth row of the tableau. If they are all nonnegative, the current basic feasible solution is optimal, and the algorithm terminates; else, choose some j for which $\overline{c}_j < 0$.

3. Consider the vector $\mathbf{u} = \mathbf{B}^{-1}\mathbf{A}_j$, which is the jth column (the pivot column) of the tableau. If no component of $\mathbf{u}$ is positive, the optimal cost is $-\infty$, and the algorithm terminates.

4. For each i for which u_i is positive, compute the ratio $x_{B(i)}/u_i$. Let ℓ be the index of a row that corresponds to the smallest ratio. The column $\mathbf{A}_{B(\ell)}$ exits the basis and the column $\mathbf{A}_j$ enters the basis.

5. Add to each row of the tableau a constant multiple of the ℓth row (the pivot row) so that u_ℓ (the pivot element) becomes one and all other entries of the pivot column become zero.

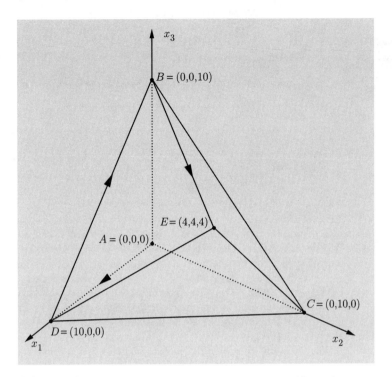

Figure 3.4: The feasible set in Example 3.5. Note that we have five extreme points. These are $A = (0,0,0)$ with cost 0, $B = (0,0,10)$ with cost -120, $C = (0,10,0)$ with cost -120, $D = (10,0,0)$ with cost -100, and $E = (4,4,4)$ with cost -136. In particular, E is the unique optimal solution.

Example 3.5 Consider the problem

$$
\begin{array}{ll}
\text{minimize} & -10x_1 - 12x_2 - 12x_3 \\
\text{subject to} & x_1 + 2x_2 + 2x_3 \le 20 \\
& 2x_1 + x_2 + 2x_3 \le 20 \\
& 2x_1 + 2x_2 + x_3 \le 20 \\
& x_1, x_2, x_3 \ge 0.
\end{array}
$$

The feasible set is shown in Figure 3.4.

After introducing slack variables, we obtain the following standard form problem:

$$
\begin{array}{ll}
\text{minimize} & -10x_1 - 12x_2 - 12x_3 \\
\text{subject to} & x_1 + 2x_2 + 2x_3 + x_4 = 20 \\
& 2x_1 + x_2 + 2x_3 + x_5 = 20 \\
& 2x_1 + 2x_2 + x_3 + x_6 = 20 \\
& x_1, \ldots, x_6 \ge 0.
\end{array}
$$

Note that $\mathbf{x} = (0,0,0,20,20,20)$ is a basic feasible solution and can be used to start the algorithm. Let accordingly, $B(1) = 4$, $B(2) = 5$, and $B(3) = 6$. The corresponding basis matrix is the identity matrix $\mathbf{I}$. To obtain the zeroth row of the initial tableau, we note that $\mathbf{c}_B = \mathbf{0}$ and, therefore, $\mathbf{c}_B'\mathbf{x}_B = 0$ and $\bar{\mathbf{c}} = \mathbf{c}$. Hence, we have the following initial tableau:

		x_1	x_2	x_3	x_4	x_5	x_6
	0	-10	-12	-12	0	0	0
$x_4 =$	20	1	2	2	1	0	0
$x_5 =$	20	2*	1	2	0	1	0
$x_6 =$	20	2	2	1	0	0	1

We note a few conventions in the format of the above tableau: the label x_i on top of the ith column indicates the variable associated with that column. The labels "$x_i =$" to the left of the tableau tell us which are the basic variables and in what order. For example, the first basic variable $x_{B(1)}$ is x_4, and its value is 20. Similarly, $x_{B(2)} = x_5 = 20$, and $x_{B(3)} = x_6 = 20$. Strictly speaking, these labels are not quite necessary. We know that the column in the tableau associated with the first basic variable must be the first unit vector. Once we observe that the column associated with the variable x_4 is the first unit vector, it follows that x_4 is the first basic variable.

We continue with our example. The reduced cost of x_1 is negative and we let that variable enter the basis. The pivot column is $\mathbf{u} = (1, 2, 2)$. We form the ratios $x_{B(i)}/u_i$, $i = 1, 2, 3$; the smallest ratio corresponds to $i = 2$ and $i = 3$. We break this tie by choosing $\ell = 2$. This determines the pivot element, which we indicate by an asterisk. The second basic variable $x_{B(2)}$, which is x_5, exits the basis. The new basis is given by $\overline{B}(1) = 4$, $\overline{B}(2) = 1$, and $\overline{B}(3) = 6$. We multiply the pivot row by 5 and add it to the zeroth row. We multiply the pivot row by $1/2$ and subtract it from the first row. We subtract the pivot row from the third row. Finally, we divide the pivot row by 2. This leads us to the new tableau:

		x_1	x_2	x_3	x_4	x_5	x_6
	100	0	-7	-2	0	5	0
$x_4 =$	10	0	1.5	1*	1	-0.5	0
$x_1 =$	10	1	0.5	1	0	0.5	0
$x_6 =$	0	0	1	-1	0	-1	1

The corresponding basic feasible solution is $\mathbf{x} = (10, 0, 0, 10, 0, 0)$. In terms of the original variables x_1, x_2, x_3, we have moved to point $D = (10, 0, 0)$ in Figure 3.4. Note that this is a degenerate basic feasible solution, because the basic variable x_6 is equal to zero. This agrees with Figure 3.4 where we observe that there are four active constraints at point D.

We have mentioned earlier that the rows of the tableau (other than the zeroth row) amount to a representation of the equality constraints $\mathbf{B}^{-1}\mathbf{Ax} = \mathbf{B}^{-1}\mathbf{b}$, which are equivalent to the original constraints $\mathbf{Ax} = \mathbf{b}$. In our current example, the tableau indicates that the equality constraints can be written in the equivalent form:

$$10 = \quad 1.5x_2 + x_3 + x_4 - 0.5x_5$$

$$10 = x_1 + 0.5x_2 + x_3 \qquad + 0.5x_5$$

$$0 = \qquad x_2 - x_3 \qquad - x_5 + x_6.$$

We now return to the simplex method. With the current tableau, the variables x_2 and x_3 have negative reduced costs. Let us choose x_3 to be the one that enters the basis. The pivot column is $\mathbf{u} = (1, 1, -1)$. Since $u_3 < 0$, we only form the ratios $x_{B(i)}/u_i$, for $i = 1, 2$. There is again a tie, which we break by letting $\ell = 1$, and the first basic variable, x_4, exits the basis. The pivot element is again indicated by an asterisk. After carrying out the necessary elementary row operations, we obtain the following new tableau:

		x_1	x_2	x_3	x_4	x_5	x_6
	120	0	-4	0	2	4	0
$x_3 =$	10	0	1.5	1	1	-0.5	0
$x_1 =$	0	1	-1	0	-1	1	0
$x_6 =$	10	0	2.5*	0	1	-1.5	1

In terms of Figure 3.4, we have moved to point $B = (0, 0, 10)$, and the cost has been reduced to -120. At this point, x_2 is the only variable with negative reduced cost. We bring x_2 into the basis, x_6 exits, and the resulting tableau is:

		x_1	x_2	x_3	x_4	x_5	x_6
	136	0	0	0	3.6	1.6	1.6
$x_3 =$	4	0	0	1	0.4	0.4	-0.6
$x_1 =$	4	1	0	0	-0.6	0.4	0.4
$x_2 =$	4	0	1	0	0.4	-0.6	0.4

We have now reached point E in Figure 3.4. Its optimality is confirmed by observing that all reduced costs are nonnegative.

In this example, the simplex method took three changes of basis to reach the optimal solution, and it traced the path $A - D - B - E$ in Figure 3.4. With different pivoting rules, a different path would have been traced. Could the simplex method have solved the problem by tracing the path $A - D - E$, which involves only two edges, with only two iterations? The answer is no. The initial and final bases differ in three columns, and therefore at least three basis changes are required. In particular, if the method were to trace the path $A - D - E$, there would be a degenerate change of basis at point D (with no edge being traversed), which would again bring the total to three.

Example 3.6 This example shows that the simplex method can indeed cycle. We consider a problem described in terms of the following initial tableau.

		x_1	x_2	x_3	x_4	x_5	x_6	x_7
	3	$-3/4$	20	$-1/2$	6	0	0	0
$x_5 =$	0	$1/4^*$	-8	-1	9	1	0	0
$x_6 =$	0	$1/2$	-12	$-1/2$	3	0	1	0
$x_7 =$	1	0	0	1	0	0	0	1

We use the following pivoting rules:

(a) We select a nonbasic variable with the most negative reduced cost $\bar{c}_j$ to be the one that enters the basis.

(b) Out of all basic variables that are eligible to exit the basis, we select the one with the smallest subscript.

We then obtain the following sequence of tableaux (the pivot element is indicated by an asterisk):

		x_1	x_2	x_3	x_4	x_5	x_6	x_7
	3	0	-4	$-7/2$	33	3	0	0
$x_1 =$	0	1	-32	-4	36	4	0	0
$x_6 =$	0	0	4^*	$3/2$	-15	-2	1	0
$x_7 =$	1	0	0	1	0	0	0	1

		x_1	x_2	x_3	x_4	x_5	x_6	x_7
	3	0	0	-2	18	1	1	0
$x_1 =$	0	1	0	8^*	-84	-12	8	0
$x_2 =$	0	0	1	$3/8$	$-15/4$	$-1/2$	$1/4$	0
$x_7 =$	1	0	0	1	0	0	0	1

		x_1	x_2	x_3	x_4	x_5	x_6	x_7
	3	$1/4$	0	0	-3	-2	3	0
$x_3 =$	0	$1/8$	0	1	$-21/2$	$-3/2$	1	0
$x_2 =$	0	$-3/64$	1	0	$3/16^*$	$1/16$	$-1/8$	0
$x_7 =$	1	$-1/8$	0	0	$21/2$	$3/2$	-1	1

		x_1	x_2	x_3	x_4	x_5	x_6	x_7
	3	$-1/2$	16	0	0	-1	1	0
$x_3 =$	0	$-5/2$	56	1	0	2^*	-6	0
$x_4 =$	0	$-1/4$	$16/3$	0	1	$1/3$	$-2/3$	0
$x_7 =$	1	$5/2$	-56	0	0	-2	6	1

		x_1	x_2	x_3	x_4	x_5	x_6	x_7
	3	$-7/4$	44	$1/2$	0	0	-2	0
$x_5 =$	0	$-5/4$	28	$1/2$	0	1	-3	0
$x_4 =$	0	$1/6$	-4	$-1/6$	1	0	$1/3^*$	0
$x_7 =$	1	0	0	1	0	0	0	1

		x_1	x_2	x_3	x_4	x_5	x_6	x_7
	3	$-3/4$	20	$-1/2$	6	0	0	0
$x_5 =$	0	$1/4$	-8	-1	9	1	0	0
$x_6 =$	0	$1/2$	-12	$-1/2$	3	0	1	0
$x_7 =$	1	0	0	1	0	0	0	1

After six pivots, we have the same basis and the same tableau that we started with. At each basis change, we had $\theta^* = 0$. In particular, for each intermediate tableau, we had the same feasible solution and the same cost. The same sequence of pivots can be repeated over and over, and the simplex method never terminates.

Comparison of the full tableau and the revised simplex methods

Let us pretend that the problem is changed to

$$\text{minimize} \quad \mathbf{c}'\mathbf{x} + \mathbf{0}'\mathbf{y}$$
$$\text{subject to} \quad \mathbf{Ax} + \mathbf{Iy} = \mathbf{b}$$
$$\mathbf{x}, \mathbf{y} \geq \mathbf{0}.$$

We implement the simplex method on this new problem, except that we never allow any of the components of the vector $\mathbf{y}$ to become basic. Then, the simplex method performs basis changes as if the vector $\mathbf{y}$ were entirely

absent. Note also that the vector of reduced costs in the augmented problem
is

$$\left[\mathbf{c}' \mid \mathbf{0}'\right] - \mathbf{c}_B'\mathbf{B}^{-1}\left[\mathbf{A} \mid \mathbf{I}\right] = \left[\bar{\mathbf{c}}' \mid -\mathbf{c}_B'\mathbf{B}^{-1}\right].$$

Thus, the simplex tableau for the augmented problem takes the form

$-\mathbf{c}_B'\mathbf{B}^{-1}\mathbf{b}$	$\bar{\mathbf{c}}'$	$-\mathbf{c}_B'\mathbf{B}^{-1}$
$\mathbf{B}^{-1}\mathbf{b}$	$\mathbf{B}^{-1}\mathbf{A}$	$\mathbf{B}^{-1}$

In particular, by following the mechanics of the full tableau method on the
above tableau, the inverse basis matrix $\mathbf{B}^{-1}$ is made available at each iteration. We can now think of the revised simplex method as being essentially
the same as the full tableau method applied to the above augmented prob-
lem, except that the part of the tableau containing $\mathbf{B}^{-1}\mathbf{A}$ is never formed
explicitly; instead, once the entering variable x_j is chosen, the pivot column
$\mathbf{B}^{-1}\mathbf{A}_j$ is computed on the fly. Thus, the revised simplex method is just
a variant of the full tableau method, with more efficient bookkeeping. If
the revised simplex method also updates the zeroth row entries that lie on
top of $\mathbf{B}^{-1}$ (by the usual elementary operations), the simplex multipliers
$\mathbf{p}' = \mathbf{c}_B'\mathbf{B}^{-1}$ become available, thus eliminating the need for solving the
linear system $\mathbf{p}'\mathbf{B} = \mathbf{c}_B'$ at each iteration.

    We now discuss the relative merits of the two methods. The full
tableau method requires a constant (and small) number of arithmetic operations for updating each entry of the tableau. Thus, the amount of computation per iteration is proportional to the size of the tableau, which is
$O(mn)$. The revised simplex method uses similar computations to update
$\mathbf{B}^{-1}$ and $\mathbf{c}_B'\mathbf{B}^{-1}$, and since only $O(m^2)$ entries are updated, the computational requirements per iteration are $O(m^2)$. In addition, the reduced
cost of each variable x_j can be computed by forming the inner product
$\mathbf{p}'\mathbf{A}_j$, which requires $O(m)$ operations. In the worst case, the reduced cost
of every variable is computed, for a total of $O(mn)$ computations per iteration. Since $m \leq n$, the worst-case computational effort per iteration is
$O(mn+m^2) = O(mn)$, under either implementation. On the other hand, if
we consider a pivoting rule that evaluates one reduced cost at a time, until
a negative reduced cost is found, a typical iteration of the revised simplex
method might require a lot less work. In the best case, if the first reduced
cost computed is negative, and the corresponding variable is chosen to enter the basis, the total computational effort is only $O(m^2)$. The conclusion
is that the revised simplex method cannot be slower than the full tableau
method, and could be much faster during most iterations.

    Another important element in favor of the revised simplex method
is that memory requirements are reduced from $O(mn)$ to $O(m^2)$. As n is
often much larger than m, this effect can be quite significant. It could be
counterargued that the memory requirements of the revised simplex method

are also $O(mn)$ because of the need to store the matrix $\mathbf{A}$. However, in most large scale problems that arise in applications, the matrix $\mathbf{A}$ is very sparse (has many zero entries) and can be stored compactly. (Note that the sparsity of $\mathbf{A}$ does not usually help in the storage of the full simplex tableau because even if $\mathbf{A}$ and $\mathbf{B}$ are sparse, $\mathbf{B}^{-1}\mathbf{A}$ is not sparse, in general.)

We summarize this discussion in the following table:

	Full tableau	**Revised simplex**
Memory	$O(mn)$	$O(m^2)$
Worst-case time	$O(mn)$	$O(mn)$
Best-case time	$O(mn)$	$O(m^2)$

Table 3.1: Comparison of the full tableau method and revised simplex. The time requirements refer to a single iteration.

Practical performance enhancements

Practical implementations of the simplex method aimed at solving problems of moderate or large size incorporate a number of additional ideas from numerical linear algebra which we briefly mention.

The first idea is related to *reinversion*. Recall that at each iteration of the revised simplex method, the inverse basis matrix $\mathbf{B}^{-1}$ is updated according to certain rules. Each such iteration may introduce roundoff or truncation errors which accumulate and may eventually lead to highly inaccurate results. For this reason, it is customary to recompute the matrix $\mathbf{B}^{-1}$ from scratch once in a while. The efficiency of such reinversions can be greatly enhanced by using suitable data structures and certain techniques from computational linear algebra.

Another set of ideas is related to the way that the inverse basis matrix $\mathbf{B}^{-1}$ is represented. Suppose that a reinversion has been just carried out and $\mathbf{B}^{-1}$ is available. Subsequent to the current iteration of the revised simplex method, we have the option of generating explicitly and storing the new inverse basis matrix $\overline{\mathbf{B}}^{-1}$. An alternative that carries the same information, is to store a matrix $\mathbf{Q}$ such that $\mathbf{Q}\mathbf{B}^{-1} = \overline{\mathbf{B}}^{-1}$. Note that $\mathbf{Q}$ basically prescribes which elementary row operations need to be applied to $\mathbf{B}^{-1}$ in order to produce $\overline{\mathbf{B}}^{-1}$. It is not a full matrix, and can be completely specified in terms of m coefficients: for each row, we need to know what multiple of the pivot row must be added to it.

Suppose now that we wish to solve the system $\overline{\mathbf{B}}\mathbf{u} = \mathbf{A}_j$ for $\mathbf{u}$, where $\mathbf{A}_j$ is the entering column, as is required by the revised simplex method. We have $\mathbf{u} = \overline{\mathbf{B}}^{-1}\mathbf{A}_j = \mathbf{Q}\mathbf{B}^{-1}\mathbf{A}_j$, which shows that we can first compute

$\mathbf{B}^{-1}\mathbf{A}_j$ and then left-multiply by $\mathbf{Q}$ (equivalently, apply a sequence of elementary row operations) to produce $\mathbf{u}$. The same idea can also be used to represent the inverse basis matrix after several simplex iterations, as a product of the initial inverse basis matrix and several sparse matrices like $\mathbf{Q}$.

The last idea we mention is the following. Subsequent to a "reinversion," one does not usually compute $\mathbf{B}^{-1}$ explicitly, but $\mathbf{B}^{-1}$ is instead represented in terms of sparse triangular matrices with a special structure.

The methods discussed in this subsection are designed to accomplish two objectives: improve numerical stability (minimize the effect of roundoff errors) and exploit sparsity in the problem data to improve both running time and memory requirements. These methods have a critical effect in practice. Besides having a better chance of producing numerically trustworthy results, they can also speed up considerably the running time of the simplex method. These techniques lie much closer to the subject of numerical linear algebra, as opposed to optimization, and for this reason we do not pursue them in any greater depth.

3.4   Anticycling: lexicography and Bland's rule

In this section, we discuss anticycling rules under which the simplex method is guaranteed to terminate, thus extending Theorem 3.3 to degenerate problems. As an important corollary, we conclude that if the optimal cost is finite, then there exists an optimal basis, that is, a basis satisfying $\mathbf{B}^{-1}\mathbf{b} \geq \mathbf{0}$ and $\bar{\mathbf{c}}' = \mathbf{c}' - \mathbf{c}'_B \mathbf{B}^{-1}\mathbf{A} \geq \mathbf{0}'$.

Lexicography

We present here the lexicographic pivoting rule and prove that it prevents the simplex method from cycling. Historically, this pivoting rule was derived by analyzing the behavior of the simplex method on a nondegenerate problem obtained by means of a small perturbation of the right-hand side vector $\mathbf{b}$. This connection is pursued in Exercise 3.15.

We start with a definition.

Definition 3.5 *A vector* $\mathbf{u} \in \Re^n$ *is said to be* **lexicographically larger** *(or* **smaller***) than another vector* $\mathbf{v} \in \Re^n$ *if* $\mathbf{u} \neq \mathbf{v}$ *and the first nonzero component of* $\mathbf{u} - \mathbf{v}$ *is positive (or negative, respectively). Symbolically, we write*

$$\mathbf{u} \overset{L}{>} \mathbf{v} \qquad or \qquad \mathbf{u} \overset{L}{<} \mathbf{v}.$$

For example,

$$(0, \ 2, \ 3, \ 0) \overset{L}{>} (0, \ 2, \ 1, \ 4),$$

$$(0, \ 4, \ 5, \ 0) \overset{L}{<} (1, \ 2, \ 1, \ 2).$$

Also, when $u \overset{L}{>} 0$, $\rightarrow u$ is lexicographically positive

---

Lexicographic pivoting rule

1. Choose an entering column $\mathbf{A}_j$ arbitrarily, as long as its reduced cost $\bar{c}_j$ is negative. Let $\mathbf{u} = \mathbf{B}^{-1}\mathbf{A}_j$ be the jth column of the tableau.

2. For each i with $u_i > 0$, divide the ith row of the tableau (including the entry in the zeroth column) by u_i and choose the lexicographically smallest row. If row ℓ is lexicographically smallest, then the ℓth basic variable $x_{B(\ell)}$ exits the basis.

Example 3.7 Consider the following tableau (the zeroth row is omitted), and suppose that the pivot column is the third one ($j = 3$).

1	0	5	3	$\cdots$
2	4	6	-1	$\cdots$
3	0	7	9	$\cdots$

Note that there is a tie in trying to determine the exiting variable because $x_{B(1)}/u_1 = 1/3$ and $x_{B(3)}/u_3 = 3/9 = 1/3$. We divide the first and third rows of the tableau by $u_1 = 3$ and $u_3 = 9$, respectively, to obtain:

1/3	0	5/3	1	$\cdots$
*	*	*	*	$\cdots$
1/3	0	7/9	1	$\cdots$

The tie between the first and third rows is resolved by performing a lexicographic comparison. Since $7/9 < 5/3$, the third row is chosen to be the pivot row, and the variable $x_{B(3)}$ exits the basis.

We note that the lexicographic pivoting rule always leads to a unique choice for the exiting variable. Indeed, if this were not the case, two of the rows in the tableau would have to be proportional. But if two rows of the matrix $\mathbf{B}^{-1}\mathbf{A}$ are proportional, the matrix $\mathbf{B}^{-1}\mathbf{A}$ has rank smaller than m and, therefore, $\mathbf{A}$ also has rank less than m, which contradicts our standing assumption that $\mathbf{A}$ has linearly independent rows.

Theorem 3.4 *Suppose that the simplex algorithm starts with all the rows in the simplex tableau, other than the zeroth row, lexicographically positive. Suppose that the lexicographic pivoting rule is followed. Then:*

(a) *Every row of the simplex tableau, other than the zeroth row, remains lexicographically positive throughout the algorithm.*

(b) *The zeroth row strictly increases lexicographically at each iteration.*

(c) *The simplex method terminates after a finite number of iterations.*

Proof.

(a) Suppose that all rows of the simplex tableau, other than the zeroth row, are lexicographically positive at the beginning of a simplex iteration. Suppose that x_j enters the basis and that the pivot row is the ℓth row. According to the lexicographic pivoting rule, we have $u_\ell > 0$ and

$$\frac{(\ell\text{th row})}{u_\ell} \stackrel{L}{<} \frac{(i\text{th row})}{u_i}, \qquad \text{if } i \neq \ell \text{ and } u_i > 0. \qquad (3.5)$$

To determine the new tableau, the ℓth row is divided by the positive pivot element u_ℓ and, therefore, remains lexicographically positive. Consider the ith row and suppose that $u_i < 0$. In order to zero the (i,j)th entry of the tableau, we need to add a positive multiple of the pivot row to the ith row. Due to the lexicographic positivity of both rows, the ith row will remain lexicographically positive after this addition. Finally, consider the ith row for the case where $u_i > 0$ and $i \neq \ell$. We have

$$(\text{new } i\text{th row}) = (\text{old } i\text{th row}) - \frac{u_i}{u_\ell}(\text{old } \ell\text{th row}).$$

Because of the lexicographic inequality (3.5), which is satisfied by the old rows, the new ith row is also lexicographically positive.

(b) At the beginning of an iteration, the reduced cost in the pivot column is negative. In order to make it zero, we need to add a positive multiple of the pivot row. Since the latter row is lexicographically positive, the zeroth row increases lexicographically.

(c) Since the zeroth row increases lexicographically at each iteration, it never returns to a previous value. Since the zeroth row is determined completely by the current basis, no basis can be repeated twice and the simplex method must terminate after a finite number of iterations. □

The lexicographic pivoting rule is straightforward to use if the simplex method is implemented in terms of the full tableau. It can also be used in conjunction with the revised simplex method, provided that the inverse basis matrix $\mathbf{B}^{-1}$ is formed explicitly (see Exercise 3.16). On the other hand, in sophisticated implementations of the revised simplex method, the matrix $\mathbf{B}^{-1}$ is never computed explicitly, and the lexicographic rule is not really suitable.

We finally note that in order to apply the lexicographic pivoting rule, an initial tableau with lexicographically positive rows is required. Let us assume that an initial tableau is available (methods for obtaining an initial tableau are discussed in the next section). We can then rename the variables so that the basic variables are the first m ones. This is equivalent to rearranging the tableau so that the first m columns of $\mathbf{B}^{-1}\mathbf{A}$ are the m unit vectors. The resulting tableau has lexicographically positive rows, as desired.

Bland's rule

The smallest subscript pivoting rule, also known as Bland's rule, is as follows.

Smallest subscript pivoting rule

1. Find the smallest j for which the reduced cost $\bar{c}_j$ is negative and have the column $\mathbf{A}_j$ enter the basis.

2. Out of all variables x_i that are tied in the test for choosing an exiting variable, select the one with the smallest value of i.

This pivoting rule is compatible with an implementation of the revised simplex method in which the reduced costs of the nonbasic variables are computed one at a time, in the natural order, until a negative one is discovered. Under this pivoting rule, it is known that cycling never occurs and the simplex method is guaranteed to terminate after a finite number of iterations.

3.5 Finding an initial basic feasible solution

In order to start the simplex method, we need to find an initial basic feasible solution. Sometimes this is straightforward. For example, suppose that we are dealing with a problem involving constraints of the form $\mathbf{A}\mathbf{x} \leq \mathbf{b}$, where $\mathbf{b} \geq \mathbf{0}$. We can then introduce nonnegative slack variables $\mathbf{s}$ and rewrite the constraints in the form $\mathbf{A}\mathbf{x} + \mathbf{s} = \mathbf{b}$. The vector $(\mathbf{x}, \mathbf{s})$ defined by $\mathbf{x} = \mathbf{0}$ and $\mathbf{s} = \mathbf{b}$ is a basic feasible solution and the corresponding basis matrix is the identity. In general, however, finding an initial basic feasible solution is not easy and requires the solution of an auxiliary linear programming problem, as will be seen shortly.

Consider the problem

$$\begin{array}{ll} \text{minimize} & \mathbf{c}'\mathbf{x} \\ \text{subject to} & \mathbf{A}\mathbf{x} = \mathbf{b} \\ & \mathbf{x} \geq \mathbf{0}. \end{array}$$

By possibly multiplying some of the equality constraints by -1, we can assume, without loss of generality, that $\mathbf{b} \geq \mathbf{0}$. We now introduce a vector $\mathbf{y} \in \Re^m$ of *artificial variables* and use the simplex method to solve the auxiliary problem

$$\begin{array}{ll} \text{minimize} & y_1 + y_2 + \cdots + y_m \\ \text{subject to} & \mathbf{A}\mathbf{x} + \mathbf{y} = \mathbf{b} \\ & \mathbf{x} \geq \mathbf{0} \\ & \mathbf{y} \geq \mathbf{0}. \end{array}$$

Initialization is easy for the auxiliary problem: by letting $\mathbf{x} = \mathbf{0}$ and $\mathbf{y} = \mathbf{b}$, we have a basic feasible solution and the corresponding basis matrix is the identity.

If $\mathbf{x}$ is a feasible solution to the original problem, this choice of $\mathbf{x}$ together with $\mathbf{y} = \mathbf{0}$, yields a zero cost solution to the auxiliary problem. Therefore, if the optimal cost in the auxiliary problem is nonzero, we conclude that the original problem is infeasible. If on the other hand, we obtain a zero cost solution to the auxiliary problem, it must satisfy $\mathbf{y} = \mathbf{0}$, and $\mathbf{x}$ is a feasible solution to the original problem.

At this point, we have accomplished our objectives only partially. We have a method that either detects infeasibility or finds a feasible solution to the original problem. However, in order to initialize the simplex method for the original problem, we need a basic feasible solution, an associated basis matrix $\mathbf{B}$, and – depending on the implementation – the corresponding tableau. All this is straightforward if the simplex method, applied to the auxiliary problem, terminates with a basis matrix $\mathbf{B}$ consisting exclusively of columns of $\mathbf{A}$. We can simply drop the columns that correspond to the artificial variables and continue with the simplex method on the original problem, using $\mathbf{B}$ as the starting basis matrix.

Driving artificial variables out of the basis

The situation is more complex if the original problem is feasible, the simplex method applied to the auxiliary problem terminates with a feasible solution $\mathbf{x}^*$ to the original problem, but some of the artificial variables are in the final basis. (Since the final value of the artificial variables is zero, this implies that we have a degenerate basic feasible solution to the auxiliary problem.) Let k be the number of columns of $\mathbf{A}$ that belong to the final basis $(k < m)$ and, without loss of generality, assume that these are the columns $\mathbf{A}_{B(1)}, \ldots, \mathbf{A}_{B(k)}$. (In particular, $x_{B(1)}, \ldots, x_{B(k)}$ are the only variables that can be at nonzero level.) Note that the columns $\mathbf{A}_{B(1)}, \ldots, \mathbf{A}_{B(k)}$ must be linearly independent since they are part of a basis. Under our standard assumption that the matrix $\mathbf{A}$ has full rank, the columns of $\mathbf{A}$ span $\Re^m$, and we can choose $m - k$ additional columns $\mathbf{A}_{B(k+1)}, \ldots, \mathbf{A}_{B(m)}$ of $\mathbf{A}$, to obtain a set of m linearly independent columns, that is, a basis consisting exclusively of columns of $\mathbf{A}$. With this basis, all nonbasic components of $\mathbf{x}^*$ are at zero level, and it follows that $\mathbf{x}^*$ is the basic feasible solution associated with this new basis as well. At this point, the artificial variables and the corresponding columns of the tableau can be dropped.

The procedure we have just described is called *driving the artificial variables out of the basis*, and depends crucially on the assumption that the matrix $\mathbf{A}$ has rank m. After all, if $\mathbf{A}$ has rank less than m, constructing a basis for $\Re^m$ using the columns of $\mathbf{A}$ is impossible and there exist redundant equality constraints that must be eliminated, as described by Theorem 2.5 in Section 2.3. All of the above can be carried out mechanically, in terms of the simplex tableau, in the following manner.

Suppose that the ℓth basic variable is an artificial variable, which is in the basis at zero level. We examine the ℓth row of the tableau and find some j such that the ℓth entry of $\mathbf{B}^{-1}\mathbf{A}_j$ is nonzero. We claim that $\mathbf{A}_j$ is linearly independent from the columns $\mathbf{A}_{B(1)}, \ldots, \mathbf{A}_{B(k)}$. To see this, note that $\mathbf{B}^{-1}\mathbf{A}_{B(i)} = \mathbf{e}_i$, $i = 1, \ldots, k$, and since $k < \ell$, the ℓth entry of these vectors is zero. It follows that the ℓth entry of any linear combination of the vectors $\mathbf{B}^{-1}\mathbf{A}_{B(1)}, \ldots, \mathbf{B}^{-1}\mathbf{A}_{B(k)}$ is also equal to zero. Since the ℓth entry of $\mathbf{B}^{-1}\mathbf{A}_j$ is nonzero, this vector is not a linear combination of the vectors $\mathbf{B}^{-1}\mathbf{A}_{B(1)}, \ldots, \mathbf{B}^{-1}\mathbf{A}_{B(k)}$. Equivalently, $\mathbf{A}_j$ is not a linear combination of the vectors $\mathbf{A}_{B(1)}, \ldots, \mathbf{A}_{B(k)}$, which proves our claim. We now bring $\mathbf{A}_j$ into the basis and have the ℓth basic variable exit the basis. This is accomplished in the usual manner: perform those elementary row operations that replace $\mathbf{B}^{-1}\mathbf{A}_j$ by the ℓth unit vector. The only difference from the usual mechanics of the simplex method is that the pivot element (the ℓth entry of $\mathbf{B}^{-1}\mathbf{A}_j$) could be negative. Because the ℓth basic variable was zero, adding a multiple of the ℓth row to the other rows does not change the values of the basic variables. This means that after the change of basis, we are still at the same basic feasible solution to the auxiliary problem, but we have reduced the number of basic artificial variables by one. We repeat this procedure as many times as needed until all artificial variables are driven out of the basis.

Let us now assume that the ℓth row of $\mathbf{B}^{-1}\mathbf{A}$ is zero, in which case the above described procedure fails. Note that the ℓth row of $\mathbf{B}^{-1}\mathbf{A}$ is equal to $\mathbf{g}'\mathbf{A}$, where $\mathbf{g}'$ is the ℓth row of $\mathbf{B}^{-1}$. Hence, $\mathbf{g}'\mathbf{A} = \mathbf{0}'$ for some nonzero vector $\mathbf{g}$, and the matrix $\mathbf{A}$ has linearly dependent rows. Since we are dealing with a feasible problem, we must also have $\mathbf{g}'\mathbf{b} = 0$. Thus, the constraint $\mathbf{g}'\mathbf{A}\mathbf{x} = \mathbf{g}'\mathbf{b}$ is redundant and can be eliminated (cf. Theorem 2.5 in Section 2.3). Since this constraint is the information provided by the ℓth row of the tableau, we can eliminate that row and continue from there.

Example 3.8 Consider the linear programming problem:

$$
\begin{aligned}
\text{minimize} \quad & x_1 + x_2 + x_3 \\
\text{subject to} \quad & x_1 + 2x_2 + 3x_3 && = 3 \\
& -x_1 + 2x_2 + 6x_3 && = 2 \\
& 4x_2 + 9x_3 && = 5 \\
& 3x_3 + x_4 && = 1 \\
& x_1, \ldots, x_4 \geq 0.
\end{aligned}
$$

In order to find a feasible solution, we form the auxiliary problem

$$
\begin{aligned}
\text{minimize} \quad & x_5 + x_6 + x_7 + x_8 \\
\text{subject to} \quad & x_1 + 2x_2 + 3x_3 + x_5 && = 3 \\
& -x_1 + 2x_2 + 6x_3 + x_6 && = 2 \\
& 4x_2 + 9x_3 + x_7 && = 5 \\
& 3x_3 + x_4 + x_8 && = 1 \\
& x_1, \ldots, x_8 \geq 0.
\end{aligned}
$$

A basic feasible solution to the auxiliary problem is obtained by letting $(x_5, x_6, x_7, x_8) = \mathbf{b} = (3, 2, 5, 1)$. The corresponding basis matrix is the identity. Furthermore, we have $\mathbf{c}_B = (1, 1, 1, 1)$. We evaluate the reduced cost of each one of the original variables x_i, which is $-\mathbf{c}'_B \mathbf{A}_i$, and form the initial tableau:

		x_1	x_2	x_3	x_4	x_5	x_6	x_7	x_8
	-11	0	-8	-21	-1	0	0	0	0
$x_5 =$	3	1	2	3	0	1	0	0	0
$x_6 =$	2	-1	2	6	0	0	1	0	0
$x_7 =$	5	0	4	9	0	0	0	1	0
$x_8 =$	1	0	0	3	1^*	0	0	0	1

We bring x_4 into the basis and have x_8 exit the basis. The basis matrix $\mathbf{B}$ is still the identity and only the zeroth row of the tableau changes. We obtain:

		x_1	x_2	x_3	x_4	x_5	x_6	x_7	x_8
	-10	0	-8	-18	0	0	0	0	1
$x_5 =$	3	1	2	3	0	1	0	0	0
$x_6 =$	2	-1	2	6	0	0	1	0	0
$x_7 =$	5	0	4	9	0	0	0	1	0
$x_4 =$	1	0	0	3^*	1	0	0	0	1

We now bring x_3 into the basis and have x_4 exit the basis. The new tableau is:

		x_1	x_2	x_3	x_4	x_5	x_6	x_7	x_8
	-4	0	-8	0	6	0	0	0	7
$x_5 =$	2	1	2	0	-1	1	0	0	-1
$x_6 =$	0	-1	2*	0	-2	0	1	0	-2
$x_7 =$	2	0	4	0	-3	0	0	1	-3
$x_3 =$	1/3	0	0	1	1/3	0	0	0	1/3

We now bring x_2 into the basis and x_6 exits. Note that this is a degenerate pivot with $\theta^* = 0$. The new tableau is:

		x_1	x_2	x_3	x_4	x_5	x_6	x_7	x_8
	-4	-4	0	0	-2	0	4	0	-1
$x_5 =$	2	2*	0	0	1	1	-1	0	1
$x_2 =$	0	$-1/2$	1	0	-1	0	1/2	0	-1
$x_7 =$	2	2	0	0	1	0	-2	1	1
$x_3 =$	1/3	0	0	1	1/3	0	0	0	1/3

We now have x_1 enter the basis and x_5 exit the basis. We obtain the following tableau:

		x_1	x_2	x_3	x_4	x_5	x_6	x_7	x_8
	0	0	0	0	0	2	2	0	1
$x_1 =$	1	1	0	0	1/2	1/2	$-1/2$	0	1/2
$x_2 =$	1/2	0	1	0	$-3/4$	1/4	1/4	0	$-3/4$
$x_7 =$	0	0	0	0	0	-1	-1	1	0
$x_3 =$	1/3	0	0	1	1/3	0	0	0	1/3

Note that the cost in the auxiliary problem has dropped to zero, indicating that we have a feasible solution to the original problem. However, the artificial variable x_7 is still in the basis, at zero level. In order to obtain a basic feasible solution to the original problem, we need to drive x_7 out of the basis. Note that x_7 is the third basic variable and that the third entry of the columns $\mathbf{B}^{-1}\mathbf{A}_j, j = 1, \ldots, 4$, associated with the original variables, is zero. This indicates that the matrix $\mathbf{A}$ has linearly dependent rows. At this point, we remove the third row of the tableau, because it corresponds to a redundant constraint, and also remove all of the artificial variables. This leaves us with the following initial tableau for the original problem:

		x_1	x_2	x_3	x_4
	*	*	*	*	*
$x_1 =$	1	1	0	0	1/2
$x_2 =$	1/2	0	1	0	−3/4
$x_3 =$	1/3	0	0	1	1/3

We may now compute the reduced costs of the original variables, fill in the zeroth row of the tableau, and start executing the simplex method on the original problem.

We observe that in this example, the artificial variable x_8 was unnecessary. Instead of starting with $x_8 = 1$, we could have started with $x_4 = 1$ thus eliminating the need for the first pivot. More generally, whenever there is a variable that appears in a single constraint and with a positive coefficient (slack variables being the typical example), we can always let that variable be in the initial basis and we do not have to associate an artificial variable with that constraint.

The two-phase simplex method

We can now summarize a complete algorithm for linear programming problems in standard form.

Phase I:

1. By multiplying some of the constraints by −1, change the problem so that $\mathbf{b} \geq \mathbf{0}$.

2. Introduce artificial variables $y_1, \ldots, y_m$, if necessary, and apply the simplex method to the auxiliary problem with cost $\sum_{i=1}^{m} y_i$.

3. If the optimal cost in the auxiliary problem is positive, the original problem is infeasible and the algorithm terminates.

4. If the optimal cost in the auxiliary problem is zero, a feasible solution to the original problem has been found. If no artificial variable is in the final basis, the artificial variables and the corresponding columns are eliminated, and a feasible basis for the original problem is available.

5. If the ℓth basic variable is an artificial one, examine the ℓth entry of the columns $\mathbf{B}^{-1}\mathbf{A}_j$, $j = 1, \ldots, n$. If all of these entries are zero, the ℓth row represents a redundant constraint and is eliminated. Otherwise, if the ℓth entry of the jth column is nonzero, apply a change of basis (with this entry serving as the pivot

element): the ℓth basic variable exits and x_j enters the basis. Repeat this operation until all artificial variables are driven out of the basis.

Phase II:

1. Let the final basis and tableau obtained from Phase I be the initial basis and tableau for Phase II.

2. Compute the reduced costs of all variables for this initial basis, using the cost coefficients of the original problem.

3. Apply the simplex method to the original problem.

The above two-phase algorithm is a complete method, in the sense that it can handle all possible outcomes. As long as cycling is avoided (due to either nondegeneracy, an anticycling rule, or luck), one of the following possibilities will materialize:

(a) If the problem is infeasible, this is detected at the end of Phase I.

(b) If the problem is feasible but the rows of **A** are linearly dependent, this is detected and corrected at the end of Phase I, by eliminating redundant equality constraints.

(c) If the optimal cost is equal to $-\infty$, this is detected while running Phase II.

(d) Else, Phase II terminates with an optimal solution.

The big-M method

We close by mentioning an alternative approach, the *big-M method*, that combines the two phases into a single one. The idea is to introduce a cost function of the form

$$\sum_{j=1}^{n} c_j x_j + M \sum_{i=1}^{m} y_i,$$

where M is a large positive constant, and where y_i are the same artificial variables as in Phase I simplex. For a sufficiently large choice of M, if the original problem is feasible and its optimal cost is finite, all of the artificial variables are eventually driven to zero (Exercise 3.26), which takes us back to the minimization of the original cost function. In fact, there is no reason for fixing a numerical value for M. We can leave M as an undetermined parameter and let the reduced costs be functions of M. Whenever M is compared to another number (in order to determine whether a reduced cost is negative), M will be always treated as being larger.

Example 3.9 We consider the same linear programming problem as in Example 3.8:

$$
\begin{aligned}
\text{minimize} \quad & x_1 + x_2 + x_3 \\
\text{subject to} \quad & x_1 + 2x_2 + 3x_3 && = 3 \\
& -x_1 + 2x_2 + 6x_3 && = 2 \\
& 4x_2 + 9x_3 && = 5 \\
& 3x_3 + x_4 && = 1 \\
& x_1, \ldots, x_4 \geq 0.
\end{aligned}
$$

We use the big-M method in conjunction with the following auxiliary problem, in which the unnecessary artificial variable x_8 is omitted.

$$
\begin{aligned}
\text{minimize} \quad & x_1 + x_2 + x_3 && + Mx_5 + Mx_6 + Mx_7 \\
\text{subject to} \quad & x_1 + 2x_2 + 3x_3 && + x_5 && = 3 \\
& -x_1 + 2x_2 + 6x_3 && + x_6 && = 2 \\
& 4x_2 + 9x_3 && + x_7 && = 5 \\
& 3x_3 + x_4 && = 1 \\
& x_1, \ldots, x_7 \geq 0.
\end{aligned}
$$

A basic feasible solution to the auxiliary problem is obtained by letting $(x_5, x_6, x_7, x_4) = \mathbf{b} = (3, 2, 5, 1)$. The corresponding basis matrix is the identity. Furthermore, we have $\mathbf{c}_B = (M, M, M, 0)$. We evaluate the reduced cost of each one of the original variables x_i, which is $c_i - \mathbf{c}_B' \mathbf{A}_i$, and form the initial tableau:

		x_1	x_2	x_3	x_4	x_5	x_6	x_7
	$-10M$	1	$-8M+1$	$-18M+1$	0	0	0	0
$x_5 =$	3	1	2	3	0	1	0	0
$x_6 =$	2	-1	2	6	0	0	1	0
$x_7 =$	5	0	4	9	0	0	0	1
$x_4 =$	1	0	0	3*	1	0	0	0

The reduced cost of x_3 is negative when M is large enough. We therefore bring x_3 into the basis and have x_4 exit. Note that in order to set the reduced cost of x_3 to zero, we need to multiply the pivot row by $6M - 1/3$ and add it to the zeroth row. The new tableau is:

		x_1	x_2	x_3	x_4	x_5	x_6	x_7
	$-4M-1/3$	1	$-8M+1$	0	$6M-1/3$	0	0	0
$x_5 =$	2	1	2	0	-1	1	0	0
$x_6 =$	0	-1	2*	0	-2	0	1	0
$x_7 =$	2	0	4	0	-3	0	0	1
$x_3 =$	1/3	0	0	1	1/3	0	0	0

The reduced cost of x_2 is negative when M is large enough. We therefore bring x_2 into the basis and x_6 exits. Note that this is a degenerate pivot with $\theta^* = 0$.

The new tableau is:

		x_1	x_2	x_3	x_4	x_5	x_6	x_7
	$-4M - \dfrac{1}{3}$	$-4M + \dfrac{3}{2}$	0	0	$-2M + \dfrac{2}{3}$	0	$4M - \dfrac{1}{2}$	0
$x_5 =$	2	2^*	0	0	1	1	-1	0
$x_2 =$	0	$-1/2$	1	0	-1	0	$1/2$	0
$x_7 =$	2	2	0	0	1	0	-2	1
$x_3 =$	$1/3$	0	0	1	$1/3$	0	0	0

We now have x_1 enter and x_5 exit the basis. We obtain the following tableau:

		x_1	x_2	x_3	x_4	x_5	x_6	x_7
	$-11/6$	0	0	0	$-1/12$	$2M - 3/4$	$2M + 1/4$	0
$x_1 =$	1	1	0	0	$1/2$	$1/2$	$-1/2$	0
$x_2 =$	$1/2$	0	1	0	$-3/4$	$1/4$	$1/4$	0
$x_7 =$	0	0	0	0	0	-1	-1	1
$x_3 =$	$1/3$	0	0	1	$1/3^*$	0	0	0

We now bring x_4 into the basis and x_3 exits. The new tableau is:

		x_1	x_2	x_3	x_4	x_5	x_6	x_7
	$-7/4$	0	0	$1/4$	0	$2M - 3/4$	$2M + 1/4$	0
$x_1 =$	$1/2$	1	0	$-3/2$	0	$1/2$	$-1/2$	0
$x_2 =$	$5/4$	0	1	$9/4$	0	$1/4$	$1/4$	0
$x_7 =$	0	0	0	0	0	-1	-1	1
$x_4 =$	1	0	0	3	1	0	0	0

With M large enough, all of the reduced costs are nonnegative and we have an optimal solution to the auxiliary problem. In addition, all of the artificial variables have been driven to zero, and we have an optimal solution to the original problem.

3.6   Column geometry and the simplex method

In this section, we introduce an alternative way of visualizing the workings of the simplex method. This approach provides some insights into why the simplex method appears to be efficient in practice.

We consider the problem

$$
\begin{aligned}
\text{minimize} \quad & \mathbf{c}'\mathbf{x} \\
\text{subject to} \quad & \mathbf{A}\mathbf{x} = \mathbf{b} \\
& \mathbf{e}'\mathbf{x} = 1 \\
& \mathbf{x} \geq \mathbf{0},
\end{aligned}
\tag{3.6}
$$

where $\mathbf{A}$ is an $m \times n$ matrix and $\mathbf{e}$ is the n-dimensional vector with all components equal to one. Although this might appear to be a special type of a linear programming problem, it turns out that every problem with a bounded feasible set can be brought into this form (Exercise 3.28). The constraint $\mathbf{e}'\mathbf{x} = 1$ is called the *convexity constraint*. We also introduce an auxiliary variable z defined by $z = \mathbf{c}'\mathbf{x}$. If $\mathbf{A}_1, \mathbf{A}_2, \ldots, \mathbf{A}_n$ are the n columns of $\mathbf{A}$, we are dealing with the problem of minimizing z subject to the nonnegativity constraints $\mathbf{x} \geq \mathbf{0}$, the convexity constraint $\sum_{i=1}^{n} x_i = 1$, and the constraint

$$
x_1 \begin{bmatrix} \mathbf{A}_1 \\ c_1 \end{bmatrix} + x_2 \begin{bmatrix} \mathbf{A}_2 \\ c_2 \end{bmatrix} + \cdots + x_n \begin{bmatrix} \mathbf{A}_n \\ c_n \end{bmatrix} = \begin{bmatrix} \mathbf{b} \\ z \end{bmatrix}.
$$

In order to capture this problem geometrically, we view the horizontal plane as an m-dimensional space containing the columns of $\mathbf{A}$, and we view the vertical axis as the one-dimensional space associated with the cost components c_i. Then, each point in the resulting three-dimensional space corresponds to a point $(\mathbf{A}_i, c_i)$; see Figure 3.5.

In this geometry, our objective is to construct a vector $(\mathbf{b}, z)$, which is a convex combination of the vectors $(\mathbf{A}_i, c_i)$, such that z is as small as possible. Note that the vectors of the form $(\mathbf{b}, z)$ lie on a vertical line, which we call the *requirement line*, and which intersects the horizontal plane at $\mathbf{b}$. If the requirement line does not intersect the convex hull of the points $(\mathbf{A}_i, c_i)$, the problem is infeasible. If it does intersect it, the problem is feasible and an optimal solution corresponds to the lowest point in the intersection of the convex hull and the requirement line. For example, in Figure 3.6, the requirement line intersects the convex hull of the points $(\mathbf{A}_i, c_i)$; the point G corresponds to an optimal solution, and its height is the optimal cost.

We now need some terminology.

Definition 3.6

(a) *A collection of vectors* $\mathbf{y}^1, \ldots, \mathbf{y}^{k+1}$ *in* $\Re^n$ *are said to be* **affinely independent** *if the vectors* $\mathbf{y}^1 - \mathbf{y}^{k+1}, \mathbf{y}^2 - \mathbf{y}^{k+1}, \ldots, \mathbf{y}^k - \mathbf{y}^{k+1}$ *are linearly independent. (Note that we must have $k \leq n$.)*

(b) *The convex hull of $k + 1$ affinely independent vectors in $\Re^n$ is called a k-dimensional* **simplex**.

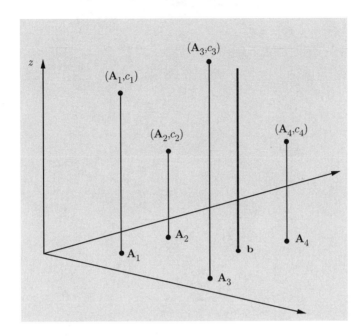

Figure 3.5: The column geometry.

Thus, three points are either collinear or they are affinely independent and determine a two-dimensional simplex (a triangle). Similarly, four points either lie on the same plane, or they are affinely independent and determine a three-dimensional simplex (a pyramid).

Let us now give an interpretation of basic feasible solutions to problem (3.6) in this geometry. Since we have added the convexity constraint, we have a total of $m+1$ equality constraints. Thus, a basic feasible solution is associated with a collection of $m+1$ linearly independent columns $(\mathbf{A}_i, 1)$ of the linear programming problem (3.6). These are in turn associated with $m+1$ of the points $(\mathbf{A}_i, c_i)$, which we call *basic points*; the remaining points $(\mathbf{A}_i, c_i)$ are called the *nonbasic points*. It is not hard to show that the $m+1$ basic points are affinely independent (Exercise 3.29) and, therefore, their convex hull is an m-dimensional simplex, which we call the *basic simplex*. Let the requirement line intersect the m-dimensional basic simplex at some point $(\mathbf{b}, z)$. The vector of weights x_i used in expressing $(\mathbf{b}, z)$ as a convex combination of the basic points, is the current basic feasible solution, and z represents its cost. For example, in Figure 3.6, the shaded triangle CDF is the basic simplex, and the point H corresponds to a basic feasible solution associated with the basic points C, D, and F.

Let us now interpret a change of basis geometrically. In a change of basis, a new point $(\mathbf{A}_j, c_j)$ becomes basic, and one of the currently basic points is to become nonbasic. For example, in Figure 3.6, if C, D, F, are the current basic points, we could make point B basic, replacing F

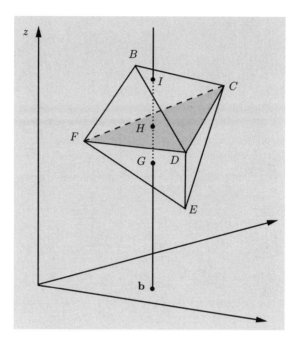

Figure 3.6: Feasibility and optimality in the column geometry.

(even though this turns out not to be profitable). The new basic simplex would be the convex hull of B, C, D, and the new basic feasible solution would correspond to point I. Alternatively, we could make point E basic, replacing C, and the new basic feasible solution would now correspond to point G. After a change of basis, the intercept of the requirement line with the new basic simplex is lower, and hence the cost decreases, if and only if the new basic point is below the plane that passes through the old basic points; we refer to the latter plane as the *dual plane*. For example, point E is below the dual plane and having it enter the basis is profitable; this is not the case for point B. In fact, the vertical distance from the dual plane to a point $(\mathbf{A}_j, c_j)$ is equal to the reduced cost of the associated variable x_j (Exercise 3.30); requiring the new basic point to be below the dual plane is therefore equivalent to requiring the entering column to have negative reduced cost.

We discuss next the selection of the basic point that will exit the basis. Each possible choice of the exiting point leads to a different basic simplex. These m basic simplices, together with the original basic simplex (before the change of basis) form the boundary (the faces) of an $(m + 1)$-dimensional simplex. The requirement line exits this $(m + 1)$-dimensional simplex through its top face and must therefore enter it by crossing some other face. This determines which one of the potential basic simplices will be obtained after the change of basis. In reference to Figure 3.6, the basic points C, D, F, determine a two-dimensional basic simplex. If point E is to become basic, we obtain a three-dimensional simplex (pyramid) with vertices C, D, E, F. The requirement line exits the pyramid through its top face with vertices C, D, F. It enters the pyramid through the face with vertices D, E, F; this is the new basic simplex.

We can now visualize pivoting through the following physical analogy. Think of the original basic simplex with vertices C, D, F, as a solid object anchored at its vertices. Grasp the corner of the basic simplex at the vertex C leaving the basis, and pull the corner down to the new basic point E. While so moving, the simplex will hinge, or *pivot*, on its anchor and stretch down to the lower position. The somewhat peculiar terms (e.g., "simplex", "pivot") associated with the simplex method have their roots in this column geometry.

Example 3.10 Consider the problem illustrated in Figure 3.7, in which $m = 1$, and the following pivoting rule: choose a point $(\mathbf{A}_i, c_i)$ below the dual plane to become basic, whose vertical distance from the dual plane is largest. According to Exercise 3.30, this is identical to the pivoting rule that selects an entering variable with the most negative reduced cost. Starting from the initial basic simplex consisting of the points $(\mathbf{A}_3, c_3)$, $(\mathbf{A}_6, c_6)$, the next basic simplex is determined by the points $(\mathbf{A}_3, c_3)$, $(\mathbf{A}_5, c_5)$, and the next one by the points $(\mathbf{A}_5, c_5)$, $(\mathbf{A}_8, c_8)$. In particular, the simplex method only takes two pivots in this case. This example indicates why the simplex method may require a rather small number of pivots, even when the number of underlying variables is large.

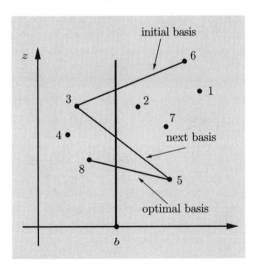

Figure 3.7: The simplex method finds the optimal basis after two iterations. Here, the point indicated by a number i corresponds to the vector $(\mathbf{A}_i, c_i)$.

3.7 Computational efficiency of the simplex method

The computational efficiency of the simplex method is determined by two factors:

(a) the computational effort at each iteration;

(b) the number of iterations.

The computational requirements of each iteration have already been discussed in Section 3.3. For example, the full tableau implementation needs $O(mn)$ arithmetic operations per iteration; the same is true for the revised simplex method in the worst case. We now turn to a discussion of the number of iterations.

The number of iterations in the worst case

Although the number of extreme points of the feasible set can increase exponentially with the number of variables and constraints, it has been observed in practice that the simplex method typically takes only $O(m)$ pivots to find an optimal solution. Unfortunately, however, this practical observation is not true for every linear programming problem. We will describe shortly a family of problems for which an exponential number of pivots may be required.

Recall that for nondegenerate problems, the simplex method always moves from one vertex to an adjacent one, each time improving the value of the cost function. We will now describe a polyhedron that has an exponential number of vertices, along with a path that visits all vertices, by taking steps from one vertex to an adjacent one that has lower cost. Once such a polyhedron is available, then the simplex method – under a pivoting rule that traces this path – needs an exponential number of pivots.

Consider the unit cube in $\Re^n$, defined by the constraints

$$0 \leq x_i \leq 1, \qquad i = 1, \ldots, n.$$

The unit cube has 2^n vertices (for each i, we may let either one of the two constraints $0 \leq x_i$ or $x_i \leq 1$ become active). Furthermore, there exists a path that travels along the edges of the cube and which visits each vertex exactly once; we call such a path a *spanning path*. It can be constructed according to the procedure illustrated in Figure 3.8.

Let us now introduce the cost function $-x_n$. Half of the vertices of the cube have zero cost and the other half have a cost of -1. Thus, the cost cannot decrease strictly with each move along the spanning path, and we do not yet have the desired example. However, if we choose some $\epsilon \in (0, 1/2)$ and consider the perturbation of the unit cube defined by the constraints

$$\epsilon \leq x_1 \leq 1, \tag{3.7}$$

$$\epsilon x_{i-1} \leq x_i \leq 1 - \epsilon x_{i-1}, \qquad i = 2, \ldots, n, \tag{3.8}$$

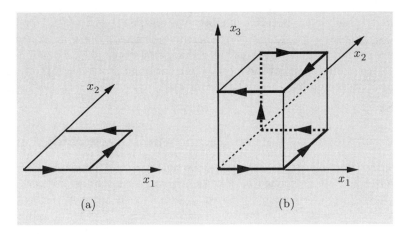

Figure 3.8: (a) A spanning path p_2 in the two-dimensional cube. (b) A spanning path p_3 in the three-dimensional cube. Notice that this path is obtained by splitting the three-dimensional cube into two two-dimensional cubes, following path p_2 in one of them, moving to the other cube, and following p_2 in the reverse order. This construction generalizes and provides a recursive definition of a spanning path for the general n-dimensional cube.

then it can be verified that the cost function decreases strictly with each move along a suitably chosen spanning path. If we start the simplex method at the first vertex on that spanning path and if our pivoting rule is to always move to the next vertex on that path, then the simplex method will require $2^n - 1$ pivots. We summarize this discussion in the following theorem whose proof is left as an exercise (Exercise 3.32).

Theorem 3.5 *Consider the linear programming problem of minimizing* $-x_n$ *subject to the constraints (3.7)-(3.8). Then:*

(a) *The feasible set has* 2^n *vertices.*

(b) *The vertices can be ordered so that each one is adjacent to and has lower cost than the previous one.*

(c) *There exists a pivoting rule under which the simplex method requires* $2^n - 1$ *changes of basis before it terminates.*

We observe in Figure 3.8 that the first and the last vertex in the spanning path are adjacent. This property persists in the perturbed polyhedron as well. Thus, with a different pivoting rule, the simplex method could terminate with a single pivot. We are thus led to the following question: is it true that for every pivoting rule there are examples where the simplex method takes an exponential number of iterations? For several popular pivoting rules, such examples have been constructed. However, these examples cannot exclude the possibility that some other pivoting rule might fare better. This is one of the most important open problems in the theory of linear programming. In the next subsection, we address a closely related issue.

The diameter of polyhedra and the Hirsch conjecture

The preceding discussion leads us to the notion of the diameter of a polyhedron P, which is defined as follows. Suppose that from any vertex of the polyhedron, we are only allowed to jump to an adjacent vertex. We define the distance $d(\mathbf{x}, \mathbf{y})$ between two vertices $\mathbf{x}$ and $\mathbf{y}$ as the minimum number of such jumps required to reach $\mathbf{y}$ starting from $\mathbf{x}$. The diameter $D(P)$ of the polyhedron P is then defined as the maximum of $d(\mathbf{x}, \mathbf{y})$ over all pairs $(\mathbf{x}, \mathbf{y})$ of vertices. Finally, we define $\Delta(n, m)$ as the maximum of $D(P)$ over all *bounded* polyhedra in $\Re^n$ that are represented in terms of m inequality constraints. The quantity $\Delta_u(n, m)$ is defined similarly, except that general, possibly unbounded, polyhedra are allowed. For example, we have

$$\Delta(2, m) = \left\lfloor \frac{m}{2} \right\rfloor,$$

and

$$\Delta_u(2, m) = m - 2;$$

see Figure 3.9.

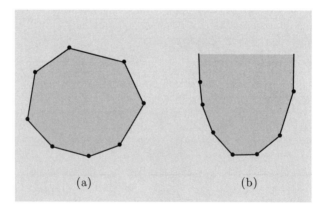

(a)   (b)

Figure 3.9: Let $n = 2$ and $m = 8$. (a) A bounded polyhedron with diameter $\lfloor m/2 \rfloor = 4$. (b) An unbounded polyhedron with diameter $m - 2 = 6$.

Suppose that the feasible set in a linear programming problem has diameter d and that the distance between vertices $\mathbf{x}$ and $\mathbf{y}$ is equal to d. If the simplex method (or any other method that proceeds from one vertex to an adjacent vertex) is initialized at $\mathbf{x}$, and if $\mathbf{y}$ happens to be the unique optimal solution, then at least d steps will be required. Now, if $\Delta(n, m)$ or $\Delta_u(n, m)$ increases exponentially with n and m, this implies that there exist examples for which the simplex method takes an exponentially increasing number of steps, no matter which pivoting rule is used. Thus, in order to have any hope of developing pivoting rules under which the simplex method requires a polynomial number of iterations, we must first establish that $\Delta(n, m)$ or $\Delta_u(n, m)$ grows with n and m at the rate of some polynomial. The practical success of the simplex method has led to the conjecture that indeed $\Delta(n, m)$ and $\Delta_u(n, m)$ do not grow exponentially fast. In fact, the following, much stronger, conjecture has been advanced:

Hirsch Conjecture: $\Delta(n, m) \leq m - n$.

Despite the significance of $\Delta(n, m)$ and $\Delta_u(n, m)$, we are far from establishing the Hirsch conjecture or even from establishing that these quantities exhibit polynomial growth. It is known (Klee and Walkup, 1967) that the Hirsch conjecture is false for unbounded polyhedra and, in particular, that

$$\Delta_u(n, m) \geq m - n + \left\lfloor \frac{n}{5} \right\rfloor .$$

Unfortunately, this is the best lower bound known; even though it disproves the Hirsch conjecture for unbounded polyhedra, it does not provide any insights as to whether the growth of $\Delta_u(n, m)$ is polynomial or exponential.

Regarding upper bounds, it has been established (Kalai and Kleitman, 1993) that the worst-case diameter grows slower than exponentially, but the available upper bound grows faster than any polynomial. In particular, the following bounds are available:

$$\Delta(n, m) \leq \Delta_u(n, m) < m^{1+\log_2 n} = (2n)^{\log_2 m} .$$

The average case behavior of the simplex method

Our discussion has been focused on the worst-case behavior of the simplex method, but this is only part of the story. Even if every pivoting rule requires an exponential number of iterations in the worst case, this is not necessarily relevant to the typical behavior of the simplex method. For this reason, there has been a fair amount of research aiming at an understanding of the typical or average behavior of the simplex method, and an explanation of its observed behavior.

The main difficulty in studying the average behavior of any algorithm lies in defining the meaning of the term "average." Basically, one needs to define a probability distribution over the set of all problems of a given size, and then take the mathematical expectation of the number of iterations required by the algorithm, when applied to a random problem drawn according to the postulated probability distribution. Unfortunately, there is no natural probability distribution over the set of linear programming problems. Nevertheless, a fair number of positive results have been obtained for a few different types of probability distributions. In one such result, a set of vectors $\mathbf{c}, \mathbf{a}_1, \ldots, \mathbf{a}_m \in \Re^n$ and scalars $b_1, \ldots, b_m$ is given. For $i = 1, \ldots, m$, we introduce either constraint $\mathbf{a}_i'\mathbf{x} \le b_i$ or $\mathbf{a}_i'\mathbf{x} \ge b_i$, with equal probability. We then have 2^m possible linear programming problems, and suppose that L of them are feasible. Haimovich (1983) has established that under a rather special pivoting rule, the simplex method requires no more than $n/2$ iterations, on the average over those L feasible problems. This linear dependence on the size of the problem agrees with observed behavior; some empirical evidence is discussed in Chapter 12.

3.8   Summary

This chapter was centered on the development of the simplex method, which is a complete algorithm for solving linear programming problems in standard form. The cornerstones of the simplex method are:

(a) the optimality conditions (nonnegativity of the reduced costs) that allow us to test whether the current basis is optimal;

(b) a systematic method for performing basis changes whenever the optimality conditions are violated.

At a high level, the simplex method simply moves from one extreme point of the feasible set to another, each time reducing the cost, until an optimal solution is reached. However, the lower level details of the simplex method, relating to the organization of the required computations and the associated bookkeeping, play an important role. We have described three different implementations: the naive one, the revised simplex method, and the full tableau implementation. Abstractly, they are all equivalent, but their mechanics are quite different. Practical implementations of the simplex method follow our general description of the revised simplex method, but the details are different, because an explicit computation of the inverse basis matrix is usually avoided.

We have seen that degeneracy can cause substantial difficulties, including the possibility of nonterminating behavior (cycling). This is because in the presence of degeneracy, a change of basis may keep us at the same basic feasible solution, with no cost improvement resulting. Cycling can be avoided if suitable rules for choosing the entering and exiting variables (pivoting rules) are applied (e.g., Bland's rule or the lexicographic pivoting rule).

Starting the simplex method requires an initial basic feasible solution, and an associated tableau. These are provided by the Phase I simplex algorithm, which is nothing but the simplex method applied to an auxiliary problem. We saw that the changeover from Phase I to Phase II involves some delicate steps whenever some artificial variables are in the final basis constructed by the Phase I algorithm.

The simplex method is a rather efficient algorithm and is incorporated in most of the commercial codes for linear programming. While the number of pivots can be an exponential function of the number of variables and constraints in the worst case, its observed behavior is a lot better, hence the practical usefulness of the method.

3.9   Exercises

Exercise 3.1 (Local minima of convex functions) Let $f : \Re^n \mapsto \Re$ be a convex function and let $S \subset \Re^n$ be a convex set. Let $\mathbf{x}^*$ be an element of S. Suppose that $\mathbf{x}^*$ is a local optimum for the problem of minimizing $f(\mathbf{x})$ over S; that is, there exists some $\epsilon > 0$ such that $f(\mathbf{x}^*) \le f(\mathbf{x})$ for all $\mathbf{x} \in S$ for which $\|\mathbf{x} - \mathbf{x}^*\| \le \epsilon$. Prove that $\mathbf{x}^*$ is globally optimal; that is, $f(\mathbf{x}^*) \le f(\mathbf{x})$ for all $\mathbf{x} \in S$.

Exercise 3.2 (Optimality conditions) Consider the problem of minimizing $\mathbf{c}'\mathbf{x}$ over a polyhedron P. Prove the following:

(a) A feasible solution $\mathbf{x}$ is optimal if and only if $\mathbf{c}'\mathbf{d} \ge 0$ for every feasible direction $\mathbf{d}$ at $\mathbf{x}$.

(b) A feasible solution $\mathbf{x}$ is the unique optimal solution if and only if $\mathbf{c}'\mathbf{d} > 0$ for every nonzero feasible direction $\mathbf{d}$ at $\mathbf{x}$.

Exercise 3.3 Let $\mathbf{x}$ be an element of the standard form polyhedron $P = \{\mathbf{x} \in \Re^n \mid \mathbf{A}\mathbf{x} = \mathbf{b}, \ \mathbf{x} \ge \mathbf{0}\}$. Prove that a vector $\mathbf{d} \in \Re^n$ is a feasible direction at $\mathbf{x}$ if and only if $\mathbf{A}\mathbf{d} = \mathbf{0}$ and $d_i \ge 0$ for every i such that $x_i = 0$.

Exercise 3.4 Consider the problem of minimizing $\mathbf{c}'\mathbf{x}$ over the set $P = \{\mathbf{x} \in \Re^n \mid \mathbf{A}\mathbf{x} = \mathbf{b}, \ \mathbf{D}\mathbf{x} \le \mathbf{f}, \ \mathbf{E}\mathbf{x} \le \mathbf{g}\}$. Let $\mathbf{x}^*$ be an element of P that satisfies $\mathbf{D}\mathbf{x}^* = \mathbf{f}, \ \mathbf{E}\mathbf{x}^* < \mathbf{g}$. Show that the set of feasible directions at the point $\mathbf{x}^*$ is the set

$$\{\mathbf{d} \in \Re^n \mid \mathbf{A}\mathbf{d} = \mathbf{0}, \ \mathbf{D}\mathbf{d} \le \mathbf{0}\}.$$

Exercise 3.5 Let $P = \{\mathbf{x} \in \Re^3 \mid x_1 + x_2 + x_3 = 1, \ \mathbf{x} \ge \mathbf{0}\}$ and consider the vector $\mathbf{x} = (0, 0, 1)$. Find the set of feasible directions at $\mathbf{x}$.

Exercise 3.6 (Conditions for a unique optimum) Let $\mathbf{x}$ be a basic feasible solution associated with some basis matrix $\mathbf{B}$. Prove the following:

(a) If the reduced cost of every nonbasic variable is positive, then $\mathbf{x}$ is the unique optimal solution.

(b) If $\mathbf{x}$ is the unique optimal solution and is nondegenerate, then the reduced cost of every nonbasic variable is positive.

Exercise 3.7 (Optimality conditions) Consider a feasible solution $\mathbf{x}$ to a standard form problem, and let $Z = \{i \mid x_i = 0\}$. Show that $\mathbf{x}$ is an optimal solution if and only if the linear programming problem

$$\begin{aligned} \text{minimize} \quad & \mathbf{c}'\mathbf{d} \\ \text{subject to} \quad & \mathbf{A}\mathbf{d} = \mathbf{0} \\ & d_i \geq 0, \qquad i \in Z, \end{aligned}$$

has an optimal cost of zero. (In this sense, deciding optimality is equivalent to solving a new linear programming problem.)

Exercise 3.8* This exercise deals with the problem of deciding whether a given degenerate basic feasible solution is optimal and shows that this is essentially as hard as solving a general linear programming problem.

Consider the linear programming problem of minimizing $\mathbf{c}'\mathbf{x}$ over all $\mathbf{x} \in P$, where $P \subset \Re^n$ is a given bounded polyhedron. Let

$$Q = \big\{ (t\mathbf{x}, t) \in \Re^{n+1} \mid \mathbf{x} \in P,\ t \in [0, 1] \big\}.$$

(a) Show that Q is a polyhedron.
(b) Give an example of P and Q, with $n = 2$, for which the zero vector (in $\Re^{n+1}$) is a degenerate basic feasible solution in Q; show the example in a figure.
(c) Show that the zero vector (in $\Re^{n+1}$) minimizes $(\mathbf{c}, 0)'\mathbf{y}$ over all $\mathbf{y} \in Q$ if and only if the optimal cost in the original linear programming problem is greater than or equal to zero.

Exercise 3.9 (Necessary and sufficient conditions for a unique optimum) Consider a linear programming problem in standard form and suppose that $\mathbf{x}^*$ is an optimal basic feasible solution. Consider an optimal basis associated with $\mathbf{x}^*$. Let B and N be the set of basic and nonbasic indices, respectively. Let I be the set of nonbasic indices i for which the corresponding reduced costs $\bar{c}_i$ are zero.

(a) Show that if I is empty, then $\mathbf{x}^*$ is the only optimal solution.
(b) Show that $\mathbf{x}^*$ is the unique optimal solution if and only if the following linear programming problem has an optimal value of zero:

$$\begin{aligned} \text{maximize} \quad & \sum_{i \in I} x_i \\ \text{subject to} \quad & \mathbf{A}\mathbf{x} = \mathbf{b} \\ & x_i = 0, \qquad i \in N \setminus I, \\ & x_i \geq 0, \qquad i \in B \cup I. \end{aligned}$$

Exercise 3.10 * Show that if $n - m = 2$, then the simplex method will not cycle, no matter which pivoting rule is used.

Exercise 3.11 * Construct an example with $n - m = 3$ and a pivoting rule under which the simplex method will cycle.

Exercise 3.12 Consider the problem

$$\begin{array}{ll} \text{minimize} & -2x_1 - x_2 \\ \text{subject to} & x_1 - x_2 \le 2 \\ & x_1 + x_2 \le 6 \\ & x_1, x_2 \ge 0. \end{array}$$

(a) Convert the problem into standard form and construct a basic feasible solution at which $(x_1, x_2) = (0, 0)$.

(b) Carry out the full tableau implementation of the simplex method, starting with the basic feasible solution of part (a).

(c) Draw a graphical representation of the problem in terms of the original variables x_1, x_2, and indicate the path taken by the simplex algorithm.

Exercise 3.13 This exercise shows that our efficient procedures for updating a tableau can be derived from a useful fact in numerical linear algebra.

(a) **(Matrix inversion lemma)** Let $\mathbf{C}$ be an $m \times m$ invertible matrix and let $\mathbf{u}, \mathbf{v}$ be vectors in $\Re^m$. Show that

$$(\mathbf{C} + \mathbf{w}\mathbf{v}')^{-1} = \mathbf{C}^{-1} - \frac{\mathbf{C}^{-1}\mathbf{w}\mathbf{v}'\mathbf{C}^{-1}}{1 + \mathbf{v}'\mathbf{C}^{-1}\mathbf{w}}.$$

(Note that $\mathbf{w}\mathbf{v}'$ is an $m \times m$ matrix). *Hint:* Multiply both sides by $(\mathbf{C} + \mathbf{w}\mathbf{v}')$.

(b) Assuming that $\mathbf{C}^{-1}$ is available, explain how to obtain $(\mathbf{C} + \mathbf{w}\mathbf{v}')^{-1}$ using only $O(m^2)$ arithmetic operations.

(c) Let $\mathbf{B}$ and $\overline{\mathbf{B}}$ be basis matrices before and after an iteration of the simplex method. Let $\mathbf{A}_{B(\ell)}$, $\mathbf{A}_{\overline{B}(\ell)}$ be the exiting and entering column, respectively. Show that

$$\overline{\mathbf{B}} - \mathbf{B} = (\mathbf{A}_{\overline{B}(\ell)} - \mathbf{A}_{B(\ell)})\mathbf{e}'_\ell,$$

where $\mathbf{e}_\ell$ is the ℓth unit vector.

(d) Note that $\mathbf{e}'_i\mathbf{B}^{-1}$ is the ith row of $\mathbf{B}^{-1}$ and $\mathbf{e}'_\ell\mathbf{B}^{-1}$ is the pivot row. Show that

$$\mathbf{e}'_i\overline{\mathbf{B}}^{-1} = \mathbf{e}'_i\mathbf{B}^{-1} - g_i\mathbf{e}'_\ell\mathbf{B}^{-1}, \qquad i = 1, \dots, m,$$

for suitable scalars g_i. Provide a formula for g_i. Interpret the above equation in terms of the mechanics for pivoting in the revised simplex method.

(e) Multiply both sides of the equation in part (d) by $[\mathbf{b} \mid \mathbf{A}]$ and obtain an interpretation of the mechanics for pivoting in the full tableau implementation.

Exercise 3.14 Suppose that a feasible tableau is available. Show how to obtain a tableau with lexicographically positive rows. *Hint:* Permute the columns.

Exercise 3.15 (Perturbation approach to lexicography) Consider a standard form problem, under the usual assumption that the rows of $\mathbf{A}$ are linearly independent. Let ϵ be a scalar and define

$$\mathbf{b}(\epsilon) = \mathbf{b} + \begin{bmatrix} \epsilon \\ \epsilon^2 \\ \vdots \\ \epsilon^m \end{bmatrix}.$$

For every $\epsilon > 0$, we define the ϵ-perturbed problem to be the linear programming problem obtained by replacing $\mathbf{b}$ with $\mathbf{b}(\epsilon)$.

(a) Given a basis matrix $\mathbf{B}$, show that the corresponding basic solution $\mathbf{x}_B(\epsilon)$ in the ϵ-perturbed problem is equal to

$$\mathbf{B}^{-1}\bigl[\mathbf{b}\mid\mathbf{I}\bigr]\begin{bmatrix}1\\\epsilon\\\vdots\\\epsilon^m\end{bmatrix}.$$

(b) Show that there exists some $\epsilon^* > 0$ such that all basic solutions to the ϵ-perturbed problem are nondegenerate, for $0 < \epsilon < \epsilon^*$.

(c) Suppose that all rows of $\mathbf{B}^{-1}\bigl[\mathbf{b}\mid\mathbf{I}\bigr]$ are lexicographically positive. Show that $\mathbf{x}_B(\epsilon)$ is a basic feasible solution to the ϵ-perturbed problem for ϵ positive and sufficiently small.

(d) Consider a feasible basis for the original problem, and assume that all rows of $\mathbf{B}^{-1}\bigl[\mathbf{b}\mid\mathbf{I}\bigr]$ are lexicographically positive. Let some nonbasic variable x_j enter the basis, and define $\mathbf{u} = \mathbf{B}^{-1}\mathbf{A}_j$. Let the exiting variable be determined as follows. For every row i such that u_i is positive, divide the ith row of $\mathbf{B}^{-1}\bigl[\mathbf{b}\mid\mathbf{I}\bigr]$ by u_i, compare the results lexicographically, and choose the exiting variable to be the one corresponding to the lexicographically smallest row. Show that this is the same choice of exiting variable as in the original simplex method applied to the ϵ-perturbed problem, when ϵ is sufficiently small.

(e) Explain why the revised simplex method, with the lexicographic rule described in part (d), is guaranteed to terminate even in the face of degeneracy.

Exercise 3.16 (Lexicography and the revised simplex method) Suppose that we have a basic feasible solution and an associated basis matrix $\mathbf{B}$ such that every row of $\mathbf{B}^{-1}$ is lexicographically positive. Consider a pivoting rule that chooses the entering variable x_j arbitrarily (as long as $\bar{c}_j < 0$) and the exiting variable as follows. Let $\mathbf{u} = \mathbf{B}^{-1}\mathbf{A}_j$. For each i with $u_i > 0$, divide the ith row of $[\mathbf{B}^{-1}\mathbf{b}\mid\mathbf{B}^{-1}]$ by u_i and choose the row which is lexicographically smallest. If row ℓ was lexicographically smallest, then the ℓth basic variable $x_{B(\ell)}$ exits the basis. Prove the following:

(a) The row vector $(-\mathbf{c}_B'\mathbf{B}^{-1}\mathbf{b}, -\mathbf{c}_B'\mathbf{B}^{-1})$ increases lexicographically at each iteration.

(b) Every row of $\mathbf{B}^{-1}$ is lexicographically positive throughout the algorithm.

(c) The revised simplex method terminates after a finite number of steps.

Exercise 3.17 Solve completely (i.e., both Phase I and Phase II) via the simplex method the following problem:

$$\begin{array}{lrcrcrcrcrcl}
\text{minimize} & 2x_1 & + & 3x_2 & + & 3x_3 & + & x_4 & - & 2x_5 & & \\
\text{subject to} & x_1 & + & 3x_2 & & & + & 4x_4 & + & x_5 & = & 2 \\
& x_1 & + & 2x_2 & & & - & 3x_4 & + & x_5 & = & 2 \\
& -x_1 & - & 4x_2 & + & 3x_3 & & & & & = & 1 \\
& x_1, & \ldots, & x_5 & \geq & 0. & & & & & &
\end{array}$$

Exercise 3.18 Consider the simplex method applied to a standard form problem and assume that the rows of the matrix $\mathbf{A}$ are linearly independent. For each of the statements that follow, give either a proof or a counterexample.

(a) An iteration of the simplex method may move the feasible solution by a positive distance while leaving the cost unchanged.

(b) A variable that has just left the basis cannot reenter in the very next iteration.

(c) A variable that has just entered the basis cannot leave in the very next iteration.

(d) If there is a nondegenerate optimal basis, then there exists a unique optimal basis.

(e) If $\mathbf{x}$ is an optimal solution, no more than m of its components can be positive, where m is the number of equality constraints.

Exercise 3.19 While solving a standard form problem, we arrive at the following tableau, with x_3, x_4, and x_5 being the basic variables:

-10	δ	-2	0	0	0
4	-1	η	1	0	0
1	α	-4	0	1	0
β	γ	3	0	0	1

The entries α, β, γ, δ, η in the tableau are unknown parameters. For each one of the following statements, find some parameter values that will make the statement true.

(a) The current solution is optimal and there are multiple optimal solutions.

(b) The optimal cost is $-\infty$.

(c) The current solution is feasible but not optimal.

Exercise 3.20 Consider a linear programming problem in standard form, described in terms of the following initial tableau:

0	0	0	0	δ	3	γ	ξ
β	0	1	0	α	1	0	3
2	0	0	1	-2	2	η	-1
3	1	0	0	0	-1	2	1

The entries α, β, γ, δ, η, ξ in the tableau are unknown parameters. Furthermore, let $\mathbf{B}$ be the basis matrix corresponding to having x_2, x_3, and x_1 (in that order) be the basic variables. For each one of the following statements, find the ranges of values of the various parameters that will make the statement to be true.

(a) Phase II of the simplex method can be applied using this as an initial tableau.

(b) The first row in the present tableau indicates that the problem is infeasible.

(c) The corresponding basic solution is feasible, but we do not have an optimal basis.

(d) The corresponding basic solution is feasible and the first simplex iteration indicates that the optimal cost is $-\infty$.

(e) The corresponding basic solution is feasible, x_6 is a candidate for entering the basis, and when x_6 is the entering variable, x_3 leaves the basis.

(f) The corresponding basic solution is feasible, x_7 is a candidate for entering the basis, but if it does, the solution and the objective value remain unchanged.

Exercise 3.21 Consider the oil refinery problem in Exercise 1.16.

(a) Use the simplex method to find an optimal solution.

(b) Suppose that the selling price of heating oil is sure to remain fixed over the next month, but the selling price of gasoline may rise. How high can it go without causing the optimal solution to change?

(c) The refinery manager can buy crude oil B on the spot market at $40/barrel, in unlimited quantities. How much should be bought?

Exercise 3.22 Consider the following linear programming problem with a single constraint:

$$\text{minimize} \quad \sum_{i=1}^{n} c_i x_i$$

$$\text{subject to} \quad \sum_{i=1}^{n} a_i x_i = b$$

$$x_i \geq 0, \qquad i = 1, \ldots, n.$$

(a) Derive a simple test for checking the feasibility of this problem.

(b) Assuming that the optimal cost is finite, develop a simple method for obtaining an optimal solution directly.

Exercise 3.23 While solving a linear programming problem by the simplex method, the following tableau is obtained at some iteration.

	0	...	0	$\bar{c}_{m+1}$	...	$\bar{c}_n$
x_1	1	...	0	$a_{1,m+1}$	...	$a_{1,n}$
⋮	⋮	...	⋮	⋮	...	⋮
x_m	0	...	1	$a_{m,m+1}$	...	$a_{m,n}$

Assume that in this tableau we have $\bar{c}_j \geq 0$ for $j = m+1, \ldots, n-1$, and $\bar{c}_n < 0$. In particular, x_n is the only candidate for entering the basis.

(a) Suppose that x_n indeed enters the basis and that this is a nondegenerate pivot (that is, $\theta^* \neq 0$). Prove that x_n will remain basic in all subsequent iterations of the algorithm and that x_n is a basic variable in any optimal basis.

(b) Suppose that x_n indeed enters the basis and that this is a degenerate pivot (that is, $\theta^* = 0$). Show that x_n need not be basic in an optimal basic feasible solution.

Exercise 3.24 Show that in Phase I of the simplex method, if an artificial variable becomes nonbasic, it need never again become basic. Thus, when an artificial variable becomes nonbasic, its column can be eliminated from the tableau.

Exercise 3.25 (The simplex method with upper bound constraints) Consider a problem of the form

$$\begin{aligned} \text{minimize} \quad & \mathbf{c'x} \\ \text{subject to} \quad & \mathbf{Ax = b} \\ & 0 \le \mathbf{x} \le \mathbf{u}, \end{aligned}$$

where $\mathbf{A}$ has linearly independent rows and dimensions $m \times n$. Assume that $u_i > 0$ for all i.

(a) Let $\mathbf{A}_{B(1)} \ldots, \mathbf{A}_{B(m)}$ be m linearly independent columns of $\mathbf{A}$ (the "basic" columns). We partition the set of all $i \ne B(1), \ldots, B(m)$ into two disjoint subsets L and U. We set $x_i = 0$ for all $i \in L$, and $x_i = u_i$ for all $i \in U$. We then solve the equation $\mathbf{Ax = b}$ for the basic variables $x_{B(1)}, \ldots, x_{B(m)}$. Show that the resulting vector $\mathbf{x}$ is a basic solution. Also, show that it is nondegenerate if and only if $0 < x_i < u_i$ for every basic variable x_i.

(b) For this part and the next, assume that the basic solution constructed in part (a) is feasible. We form the simplex tableau and compute the reduced costs as usual. Let x_j be some nonbasic variable such that $x_j = 0$ and $\bar{c}_j < 0$. As in Section 3.2, we increase x_j by θ, and adjust the basic variables from $\mathbf{x}_B$ to $\mathbf{x}_B - \theta \mathbf{B}^{-1} \mathbf{A}_j$. Given that we wish to preserve feasibility, what is the largest possible value of θ? How are the new basic columns determined?

(c) Let x_j be some nonbasic variable such that $x_j = u_j$ and $\bar{c}_j > 0$. We decrease x_j by θ, and adjust the basic variables from $\mathbf{x}_B$ to $\mathbf{x}_B + \theta \mathbf{B}^{-1} \mathbf{A}_j$. Given that we wish to preserve feasibility, what is the largest possible value of θ? How are the new basic columns determined?

(d) Assuming that every basic feasible solution is nondegenerate, show that the cost strictly decreases with each iteration and the method terminates.

Exercise 3.26 (The big-M method) Consider the variant of the big-M method in which M is treated as an undetermined large parameter. Prove the following.

(a) If the simplex method terminates with a solution $(\mathbf{x}, \mathbf{y})$ for which $\mathbf{y} = \mathbf{0}$, then $\mathbf{x}$ is an optimal solution to the original problem.

(b) If the simplex method terminates with a solution $(\mathbf{x}, \mathbf{y})$ for which $\mathbf{y} \ne \mathbf{0}$, then the original problem is infeasible.

(c) If the simplex method terminates with an indication that the optimal cost in the auxiliary problem is $-\infty$, show that the original problem is either infeasible or its optimal cost is $-\infty$. *Hint:* When the simplex method terminates, it has discovered a feasible direction $\mathbf{d} = (\mathbf{d}_x, \mathbf{d}_y)$ of cost decrease. Show that $\mathbf{d}_y = \mathbf{0}$.

(d) Provide examples to show that both alternatives in part (c) are possible.

Exercise 3.27 *

(a) Suppose that we wish to find a vector $\mathbf{x} \in \Re^n$ that satisfies $\mathbf{Ax} = \mathbf{0}$ and $\mathbf{x} \geq \mathbf{0}$, and such that the number of positive components of $\mathbf{x}$ is maximized. Show that this can be accomplished by solving the linear programming problem

$$\text{maximize} \quad \sum_{i=1}^{n} y_i$$
$$\text{subject to} \quad \mathbf{A}(\mathbf{z} + \mathbf{y}) = \mathbf{0}$$
$$y_i \leq 1, \qquad \text{for all } i,$$
$$\mathbf{z}, \mathbf{y} \geq \mathbf{0}.$$

(b) Suppose that we wish to find a vector $\mathbf{x} \in \Re^n$ that satisfies $\mathbf{Ax} = \mathbf{b}$ and $\mathbf{x} \geq \mathbf{0}$, and such that the number of positive components of $\mathbf{x}$ is maximized. Show how this can be accomplished by solving a single linear programming problem.

Exercise 3.28 Consider a linear programming problem in standard form with a bounded feasible set. Furthermore, suppose that we know the value of a scalar U such that any feasible solution satisfies $x_i \leq U$, for all i. Show that the problem can be transformed into an equivalent one that contains the constraint $\sum_{i=1}^{n} x_i = 1$.

Exercise 3.29 Consider the simplex method, viewed in terms of column geometry. Show that the $m + 1$ basic points $(\mathbf{A}_i, c_i)$, as defined in Section 3.6, are affinely independent.

Exercise 3.30 Consider the simplex method, viewed in terms of column geometry. In the terminology of Section 3.6, show that the vertical distance from the dual plane to a point $(\mathbf{A}_j, c_j)$ is equal to the reduced cost of the variable x_j.

Exercise 3.31 Consider the linear programming problem

$$
\begin{array}{lrcrcrcrcl}
\text{minimize} & x_1 & + & 3x_2 & + & 2x_3 & + & 2x_4 & & \\
\text{subject to} & 2x_1 & + & 3x_2 & + & x_3 & + & x_4 & = & b_1 \\
& x_1 & + & 2x_2 & + & x_3 & + & 3x_4 & = & b_2 \\
& x_1 & + & x_2 & + & x_3 & + & x_4 & = & 1 \\
& & & & x_1, \ldots, x_4 & \geq & 0, & & &
\end{array}
$$

where b_1, b_2 are free parameters. Let $P(b_1, b_2)$ be the feasible set. Use the column geometry of linear programming to answer the following questions.

(a) Characterize explicitly (preferably with a picture) the set of all (b_1, b_2) for which $P(b_1, b_2)$ is nonempty.

(b) Characterize explicitly (preferably with a picture) the set of all (b_1, b_2) for which some basic feasible solution is degenerate.

(c) There are four bases in this problem; in the ith basis, all variables except for x_i are basic. For every (b_1, b_2) for which there exists a degenerate basic feasible solution, enumerate all bases that correspond to each degenerate basic feasible solution.

(d) For $i = 1, \ldots, 4$, let $S_i = \{(b_1, b_2) \mid \text{the } i\text{th basis is optimal}\}$. Identify, preferably with a picture, the sets $S_1, \ldots, S_4$.

(e) For which values of (b_1, b_2) is the optimal solution degenerate?

(f) Let $b_1 = 9/5$ and $b_2 = 7/5$. Suppose that we start the simplex method with x_2, x_3, x_4 as the basic variables. Which path will the simplex method follow?

Exercise 3.32 * Prove Theorem 3.5.

Exercise 3.33 Consider a polyhedron in standard form, and let $\mathbf{x}$, $\mathbf{y}$ be two different basic feasible solutions. If we are allowed to move from any basic feasible solution to an adjacent one in a single step, show that we can go from $\mathbf{x}$ to $\mathbf{y}$ in a finite number of steps.

3.10 Notes and sources

3.2. The simplex method was pioneered by Dantzig in 1947, who later wrote a comprehensive text on the subject (Dantzig, 1963).

3.3. For more discussion of practical implementations of the simplex method based on products of sparse matrices, instead of $\mathbf{B}^{-1}$, see the books by Gill, Murray, and Wright (1981), Chvátal (1983), Murty (1983), and Luenberger (1984). An excellent introduction to numerical linear algebra is the text by Golub and Van Loan (1983). Example 3.6, which shows the possibility of cycling, is due to Beale (1955).

  If we have upper bounds for all or some of the variables, instead of converting the problem to standard form, we can use a suitable adaptation of the simplex method. This is developed in Exercise 3.25 and in the textbooks that we mentioned earlier.

3.4. The lexicographic anticycling rule is due to Dantzig, Orden, and Wolfe (1955). It can be viewed as an outgrowth of a perturbation method developed by Orden and also by Charnes (1952). For an exposition of the perturbation method, see Chvátal (1983) and Murty (1983), as well as Exercise 3.15. The smallest subscript rule is due to Bland (1977). A proof that Bland's rule avoids cycling can also be found in Papadimitriou and Steiglitz (1982), Chvátal (1983), or Murty (1983).

3.6. The column geometry interpretation of the simplex method is due to Dantzig (1963). For further discussion, see Stone and Tovey (1991).

3.7. The example showing that the simplex method can take an exponential number of iterations is due to Klee and Minty (1972). The Hirsch conjecture was made by Hirsch in 1957. The first results on the average case behavior of the simplex method were obtained by Borgwardt (1982) and Smale (1983). Schrijver (1986) contains an overview of the early research in this area, as well as proof of the $n/2$ bound on the number of pivots due to Haimovich (1983).

3.9. The results in Exercises 3.10 and 3.11, which deal with the smallest examples of cycling, are due to Marshall and Suurballe (1969). The matrix inversion lemma [Exercise 3.13(a)] is known as the Sherman-Morrison formula.

Chapter 4

Duality theory

Contents

In this chapter, we start with a linear programming problem, called the primal, and introduce another linear programming problem, called the dual. Duality theory deals with the relation between these two problems and uncovers the deeper structure of linear programming. It is a powerful theoretical tool that has numerous applications, provides new geometric insights, and leads to another algorithm for linear programming (the dual simplex method).

4.1   Motivation

Duality theory can be motivated as an outgrowth of the Lagrange multiplier method, often used in calculus to minimize a function subject to equality constraints. For example, in order to solve the problem

$$\begin{aligned} \text{minimize} \quad & x^2 + y^2 \\ \text{subject to} \quad & x + y = 1, \end{aligned}$$

we introduce a Lagrange multiplier p and form the Lagrangean $L(x, y, p)$ defined by

$$L(x, y, p) = x^2 + y^2 + p(1 - x - y).$$

While keeping p fixed, we minimize the Lagrangean over all x and y, subject to no constraints, which can be done by setting $\partial L/\partial x$ and $\partial L/\partial y$ to zero. The optimal solution to this unconstrained problem is

$$x = y = \frac{p}{2},$$

and depends on p. The constraint $x + y = 1$ gives us the additional relation $p = 1$, and the optimal solution to the original problem is $x = y = 1/2$.

The main idea in the above example is the following. Instead of enforcing the hard constraint $x + y = 1$, we allow it to be violated and associate a Lagrange multiplier, or *price*, p with the amount $1 - x - y$ by which it is violated. This leads to the unconstrained minimization of $x^2 + y^2 + p(1 - x - y)$. When the price is properly chosen ($p = 1$, in our example), the optimal solution to the constrained problem is also optimal for the unconstrained problem. In particular, under that specific value of p, the presence or absence of the hard constraint does not affect the optimal cost.

The situation in linear programming is similar: we associate a price variable with each constraint and start searching for prices under which the presence or absence of the constraints does not affect the optimal cost. It turns out that the right prices can be found by solving a new linear programming problem, called the *dual* of the original. We now motivate the form of the dual problem.

Consider the standard form problem

$$\text{minimize} \quad \mathbf{c}'\mathbf{x}$$
$$\text{subject to} \quad \mathbf{A}\mathbf{x} = \mathbf{b}$$
$$\mathbf{x} \geq \mathbf{0},$$

which we call the *primal* problem, and let $\mathbf{x}^*$ be an optimal solution, assumed to exist. We introduce a *relaxed* problem in which the constraint $\mathbf{A}\mathbf{x} = \mathbf{b}$ is replaced by a penalty $\mathbf{p}'(\mathbf{b} - \mathbf{A}\mathbf{x})$, where $\mathbf{p}$ is a price vector of the same dimension as $\mathbf{b}$. We are then faced with the problem

$$\text{minimize} \quad \mathbf{c}'\mathbf{x} + \mathbf{p}'(\mathbf{b} - \mathbf{A}\mathbf{x})$$
$$\text{subject to} \quad \mathbf{x} \geq \mathbf{0}.$$

Let $g(\mathbf{p})$ be the optimal cost for the relaxed problem, as a function of the price vector $\mathbf{p}$. The relaxed problem allows for more options than those present in the primal problem, and we expect $g(\mathbf{p})$ to be no larger than the optimal primal cost $\mathbf{c}'\mathbf{x}^*$. Indeed,

$$g(\mathbf{p}) = \min_{\mathbf{x} \geq \mathbf{0}} \left[\mathbf{c}'\mathbf{x} + \mathbf{p}'(\mathbf{b} - \mathbf{A}\mathbf{x}) \right] \leq \mathbf{c}'\mathbf{x}^* + \mathbf{p}'(\mathbf{b} - \mathbf{A}\mathbf{x}^*) = \mathbf{c}'\mathbf{x}^*,$$

where the last inequality follows from the fact that $\mathbf{x}^*$ is a feasible solution to the primal problem, and satisfies $\mathbf{A}\mathbf{x}^* = \mathbf{b}$. Thus, each $\mathbf{p}$ leads to a lower bound $g(\mathbf{p})$ for the optimal cost $\mathbf{c}'\mathbf{x}^*$. The problem

$$\text{maximize} \quad g(\mathbf{p})$$
$$\text{subject to} \quad \text{no constraints}$$

can be then interpreted as a search for the tightest possible lower bound of this type, and is known as the *dual* problem. The main result in duality theory asserts that the optimal cost in the dual problem is equal to the optimal cost $\mathbf{c}'\mathbf{x}^*$ in the primal. In other words, when the prices are chosen according to an optimal solution for the dual problem, the option of violating the constraints $\mathbf{A}\mathbf{x} = \mathbf{b}$ is of no value.

Using the definition of $g(\mathbf{p})$, we have

$$g(\mathbf{p}) = \min_{\mathbf{x} \geq \mathbf{0}} \left[\mathbf{c}'\mathbf{x} + \mathbf{p}'(\mathbf{b} - \mathbf{A}\mathbf{x}) \right]$$
$$= \mathbf{p}'\mathbf{b} + \min_{\mathbf{x} \geq \mathbf{0}}(\mathbf{c}' - \mathbf{p}'\mathbf{A})\mathbf{x}.$$

Note that

$$\min_{\mathbf{x} \geq \mathbf{0}}(\mathbf{c}' - \mathbf{p}'\mathbf{A})\mathbf{x} = \begin{cases} 0, & \text{if } \mathbf{c}' - \mathbf{p}'\mathbf{A} \geq \mathbf{0}', \\ -\infty, & \text{otherwise.} \end{cases}$$

In maximizing $g(\mathbf{p})$, we only need to consider those values of $\mathbf{p}$ for which $g(\mathbf{p})$ is not equal to $-\infty$. We therefore conclude that the dual problem is the same as the linear programming problem

$$\text{maximize} \quad \mathbf{p}'\mathbf{b}$$
$$\text{subject to} \quad \mathbf{p}'\mathbf{A} \leq \mathbf{c}'.$$

In the preceding example, we started with the equality constraint $\mathbf{Ax} = \mathbf{b}$ and we ended up with no constraints on the sign of the price vector $\mathbf{p}$. If the primal problem had instead inequality constraints of the form $\mathbf{Ax} \geq \mathbf{b}$, they could be replaced by $\mathbf{Ax} - \mathbf{s} = \mathbf{b}$, $\mathbf{s} \geq \mathbf{0}$. The equality constraint can be written in the form

$$[\mathbf{A} \mid -\mathbf{I}] \begin{bmatrix} \mathbf{x} \\ \mathbf{s} \end{bmatrix} = \mathbf{0},$$

which leads to the dual constraints

$$\mathbf{p}'[\mathbf{A} \mid -\mathbf{I}] \leq [\mathbf{c}' \mid \mathbf{0}'],$$

or, equivalently,

$$\mathbf{p}'\mathbf{A} \leq \mathbf{c}', \quad \mathbf{p} \geq \mathbf{0}.$$

Also, if the vector $\mathbf{x}$ is free rather than sign-constrained, we use the fact

$$\min_{\mathbf{x}}(\mathbf{c}' - \mathbf{p}'\mathbf{A})\mathbf{x} = \begin{cases} 0, & \text{if } \mathbf{c}' - \mathbf{p}'\mathbf{A} = \mathbf{0}', \\ -\infty, & \text{otherwise}, \end{cases}$$

to end up with the constraint $\mathbf{p}'\mathbf{A} = \mathbf{c}'$ in the dual problem. These considerations motivate the general form of the dual problem which we introduce in the next section.

In summary, the construction of the dual of a primal minimization problem can be viewed as follows. We have a vector of parameters (dual variables) $\mathbf{p}$, and for every $\mathbf{p}$ we have a method for obtaining a lower bound on the optimal primal cost. The dual problem is a maximization problem that looks for the tightest such lower bound. For some vectors $\mathbf{p}$, the corresponding lower bound is equal to $-\infty$, and does not carry any useful information. Thus, we only need to maximize over those $\mathbf{p}$ that lead to nontrivial lower bounds, and this is what gives rise to the dual constraints.

4.2   The dual problem

Let $\mathbf{A}$ be a matrix with rows $\mathbf{a}_i'$ and columns $\mathbf{A}_j$. Given a *primal* problem with the structure shown on the left, its *dual* is defined to be the maximization problem shown on the right:

minimize	$\mathbf{c}'\mathbf{x}$		maximize	$\mathbf{p}'\mathbf{b}$	
subject to	$\mathbf{a}_i'\mathbf{x} \geq b_i,$	$i \in M_1,$	subject to	$p_i \geq 0,$	$i \in M_1,$
	$\mathbf{a}_i'\mathbf{x} \leq b_i,$	$i \in M_2,$		$p_i \leq 0,$	$i \in M_2,$
	$\mathbf{a}_i'\mathbf{x} = b_i,$	$i \in M_3,$		p_i free,	$i \in M_3,$
	$x_j \geq 0,$	$j \in N_1,$		$\mathbf{p}'\mathbf{A}_j \leq c_j,$	$j \in N_1,$
	$x_j \leq 0,$	$j \in N_2,$		$\mathbf{p}'\mathbf{A}_j \geq c_j,$	$j \in N_2,$
	x_j free,	$j \in N_3,$		$\mathbf{p}'\mathbf{A}_j = c_j,$	$j \in N_3.$

Notice that for each constraint in the primal (other than the sign constraints), we introduce a variable in the dual problem; for each variable in the primal, we introduce a constraint in the dual. Depending on whether the primal constraint is an equality or inequality constraint, the corresponding dual variable is either free or sign-constrained, respectively. In addition, depending on whether a variable in the primal problem is free or sign-constrained, we have an equality or inequality constraint, respectively, in the dual problem. We summarize these relations in Table 4.1.

PRIMAL	minimize	maximize	DUAL
	$\geq b_i$	≥ 0	
constraints	$\leq b_i$	≤ 0	**variables**
	$= b_i$	free	
	≥ 0	$\leq c_j$	
variables	≤ 0	$\geq c_j$	**constraints**
	free	$= c_j$	

Table 4.1: Relation between primal and dual variables and constraints.

If we start with a maximization problem, we can always convert it into an equivalent minimization problem, and then form its dual according to the rules we have described. However, to avoid confusion, we will adhere to the convention that the primal is a minimization problem, and its dual is a maximization problem. Finally, we will keep referring to the objective function in the dual problem as a "cost" that is being maximized.

A problem and its dual can be stated more compactly, in matrix notation, if a particular form is assumed for the primal. We have, for example, the following pairs of primal and dual problems:

$$\begin{array}{ll} \text{minimize} & \mathbf{c}'\mathbf{x} \\ \text{subject to} & \mathbf{A}\mathbf{x} = \mathbf{b} \\ & \mathbf{x} \geq \mathbf{0}, \end{array} \qquad \begin{array}{ll} \text{maximize} & \mathbf{p}'\mathbf{b} \\ \text{subject to} & \mathbf{p}'\mathbf{A} \leq \mathbf{c}', \end{array}$$

and

$$\begin{array}{ll} \text{minimize} & \mathbf{c}'\mathbf{x} \\ \text{subject to} & \mathbf{A}\mathbf{x} \geq \mathbf{b}, \end{array} \qquad \begin{array}{ll} \text{maximize} & \mathbf{p}'\mathbf{b} \\ \text{subject to} & \mathbf{p}'\mathbf{A} = \mathbf{c}' \\ & \mathbf{p} \geq \mathbf{0}. \end{array}$$

Example 4.1 Consider the primal problem shown on the left and its dual shown on the right:

$$
\begin{array}{ll}
\text{minimize} & x_1 + 2x_2 + 3x_3 \\
\text{subject to} & -x_1 + 3x_2 \qquad = 5 \\
& 2x_1 - \ \ x_2 + 3x_3 \geq 6 \\
& \qquad\qquad\qquad x_3 \leq 4 \\
& x_1 \geq 0 \\
& x_2 \leq 0 \\
& x_3 \ \text{free},
\end{array}
\qquad
\begin{array}{ll}
\text{maximize} & 5p_1 + 6p_2 + 4p_3 \\
\text{subject to} & p_1 \ \text{free} \\
& p_2 \geq 0 \\
& p_3 \leq 0 \\
& -p_1 + 2p_2 \qquad \leq 1 \\
& 3p_1 - \ \ p_2 \qquad \geq 2 \\
& \qquad 3p_2 + \ p_3 = 3.
\end{array}
$$

We transform the dual into an equivalent minimization problem, rename the variables from p_1, p_2, p_3 to x_1, x_2, x_3, and multiply the three last constraints by -1. The resulting problem is shown on the left. Then, on the right, we show its dual:

$$
\begin{array}{ll}
\text{minimize} & -5x_1 - 6x_2 - 4x_3 \\
\text{subject to} & x_1 \ \text{free} \\
& x_2 \geq 0 \\
& x_3 \leq 0 \\
& x_1 - 2x_2 \qquad \geq -1 \\
& -3x_1 + \ \ x_2 \qquad \leq -2 \\
& \qquad - 3x_2 - \ x_3 = -3,
\end{array}
\qquad
\begin{array}{ll}
\text{maximize} & -p_1 - 2p_2 - 3p_3 \\
\text{subject to} & p_1 - 3p_2 \qquad = -5 \\
& -2p_1 + \ p_2 - 3p_3 \leq -6 \\
& \qquad\qquad - \ p_3 \geq -4 \\
& p_1 \geq 0 \\
& p_2 \leq 0 \\
& p_3 \ \text{free}.
\end{array}
$$

We observe that the latter problem is equivalent to the primal problem we started with. (The first three constraints in the latter problem are the same as the first three constraints in the original problem, multiplied by -1. Also, if the maximization in the latter problem is changed to a minimization, by multiplying the objective function by -1, we obtain the cost function in the original problem.)

The first primal problem considered in Example 4.1 had all of the ingredients of a general linear programming problem. This suggests that the conclusion reached at the end of the example should hold in general. Indeed, we have the following result. Its proof needs nothing more than the steps followed in Example 4.1, with abstract symbols replacing specific numbers, and will therefore be omitted.

Theorem 4.1 *If we transform the dual into an equivalent minimization problem and then form its dual, we obtain a problem equivalent to the original problem.*

A compact statement that is often used to describe Theorem 4.1 is that "the dual of the dual is the primal."

Any linear programming problem can be manipulated into one of several equivalent forms, for example, by introducing slack variables or by using the difference of two nonnegative variables to replace a single free variable. Each equivalent form leads to a somewhat different form for the dual problem. Nevertheless, the examples that follow indicate that the duals of equivalent problems are equivalent.

Example 4.2 Consider the primal problem shown on the left and its dual shown on the right:

$$\begin{array}{ll}
\text{minimize} & \mathbf{c}'\mathbf{x} \\
\text{subject to} & \mathbf{A}\mathbf{x} \geq \mathbf{b} \\
& \mathbf{x} \text{ free,}
\end{array}
\qquad
\begin{array}{ll}
\text{maximize} & \mathbf{p}'\mathbf{b} \\
\text{subject to} & \mathbf{p} \geq \mathbf{0} \\
& \mathbf{p}'\mathbf{A} = \mathbf{c}'.
\end{array}$$

We transform the primal problem by introducing surplus variables and then obtain its dual:

$$\begin{array}{ll}
\text{minimize} & \mathbf{c}'\mathbf{x} + \mathbf{0}'\mathbf{s} \\
\text{subject to} & \mathbf{A}\mathbf{x} - \mathbf{s} = \mathbf{b} \\
& \mathbf{x} \text{ free} \\
& \mathbf{s} \geq \mathbf{0},
\end{array}
\qquad
\begin{array}{ll}
\text{maximize} & \mathbf{p}'\mathbf{b} \\
\text{subject to} & \mathbf{p} \text{ free} \\
& \mathbf{p}'\mathbf{A} = \mathbf{c}' \\
& -\mathbf{p} \leq \mathbf{0}.
\end{array}$$

Alternatively, if we take the original primal problem and replace $\mathbf{x}$ by sign-constrained variables, we obtain the following pair of problems:

$$\begin{array}{ll}
\text{minimize} & \mathbf{c}'\mathbf{x}^+ - \mathbf{c}'\mathbf{x}^- \\
\text{subject to} & \mathbf{A}\mathbf{x}^+ - \mathbf{A}\mathbf{x}^- \geq \mathbf{b} \\
& \mathbf{x}^+ \geq \mathbf{0} \\
& \mathbf{x}^- \geq \mathbf{0},
\end{array}
\qquad
\begin{array}{ll}
\text{maximize} & \mathbf{p}'\mathbf{b} \\
\text{subject to} & \mathbf{p} \geq \mathbf{0} \\
& \mathbf{p}'\mathbf{A} \leq \mathbf{c}' \\
& -\mathbf{p}'\mathbf{A} \leq -\mathbf{c}'.
\end{array}$$

Note that we have three equivalent forms of the primal. We observe that the constraint $\mathbf{p} \geq \mathbf{0}$ is equivalent to the constraint $-\mathbf{p} \leq \mathbf{0}$. Furthermore, the constraint $\mathbf{p}'\mathbf{A} = \mathbf{c}'$ is equivalent to the two constraints $\mathbf{p}'\mathbf{A} \leq \mathbf{c}'$ and $-\mathbf{p}'\mathbf{A} \leq -\mathbf{c}'$. Thus, the duals of the three variants of the primal problem are also equivalent.

The next example is in the same spirit and examines the effect of removing redundant equality constraints in a standard form problem.

Example 4.3 Consider a standard form problem, assumed feasible, and its dual:

$$\begin{array}{ll}
\text{minimize} & \mathbf{c}'\mathbf{x} \\
\text{subject to} & \mathbf{A}\mathbf{x} = \mathbf{b} \\
& \mathbf{x} \geq \mathbf{0},
\end{array}
\qquad
\begin{array}{ll}
\text{maximize} & \mathbf{p}'\mathbf{b} \\
\text{subject to} & \mathbf{p}'\mathbf{A} \leq \mathbf{c}'.
\end{array}$$

Let $\mathbf{a}_1', \ldots, \mathbf{a}_m'$ be the rows of $\mathbf{A}$ and suppose that $\mathbf{a}_m = \sum_{i=1}^{m-1} \gamma_i \mathbf{a}_i$ for some scalars $\gamma_1, \ldots, \gamma_{m-1}$. In particular, the last equality constraint is redundant and can be eliminated. By considering an arbitrary feasible solution $\mathbf{x}$, we obtain

$$b_m = \mathbf{a}_m'\mathbf{x} = \sum_{i=1}^{m-1} \gamma_i \mathbf{a}_i'\mathbf{x} = \sum_{i=1}^{m-1} \gamma_i b_i. \tag{4.1}$$

Note that the dual constraints are of the form $\sum_{i=1}^{m} p_i \mathbf{a}_i' \leq \mathbf{c}'$ and can be rewritten as

$$\sum_{i=1}^{m-1} (p_i + \gamma_i p_m) \mathbf{a}_i' \leq \mathbf{c}'.$$

Furthermore, using Eq. (4.1), the dual cost $\sum_{i=1}^{m} p_i b_i$ is equal to

$$\sum_{i=1}^{m-1} (p_i + \gamma_i p_m) b_i.$$

If we now let $q_i = p_i + \gamma_i p_m$, we see that the dual problem is equivalent to

$$\text{maximize} \quad \sum_{i=1}^{m-1} q_i b_i$$

$$\text{subject to} \quad \sum_{i=1}^{m-1} q_i \mathbf{a}_i' \leq \mathbf{c}'.$$

We observe that this is the exact same dual that we would have obtained if we had eliminated the last (and redundant) constraint in the primal problem, before forming the dual.

The conclusions of the preceding two examples are summarized and generalized by the following result.

Theorem 4.2 *Suppose that we have transformed a linear programming problem Π_1 to another linear programming problem Π_2, by a sequence of transformations of the following types:*

(a) *Replace a free variable with the difference of two nonnegative variables.*

(b) *Replace an inequality constraint by an equality constraint involving a nonnegative slack variable.*

(c) *If some row of the matrix $\mathbf{A}$ in a feasible standard form problem is a linear combination of the other rows, eliminate the corresponding equality constraint.*

Then, the duals of Π_1 and Π_2 are equivalent, i.e., they are either both infeasible, or they have the same optimal cost.

The proof of Theorem 4.2 involves a combination of the various steps in Examples 4.2 and 4.3, and is left to the reader.

4.3 The duality theorem

We saw in Section 4.1 that for problems in standard form, the cost $g(\mathbf{p})$ of any dual solution provides a lower bound for the optimal cost. We now show that this property is true in general.

Theorem 4.3 (Weak duality) *If $\mathbf{x}$ is a feasible solution to the primal problem and $\mathbf{p}$ is a feasible solution to the dual problem, then*

$$\mathbf{p}'\mathbf{b} \leq \mathbf{c}'\mathbf{x}.$$

Proof. For any vectors $\mathbf{x}$ and $\mathbf{p}$, we define

$$u_i = p_i(\mathbf{a}_i'\mathbf{x} - b_i),$$
$$v_j = (c_j - \mathbf{p}'\mathbf{A}_j)x_j.$$

Suppose that $\mathbf{x}$ and $\mathbf{p}$ are primal and dual feasible, respectively. The definition of the dual problem requires the sign of p_i to be the same as the sign of $\mathbf{a}_i'\mathbf{x} - b_i$, and the sign of $c_j - \mathbf{p}'\mathbf{A}_j$ to be the same as the sign of x_j. Thus, primal and dual feasibility imply that

$$u_i \geq 0, \qquad \forall\ i,$$

and

$$v_j \geq 0, \qquad \forall\ j.$$

Notice that

$$\sum_i u_i = \mathbf{p}'\mathbf{A}\mathbf{x} - \mathbf{p}'\mathbf{b},$$

and

$$\sum_j v_j = \mathbf{c}'\mathbf{x} - \mathbf{p}'\mathbf{A}\mathbf{x}.$$

We add these two equalities and use the nonnegativity of u_i, v_j, to obtain

$$0 \leq \sum_i u_i + \sum_j v_j = \mathbf{c}'\mathbf{x} - \mathbf{p}'\mathbf{b}. \qquad \square$$

The weak duality theorem is not a deep result, yet it does provide some useful information about the relation between the primal and the dual. We have, for example, the following corollary.

Corollary 4.1

(a) *If the optimal cost in the primal is $-\infty$, then the dual problem must be infeasible.*

(b) *If the optimal cost in the dual is $+\infty$, then the primal problem must be infeasible.*

Proof. Suppose that the optimal cost in the primal problem is $-\infty$ and that the dual problem has a feasible solution $\mathbf{p}$. By weak duality, $\mathbf{p}$ satisfies $\mathbf{p}'\mathbf{b} \leq \mathbf{c}'\mathbf{x}$ for every primal feasible $\mathbf{x}$. Taking the minimum over all primal feasible $\mathbf{x}$, we conclude that $\mathbf{p}'\mathbf{b} \leq -\infty$. This is impossible and shows that the dual cannot have a feasible solution, thus establishing part (a). Part (b) follows by a symmetrical argument. $\qquad \square$

Another important corollary of the weak duality theorem is the following.

> **Corollary 4.2** *Let* **x** *and* **p** *be feasible solutions to the primal and the dual, respectively, and suppose that* $\mathbf{p'b} = \mathbf{c'x}$. *Then,* **x** *and* **p** *are optimal solutions to the primal and the dual, respectively.*

Proof. Let **x** and **p** be as in the statement of the corollary. For every primal feasible solution **y**, the weak duality theorem yields $\mathbf{c'x} = \mathbf{p'b} \leq \mathbf{c'y}$, which proves that **x** is optimal. The proof of optimality of **p** is similar. □

The next theorem is the central result on linear programming duality.

> **Theorem 4.4 (Strong duality)** *If a linear programming problem has an optimal solution, so does its dual, and the respective optimal costs are equal.*

Proof. Consider the standard form problem

$$\begin{aligned}
\text{minimize} \quad & \mathbf{c'x} \\
\text{subject to} \quad & \mathbf{Ax} = \mathbf{b} \\
& \mathbf{x} \geq \mathbf{0}.
\end{aligned}$$

Let us assume temporarily that the rows of **A** are linearly independent and that there exists an optimal solution. Let us apply the simplex method to this problem. As long as cycling is avoided, e.g., by using the lexicographic pivoting rule, the simplex method terminates with an optimal solution **x** and an optimal basis **B**. Let $\mathbf{x}_B = \mathbf{B}^{-1}\mathbf{b}$ be the corresponding vector of basic variables. When the simplex method terminates, the reduced costs must be nonnegative and we obtain

$$\mathbf{c'} - \mathbf{c}_B' \mathbf{B}^{-1} \mathbf{A} \geq \mathbf{0'},$$

where $\mathbf{c}_B'$ is the vector with the costs of the basic variables. Let us define a vector **p** by letting $\mathbf{p'} = \mathbf{c}_B' \mathbf{B}^{-1}$. We then have $\mathbf{p'A} \leq \mathbf{c'}$, which shows that **p** is a feasible solution to the dual problem

$$\begin{aligned}
\text{maximize} \quad & \mathbf{p'b} \\
\text{subject to} \quad & \mathbf{p'A} \leq \mathbf{c'}.
\end{aligned}$$

In addition,

$$\mathbf{p'b} = \mathbf{c}_B' \mathbf{B}^{-1} \mathbf{b} = \mathbf{c}_B' \mathbf{x}_B = \mathbf{c'x}.$$

It follows that **p** is an optimal solution to the dual (cf. Corollary 4.2), and the optimal dual cost is equal to the optimal primal cost.

If we are dealing with a general linear programming problem Π_1 that has an optimal solution, we first transform it into an equivalent standard form problem Π_2, with the same optimal cost, and in which the rows of the matrix $\mathbf{A}$ are linearly independent. Let D_1 and D_2 be the duals of Π_1 and Π_2, respectively. By Theorem 4.2, the dual problems D_1 and D_2 have the same optimal cost. We have already proved that Π_2 and D_2 have the same optimal cost. It follows that Π_1 and D_1 have the same optimal cost (see Figure 4.1).   □

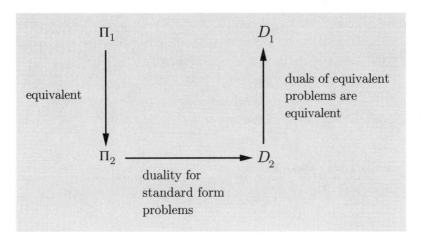

Figure 4.1: Proof of the duality theorem for general linear programming problems.

The preceding proof shows that an optimal solution to the dual problem is obtained as a byproduct of the simplex method as applied to a primal problem in standard form. It is based on the fact that the simplex method is guaranteed to terminate and this, in turn, depends on the existence of pivoting rules that prevent cycling. There is an alternative derivation of the duality theorem, which provides a geometric, algorithm-independent view of the subject, and which is developed in Section 4.7. At this point, we provide an illustration that conveys most of the content of the geometric proof.

Example 4.4 Consider a solid ball constrained to lie in a polyhedron defined by inequality constraints of the form $\mathbf{a}_i'\mathbf{x} \geq b_i$. If left under the influence of gravity, this ball reaches equilibrium at the lowest corner $\mathbf{x}^*$ of the polyhedron; see Figure 4.2. This corner is an optimal solution to the problem

$$\begin{aligned} \text{minimize} \quad & \mathbf{c}'\mathbf{x} \\ \text{subject to} \quad & \mathbf{a}_i'\mathbf{x} \geq b_i, \qquad \forall\ i, \end{aligned}$$

where $\mathbf{c}$ is a vertical vector pointing upwards. At equilibrium, gravity is counterbalanced by the forces exerted on the ball by the "walls" of the polyhedron. The latter forces are normal to the walls, that is, they are aligned with the vectors $\mathbf{a}_i$. We conclude that $\mathbf{c} = \sum_i p_i \mathbf{a}_i$, for some nonnegative coefficients p_i; in particular, the vector $\mathbf{p}$ is a feasible solution to the dual problem

$$\begin{array}{ll} \text{maximize} & \mathbf{p}'\mathbf{b} \\ \text{subject to} & \mathbf{p}'\mathbf{A} = \mathbf{c}' \\ & \mathbf{p} \geq \mathbf{0}. \end{array}$$

Given that forces can only be exerted by the walls that touch the ball, we must have $p_i = 0$, whenever $\mathbf{a}_i'\mathbf{x}^* > b_i$. Consequently, $p_i(b_i - \mathbf{a}_i'\mathbf{x}^*) = 0$ for all i. We therefore have $\mathbf{p}'\mathbf{b} = \sum_i p_i b_i = \sum_i p_i \mathbf{a}_i'\mathbf{x}^* = \mathbf{c}'\mathbf{x}^*$. It follows (Corollary 4.2) that $\mathbf{p}$ is an optimal solution to the dual, and the optimal dual cost is equal to the optimal primal cost.

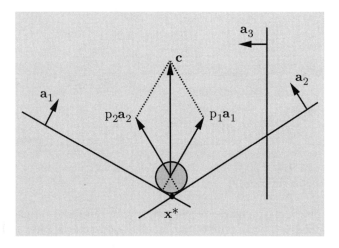

Figure 4.2: A mechanical analogy of the duality theorem.

Recall that in a linear programming problem, exactly one of the following three possibilities will occur:

(a) There is an optimal solution.

(b) The problem is "unbounded"; that is, the optimal cost is $-\infty$ (for minimization problems), or $+\infty$ (for maximization problems).

(c) The problem is infeasible.

This leads to nine possible combinations for the primal and the dual, which are shown in Table 4.2. By the strong duality theorem, if one problem has an optimal solution, so does the other. Furthermore, as discussed earlier, the weak duality theorem implies that if one problem is unbounded, the other must be infeasible. This allows us to mark some of the entries in Table 4.2 as "impossible."

	Finite optimum	Unbounded	Infeasible
Finite optimum	Possible	Impossible	Impossible
Unbounded	Impossible	Impossible	Possible
Infeasible	Impossible	Possible	Possible

Table 4.2: The different possibilities for the primal and the dual.

The case where both problems are infeasible can indeed occur, as shown by the following example.

Example 4.5 Consider the infeasible primal

$$\begin{array}{ll} \text{minimize} & x_1 + 2x_2 \\ \text{subject to} & x_1 + x_2 = 1 \\ & 2x_1 + 2x_2 = 3. \end{array}$$

Its dual is

$$\begin{array}{ll} \text{maximize} & p_1 + 3p_2 \\ \text{subject to} & p_1 + 2p_2 = 1 \\ & p_1 + 2p_2 = 2, \end{array}$$

which is also infeasible.

There is another interesting relation between the primal and the dual which is known as Clark's theorem (Clark, 1961). It asserts that unless both problems are infeasible, at least one of them must have an unbounded feasible set (Exercise 4.21).

Complementary slackness

An important relation between primal and dual optimal solutions is provided by the *complementary slackness* conditions, which we present next.

> **Theorem 4.5 (Complementary slackness)** *Let* $\mathbf{x}$ *and* $\mathbf{p}$ *be feasible solutions to the primal and the dual problem, respectively. The vectors* $\mathbf{x}$ *and* $\mathbf{p}$ *are optimal solutions for the two respective problems if and only if:*
> $$\begin{array}{ll} p_i(\mathbf{a}_i'\mathbf{x} - b_i) = 0, & \forall\, i, \\ (c_j - \mathbf{p}'\mathbf{A}_j)x_j = 0, & \forall\, j. \end{array}$$

Proof. In the proof of Theorem 4.3, we defined $u_i = p_i(\mathbf{a}_i'\mathbf{x} - b_i)$ and $v_j = (c_j - \mathbf{p}'\mathbf{A}_j)x_j$, and noted that for $\mathbf{x}$ primal feasible and $\mathbf{p}$ dual feasible, we have $u_i \geq 0$ and $v_j \geq 0$ for all i and j. In addition, we showed that

$$\mathbf{c}'\mathbf{x} - \mathbf{p}'\mathbf{b} = \sum_i u_i + \sum_j v_j.$$

By the strong duality theorem, if $\mathbf{x}$ and $\mathbf{p}$ are optimal, then $\mathbf{c}'\mathbf{x} = \mathbf{p}'\mathbf{b}$, which implies that $u_i = v_j = 0$ for all i, j. Conversely, if $u_i = v_j = 0$ for all i, j, then $\mathbf{c}'\mathbf{x} = \mathbf{p}'\mathbf{b}$, and Corollary 4.2 implies that $\mathbf{x}$ and $\mathbf{p}$ are optimal. $\square$

   The first complementary slackness condition is automatically satisfied by every feasible solution to a problem in standard form. If the primal problem is not in standard form and has a constraint like $\mathbf{a}_i'\mathbf{x} \geq b_i$, the corresponding complementary slackness condition asserts that the dual variable p_i is zero unless the constraint is active. An intuitive explanation is that a constraint which is not active at an optimal solution can be removed from the problem without affecting the optimal cost, and there is no point in associating a nonzero price with such a constraint. Note also the analogy with Example 4.4, where "forces" were only exerted by the active constraints.

   If the primal problem is in standard form and a nondegenerate optimal basic feasible solution is known, the complementary slackness conditions determine a unique solution to the dual problem. We illustrate this fact in the next example.

Example 4.6 Consider a problem in standard form and its dual:

$$\begin{array}{llll}
\text{minimize} & 13x_1 + 10x_2 + 6x_3 & \text{maximize} & 8p_1 + 3p_2 \\
\text{subject to} & 5x_1 + x_2 + 3x_3 = 8 & \text{subject to} & 5p_1 + 3p_2 \leq 13 \\
& 3x_1 + x_2 = 3 & & p_1 + p_2 \leq 10 \\
& x_1, x_2, x_3 \geq 0, & & 3p_1 \leq 6.
\end{array}$$

As will be verified shortly, the vector $\mathbf{x}^* = (1, 0, 1)$ is a nondegenerate optimal solution to the primal problem. Assuming this to be the case, we use the complementary slackness conditions to construct the optimal solution to the dual. The condition $p_i(\mathbf{a}_i'\mathbf{x}^* - b_i) = 0$ is automatically satisfied for each i, since the primal is in standard form. The condition $(c_j - \mathbf{p}'\mathbf{A}_j)x_j^* = 0$ is clearly satisfied for $j = 2$, because $x_2^* = 0$. However, since $x_1^* > 0$ and $x_3^* > 0$, we obtain

$$5p_1 + 3p_2 = 13,$$

and

$$3p_1 = 6,$$

which we can solve to obtain $p_1 = 2$ and $p_2 = 1$. Note that this is a dual feasible solution whose cost is equal to 19, which is the same as the cost of $\mathbf{x}^*$. This verifies that $\mathbf{x}^*$ is indeed an optimal solution as claimed earlier.

   We now generalize the above example. Suppose that x_j is a basic variable in a nondegenerate optimal basic feasible solution to a primal problem in standard form. Then, the complementary slackness condition $(c_j - \mathbf{p}' \mathbf{A}_j) x_j = 0$ yields $\mathbf{p}' \mathbf{A}_j = c_j$ for every such j. Since the basic columns $\mathbf{A}_j$ are linearly independent, we obtain a system of equations for $\mathbf{p}$ which has a unique solution, namely, $\mathbf{p}' = \mathbf{c}'_B \mathbf{B}^{-1}$. A similar conclusion can also be drawn for problems not in standard form (Exercise 4.12). On the other hand, if we are given a degenerate optimal basic feasible solution to the primal, complementary slackness may be of very little help in determining an optimal solution to the dual problem (Exercise 4.17).

We finally mention that if the primal constraints are of the form $\mathbf{Ax} \geq \mathbf{b}$, $\mathbf{x} \geq \mathbf{0}$, and the primal problem has an optimal solution, then there exist optimal solutions to the primal and the dual which satisfy *strict complementary slackness*; that is, a variable in one problem is nonzero if and only if the corresponding constraint in the other problem is active (Exercise 4.20). This result has some interesting applications in discrete optimization, but these lie outside the scope of this book.

A geometric view

We now develop a geometric view that allows us to visualize pairs of primal and dual vectors without having to draw the dual feasible set.

We consider the primal problem

$$\text{minimize} \quad \mathbf{c}'\mathbf{x}$$
$$\text{subject to} \quad \mathbf{a}'_i \mathbf{x} \geq b_i, \qquad i = 1, \ldots, m,$$

where the dimension of $\mathbf{x}$ is equal to n. We assume that the vectors $\mathbf{a}_i$ span $\Re^n$. The corresponding dual problem is

$$\text{maximize} \quad \mathbf{p}'\mathbf{b}$$
$$\text{subject to} \quad \sum_{i=1}^m p_i \mathbf{a}_i = \mathbf{c}$$
$$\mathbf{p} \geq \mathbf{0}.$$

Let I be a subset of $\{1, \ldots, m\}$ of cardinality n, such that the vectors $\mathbf{a}_i$, $i \in I$, are linearly independent. The system $\mathbf{a}'_i \mathbf{x} = b_i$, $i \in I$, has a unique solution, denoted by $\mathbf{x}^I$, which is a basic solution to the primal problem (cf. Definition 2.9 in Section 2.2). We assume, that $\mathbf{x}^I$ is nondegenerate, that is, $\mathbf{a}'_i \mathbf{x} \neq b_i$ for $i \notin I$.

Let $\mathbf{p} \in \Re^m$ be a dual vector (not necessarily dual feasible), and let us consider what is required for $\mathbf{x}^I$ and $\mathbf{p}$ to be optimal solutions to the primal and the dual problem, respectively. We need:

    (a) $\mathbf{a}'_i \mathbf{x}^I \geq b_i$, for all i,   (primal feasibility),

    (b) $p_i = 0$, for all $i \notin I$,   (complementary slackness),

    (c) $\sum_{i=1}^m p_i \mathbf{a}_i = \mathbf{c}$,   (dual feasibility),

    (d) $\mathbf{p} \geq \mathbf{0}$,   (dual feasibility).

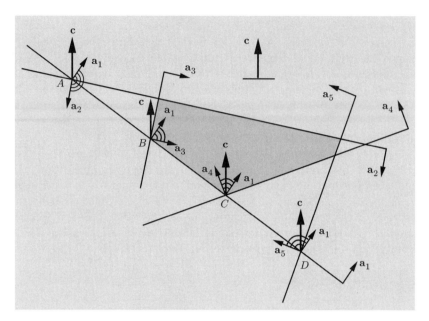

Figure 4.3: Consider a primal problem with two variables and five inequality constraints ($n = 2$, $m = 5$), and suppose that no two of the vectors $\mathbf{a}_i$ are collinear. Every two-element subset I of $\{1, 2, 3, 4, 5\}$ determines basic solutions $\mathbf{x}^I$ and $\mathbf{p}^I$ of the primal and the dual, respectively.

If $I = \{1, 2\}$, $\mathbf{x}^I$ is primal infeasible (point A) and $\mathbf{p}^I$ is dual infeasible, because $\mathbf{c}$ cannot be expressed as a nonnegative linear combination of the vectors $\mathbf{a}_1$ and $\mathbf{a}_2$.

If $I = \{1, 3\}$, $\mathbf{x}^I$ is primal feasible (point B) and $\mathbf{p}^I$ is dual infeasible.

If $I = \{1, 4\}$, $\mathbf{x}^I$ is primal feasible (point C) and $\mathbf{p}^I$ is dual feasible, because $\mathbf{c}$ can be expressed as a nonnegative linear combination of the vectors $\mathbf{a}_1$ and $\mathbf{a}_4$. In particular, $\mathbf{x}^I$ and $\mathbf{p}^I$ are optimal.

If $I = \{1, 5\}$, $\mathbf{x}^I$ is primal infeasible (point D) and $\mathbf{p}^I$ is dual feasible.

Given the complementary slackness condition (b), condition (c) becomes

$$\sum_{i \in I} p_i \mathbf{a}_i = \mathbf{c}.$$

Since the vectors $\mathbf{a}_i$, $i \in I$, are linearly independent, the latter equation has a unique solution that we denote by $\mathbf{p}^I$. In fact, it is readily seen that the vectors $\mathbf{a}_i$, $i \in I$, form a basis for the dual problem (which is in standard form) and $\mathbf{p}^I$ is the associated basic solution. For the vector $\mathbf{p}^I$ to be dual feasible, we also need it to be nonnegative. We conclude that once the complementary slackness condition (b) is enforced, feasibility of

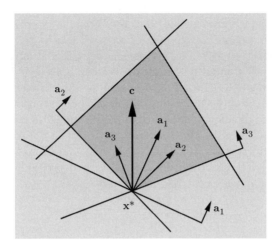

Figure 4.4: The vector $\mathbf{x}^*$ is a degenerate basic feasible solution of the primal. If we choose $I = \{1,2\}$, the corresponding dual basic solution $\mathbf{p}^I$ is infeasible, because $\mathbf{c}$ is not a nonnegative linear combination of $\mathbf{a}_1$, $\mathbf{a}_2$. On the other hand, if we choose $I = \{1,3\}$ or $I = \{2,3\}$, the resulting dual basic solution $\mathbf{p}^I$ is feasible and, therefore, optimal.

the resulting dual vector $\mathbf{p}^I$ is equivalent to $\mathbf{c}$ being a nonnegative linear combination of the vectors $\mathbf{a}_i$, $i \in I$, associated with the active primal constraints. This allows us to visualize dual feasibility without having to draw the dual feasible set; see Figure 4.3.

If $\mathbf{x}^*$ is a degenerate basic solution to the primal, there can be several subsets I such that $\mathbf{x}^I = \mathbf{x}^*$. Using different choices for I, and by solving the system $\sum_{i \in I} p_i \mathbf{a}_i = \mathbf{c}$, we may obtain several dual basic solutions $\mathbf{p}^I$. It may then well be the case that some of them are dual feasible and some are not; see Figure 4.4. Still, if $\mathbf{p}^I$ is dual feasible (i.e., all p_i are nonnegative) and if $\mathbf{x}^*$ is primal feasible, then they are both optimal, because we have been enforcing complementary slackness and Theorem 4.5 applies.

4.4   Optimal dual variables as marginal costs

In this section, we elaborate on the interpretation of the dual variables as prices. This theme will be revisited, in more depth, in Chapter 5.

Consider the standard form problem

$$\begin{aligned}
\text{minimize} \quad & \mathbf{c}'\mathbf{x} \\
\text{subject to} \quad & \mathbf{A}\mathbf{x} = \mathbf{b} \\
& \mathbf{x} \geq \mathbf{0}.
\end{aligned}$$

We assume that the rows of $\mathbf{A}$ are linearly independent and that there is a nondegenerate basic feasible solution $\mathbf{x}^*$ which is optimal. Let $\mathbf{B}$ be the corresponding basis matrix and let $\mathbf{x}_B = \mathbf{B}^{-1}\mathbf{b}$ be the vector of basic variables, which is positive, by nondegeneracy. Let us now replace $\mathbf{b}$ by $\mathbf{b} + \mathbf{d}$, where $\mathbf{d}$ is a small perturbation vector. Since $\mathbf{B}^{-1}\mathbf{b} > \mathbf{0}$, we also have $\mathbf{B}^{-1}(\mathbf{b} + \mathbf{d}) > \mathbf{0}$, as long as $\mathbf{d}$ is small. This implies that the same basis leads to a basic feasible solution of the perturbed problem as well. Perturbing the right-hand side vector $\mathbf{b}$ has no effect on the reduced costs associated with this basis. By the optimality of $\mathbf{x}^*$ in the original problem, the vector of reduced costs $\mathbf{c}' - \mathbf{c}_B'\mathbf{B}^{-1}\mathbf{A}$ is nonnegative and this establishes that the same basis is optimal for the perturbed problem as well. Thus, the optimal cost in the perturbed problem is

$$\mathbf{c}_B'\mathbf{B}^{-1}(\mathbf{b} + \mathbf{d}) = \mathbf{p}'(\mathbf{b} + \mathbf{d}),$$

where $\mathbf{p}' = \mathbf{c}_B'\mathbf{B}^{-1}$ is an optimal solution to the dual problem. Therefore, a small change of $\mathbf{d}$ in the right-hand side vector $\mathbf{b}$ results in a change of $\mathbf{p}'\mathbf{d}$ in the optimal cost. We conclude that each component p_i of the optimal dual vector can be interpreted as the *marginal cost* (or *shadow price*) per unit increase of the ith requirement b_i.

   We conclude with yet another interpretation of duality, for standard form problems. In order to develop some concrete intuition, we phrase our discussion in terms of the diet problem (Example 1.3 in Section 1.1). We interpret each vector $\mathbf{A}_j$ as the nutritional content of the jth available food, and view $\mathbf{b}$ as the nutritional content of an ideal food that we wish to synthesize. Let us interpret p_i as the "fair" price per unit of the ith nutrient. A unit of the jth food has a value of c_j at the food market, but it also has a value of $\mathbf{p}'\mathbf{A}_j$ if priced at the nutrient market. Complementary slackness asserts that every food which is used (at a nonzero level) to synthesize the ideal food, should be consistently priced at the two markets. Thus, duality is concerned with two alternative ways of cost accounting. The value of the ideal food, as computed in the food market, is $\mathbf{c}'\mathbf{x}^*$, where $\mathbf{x}^*$ is an optimal solution to the primal problem; the value of the ideal food, as computed in the nutrient market, is $\mathbf{p}'\mathbf{b}$. The duality relation $\mathbf{c}'\mathbf{x}^* = \mathbf{p}'\mathbf{b}$ states that when prices are chosen appropriately, the two accounting methods should give the same results.

4.5 Standard form problems and the dual simplex method

In this section, we concentrate on the case where the primal problem is in standard form. We develop the *dual simplex method*, which is an alternative to the simplex method of Chapter 3. We also comment on the relation between the basic feasible solutions to the primal and the dual, including a discussion of dual degeneracy.

In the proof of the strong duality theorem, we considered the simplex method applied to a primal problem in standard form and defined a dual vector $\mathbf{p}$ by letting $\mathbf{p}' = \mathbf{c}_B' \mathbf{B}^{-1}$. We then noted that the primal optimality condition $\mathbf{c}' - \mathbf{c}_B' \mathbf{B}^{-1} \mathbf{A} \geq \mathbf{0}'$ is the same as the dual feasibility condition $\mathbf{p}' \mathbf{A} \leq \mathbf{c}'$. We can thus think of the simplex method as an algorithm that maintains primal feasibility and works towards dual feasibility. A method with this property is generally called a *primal* algorithm. An alternative is to start with a dual feasible solution and work towards primal feasibility. A method of this type is called a *dual* algorithm. In this section, we present a dual simplex method, implemented in terms of the full tableau. We argue that it does indeed solve the dual problem, and we show that it moves from one basic feasible solution of the dual problem to another. An alternative implementation that only keeps track of the matrix $\mathbf{B}^{-1}$, instead of the entire tableau, is called a *revised dual simplex* method (Exercise 4.23).

The dual simplex method

Let us consider a problem in standard form, under the usual assumption that the rows of the matrix $\mathbf{A}$ are linearly independent. Let $\mathbf{B}$ be a basis matrix, consisting of m linearly independent columns of $\mathbf{A}$, and consider the corresponding tableau

$-\mathbf{c}_B' \mathbf{B}^{-1} \mathbf{b}$	$\bar{\mathbf{c}}'$
$\mathbf{B}^{-1} \mathbf{b}$	$\mathbf{B}^{-1} \mathbf{A}$

or, in more detail,

$-\mathbf{c}_B' \mathbf{x}_B$	$\bar{c}_1$	$\cdots$	$\bar{c}_n$
$x_{B(1)}$			
$\vdots$	$\mathbf{B}^{-1} \mathbf{A}_1$	$\cdots$	$\mathbf{B}^{-1} \mathbf{A}_n$
$x_{B(m)}$			

We do not require $\mathbf{B}^{-1} \mathbf{b}$ to be nonnegative, which means that we have a basic, but not necessarily feasible solution to the primal problem. However, we assume that $\bar{\mathbf{c}} \geq \mathbf{0}$; equivalently, the vector $\mathbf{p}' = \mathbf{c}_B' \mathbf{B}^{-1}$ satisfies $\mathbf{p}' \mathbf{A} \leq \mathbf{c}'$, and we have a feasible solution to the dual problem. The cost of this dual feasible solution is $\mathbf{p}' \mathbf{b} = \mathbf{c}_B' \mathbf{B}^{-1} \mathbf{b} = \mathbf{c}_B' \mathbf{x}_B$, which is the negative of the entry at the upper left corner of the tableau. If the inequality $\mathbf{B}^{-1} \mathbf{b} \geq \mathbf{0}$ happens to hold, we also have a primal feasible solution with the same cost, and optimal solutions to both problems have been found. If the inequality $\mathbf{B}^{-1} \mathbf{b} \geq \mathbf{0}$ fails to hold, we perform a change of basis in a manner we describe next.

We find some ℓ such that $x_{B(\ell)} < 0$ and consider the ℓth row of the tableau, called the *pivot row*; this row is of the form $(x_{B(\ell)}, v_1, \ldots, v_n)$, where v_i is the ℓth component of $\mathbf{B}^{-1}\mathbf{A}_i$. For each i with $v_i < 0$ (if such i exist), we form the ratio $\bar{c}_i/|v_i|$ and let j be an index for which this ratio is smallest; that is, $v_j < 0$ and

$$\frac{\bar{c}_j}{|v_j|} = \min_{\{i|v_i<0\}} \frac{\bar{c}_i}{|v_i|}. \tag{4.2}$$

(We call the corresponding entry v_j the *pivot element*. Note that x_j must be a nonbasic variable, since the jth column in the tableau contains the negative element v_j.) We then perform a change of basis: column $\mathbf{A}_j$ enters the basis and column $\mathbf{A}_{B(\ell)}$ exits. This change of basis (or *pivot*) is effected exactly as in the primal simplex method: we add to each row of the tableau a multiple of the pivot row so that all entries in the pivot column are set to zero, with the exception of the pivot element which is set to 1. In particular, in order to set the reduced cost in the pivot column to zero, we multiply the pivot row by $\bar{c}_j/|v_j|$ and add it to the zeroth row. For every i, the new value of $\bar{c}_i$ is equal to

$$\bar{c}_i + v_i \frac{\bar{c}_j}{|v_j|},$$

which is nonnegative because of the way that j was selected [cf. Eq. (4.2)]. We conclude that the reduced costs in the new tableau will also be nonnegative and dual feasibility has been maintained.

Example 4.7 Consider the tableau

		x_1	x_2	x_3	x_4	x_5
	0	2	6	10	0	0
$x_4 =$	2	-2	4	1	1	0
$x_5 =$	-1	4	-2^*	-3	0	1

Since $x_{B(2)} < 0$, we choose the second row to be the pivot row. Negative entries of the pivot row are found in the second and third column. We compare the corresponding ratios $6/|-2|$ and $10/|-3|$. The smallest ratio is $6/|-2|$ and, therefore, the second column enters the basis. (The pivot element is indicated by an asterisk.) We multiply the pivot row by 3 and add it to the zeroth row. We multiply the pivot row by 2 and add it to the first row. We then divide the pivot row by -2. The new tableau is

		x_1	x_2	x_3	x_4	x_5
	-3	14	0	1	0	3
$x_4 =$	0	6	0	-5	1	2
$x_2 =$	$1/2$	-2	1	$3/2$	0	$-1/2$

The cost has increased to 3. Furthermore, we now have $\mathbf{B}^{-1}\mathbf{b} \geq \mathbf{0}$, and an optimal solution has been found.

Note that the pivot element v_j is always chosen to be negative, whereas the corresponding reduced cost $\bar{c}_j$ is nonnegative. Let us temporarily assume that $\bar{c}_j$ is in fact positive. Then, in order to replace $\bar{c}_j$ by zero, we need to add a positive multiple of the pivot row to the zeroth row. Since $x_{B(\ell)}$ is negative, this has the effect of adding a negative quantity to the upper left corner. Equivalently, the dual cost increases. Thus, as long as the reduced cost of every nonbasic variable is nonzero, the dual cost increases with each basis change, and no basis will ever be repeated in the course of the algorithm. It follows that the algorithm must eventually terminate and this can happen in one of two ways:

(a) We have $\mathbf{B}^{-1}\mathbf{b} \geq \mathbf{0}$ and an optimal solution.

(b) All of the entries $v_1, \ldots, v_n$ in the pivot row are nonnegative and we are therefore unable to locate a pivot element. In full analogy with the primal simplex method, this implies that the optimal dual cost is equal to $+\infty$ and the primal problem is infeasible; the proof is left as an exercise (Exercise 4.22).

We now provide a summary of the algorithm.

An iteration of the dual simplex method

1. A typical iteration starts with the tableau associated with a basis matrix $\mathbf{B}$ and with all reduced costs nonnegative.

2. Examine the components of the vector $\mathbf{B}^{-1}\mathbf{b}$ in the zeroth column of the tableau. If they are all nonnegative, we have an optimal basic feasible solution and the algorithm terminates; else, choose some ℓ such that $x_{B(\ell)} < 0$.

3. Consider the ℓth row of the tableau, with elements $x_{B(\ell)}, v_1, \ldots, v_n$ (the pivot row). If $v_i \geq 0$ for all i, then the optimal dual cost is $+\infty$ and the algorithm terminates.

4. For each i such that $v_i < 0$, compute the ratio $\bar{c}_i / |v_i|$ and let j be the index of a column that corresponds to the smallest ratio. The column $\mathbf{A}_{B(\ell)}$ exits the basis and the column $\mathbf{A}_j$ takes its place.

5. Add to each row of the tableau a multiple of the ℓth row (the pivot row) so that v_j (the pivot element) becomes 1 and all other entries of the pivot column become 0.

Let us now consider the possibility that the reduced cost $\bar{c}_j$ in the pivot column is zero. In this case, the zeroth row of the tableau does not change and the dual cost $\mathbf{c}_B'\mathbf{B}^{-1}\mathbf{b}$ remains the same. The proof of termination given earlier does not apply and the algorithm can cycle. This can be avoided by employing a suitable anticycling rule, such as the following.

Lexicographic pivoting rule for the dual simplex method

   1. Choose any row ℓ such that $x_{B(\ell)} < 0$, to be the pivot row.

   2. Determine the index j of the entering column as follows. For each column with $v_i < 0$, divide all entries by $|v_i|$, and then choose the lexicographically smallest column. If there is a tie between several lexicographically smallest columns, choose the one with the smallest index.

If the dual simplex method is initialized so that every column of the tableau [that is, each vector $(\bar{c}_j, \mathbf{B}^{-1}\mathbf{A}_j)$] is lexicographically positive, and if the above lexicographic pivoting rule is used, the method terminates in a finite number of steps. The proof is similar to the proof of the corresponding result for the primal simplex method (Theorem 3.4) and is left as an exercise (Exercise 4.24).

When should we use the dual simplex method

At this point, it is natural to ask when the dual simplex method should be used. One such case arises when a basic feasible solution of the dual problem is readily available. Suppose, for example, that we already have an optimal basis for some linear programming problem, and that we wish to solve the same problem for a different choice of the right-hand side vector **b**. The optimal basis for the original problem may be primal infeasible under the new value of **b**. On the other hand, a change in **b** does not affect the reduced costs and we still have a dual feasible solution. Thus, instead of solving the new problem from scratch, it may be preferable to apply the dual simplex algorithm starting from the optimal basis for the original problem. This idea will be considered in more detail in Chapter 5.

The geometry of the dual simplex method

Our development of the dual simplex method was based entirely on tableau manipulations and algebraic arguments. We now present an alternative viewpoint based on geometric considerations.

We continue assuming that we are dealing with a problem in standard form and that the matrix **A** has linearly independent rows. Let **B** be a basis matrix with columns $\mathbf{A}_{B(1)}, \ldots, \mathbf{A}_{B(m)}$. This basis matrix determines a basic solution to the primal problem with $\mathbf{x}_B = \mathbf{B}^{-1}\mathbf{b}$. The same basis can also be used to determine a dual vector **p** by means of the equations

$$\mathbf{p}'\mathbf{A}_{B(i)} = c_{B(i)}, \qquad i = 1, \ldots, m.$$

These are m equations in m unknowns; since the columns $\mathbf{A}_{B(1)}, \ldots, \mathbf{A}_{B(m)}$ are linearly independent, there is a unique solution $\mathbf{p}$. For such a vector $\mathbf{p}$, the number of linearly independent active dual constraints is equal to the dimension of the dual vector, and it follows that we have a basic solution to the dual problem. In matrix notation, the dual basic solution $\mathbf{p}$ satisfies $\mathbf{p}'\mathbf{B} = \mathbf{c}'_B$, or $\mathbf{p}' = \mathbf{c}'_B\mathbf{B}^{-1}$, which was referred to as the vector of simplex multipliers in Chapter 3. If $\mathbf{p}$ is also dual feasible, that is, if $\mathbf{p}'\mathbf{A} \le \mathbf{c}'$, then $\mathbf{p}$ is a basic feasible solution of the dual problem.

To summarize, a basis matrix $\mathbf{B}$ is associated with a basic solution to the primal problem and also with a basic solution to the dual. A basic solution to the primal (respectively, dual) which is primal (respectively, dual) feasible, is a basic feasible solution to the primal (respectively, dual).

We now have a geometric interpretation of the dual simplex method: at every iteration, we have a basic feasible solution to the dual problem. The basic feasible solutions obtained at any two consecutive iterations have $m-1$ linearly independent active constraints in common (the reduced costs of the $m - 1$ variables that are common to both bases are zero); thus, consecutive basic feasible solutions are either adjacent or they coincide.

Example 4.8 Consider the following standard form problem and its dual:

$$
\begin{array}{ll}
\text{minimize} & x_1 + x_2 \\
\text{subject to} & x_1 + 2x_2 - x_3 = 2 \\
& x_1 - x_4 = 1 \\
& x_1, x_2, x_3, x_4 \ge 0,
\end{array}
\qquad
\begin{array}{ll}
\text{maximize} & 2p_1 + p_2 \\
\text{subject to} & p_1 + p_2 \le 1 \\
& 2p_1 \le 1 \\
& p_1, p_2 \ge 0.
\end{array}
$$

The feasible set of the primal problem is 4-dimensional. If we eliminate the variables x_3 and x_4, we obtain the equivalent problem

$$
\begin{array}{ll}
\text{minimize} & x_1 + x_2 \\
\text{subject to} & x_1 + 2x_2 \ge 2 \\
& x_1 \ge 1 \\
& x_1, x_2 \ge 0.
\end{array}
$$

The feasible sets of the equivalent primal problem and of the dual are shown in Figures 4.5(a) and 4.5(b), respectively.

There is a total of five different bases in the standard form primal problem and five different basic solutions. These correspond to the points A, B, C, D, and E in Figure 4.5(a). The same five bases also lead to five basic solutions to the dual problem, which are points A, B, C, D, and E in Figure 4.5(b).

For example, if we choose the columns $\mathbf{A}_3$ and $\mathbf{A}_4$ to be the basic columns, we have the infeasible primal basic solution $\mathbf{x} = (0, 0, -2, -1)$ (point A). The corresponding dual basic solution is obtained by letting $\mathbf{p}'\mathbf{A}_3 = c_3 = 0$ and $\mathbf{p}'\mathbf{A}_4 = c_4 = 0$, which yields $\mathbf{p} = (0, 0)$. This is a basic feasible solution of the dual problem and can be used to start the dual simplex method. The associated initial tableau is

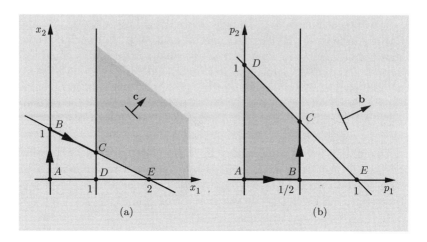

Figure 4.5: The feasible sets in Example 4.8.

	x_1	x_2	x_3	x_4
0	1	1	0	0
$x_3 =$	-2	-1	-2^*	1	0
$x_4 =$	-1	-1	0	0	1

We carry out two iterations of the dual simplex method to obtain the following two tableaux:

	x_1	x_2	x_3	x_4
-1	1/2	0	1/2	0
$x_2 =$	1	1/2	1	$-1/2$	0
$x_4 =$	-1	-1^*	0	0	1

	x_1	x_2	x_3	x_4
$-3/2$	0	0	1/2	1/2
$x_2 =$	1/2	0	1	$-1/2$	1/2
$x_1 =$	1	1	0	0	-1

This sequence of tableaux corresponds to the path $A - B - C$ in either figure. In the primal space, the path traces a sequence of infeasible basic solutions until, at optimality, it becomes feasible. In the dual space, the algorithm behaves exactly like the primal simplex method: it moves through a sequence of (dual) basic feasible solutions, while at each step improving the cost function.

Having observed that the dual simplex method moves from one basic feasible solution of the dual to an adjacent one, it may be tempting to say that the dual simplex method is simply the primal simplex method applied to the dual. This is a somewhat ambiguous statement, however, because the dual problem is not in standard form. If we were to convert it to standard form and then apply the primal simplex method, the resulting method is not necessarily identical to the dual simplex method (Exercise 4.25). A more accurate statement is to simply say that the dual simplex method is a variant of the simplex method tailored to problems defined exclusively in terms of linear inequality constraints.

Duality and degeneracy

Let us keep assuming that we are dealing with a standard form problem in which the rows of the matrix $\mathbf{A}$ are linearly independent. Any basis matrix $\mathbf{B}$ leads to an associated dual basic solution given by $\mathbf{p}' = \mathbf{c}'_B \mathbf{B}^{-1}$. At this basic solution, the dual constraint $\mathbf{p}'\mathbf{A}_j = c_j$ is active if and only if $\mathbf{c}'_B \mathbf{B}^{-1}\mathbf{A}_j = c_j$, that is, if and only if the reduced cost $\bar{c}_j$ is zero. Since $\mathbf{p}$ is m-dimensional, dual degeneracy amounts to having more than m reduced costs that are zero. Given that the reduced costs of the m basic variables must be zero, dual degeneracy is obtained whenever there exists a nonbasic variable whose reduced cost is zero.

The example that follows deals with the relation between basic solutions to the primal and the dual in the face of degeneracy.

Example 4.9 Consider the following standard from problem and its dual:

minimize	$3x_1 + x_2$		maximize	$2p_1$
subject to	$x_1 + x_2 - x_3$	$= 2$	subject to	$p_1 + 2p_2 \leq 3$
	$2x_1 - x_2 \quad - x_4$	$= 0$		$p_1 - p_2 \leq 1$
	$x_1, x_2, x_3, x_4 \geq 0,$			$p_1, p_2 \geq 0.$

We eliminate x_3 and x_4 to obtain the equivalent primal problem

$$\begin{array}{ll} \text{minimize} & 3x_1 + x_2 \\ \text{subject to} & x_1 + x_2 \geq 2 \\ & 2x_1 - x_2 \geq 0 \\ & x_1, x_2 \geq 0. \end{array}$$

The feasible set of the equivalent primal and of the dual is shown in Figures 4.6(a) and 4.6(b), respectively.

There is a total of six different bases in the standard form primal problem, but only four different basic solutions [points A, B, C, D in Figure 4.6(a)]. In the dual problem, however, the six bases lead to six distinct basic solutions [points A, A', A'', B, C, D in Figure 4.6(b)].

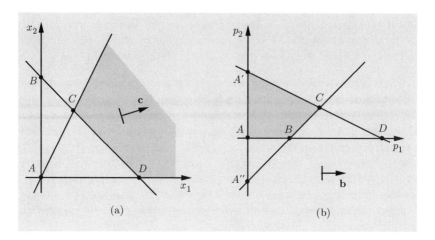

Figure 4.6: The feasible sets in Example 4.9.

For example, if we let columns $\mathbf{A}_3$ and $\mathbf{A}_4$ be basic, the primal basic solution has $x_1 = x_2 = 0$ and the corresponding dual basic solution is $(p_1, p_2) = (0, 0)$. Note that this is a basic feasible solution of the dual problem. If we let columns $\mathbf{A}_1$ and $\mathbf{A}_3$ be basic, the primal basic solution has again $x_1 = x_2 = 0$. For the dual problem, however, the equations $\mathbf{p}'\mathbf{A}_1 = c_1$ and $\mathbf{p}'\mathbf{A}_3 = c_3$ yield $(p_1, p_2) = (0, 3/2)$, which is a basic feasible solution of the dual, namely, point A' in Figure 4.6(b). Finally, if we let columns $\mathbf{A}_2$ and $\mathbf{A}_3$ be basic, we still have the same primal solution. For the dual problem, the equations $\mathbf{p}'\mathbf{A}_2 = c_1$ and $\mathbf{p}'\mathbf{A}_3 = c_3$ yield $(p_1, p_2) = (0, -1)$, which is an infeasible basic solution to the dual, namely, point A'' in Figure 4.6(b).

Example 4.9 has established that different bases may lead to the same basic solution for the primal problem, but to different basic solutions for the dual. Furthermore, out of the different basic solutions to the dual problem, it may be that some are feasible and some are infeasible.

We conclude with a summary of some properties of bases and basic solutions, for standard form problems, that were discussed in this section.

(a) Every basis determines a basic solution to the primal, but also a corresponding basic solution to the dual, namely, $\mathbf{p}' = \mathbf{c}'_B \mathbf{B}^{-1}$.

(b) This dual basic solution is feasible if and only if all of the reduced costs are nonnegative.

(c) Under this dual basic solution, the reduced costs that are equal to zero correspond to active constraints in the dual problem.

(d) This dual basic solution is degenerate if and only if some nonbasic variable has zero reduced cost.

4.6   Farkas' lemma and linear inequalities

Suppose that we wish to determine whether a given system of linear inequalities is infeasible. In this section, we approach this question using duality theory, and we show that infeasibility of a given system of linear inequalities is equivalent to the feasibility of another, related, system of linear inequalities. Intuitively, the latter system of linear inequalities can be interpreted as a search for a *certificate of infeasibility* for the former system.

To be more specific, consider a set of standard form constraints $\mathbf{Ax} = \mathbf{b}$ and $\mathbf{x} \geq \mathbf{0}$. Suppose that there exists some vector $\mathbf{p}$ such that $\mathbf{p'A} \geq \mathbf{0'}$ and $\mathbf{p'b} < 0$. Then, for any $\mathbf{x} \geq \mathbf{0}$, we have $\mathbf{p'Ax} \geq 0$ and since $\mathbf{p'b} < 0$, it follows that $\mathbf{p'Ax} \neq \mathbf{p'b}$. We conclude that $\mathbf{Ax} \neq \mathbf{b}$, for all $\mathbf{x} \geq \mathbf{0}$. This argument shows that if we can find a vector $\mathbf{p}$ satisfying $\mathbf{p'A} \geq \mathbf{0'}$ and $\mathbf{p'b} < 0$, the standard form constraints cannot have any feasible solution, and such a vector $\mathbf{p}$ is a certificate of infeasibility. Farkas' lemma below states that whenever a standard form problem is infeasible, such a certificate of infeasibility $\mathbf{p}$ is guaranteed to exist.

Theorem 4.6 (Farkas' lemma) *Let* $\mathbf{A}$ *be a matrix of dimensions* $m \times n$ *and let* $\mathbf{b}$ *be a vector in* $\Re^m$. *Then, exactly one of the following two alternatives holds:*

(a) *There exists some* $\mathbf{x} \geq \mathbf{0}$ *such that* $\mathbf{Ax} = \mathbf{b}$.

(b) *There exists some vector* $\mathbf{p}$ *such that* $\mathbf{p'A} \geq \mathbf{0'}$ *and* $\mathbf{p'b} < 0$.

Proof. One direction is easy. If there exists some $\mathbf{x} \geq \mathbf{0}$ satisfying $\mathbf{Ax} = \mathbf{b}$, and if $\mathbf{p'A} \geq \mathbf{0'}$, then $\mathbf{p'b} = \mathbf{p'Ax} \geq 0$, which shows that the second alternative cannot hold.

Let us now assume that there exists no vector $\mathbf{x} \geq \mathbf{0}$ satisfying $\mathbf{Ax} = \mathbf{b}$. Consider the pair of problems

$$
\begin{array}{ll}
\text{maximize} & \mathbf{0'x} \\
\text{subject to} & \mathbf{Ax} = \mathbf{b} \\
& \mathbf{x} \geq \mathbf{0},
\end{array}
\qquad\qquad
\begin{array}{ll}
\text{minimize} & \mathbf{p'b} \\
\text{subject to} & \mathbf{p'A} \geq \mathbf{0'},
\end{array}
$$

and note that the first is the dual of the second. The maximization problem is infeasible, which implies that the minimization problem is either unbounded (the optimal cost is $-\infty$) or infeasible. Since $\mathbf{p} = \mathbf{0}$ is a feasible solution to the minimization problem, it follows that the minimization problem is unbounded. Therefore, there exists some $\mathbf{p}$ which is feasible, that is, $\mathbf{p'A} \geq \mathbf{0'}$, and whose cost is negative, that is, $\mathbf{p'b} < 0$.   □

We now provide a geometric illustration of Farkas' lemma (see Figure 4.7). Let $\mathbf{A}_1, \ldots, \mathbf{A}_n$ be the columns of the matrix $\mathbf{A}$ and note that $\mathbf{Ax} = \sum_{i=1}^{n} \mathbf{A}_i x_i$. Therefore, the existence of a vector $\mathbf{x} \geq \mathbf{0}$ satisfying

$\mathbf{Ax} = \mathbf{b}$ is the same as requiring that $\mathbf{b}$ lies in the set of all nonnegative linear combinations of the vectors $\mathbf{A}_1, \ldots, \mathbf{A}_n$, which is the shaded region in Figure 4.7. If $\mathbf{b}$ does not belong to the shaded region (in which case the first alternative in Farkas' lemma does not hold), we expect intuitively that we can find a vector $\mathbf{p}$ and an associated hyperplane $\{\mathbf{z} \mid \mathbf{p}'\mathbf{z} = 0\}$ such that $\mathbf{b}$ lies on one side of the hyperplane while the shaded region lies on the other side. We then have $\mathbf{p}'\mathbf{b} < 0$ and $\mathbf{p}'\mathbf{A}_i \geq 0$ for all i, or, equivalently, $\mathbf{p}'\mathbf{A} \geq \mathbf{0}'$, and the second alternative holds.

Farkas' lemma predates the development of linear programming, but duality theory leads to a simple proof. A different proof, based on the geometric argument we just gave, is provided in the next section. Finally, there is an equivalent statement of Farkas' lemma which is sometimes more convenient.

Corollary 4.3 Let $\mathbf{A}_1, \ldots, \mathbf{A}_n$ and $\mathbf{b}$ be given vectors and suppose that any vector $\mathbf{p}$ that satisfies $\mathbf{p}'\mathbf{A}_i \geq 0$, $i = 1, \ldots, n$, must also satisfy $\mathbf{p}'\mathbf{b} \geq 0$. Then, $\mathbf{b}$ can be expressed as a nonnegative linear combination of the vectors $\mathbf{A}_1, \ldots, \mathbf{A}_n$.

Our next result is of a similar character.

Theorem 4.7 Suppose that the system of linear inequalities $\mathbf{Ax} \leq \mathbf{b}$ has at least one solution, and let d be some scalar. Then, the following are equivalent:

(a) Every feasible solution to the system $\mathbf{Ax} \leq \mathbf{b}$ satisfies $\mathbf{c}'\mathbf{x} \leq d$.

(b) There exists some $\mathbf{p} \geq \mathbf{0}$ such that $\mathbf{p}'\mathbf{A} = \mathbf{c}'$ and $\mathbf{p}'\mathbf{b} \leq d$.

Proof.   Consider the following pair of problems

$$
\begin{array}{ll}
\text{maximize} & \mathbf{c}'\mathbf{x} \\
\text{subject to} & \mathbf{Ax} \leq \mathbf{b},
\end{array}
\qquad
\begin{array}{ll}
\text{minimize} & \mathbf{p}'\mathbf{b} \\
\text{subject to} & \mathbf{p}'\mathbf{A} = \mathbf{c}' \\
& \mathbf{p} \geq \mathbf{0},
\end{array}
$$

and note that the first is the dual of the second. If the system $\mathbf{Ax} \leq \mathbf{b}$ has a feasible solution and if every feasible solution satisfies $\mathbf{c}'\mathbf{x} \leq d$, then the first problem has an optimal solution and the optimal cost is bounded above by d. By the strong duality theorem, the second problem also has an optimal solution $\mathbf{p}$ whose cost is bounded above by d. This optimal solution satisfies $\mathbf{p}'\mathbf{A} = \mathbf{c}'$, $\mathbf{p} \geq \mathbf{0}$, and $\mathbf{p}'\mathbf{b} \leq d$.

Conversely, if some $\mathbf{p}$ satisfies $\mathbf{p}'\mathbf{A} = \mathbf{c}'$, $\mathbf{p} \geq \mathbf{0}$, and $\mathbf{p}'\mathbf{b} \leq d$, then the weak duality theorem asserts that every feasible solution to the first problem must also satisfy $\mathbf{c}'\mathbf{x} \leq d$.   □

Results such as Theorems 4.6 and 4.7 are often called *theorems of the*

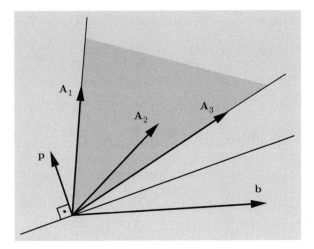

Figure 4.7: If the vector **b** does not belong to the set of all nonnegative linear combinations of $\mathbf{A}_1, \ldots, \mathbf{A}_n$, then we can find a hyperplane $\{\mathbf{z} \mid \mathbf{p}'\mathbf{z} = 0\}$ that separates it from that set.

alternative. There are several more results of this type; see, for example, Exercises 4.26, 4.27, and 4.28.

Applications of Farkas' lemma to asset pricing

Consider a market that operates for a single period, and in which n different assets are traded. Depending on the events during that single period, there are m possible states of nature at the end of the period. If we invest one dollar in some asset i and the state of nature turns out to be s, we receive a payoff of r_{si}. Thus, each asset i is described by a payoff vector $(r_{1i}, \ldots, r_{mi})$. The following $m \times n$ payoff matrix gives the payoffs of each of the n assets for each of the m states of nature:

$$\mathbf{R} = \begin{bmatrix} r_{11} & \cdots & r_{1n} \\ \vdots & \ddots & \vdots \\ r_{m1} & \cdots & r_{mn} \end{bmatrix}.$$

Let x_i be the amount held of asset i. A portfolio of assets is then a vector $\mathbf{x} = (x_1, \ldots, x_n)$. The components of a portfolio $\mathbf{x}$ can be either positive or negative. A positive value of x_i indicates that one has bought x_i units of asset i and is thus entitled to receive $r_{si}x_i$ if state s materializes. A negative value of x_i indicates a "short" position in asset i: this amounts to selling $|x_i|$ units of asset i at the beginning of the period, with a promise to buy them back at the end. Hence, one must pay out $r_{si}|x_i|$ if state s occurs, which is the same as receiving a payoff of $r_{si}x_i$.

The wealth in state s that results from a portfolio $\mathbf{x}$ is given by

$$w_s = \sum_{i=1}^{n} r_{si} x_i.$$

We introduce the vector $\mathbf{w} = (w_1, \ldots, w_m)$, and we obtain

$$\mathbf{w} = \mathbf{R}\mathbf{x}.$$

Let p_i be the price of asset i in the beginning of the period, and let $\mathbf{p} = (p_1, \ldots, p_n)$ be the vector of asset prices. Then, the cost of acquiring a portfolio $\mathbf{x}$ is given by $\mathbf{p}'\mathbf{x}$.

The central problem in asset pricing is to determine what the prices p_i should be. In order to address this question, we introduce the *absence of arbitrage* condition, which underlies much of finance theory: asset prices should always be such that no investor can get a guaranteed nonnegative payoff out of a negative investment. In other words, any portfolio that pays off nonnegative amounts in every state of nature, must be valuable to investors, so it must have nonnegative cost. Mathematically, the absence of arbitrage condition can be expressed as follows:

$$\text{if } \mathbf{R}\mathbf{x} \geq \mathbf{0}, \text{ then we must have } \mathbf{p}'\mathbf{x} \geq 0.$$

Given a particular set of assets, as described by the payoff matrix $\mathbf{R}$, only certain prices $\mathbf{p}$ are consistent with the absence of arbitrage. What characterizes such prices? What restrictions does the assumption of no arbitrage impose on asset prices? The answer is provided by Farkas' lemma.

Theorem 4.8 *The absence of arbitrage condition holds if and only if there exists a nonnegative vector $\mathbf{q} = (q_1, \ldots, q_m)$, such that the price of each asset i is given by*

$$p_i = \sum_{s=1}^{m} q_s r_{si}.$$

Proof.   The absence of arbitrage condition states that there exists no vector $\mathbf{x}$ such that $\mathbf{x}'\mathbf{R}' \geq \mathbf{0}'$ and $\mathbf{x}'\mathbf{p} < 0$. This is of the same form as condition (b) in the statement of Farkas' lemma (Theorem 4.6). (Note that here $\mathbf{p}$ plays the role of $\mathbf{b}$, and $\mathbf{R}'$ plays the role of $\mathbf{A}$.) Therefore, by Farkas' lemma, the absence of arbitrage condition holds if and only if there exists some nonnegative vector $\mathbf{q}$ such that $\mathbf{R}'\mathbf{q} = \mathbf{p}$, which is the same as the condition in the theorem's statement. $\square$

Theorem 4.8 asserts that whenever the market works efficiently enough to eliminate the possibility of arbitrage, there must exist "state prices" q_s

that can be used to value the existing assets. Intuitively, it establishes a nonnegative price q_s for an elementary asset that pays one dollar if the state of nature is s, and nothing otherwise. It then requires that every asset must be consistently priced, its total value being the sum of the values of the elementary assets from which it is composed. There is an alternative interpretation of the variables q_s as being (unnormalized) probabilities of the different states s, which, however, we will not pursue. In general, the state price vector $\mathbf{q}$ will not be unique, unless the number of assets equals or exceeds the number of states.

The no arbitrage condition is very simple, and yet very powerful. It is the key element behind many important results in financial economics, but these lie beyond the scope of this text. (See, however, Exercise 4.33 for an application in options pricing.)

4.7 From separating hyperplanes to duality*

Let us review the path followed in our development of duality theory. We started from the fact that the simplex method, in conjunction with an anticycling rule, is guaranteed to terminate. We then exploited the termination conditions of the simplex method to derive the strong duality theorem. We finally used the duality theorem to derive Farkas' lemma, which we interpreted in terms of a hyperplane that separates $\mathbf{b}$ from the columns of $\mathbf{A}$. In this section, we show that the reverse line of argument is also possible. We start from first principles and prove a general result on separating hyperplanes. We then establish Farkas' lemma, and conclude by showing that the duality theorem follows from Farkas' lemma. This line of argument is more elegant and fundamental because instead of relying on the rather complicated development of the simplex method, it only involves a small number of basic geometric concepts. Furthermore, it can be naturally generalized to nonlinear optimization problems.

Closed sets and Weierstrass' theorem

Before we proceed any further, we need to develop some background material. A set $S \subset \Re^n$ is called *closed* if it has the following property: if $\mathbf{x}^1, \mathbf{x}^2, \ldots$ is a sequence of elements of S that converges to some $\mathbf{x} \in \Re^n$, then $\mathbf{x} \in S$. In other words, S contains the limit of any sequence of elements of S. Intuitively, the set S contains its boundary.

Theorem 4.9 *Every polyhedron is closed.*

Proof. Consider the polyhedron $P = \{\mathbf{x} \in \Re^n \mid \mathbf{A}\mathbf{x} \geq \mathbf{b}\}$. Suppose that $\mathbf{x}^1, \mathbf{x}^2, \ldots$ is a sequence of elements of P that converges to some $\mathbf{x}^*$. We have to show that $\mathbf{x}^* \in P$. For each k, we have $\mathbf{x}^k \in P$ and, therefore, $\mathbf{A}\mathbf{x}^k \geq \mathbf{b}$. Taking the limit, we obtain $\mathbf{A}\mathbf{x}^* = \mathbf{A}\left(\lim_{k\to\infty} \mathbf{x}^k\right) = \lim_{k\to\infty}\left(\mathbf{A}\mathbf{x}^k\right) \geq \mathbf{b}$, and $\mathbf{x}^*$ belongs to P. □

The following is a fundamental result from real analysis that provides us with conditions for the existence of an optimal solution to an optimization problem. The proof lies beyond the scope of this book and is omitted.

Theorem 4.10 (Weierstrass' theorem) *If $f : \Re^n \mapsto \Re$ is a continuous function, and if S is a nonempty, closed, and bounded subset of $\Re^n$, then there exists some $\mathbf{x}^* \in S$ such that $f(\mathbf{x}^*) \leq f(\mathbf{x})$ for all $\mathbf{x} \in S$. Similarly, there exists some $\mathbf{y}^* \in S$ such that $f(\mathbf{y}^*) \geq f(\mathbf{x})$ for all $\mathbf{x} \in S$.*

Weierstrass' theorem is not valid if the set S is not closed. Consider, for example, the set $S = \{x \in \Re \mid x > 0\}$. This set is not closed because we can form a sequence of elements of S that converge to zero, but $x = 0$ does not belong to S. We then observe that the cost function $f(x) = x$ is not minimized at any point in S; for every $x > 0$, there exists another positive number with smaller cost, and no feasible x can be optimal. Ultimately, the reason that S is not closed is that the feasible set was defined by means of *strict* inequalities. The definition of polyhedra and linear programming problems does not allow for strict inequalities in order to avoid situations of this type.

The separating hyperplane theorem

The result that follows is "geometrically obvious" but nevertheless extremely important in the study of convex sets and functions. It states that if we are given a closed and nonempty convex set S and a point $\mathbf{x}^* \notin S$, then we can find a hyperplane, called a *separating hyperplane*, such that S and $\mathbf{x}^*$ lie in different halfspaces (Figure 4.8).

Theorem 4.11 (Separating hyperplane theorem) *Let S be a nonempty closed convex subset of $\Re^n$ and let $\mathbf{x}^* \in \Re^n$ be a vector that does not belong to S. Then, there exists some vector $\mathbf{c} \in \Re^n$ such that $\mathbf{c}'\mathbf{x}^* < \mathbf{c}'\mathbf{x}$ for all $\mathbf{x} \in S$.*

Proof. Let $\|\cdot\|$ be the Euclidean norm defined by $\|\mathbf{x}\| = (\mathbf{x}'\mathbf{x})^{1/2}$. Let us fix some element $\mathbf{w}$ of S, and let

$$B = \left\{\mathbf{x} \mid \|\mathbf{x} - \mathbf{x}^*\| \leq \|\mathbf{w} - \mathbf{x}^*\|\right\},$$

and $D = S \cap B$ [Figure 4.9(a)]. The set D is nonempty, because $\mathbf{w} \in D$.

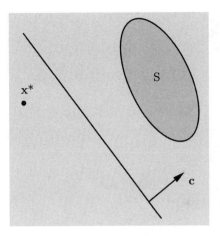

Figure 4.8: A hyperplane that separates the point $\mathbf{x}^*$ from the convex set S.

Furthermore, D is the intersection of the closed set S with the closed set B and is also closed. Finally, D is a bounded set because B is bounded. Consider the quantity $\|\mathbf{x} - \mathbf{x}^*\|$, where $\mathbf{x}$ ranges over the set D. This is a continuous function of $\mathbf{x}$. Since D is nonempty, closed, and bounded, Weierstrass' theorem implies that there exists some $\mathbf{y} \in D$ such that

$$\|\mathbf{y} - \mathbf{x}^*\| \le \|\mathbf{x} - \mathbf{x}^*\|, \qquad \forall\, \mathbf{x} \in D.$$

For any $\mathbf{x} \in S$ that does not belong to D, we have $\|\mathbf{x} - \mathbf{x}^*\| > \|\mathbf{w} - \mathbf{x}^*\| \ge \|\mathbf{y} - \mathbf{x}^*\|$. We conclude that $\mathbf{y}$ minimizes $\|\mathbf{x} - \mathbf{x}^*\|$ over all $\mathbf{x} \in S$.

We have so far established that there exists an element $\mathbf{y}$ of S which is closest to $\mathbf{x}^*$. We now show that the vector $\mathbf{c} = \mathbf{y} - \mathbf{x}^*$ has the desired property [see Figure 4.9(b)].

Let $\mathbf{x} \in S$. For any λ satisfying $0 < \lambda \le 1$, we have $\mathbf{y} + \lambda(\mathbf{x} - \mathbf{y}) \in S$, because S is convex. Since $\mathbf{y}$ minimizes $\|\mathbf{x} - \mathbf{x}^*\|$ over all $\mathbf{x} \in S$, we obtain

$$\begin{aligned}\|\mathbf{y} - \mathbf{x}^*\|^2 &\le \|\mathbf{y} + \lambda(\mathbf{x} - \mathbf{y}) - \mathbf{x}^*\|^2 \\ &= \|\mathbf{y} - \mathbf{x}^*\|^2 + 2\lambda(\mathbf{y} - \mathbf{x}^*)'(\mathbf{x} - \mathbf{y}) + \lambda^2\|\mathbf{x} - \mathbf{y}\|^2,\end{aligned}$$

which yields

$$2\lambda(\mathbf{y} - \mathbf{x}^*)'(\mathbf{x} - \mathbf{y}) + \lambda^2\|\mathbf{x} - \mathbf{y}\|^2 \ge 0.$$

We divide by λ and then take the limit as λ decreases to zero. We obtain

$$(\mathbf{y} - \mathbf{x}^*)'(\mathbf{x} - \mathbf{y}) \ge 0.$$

[This inequality states that the angle θ in Figure 4.9(b) is no larger than 90 degrees.] Thus,

$$(\mathbf{y} - \mathbf{x}^*)'\mathbf{x} \ge (\mathbf{y} - \mathbf{x}^*)'\mathbf{y}$$

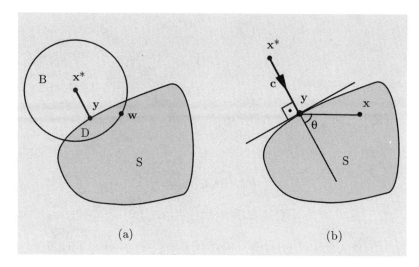

Figure 4.9: Illustration of the proof of the separating hyperplane theorem.

$$= (\mathbf{y} - \mathbf{x}^*)'\mathbf{x}^* + (\mathbf{y} - \mathbf{x}^*)'(\mathbf{y} - \mathbf{x}^*)$$
$$> (\mathbf{y} - \mathbf{x}^*)'\mathbf{x}^*.$$

Setting $\mathbf{c} = \mathbf{y} - \mathbf{x}^*$ proves the theorem.   □

Farkas' lemma revisited

We now show that Farkas' lemma is a consequence of the separating hyperplane theorem.

We will only be concerned with the difficult half of Farkas' lemma. In particular, we will prove that if the system $\mathbf{Ax} = \mathbf{b}$, $\mathbf{x} \geq \mathbf{0}$, does not have a solution, then there exists a vector $\mathbf{p}$ such that $\mathbf{p}'\mathbf{A} \geq \mathbf{0}'$ and $\mathbf{p}'\mathbf{b} < 0$.

Let

$$S = \{\mathbf{Ax} \mid \mathbf{x} \geq \mathbf{0}\}$$
$$= \{\mathbf{y} \mid \text{there exists } \mathbf{x} \text{ such that } \mathbf{y} = \mathbf{Ax}, \ \mathbf{x} \geq \mathbf{0}\},$$

and suppose that the vector $\mathbf{b}$ does not belong to S. The set S is clearly convex; it is also nonempty because $\mathbf{0} \in S$. Finally, the set S is closed; this may seem obvious, but is not easy to prove. For one possible proof, note that S is the projection of the polyhedron $\{(\mathbf{x}, \mathbf{y}) \mid \mathbf{y} = \mathbf{Ax}, \ \mathbf{x} \geq \mathbf{0}\}$ onto the $\mathbf{y}$ coordinates, is itself a polyhedron (see Section 2.8), and is therefore closed. An alternative proof is outlined in Exercise 4.37.

We now invoke the separating hyperplane theorem to separate $\mathbf{b}$ from S and conclude that there exists a vector $\mathbf{p}$ such that $\mathbf{p}'\mathbf{b} < \mathbf{p}'\mathbf{y}$ for every

$\mathbf{y} \in S$. Since $\mathbf{0} \in S$, we must have $\mathbf{p}'\mathbf{b} < 0$. Furthermore, for every column $\mathbf{A}_i$ of $\mathbf{A}$ and every $\lambda > 0$, we have $\lambda\mathbf{A}_i \in S$ and $\mathbf{p}'\mathbf{b} < \lambda\mathbf{p}'\mathbf{A}_i$. We divide both sides of the latter inequality by λ and then take the limit as λ tends to infinity, to conclude that $\mathbf{p}'\mathbf{A}_i \geq 0$. Since this is true for every i, we obtain $\mathbf{p}'\mathbf{A} \geq \mathbf{0}'$ and the proof is complete.

The duality theorem revisited

We will now derive the duality theorem as a corollary of Farkas' lemma. We only provide the proof for the case where the primal constraints are of the form $\mathbf{Ax} \geq \mathbf{b}$. The proof for the general case can be constructed along the same lines at the expense of more notation (Exercise 4.38). We also note that the proof given here is very similar to the line of argument used in the heuristic explanation of the duality theorem in Example 4.4.

We consider the following pair of primal and dual problems

$$
\begin{array}{ll}
\text{minimize} \quad \mathbf{c}'\mathbf{x} & \qquad\qquad \text{maximize} \quad \mathbf{p}'\mathbf{b} \\
\text{subject to} \quad \mathbf{Ax} \geq \mathbf{b}, & \qquad\qquad \text{subject to} \quad \mathbf{p}'\mathbf{A} = \mathbf{c}' \\
& \qquad\qquad\qquad\qquad\qquad\quad \mathbf{p} \geq \mathbf{0},
\end{array}
$$

and we assume that the primal has an optimal solution $\mathbf{x}^*$. We will show that the dual problem also has a feasible solution with the same cost. Once this is done, the strong duality theorem follows from weak duality (cf. Corollary 4.2).

Let $I = \{i \mid \mathbf{a}_i'\mathbf{x}^* = b_i\}$ be the set of indices of the constraints that are active at $\mathbf{x}^*$. We will first show that any vector $\mathbf{d}$ that satisfies $\mathbf{a}_i'\mathbf{d} \geq 0$ for every $i \in I$, must also satisfy $\mathbf{c}'\mathbf{d} \geq 0$. Consider such a vector $\mathbf{d}$ and let ϵ be a positive scalar. We then have $\mathbf{a}_i'(\mathbf{x}^* + \epsilon\mathbf{d}) \geq \mathbf{a}_i\mathbf{x}^* = b_i$ for all $i \in I$. In addition, if $i \notin I$ and if ϵ is sufficiently small, the inequality $\mathbf{a}_i'\mathbf{x}^* > b_i$ implies that $\mathbf{a}_i'(\mathbf{x}^* + \epsilon\mathbf{d}) > b_i$. We conclude that when ϵ is sufficiently small, $\mathbf{x}^* + \epsilon\mathbf{d}$ is a feasible solution. By the optimality of $\mathbf{x}^*$, we obtain $\mathbf{c}'\mathbf{d} \geq 0$, which establishes our claim. By Farkas' lemma (cf. Corollary 4.3), $\mathbf{c}$ can be expressed as a nonnegative linear combination of the vectors $\mathbf{a}_i$, $i \in I$, and there exist nonnegative scalars p_i, $i \in I$, such that

$$\mathbf{c} = \sum_{i \in I} p_i \mathbf{a}_i. \tag{4.3}$$

For $i \notin I$, we define $p_i = 0$. We then have $\mathbf{p} \geq \mathbf{0}$ and Eq. (4.3) shows that the vector $\mathbf{p}$ satisfies the dual constraint $\mathbf{p}'\mathbf{A} = \mathbf{c}'$. In addition,

$$\mathbf{p}'\mathbf{b} = \sum_{i \in I} p_i b_i = \sum_{i \in I} p_i \mathbf{a}_i'\mathbf{x}^* = \mathbf{c}'\mathbf{x}^*,$$

which shows that the cost of this dual feasible solution $\mathbf{p}$ is the same as the optimal primal cost. The duality theorem now follows from Corollary 4.2.

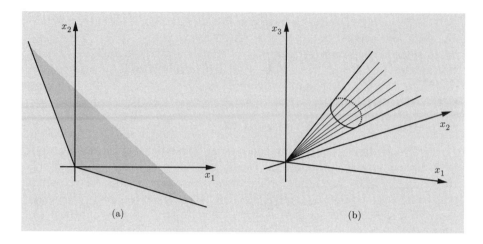

Figure 4.10: Examples of cones.

In conclusion, we have accomplished the goals that were set out in the beginning of this section. We proved the separating hyperplane theorem, which is a very intuitive and seemingly simple result, but with many important ramifications in optimization and other areas in mathematics. We used the separating hyperplane theorem to establish Farkas' lemma, and finally showed that the strong duality theorem is an easy consequence of Farkas' lemma.

4.8 Cones and extreme rays

We have seen in Chapter 2, that if the optimal cost in a linear programming problem is finite, then our search for an optimal solution can be restricted to finitely many points, namely, the basic feasible solutions, assuming one exists. In this section, we wish to develop a similar result for the case where the optimal cost is $-\infty$. In particular, we will show that the optimal cost is $-\infty$ if and only if there exists a cost reducing direction along which we can move without ever leaving the feasible set. Furthermore, our search for such a direction can be restricted to a finite set of suitably defined "extreme rays."

Cones

The first step in our development is to introduce the concept of a cone.

Definition 4.1 *A set $C \subset \Re^n$ is a **cone** if $\lambda \mathbf{x} \in C$ for all $\lambda \geq 0$ and all $\mathbf{x} \in C$.*

Notice that if C is a nonempty cone, then $\mathbf{0} \in C$. To this see, consider an arbitrary element $\mathbf{x}$ of C and set $\lambda = 0$ in the definition of a cone; see also Figure 4.10. A polyhedron of the form $P = \{\mathbf{x} \in \Re^n \mid \mathbf{Ax} \geq \mathbf{0}\}$ is easily seen to be a nonempty cone and is called a *polyhedral cone*.

Let $\mathbf{x}$ be a nonzero element of a polyhedral cone C. We then have $3\mathbf{x}/2 \in C$ and $\mathbf{x}/2 \in C$. Since $\mathbf{x}$ is the average of $3\mathbf{x}/2$ and $\mathbf{x}/2$, it is not an extreme point and, therefore, the only possible extreme point is the zero vector. If the zero vector is indeed an extreme point, we say that the cone is *pointed*. Whether this will be the case or not is determined by the criteria provided by our next result.

Theorem 4.12 *Let $C \subset \Re^n$ be the polyhedral cone defined by the constraints $\mathbf{a}_i'\mathbf{x} \geq 0$, $i = 1, \ldots, m$. Then, the following are equivalent:*

(a) *The zero vector is an extreme point of C.*

(b) *The cone C does not contain a line.*

(c) *There exist n vectors out of the family $\mathbf{a}_1, \ldots, \mathbf{a}_m$, which are linearly independent.*

Proof. This result is a special case of Theorem 2.6 in Section 2.5. □

Rays and recession cones

Consider a nonempty polyhedron

$$P = \{\mathbf{x} \in \Re^n \mid \mathbf{Ax} \geq \mathbf{b}\},$$

and let us fix some $\mathbf{y} \in P$. We define the *recession cone at* $\mathbf{y}$ as the set of all directions $\mathbf{d}$ along which we can move indefinitely away from $\mathbf{y}$, without leaving the set P. More formally, the recession cone is defined as the set

$$\{\mathbf{d} \in \Re^n \mid \mathbf{A}(\mathbf{y} + \lambda\mathbf{d}) \geq \mathbf{b}, \text{ for all } \lambda \geq 0\}.$$

It is easily seen that this set is the same as

$$\{\mathbf{d} \in \Re^n \mid \mathbf{Ad} \geq \mathbf{0}\},$$

and is a polyhedral cone. This shows that the recession cone is independent of the starting point $\mathbf{y}$; see Figure 4.11. The nonzero elements of the recession cone are called the *rays* of the polyhedron P.

For the case of a nonempty polyhedron $P = \{\mathbf{x} \in \Re^n \mid \mathbf{Ax} = \mathbf{b}, \mathbf{x} \geq \mathbf{0}\}$ in standard form, the recession cone is seen to be the set of all vectors $\mathbf{d}$ that satisfy

$$\mathbf{Ad} = \mathbf{0}, \qquad \mathbf{d} \geq \mathbf{0}.$$

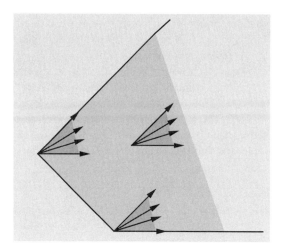

Figure 4.11: The recession cone at different elements of a polyhedron.

Extreme rays

We now define the extreme rays of a polyhedron. Intuitively, these are the directions associated with "edges" of the polyhedron that extend to infinity; see Figure 4.12 for an illustration.

Definition 4.2

(a) *A nonzero element* **x** *of a polyhedral cone* $C \subset \Re^n$ *is called an* **extreme ray** *if there are* $n-1$ *linearly independent constraints that are active at* **x**.

(b) *An extreme ray of the recession cone associated with a nonempty polyhedron* P *is also called an* **extreme ray** *of* P.

Note that a positive multiple of an extreme ray is also an extreme ray. We say that two extreme rays are *equivalent* if one is a positive multiple of the other. Note that for this to happen, they must correspond to the same $n-1$ linearly independent active constraints. Any $n-1$ linearly independent constraints define a line and can lead to at most two nonequivalent extreme rays (one being the negative of the other). Given that there is a finite number of ways that we can choose $n-1$ constraints to become active, and as long as we do not distinguish between equivalent extreme rays, we conclude that the number of extreme rays of a polyhedron is finite. A finite collection of extreme rays will be said to be a *complete set of extreme rays* if it contains exactly one representative from each equivalence class.

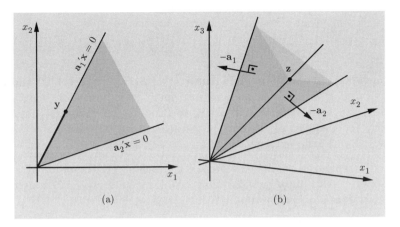

Figure 4.12: Extreme rays of polyhedral cones. (a) The vector **y** is an extreme ray because $n = 2$ and the constraint $\mathbf{a}_1'\mathbf{x} = 0$ is active at **y**. (b) A polyhedral cone defined by three linearly independent constraints of the form $\mathbf{a}_i'\mathbf{x} \geq 0$. The vector **z** is an extreme ray because $n = 3$ and the two linearly independent constraints $\mathbf{a}_1'\mathbf{x} \geq 0$ and $\mathbf{a}_2'\mathbf{x} \geq 0$ are active at **z**.

The definition of extreme rays mimics the definition of basic feasible solutions. An alternative and equivalent definition, resembling the definition of extreme points of polyhedra, is explored in Exercise 4.39.

Characterization of unbounded linear programming problems

We now derive conditions under which the optimal cost in a linear programming problem is equal to $-\infty$, first for the case where the feasible set is a cone, and then for the general case.

Theorem 4.13 *Consider the problem of minimizing $\mathbf{c}'\mathbf{x}$ over a pointed polyhedral cone $C = \{\mathbf{x} \in \Re^n \mid \mathbf{a}_i'\mathbf{x} \geq 0, \ i = 1,\ldots,m\}$. The optimal cost is equal to $-\infty$ if and only if some extreme ray $\mathbf{d}$ of C satisfies $\mathbf{c}'\mathbf{d} < 0$.*

Proof. One direction of the result is trivial because if some extreme ray has negative cost, then the cost becomes arbitrarily negative by moving along this ray.

For the converse, suppose that the optimal cost is $-\infty$. In particular, there exists some $\mathbf{x} \in C$ whose cost is negative and, by suitably scaling $\mathbf{x}$, we can assume that $\mathbf{c'x} = -1$. In particular, the polyhedron

$$P = \left\{ \mathbf{x} \in \Re^n \mid \mathbf{a}_1'\mathbf{x} \geq 0, \ldots, \mathbf{a}_m'\mathbf{x} \geq 0, \mathbf{c'x} = -1 \right\}$$

is nonempty. Since C is pointed, the vectors $\mathbf{a}_1, \ldots, \mathbf{a}_m$ span $\Re^n$ and this implies that P has at least one extreme point; let $\mathbf{d}$ be one of them. At $\mathbf{d}$, we have n linearly independent active constraints, which means that $n - 1$ linearly independent constraints of the form $\mathbf{a}_i'\mathbf{x} \geq 0$ must be active. It follows that $\mathbf{d}$ is an extreme ray of C. □

By exploiting duality, Theorem 4.13 leads to a criterion for unbound-edness in general linear programming problems. Interestingly enough, this criterion does not involve the right-hand side vector $\mathbf{b}$.

Theorem 4.14 *Consider the problem of minimizing $\mathbf{c'x}$ subject to $\mathbf{Ax} \geq \mathbf{b}$, and assume that the feasible set has at least one extreme point. The optimal cost is equal to $-\infty$ if and only if some extreme ray $\mathbf{d}$ of the feasible set satisfies $\mathbf{c'd} < 0$.*

Proof. One direction of the result is trivial because if an extreme ray has negative cost, then the cost becomes arbitrarily negative by starting at a feasible solution and moving along the direction of this ray.

For the proof of the reverse direction, we consider the dual problem:

$$\begin{aligned} \text{maximize} \quad & \mathbf{p'b} \\ \text{subject to} \quad & \mathbf{p'A} = \mathbf{c'} \\ & \mathbf{p} \geq \mathbf{0}. \end{aligned}$$

If the primal problem is unbounded, the dual problem is infeasible. Then, the related problem

$$\begin{aligned} \text{maximize} \quad & \mathbf{p'0} \\ \text{subject to} \quad & \mathbf{p'A} = \mathbf{c'} \\ & \mathbf{p} \geq \mathbf{0}, \end{aligned}$$

is also infeasible. This implies that the associated primal problem

$$\begin{aligned} \text{minimize} \quad & \mathbf{c'x} \\ \text{subject to} \quad & \mathbf{Ax} \geq \mathbf{0}, \end{aligned}$$

is either unbounded or infeasible. Since $\mathbf{x} = \mathbf{0}$ is one feasible solution, it must be unbounded. Since the primal feasible set has at least one extreme point, the rows of $\mathbf{A}$ span $\Re^n$, where n is the dimension of $\mathbf{x}$. It follows that the recession cone $\{\mathbf{x} \mid \mathbf{Ax} \geq \mathbf{0}\}$ is pointed and, by Theorem 4.13, there exists an extreme ray $\mathbf{d}$ of the recession cone satisfying $\mathbf{c'd} < 0$. By definition, this is an extreme ray of the feasible set. □

The unboundedness criterion in the simplex method

We end this section by pointing out that if we have a standard form problem in which the optimal cost is $-\infty$, the simplex method provides us at termination with an extreme ray.

Indeed, consider what happens when the simplex method terminates with an indication that the optimal cost is $-\infty$. At that point, we have a basis matrix $\mathbf{B}$, a nonbasic variable x_j with negative reduced cost, and the jth column $\mathbf{B}^{-1}\mathbf{A}_j$ of the tableau has no positive elements. Consider the jth basic direction $\mathbf{d}$, which is the vector that satisfies $\mathbf{d}_B = -\mathbf{B}^{-1}\mathbf{A}_j$, $d_j = 1$, and $d_i = 0$ for every nonbasic index i other than j. Then, the vector $\mathbf{d}$ satisfies $\mathbf{Ad} = \mathbf{0}$ and $\mathbf{d} \geq \mathbf{0}$, and belongs to the recession cone. It is also a direction of cost decrease, since the reduced cost $\bar{c}_j$ of the entering variable is negative.

Out of the constraints defining the recession cone, the jth basic direction $\mathbf{d}$ satisfies $n-1$ linearly independent such constraints with equality: these are the constraints $\mathbf{Ad} = \mathbf{0}$ (m of them) and the constraints $d_i = 0$ for i nonbasic and different than j ($n - m - 1$ of them). We conclude that $\mathbf{d}$ is an extreme ray.

4.9   Representation of polyhedra

In this section, we establish one of the fundamental results of linear programming theory. In particular, we show that any element of a polyhedron that has at least one extreme point can be represented as a convex combination of extreme points plus a nonnegative linear combination of extreme rays. A precise statement is given by our next result. A generalization to the case of general polyhedra is developed in Exercise 4.47.

Theorem 4.15 (Resolution theorem) *Let*

$$P = \left\{\mathbf{x} \in \Re^n \mid \mathbf{Ax} \geq \mathbf{b}\right\}$$

be a nonempty polyhedron with at least one extreme point. Let $\mathbf{x}^1, \ldots, \mathbf{x}^k$ *be the extreme points, and let* $\mathbf{w}^1, \ldots, \mathbf{w}^r$ *be a complete set of extreme rays of* P. *Let*

$$Q = \left\{\sum_{i=1}^{k}\lambda_i\mathbf{x}^i + \sum_{j=1}^{r}\theta_j\mathbf{w}^j \;\middle|\; \lambda_i \geq 0, \; \theta_j \geq 0, \; \sum_{i=1}^{k}\lambda_i = 1\right\}.$$

Then, $Q = P$.

Proof. We first prove that $Q \subset P$. Let

$$\mathbf{x} = \sum_{i=1}^{k} \lambda_i \mathbf{x}^i + \sum_{j=1}^{r} \theta_j \mathbf{w}^j$$

be an element of Q, where the coefficients λ_i and θ_j are nonnegative, and $\sum_{i=1}^{k} \lambda_i = 1$. The vector $\mathbf{y} = \sum_{i=1}^{k} \lambda_i \mathbf{x}^i$ is a convex combination of elements of P. It therefore belongs to P and satisfies $\mathbf{Ay} \geq \mathbf{b}$. We also have $\mathbf{Aw}^j \geq \mathbf{0}$ for every j, which implies that the vector $\mathbf{z} = \sum_{j=1}^{r} \theta_j \mathbf{w}^j$ satisfies $\mathbf{Az} \geq \mathbf{0}$. It then follows that the vector $\mathbf{x} = \mathbf{y} + \mathbf{z}$ satisfies $\mathbf{Ax} \geq \mathbf{b}$ and belongs to P.

For the reverse inclusion, we assume that P is not a subset of Q and we will derive a contradiction. Let $\mathbf{z}$ be an element of P that does not belong to Q. Consider the linear programming problem

$$
\begin{aligned}
\text{maximize} \quad & \sum_{i=1}^{k} 0 \lambda_i + \sum_{j=1}^{r} 0 \theta_j \\
\text{subject to} \quad & \sum_{i=1}^{k} \lambda_i \mathbf{x}^i + \sum_{j=1}^{r} \theta_j \mathbf{w}^j = \mathbf{z} \\
& \sum_{i=1}^{k} \lambda_i = 1 \\
& \lambda_i \geq 0, \qquad i = 1, \dots, k, \\
& \theta_j \geq 0, \qquad j = 1, \dots, r,
\end{aligned}
\tag{4.4}
$$

which is infeasible because $\mathbf{z} \notin Q$. This problem is the dual of the problem

$$
\begin{aligned}
\text{minimize} \quad & \mathbf{p}'\mathbf{z} + q \\
\text{subject to} \quad & \mathbf{p}'\mathbf{x}^i + q \geq 0, \qquad i = 1, \dots, k, \\
& \mathbf{p}'\mathbf{w}^j \geq 0, \qquad j = 1, \dots, r.
\end{aligned}
\tag{4.5}
$$

Because the latter problem has a feasible solution, namely, $\mathbf{p} = \mathbf{0}$ and $q = 0$, the optimal cost is $-\infty$, and there exists a feasible solution $(\mathbf{p}, q)$ whose cost $\mathbf{p}'\mathbf{z} + q$ is negative. On the other hand, $\mathbf{p}'\mathbf{x}^i + q \geq 0$ for all i and this implies that $\mathbf{p}'\mathbf{z} < \mathbf{p}'\mathbf{x}^i$ for all i. We also have $\mathbf{p}'\mathbf{w}^j \geq 0$ for all j. [1]

Having fixed $\mathbf{p}$ as above, we now consider the linear programming problem

$$
\begin{aligned}
\text{minimize} \quad & \mathbf{p}'\mathbf{x} \\
\text{subject to} \quad & \mathbf{Ax} \geq \mathbf{b}.
\end{aligned}
$$

If the optimal cost is finite, there exists an extreme point $\mathbf{x}^i$ which is optimal. Since $\mathbf{z}$ is a feasible solution, we obtain $\mathbf{p}'\mathbf{x}^i \leq \mathbf{p}'\mathbf{z}$, which is a

---

[1] For an intuitive view of this proof, the purpose of this paragraph was to construct a hyperplane that separates $\mathbf{z}$ from Q.

contradiction. If the optimal cost is $-\infty$, Theorem 4.14 implies that there exists an extreme ray $\mathbf{w}^j$ such that $\mathbf{p}'\mathbf{w}^j < 0$, which is again a contradiction. □

Example 4.10 Consider the unbounded polyhedron defined by the constraints

$$x_1 - x_2 \geq -2$$
$$x_1 + x_2 \geq 1$$
$$x_1, x_2 \geq 0$$

(see Figure 4.13). This polyhedron has three extreme points, namely, $\mathbf{x}^1 = (0, 2)$, $\mathbf{x}^2 = (0, 1)$, and $\mathbf{x}^3 = (1, 0)$. The recession cone C is described by the inequalities $d_1 - d_2 \geq 0$, $d_1 + d_2 \geq 0$, and $d_1, d_2 \geq 0$. We conclude that $C = \{(d_1, d_2) \mid 0 \leq d_2 \leq d_1\}$. This cone has two extreme rays, namely, $\mathbf{w}^1 = (1, 1)$ and $\mathbf{w}^2 = (1, 0)$. The vector $\mathbf{y} = (2, 2)$ is an element of the polyhedron and can be represented as

$$\mathbf{y} = \begin{bmatrix} 2 \\ 2 \end{bmatrix} = \begin{bmatrix} 0 \\ 1 \end{bmatrix} + \begin{bmatrix} 1 \\ 1 \end{bmatrix} + \begin{bmatrix} 1 \\ 0 \end{bmatrix} = \mathbf{x}^2 + \mathbf{w}^1 + \mathbf{w}^2.$$

However, this representation is not unique; for example, we also have

$$\mathbf{y} = \begin{bmatrix} 2 \\ 2 \end{bmatrix} = \frac{1}{2}\begin{bmatrix} 0 \\ 1 \end{bmatrix} + \frac{1}{2}\begin{bmatrix} 1 \\ 1 \end{bmatrix} + \frac{3}{2}\begin{bmatrix} 1 \\ 1 \end{bmatrix} = \frac{1}{2}\mathbf{x}^2 + \frac{1}{2}\mathbf{x}^3 + \frac{3}{2}\mathbf{w}^1.$$

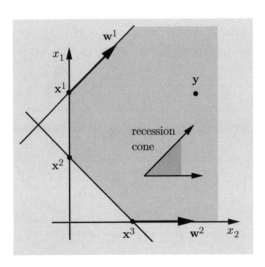

Figure 4.13: The polyhedron of Example 4.10.

We note that the set Q in Theorem 4.15 is the image of the polyhedron

$$H = \left\{ (\lambda_1, \ldots, \lambda_k, \theta_1, \ldots, \theta_r) \;\middle|\; \sum_{i=1}^{k} \lambda_i = 1, \; \lambda_i \geq 0, \; \theta_j \geq 0 \right\},$$

under the linear mapping

$$(\lambda_1, \ldots, \lambda_k, \theta_1, \ldots, \theta_r) \;\mapsto\; \sum_{i=1}^{k} \lambda_i \mathbf{x}^i + \sum_{j=1}^{r} \theta_j \mathbf{w}^j.$$

Thus, one corollary of the resolution theorem is that every polyhedron is the image, under a linear mapping, of a polyhedron H with this particular structure.

We now specialize Theorem 4.15 to the case of bounded polyhedra, to recover a result that was also proved in Section 2.7, using a different line of argument.

Corollary 4.4 *A nonempty bounded polyhedron is the convex hull of its extreme points.*

Proof. Let $P = \{\mathbf{x} \mid \mathbf{A}\mathbf{x} \geq \mathbf{b}\}$ be a nonempty bounded polyhedron. If $\mathbf{d}$ is a nonzero element of the cone $C = \{\mathbf{x} \mid \mathbf{A}\mathbf{x} \geq \mathbf{0}\}$ and $\mathbf{x}$ is an element of P, we have $\mathbf{x} + \lambda \mathbf{d} \in P$ for all $\lambda \geq 0$, contradicting the boundedness of P. We conclude that C consists of only the zero vector and does not have any extreme rays. The result then follows from Theorem 4.15. $\square$

There is another corollary of Theorem 4.15 that deals with cones, and which is proved by noting that a cone can have no extreme points other than the zero vector.

Corollary 4.5 *Assume that the cone $C = \{\mathbf{x} \mid \mathbf{A}\mathbf{x} \geq \mathbf{0}\}$ is pointed. Then, every element of C can be expressed as a nonnegative linear combination of the extreme rays of C.*

Converse to the resolution theorem

Let us say that a set Q is *finitely generated* if it is specified in the form

$$Q = \left\{ \sum_{i=1}^{k} \lambda_i \mathbf{x}^i + \sum_{j=1}^{r} \theta_j \mathbf{w}^j \;\middle|\; \lambda_i \geq 0, \; \theta_j \geq 0, \; \sum_{i=1}^{k} \lambda_i = 1 \right\}, \qquad (4.6)$$

where $\mathbf{x}^1, \ldots, \mathbf{x}^k$ and $\mathbf{w}^1, \ldots, \mathbf{w}^r$ are some given elements of $\Re^n$. The resolution theorem states that a polyhedron with at least one extreme point is a finitely generated set (this is also true for general polyhedra; see Exercise 4.47). We now discuss a converse result, which states that every finitely generated set is a polyhedron.

As observed earlier, a finitely generated set Q can be viewed as the image of the polyhedron

$$H = \left\{ (\lambda_1, \ldots, \lambda_k, \theta_1, \ldots, \theta_r) \ \Big| \ \sum_{i=1}^{k} \lambda_i = 1, \ \lambda_i \geq 0, \ \theta_j \geq 0 \right\}$$

under a certain linear mapping. Thus, the results of Section 2.8 apply and establish that a finitely generated set is indeed a polyhedron. We record this result and also present a proof based on duality.

> **Theorem 4.16** *A finitely generated set is a polyhedron. In particular, the convex hull of finitely many vectors is a (bounded) polyhedron.*

Proof. Consider the linear programming problem (4.4) that was used in the proof of Theorem 4.15. A given vector $\mathbf{z}$ belongs to a finitely generated set Q of the form (4.6) if and only if the problem (4.4) has a feasible solution. Using duality, this is the case if and only if problem (4.5) has finite optimal cost. We convert problem (4.5) to standard form by introducing nonnegative variables $\mathbf{p}^+, \mathbf{p}^-, q^+, q^-$, such that $\mathbf{p} = \mathbf{p}^+ - \mathbf{p}^-$, and $q = q^+ - q^-$, as well as surplus variables. Since standard form polyhedra contain no lines, Theorem 4.13 shows that the optimal cost in the standard form problem is finite if and only if

$$(\mathbf{p}^+)'\mathbf{z} - (\mathbf{p}^-)'\mathbf{z} + q^+ - q^- \geq 0,$$

for each one of its finitely many extreme rays. Hence, $\mathbf{z} \in Q$ if and only if $\mathbf{z}$ satisfies a finite collection of linear inequalities. This shows that Q is a polyhedron. ☐

In conclusion, we have two ways of representing a polyhedron:

(a) in terms of a finite set of linear constraints;

(b) as a finitely generated set, in terms of its extreme points and extreme rays.

These two descriptions are mathematically equivalent, but can be quite different from a practical viewpoint. For example, we may be able to describe a polyhedron in terms of a small number of linear constraints. If on the other hand, this polyhedron has many extreme points, a description as a finitely generated set can be much more complicated. Furthermore, passing from one type of description to the other is, in general, a complicated computational task.

4.10   General linear programming duality*

In the definition of the dual problem (Section 4.2), we associated a dual variable p_i with each constraint of the form $\mathbf{a}_i'\mathbf{x} = b_i$, $\mathbf{a}_i'\mathbf{x} \geq b_i$, or $\mathbf{a}_i'\mathbf{x} \leq b_i$.

However, no dual variables were associated with constraints of the form $x_i \geq 0$ or $x_i \leq 0$. In the same spirit, and in a more general approach to linear programming duality, we can choose arbitrarily which constraints will be associated with price variables and which ones will not. In this section, we develop a general duality theorem that covers such a situation.

Consider the primal problem

$$\begin{array}{ll} \text{minimize} & \mathbf{c'x} \\ \text{subject to} & \mathbf{Ax} \geq \mathbf{b} \\ & \mathbf{x} \in P, \end{array}$$

where P is the polyhedron

$$P = \big\{ \mathbf{x} \mid \mathbf{Dx} \geq \mathbf{d} \big\}.$$

We associate a dual vector $\mathbf{p}$ with the constraint $\mathbf{Ax} \geq \mathbf{b}$. The constraint $\mathbf{x} \in P$ is a generalization of constraints of the form $x_i \geq 0$ or $x_i \leq 0$ and dual variables are not associated with it.

As in Section 4.1, we define the *dual objective* $g(\mathbf{p})$ by

$$g(\mathbf{p}) = \min_{\mathbf{x} \in P} \Big[\mathbf{c'x} + \mathbf{p'}(\mathbf{b} - \mathbf{Ax}) \Big]. \tag{4.7}$$

The *dual problem* is then defined as

$$\begin{array}{ll} \text{maximize} & g(\mathbf{p}) \\ \text{subject to} & \mathbf{p} \geq \mathbf{0}. \end{array}$$

We first provide a generalization of the weak duality theorem.

Theorem 4.17 (Weak duality) *If $\mathbf{x}$ is primal feasible ($\mathbf{Ax} \geq \mathbf{b}$ and $\mathbf{x} \in P$), and $\mathbf{p}$ is dual feasible ($\mathbf{p} \geq \mathbf{0}$), then $g(\mathbf{p}) \leq \mathbf{c'x}$.*

Proof. If $\mathbf{x}$ and $\mathbf{p}$ are primal and dual feasible, respectively, then $\mathbf{p'}(\mathbf{b} - \mathbf{Ax}) \leq 0$, which implies that

$$\begin{aligned} g(\mathbf{p}) &= \min_{\mathbf{y} \in P} \Big[\mathbf{c'y} + \mathbf{p'}(\mathbf{b} - \mathbf{Ay}) \Big] \\ &\leq \mathbf{c'x} + \mathbf{p'}(\mathbf{b} - \mathbf{Ax}) \\ &\leq \mathbf{c'x}. \qquad\qquad \square \end{aligned}$$

We also have the following generalization of the strong duality theorem.

Theorem 4.18 (Strong duality) *If the primal problem has an optimal solution, so does the dual, and the respective optimal costs are equal.*

Proof. Since $P = \{\mathbf{x} \mid \mathbf{Dx} \geq \mathbf{d}\}$, the primal problem is of the form

$$\begin{array}{ll} \text{minimize} & \mathbf{c}'\mathbf{x} \\ \text{subject to} & \mathbf{Ax} \geq \mathbf{b} \\ & \mathbf{Dx} \geq \mathbf{d}, \end{array}$$

and we assume that it has an optimal solution. Its dual, which is

$$\begin{array}{ll} \text{maximize} & \mathbf{p}'\mathbf{b} + \mathbf{q}'\mathbf{d} \\ \text{subject to} & \mathbf{p}'\mathbf{A} + \mathbf{q}'\mathbf{D} = \mathbf{c}' \\ & \mathbf{p} \geq \mathbf{0} \\ & \mathbf{q} \geq \mathbf{0}, \end{array} \tag{4.8}$$

must then have the same optimal cost. For any fixed $\mathbf{p}$, the vector $\mathbf{q}$ should be chosen optimally in the problem (4.8). Thus, the dual problem (4.8) can also be written as

$$\begin{array}{ll} \text{maximize} & \mathbf{p}'\mathbf{b} + f(\mathbf{p}) \\ \text{subject to} & \mathbf{p} \geq \mathbf{0}, \end{array}$$

where $f(\mathbf{p})$ is the optimal cost in the problem

$$\begin{array}{ll} \text{maximize} & \mathbf{q}'\mathbf{d} \\ \text{subject to} & \mathbf{q}'\mathbf{D} = \mathbf{c}' - \mathbf{p}'\mathbf{A} \\ & \mathbf{q} \geq \mathbf{0}. \end{array} \tag{4.9}$$

[If the latter problem is infeasible, we set $f(\mathbf{p}) = -\infty$.] Using the strong duality theorem for problem (4.9), we obtain

$$f(\mathbf{p}) = \min_{\mathbf{Dx} \geq \mathbf{d}} (\mathbf{c}'\mathbf{x} - \mathbf{p}'\mathbf{Ax}).$$

We conclude that the dual problem (4.8) has the same optimal cost as the problem

$$\begin{array}{ll} \text{maximize} & \mathbf{p}'\mathbf{b} + \min_{\mathbf{Dx} \geq \mathbf{d}} (\mathbf{c}'\mathbf{x} - \mathbf{p}'\mathbf{Ax}) \\ \text{subject to} & \mathbf{p} \geq \mathbf{0}. \end{array}$$

By comparing with Eq. (4.7), we see that this is the same as maximizing $g(\mathbf{p})$ over all $\mathbf{p} \geq \mathbf{0}$. $\qquad\square$

The idea of selectively assigning dual variables to some of the constraints is often used in order to treat "simpler" constraints differently than more "complex" ones, and has numerous applications in large scale optimization. (Applications to integer programming are discussed in Section 11.4.) Finally, let us point out that the approach in this section extends to certain nonlinear optimization problems. For example, if we replace the linear cost function $\mathbf{c}'\mathbf{x}$ by a general convex function $c(\mathbf{x})$, and the polyhedron P by a general convex set, we can again define the dual objective according to the formula

$$g(\mathbf{p}) = \min_{\mathbf{x} \in P} \left[c(\mathbf{x}) + \mathbf{p}'(\mathbf{b} - \mathbf{A}\mathbf{x}) \right].$$

It turns out that the strong duality theorem remains valid for such nonlinear problems, under suitable technical conditions, but this lies beyond the scope of this book.

4.11 Summary

We summarize here the main ideas that have been developed in this chapter.

Given a (primal) linear programming problem, we can associate with it another (dual) linear programming problem, by following a set of mechanical rules. The definition of the dual problem is consistent, in the sense that the duals of equivalent primal problems are themselves equivalent.

Each dual variable is associated with a particular primal constraint and can be viewed as a penalty for violating that constraint. By replacing the primal constraints with penalty terms, we increase the set of available options, and this allows us to construct primal solutions whose cost is less than the optimal cost. In particular, every dual feasible vector leads to a lower bound on the optimal cost of the primal problem (this is the essence of the weak duality theorem). The maximization in the dual problem is then a search for the tightest such lower bound. The strong duality theorem asserts that the tightest such lower bound is equal to the optimal primal cost.

An optimal dual variable can also be interpreted as a marginal cost, that is, as the rate of change of the optimal primal cost when we perform a small perturbation of the right-hand side vector $\mathbf{b}$, assuming nondegeneracy.

A useful relation between optimal primal and dual solutions is provided by the complementary slackness conditions. Intuitively, these conditions require that any constraint that is inactive at an optimal solution carries a zero price, which is compatible with the interpretation of prices as marginal costs.

We saw that every basis matrix in a standard form problem determines not only a primal basic solution, but also a basic dual solution. This observation is at the heart of the dual simplex method. This method is similar to the primal simplex method in that it generates a sequence of primal basic solutions, together with an associated sequence of dual basic solutions. It is different, however, in that the dual basic solutions are dual feasible, with ever improving costs, while the primal basic solutions are infeasible (except for the last one). We developed the dual simplex method by simply describing its mechanics and by providing an algebraic justification.

Nevertheless, the dual simplex method also has a geometric interpretation. It keeps moving from one dual basic feasible solution to an adjacent one and, in this respect, it is similar to the primal simplex method applied to the dual problem.

All of duality theory can be developed by exploiting the termination conditions of the simplex method, and this was our initial approach to the subject. We also pursued an alternative line of development that proceeded from first principles and used geometric arguments. This is a more direct and more general approach, but requires more abstract reasoning.

Duality theory provided us with some powerful tools based on which we were able to enhance our geometric understanding of polyhedra. We derived a few theorems of the alternative (like Farkas' lemma), which are surprisingly powerful and have applications in a wide variety of contexts. In fact, Farkas' lemma can be viewed as the core of linear programming duality theory. Another major result that we derived is the resolution theorem, which allows us to express any element of a nonempty polyhedron with at least one extreme point as a convex combination of its extreme points plus a nonnegative linear combination of its extreme rays; in other words, every polyhedron is "finitely generated." The converse is also true, and every finitely generated set is a polyhedron (can be represented in terms of linear inequality constraints). Results of this type play a key role in confirming our intuitive geometric understanding of polyhedra and linear programming. They allow us to develop alternative views of certain situations and lead to deeper understanding. Many such results have an "obvious" geometric content and are often taken for granted. Nevertheless, as we have seen, rigorous proofs can be quite elaborate.

4.12   Exercises

Exercise 4.1 Consider the linear programming problem:

$$
\begin{array}{llrcrcrcrcl}
\text{minimize} & x_1 & - & x_2 & & & & & \\
\text{subject to} & 2x_1 & + & 3x_2 & - & x_3 & + & x_4 & \leq & 0 \\
& 3x_1 & + & x_2 & + & 4x_3 & - & 2x_4 & \geq & 3 \\
& -x_1 & - & x_2 & + & 2x_3 & + & x_4 & = & 6 \\
& x_1 & \leq & 0 & & & & & \\
& x_2, x_3 & \geq & 0. & & & & &
\end{array}
$$

Write down the corresponding dual problem.

Exercise 4.2 Consider the primal problem

$$
\begin{array}{ll}
\text{minimize} & \mathbf{c}'\mathbf{x} \\
\text{subject to} & \mathbf{Ax} \geq \mathbf{b} \\
& \mathbf{x} \geq \mathbf{0}.
\end{array}
$$

Form the dual problem and convert it into an equivalent minimization problem. Derive a set of conditions on the matrix $\mathbf{A}$ and the vectors $\mathbf{b}$, $\mathbf{c}$, under which the dual is identical to the primal, and construct an example in which these conditions are satisfied.

Exercise 4.3 The purpose of this exercise is to show that solving linear programming problems is no harder than solving systems of linear inequalities.

Suppose that we are given a subroutine which, given a system of linear inequality constraints, either produces a solution or decides that no solution exists. Construct a simple algorithm that uses a single call to this subroutine and which finds an optimal solution to any linear programming problem that has an optimal solution.

Exercise 4.4 Let $\mathbf{A}$ be a symmetric square matrix. Consider the linear programming problem

$$\begin{aligned}
\text{minimize} \quad & \mathbf{c}'\mathbf{x} \\
\text{subject to} \quad & \mathbf{A}\mathbf{x} \geq \mathbf{c} \\
& \mathbf{x} \geq \mathbf{0}.
\end{aligned}$$

Prove that if $\mathbf{x}^*$ satisfies $\mathbf{A}\mathbf{x}^* = \mathbf{c}$ and $\mathbf{x}^* \geq \mathbf{0}$, then $\mathbf{x}^*$ is an optimal solution.

Exercise 4.5 Consider a linear programming problem in standard form and assume that the rows of $\mathbf{A}$ are linearly independent. For each one of the following statements, provide either a proof or a counterexample.

(a) Let $\mathbf{x}^*$ be a basic feasible solution. Suppose that for every basis corresponding to $\mathbf{x}^*$, the associated basic solution to the dual is infeasible. Then, the optimal cost must be strictly less that $\mathbf{c}'\mathbf{x}^*$.

(b) The dual of the auxiliary primal problem considered in Phase I of the simplex method is always feasible.

(c) Let p_i be the dual variable associated with the ith equality constraint in the primal. Eliminating the ith primal equality constraint is equivalent to introducing the additional constraint $p_i = 0$ in the dual problem.

(d) If the unboundedness criterion in the primal simplex algorithm is satisfied, then the dual problem is infeasible.

Exercise 4.6* (**Duality in Chebychev approximation**) Let $\mathbf{A}$ be an $m \times n$ matrix and let $\mathbf{b}$ be a vector in $\Re^m$. We consider the problem of minimizing $\|\mathbf{A}\mathbf{x} - \mathbf{b}\|_\infty$ over all $\mathbf{x} \in \Re^n$. Here $\| \cdot \|_\infty$ is the vector norm defined by $\|\mathbf{y}\|_\infty = \max_i |y_i|$. Let v be the value of the optimal cost.

(a) Let $\mathbf{p}$ be any vector in $\Re^m$ that satisfies $\sum_{i=1}^m |p_i| = 1$ and $\mathbf{p}'\mathbf{A} = \mathbf{0}'$. Show that $\mathbf{p}'\mathbf{b} \leq v$.

(b) In order to obtain the best possible lower bound of the form considered in part (a), we form the linear programming problem

$$\begin{aligned}
\text{maximize} \quad & \mathbf{p}'\mathbf{b} \\
\text{subject to} \quad & \mathbf{p}'\mathbf{A} = \mathbf{0}' \\
& \sum_{i=1}^m |p_i| \leq 1.
\end{aligned}$$

Show that the optimal cost in this problem is equal to v.

Exercise 4.7 (Duality in piecewise linear convex optimization) Consider the problem of minimizing $\max_{i=1,\ldots,m}(\mathbf{a}_i'\mathbf{x} - b_i)$ over all $\mathbf{x} \in \Re^n$. Let v be the value of the optimal cost, assumed finite. Let $\mathbf{A}$ be the matrix with rows $\mathbf{a}_1,\ldots,\mathbf{a}_m$, and let $\mathbf{b}$ be the vector with components $b_1,\ldots,b_m$.

(a) Consider any vector $\mathbf{p} \in \Re^m$ that satisfies $\mathbf{p}'\mathbf{A} = \mathbf{0}'$, $\mathbf{p} \geq \mathbf{0}$, and $\sum_{i=1}^m p_i = 1$. Show that $-\mathbf{p}'\mathbf{b} \leq v$.

(b) In order to obtain the best possible lower bound of the form considered in part (a), we form the linear programming problem

$$
\begin{aligned}
\text{maximize} \quad & -\mathbf{p}'\mathbf{b} \\
\text{subject to} \quad & \mathbf{p}'\mathbf{A} = \mathbf{0}' \\
& \mathbf{p}'\mathbf{e} = 1 \\
& \mathbf{p} \geq \mathbf{0},
\end{aligned}
$$

where $\mathbf{e}$ is the vector with all components equal to 1. Show that the optimal cost in this problem is equal to v.

Exercise 4.8 Consider the linear programming problem of minimizing $\mathbf{c}'\mathbf{x}$ subject to $\mathbf{A}\mathbf{x} = \mathbf{b}$, $\mathbf{x} \geq \mathbf{0}$. Let $\mathbf{x}^*$ be an optimal solution, assumed to exist, and let $\mathbf{p}^*$ be an optimal solution to the dual.

(a) Let $\tilde{\mathbf{x}}$ be an optimal solution to the primal, when $\mathbf{c}$ is replaced by some $\tilde{\mathbf{c}}$. Show that $(\tilde{\mathbf{c}} - \mathbf{c})'(\tilde{\mathbf{x}} - \mathbf{x}^*) \leq 0$.

(b) Let the cost vector be fixed at $\mathbf{c}$, but suppose that we now change $\mathbf{b}$ to $\tilde{\mathbf{b}}$, and let $\tilde{\mathbf{x}}$ be a corresponding optimal solution to the primal. Prove that $(\mathbf{p}^*)'(\tilde{\mathbf{b}} - \mathbf{b}) \leq \mathbf{c}'(\tilde{\mathbf{x}} - \mathbf{x}^*)$.

Exercise 4.9 (Back-propagation of dual variables in a multiperiod problem) A company makes a product that can be either sold or stored to meet future demand. Let $t = 1,\ldots,T$ denote the periods of the planning horizon. Let b_t be the production volume during period t, which is assumed to be known in advance. During each period t, a quantity x_t of the product is sold, at a unit price of d_t. Furthermore, a quantity y_t can be sent to long-term storage, at a unit transportation cost of c. Alternatively, a quantity w_t can be retrieved from storage, at zero cost. We assume that when the product is prepared for long-term storage, it is partly damaged, and only a fraction f of the total survives. Demand is assumed to be unlimited. The main question is whether it is profitable to store some of the production, in anticipation of higher prices in the future. This leads us to the following problem, where z_t stands for the amount kept in long-term storage, at the end of period t:

$$
\begin{aligned}
\text{maximize} \quad & \sum_{t=1}^T \alpha^{t-1}(d_t x_t - c y_t) + \alpha^T d_{T+1} z_T \\
\text{subject to} \quad & x_t + y_t - w_t = b_t, && t = 1,\ldots,T, \\
& z_t + w_t - z_{t-1} - f y_t = 0, && t = 1,\ldots,T, \\
& z_0 = 0, \\
& x_t, y_t, w_t, z_t \geq 0.
\end{aligned}
$$

Here, d_{T+1} is the salvage prive for whatever inventory is left at the end of period T. Furthermore, α is a discount factor, with $0 < \alpha < 1$, reflecting the fact that future revenues are valued less than current ones.

(a) Let p_t and q_t be dual variables associated with the first and second equality constraint, respectively. Write down the dual problem.

(b) Assume that $0 < f < 1$, $b_t \geq 0$, and $c \geq 0$. Show that the following formulae provide an optimal solution to the dual problem:

$$
\begin{aligned}
q_T &= \alpha^T d_{T+1}, \\
p_T &= \max\left\{\alpha^{T-1} d_T, \ f q_T - \alpha^{T-1} c\right\}, \\
q_t &= \max\left\{q_{t+1}, \alpha^{t-1} d_t\right\}, &\quad t = 1, \ldots, T-1, \\
p_t &= \max\left\{\alpha^{t-1} d_t, \ f q_t - \alpha^{t-1} c\right\}, &\quad t = 1, \ldots, T-1.
\end{aligned}
$$

(c) Explain how the result in part (b) can be used to compute an optimal solution to the original problem. Primal and dual nondegeneracy can be assumed.

Exercise 4.10 (Saddle points of the Lagrangean) Consider the standard form problem of minimizing $\mathbf{c'x}$ subject to $\mathbf{Ax} = \mathbf{b}$ and $\mathbf{x} \geq \mathbf{0}$. We define the *Lagrangean* by

$$L(\mathbf{x}, \mathbf{p}) = \mathbf{c'x} + \mathbf{p'}(\mathbf{b} - \mathbf{Ax}).$$

Consider the following "game": player 1 chooses some $\mathbf{x} \geq \mathbf{0}$, and player 2 chooses some $\mathbf{p}$; then, player 1 pays to player 2 the amount $L(\mathbf{x}, \mathbf{p})$. Player 1 would like to minimize $L(\mathbf{x}, \mathbf{p})$, while player 2 would like to maximize it.

A pair $(\mathbf{x}^*, \mathbf{p}^*)$, with $\mathbf{x}^* \geq \mathbf{0}$, is called an *equilibrium* point (or a *saddle point*, or a *Nash equilibrium*) if

$$L(\mathbf{x}^*, \mathbf{p}) \leq L(\mathbf{x}^*, \mathbf{p}^*) \leq L(\mathbf{x}, \mathbf{p}^*), \qquad \forall \, \mathbf{x} \geq \mathbf{0}, \ \forall \, \mathbf{p}.$$

(Thus, we have an equilibrium if no player is able to improve her performance by unilaterally modifying her choice.)

Show that a pair $(\mathbf{x}^*, \mathbf{p}^*)$ is an equilibrium if and only if $\mathbf{x}^*$ and $\mathbf{p}^*$ are optimal solutions to the standard form problem under consideration and its dual, respectively.

Exercise 4.11 Consider a linear programming problem in standard form which is infeasible, but which becomes feasible and has finite optimal cost when the last equality constraint is omitted. Show that the dual of the original (infeasible) problem is feasible and the optimal cost is infinite.

Exercise 4.12* (Degeneracy and uniqueness – I) Consider a general linear programming problem and suppose that we have a nondegenerate basic feasible solution to the primal. Show that the complementary slackness conditions lead to a system of equations for the dual vector that has a unique solution.

Exercise 4.13* (Degeneracy and uniqueness – II) Consider the following pair of problems that are duals of each other:

$$
\begin{array}{ll}
\text{minimize} \quad \mathbf{c'x} & \qquad \text{maximize} \quad \mathbf{p'b} \\
\text{subject to} \quad \mathbf{Ax} = \mathbf{b} & \qquad \text{subject to} \quad \mathbf{p'A} \leq \mathbf{c'}. \\
\qquad\qquad\quad \mathbf{x} \geq \mathbf{0},
\end{array}
$$

(a) Prove that if one problem has a nondegenerate and unique optimal solution, so does the other.

(b) Suppose that we have a nondegenerate optimal basis for the primal and that the reduced cost for one of the basic variables is zero. What does the result of part (a) imply? Is it true that there must exist another optimal basis?

Exercise 4.14 (Degeneracy and uniqueness – III) Give an example in which the primal problem has a degenerate optimal basic feasible solution, but the dual has a unique optimal solution. (The example need not be in standard form.)

Exercise 4.15 (Degeneracy and uniqueness – IV) Consider the problem

$$
\begin{aligned}
\text{minimize}\quad & x_2 \\
\text{subject to}\quad & x_2 = 1 \\
& x_1 \geq 0 \\
& x_2 \geq 0.
\end{aligned}
$$

Write down its dual. For both the primal and the dual problem determine whether they have unique optimal solutions and whether they have nondegenerate optimal solutions. Is this example in agreement with the statement that nondegeneracy of an optimal basic feasible solution in one problem implies uniqueness of optimal solutions for the other? Explain.

Exercise 4.16 Give an example of a pair (primal and dual) of linear programming problems, both of which have multiple optimal solutions.

Exercise 4.17 This exercise is meant to demonstrate that knowledge of a primal optimal solution does not necessarily contain information that can be exploited to determine a dual optimal solution. In particular, determining an optimal solution to the dual is as hard as solving a system of linear inequalities, even if an optimal solution to the primal is available.

Consider the problem of minimizing $c'x$ subject to $Ax \geq 0$, and suppose that we are told that the zero vector is optimal. Let the dimensions of A be $m \times n$, and suppose that we have an algorithm that determines a dual optimal solution and whose running time $O\big((m+n)^k\big)$, for some constant k. (Note that if $x = 0$ is not an optimal primal solution, the dual has no feasible solution, and we assume that in this case our algorithm exits with an error message.) Assuming the availability of the above algorithm, construct a new algorithm that takes as input a system of m linear inequalities in n variables, runs for $O\big((m+n)^k\big)$ time, and either finds a feasible solution or determines that no feasible solution exists.

Exercise 4.18 Consider a problem in standard form. Suppose that the matrix A has dimensions $m \times n$ and its rows are linearly independent. Suppose that all basic solutions to the primal and to the dual are nondegenerate. Let x be a feasible solution to the primal and let p be a dual vector (not necessarily feasible), such that the pair (x, p) satisfies complementary slackness.

(a) Show that there exist m columns of A that are linearly independent and such that the corresponding components of x are all positive.

(b) Show that $\mathbf{x}$ and $\mathbf{p}$ are basic solutions to the primal and the dual, respectively.

(c) Show that the result of part (a) is false if the nondegeneracy assumption is removed.

Exercise 4.19 Let $P = \{\mathbf{x} \in \Re^n \mid \mathbf{A}\mathbf{x} = \mathbf{b}, \ \mathbf{x} \geq \mathbf{0}\}$ be a nonempty polyhedron, and let m be the dimension of the vector $\mathbf{b}$. We call x_j a *null variable* if $x_j = 0$ whenever $\mathbf{x} \in P$.

(a) Suppose that there exists some $\mathbf{p} \in \Re^m$ for which $\mathbf{p}'\mathbf{A} \geq \mathbf{0}'$, $\mathbf{p}'\mathbf{b} = 0$, and such that the jth component of $\mathbf{p}'\mathbf{A}$ is positive. Prove that x_j is a null variable.

(b) Prove the converse of (a): if x_j is a null variable, then there exists some $\mathbf{p} \in \Re^m$ with the properties stated in part (a).

(c) If x_j is not a null variable, then by definition, there exists some $\mathbf{y} \in P$ for which $y_j > 0$. Use the results in parts (a) and (b) to prove that there exist $\mathbf{x} \in P$ and $\mathbf{p} \in \Re^m$ such that:

$$\mathbf{p}'\mathbf{A} \geq \mathbf{0}', \qquad \mathbf{p}'\mathbf{b} = 0, \qquad \mathbf{x} + \mathbf{A}'\mathbf{p} > \mathbf{0}.$$

Exercise 4.20 * (Strict complementary slackness)

(a) Consider the following linear programming problem and its dual

$$
\begin{array}{llll}
\text{minimize} & \mathbf{c}'\mathbf{x} & \text{maximize} & \mathbf{p}'\mathbf{b} \\
\text{subject to} & \mathbf{A}\mathbf{x} = \mathbf{b} & \text{subject to} & \mathbf{p}'\mathbf{A} \leq \mathbf{c}', \\
& \mathbf{x} \geq \mathbf{0}, & &
\end{array}
$$

and assume that both problems have an optimal solution. Fix some j. Suppose that every optimal solution to the primal satisfies $x_j = 0$. Show that there exists an optimal solution $\mathbf{p}$ to the dual such that $\mathbf{p}'\mathbf{A}_j < c_j$. (Here, $\mathbf{A}_j$ is the jth column of $\mathbf{A}$.) *Hint:* Let d be the optimal cost. Consider the problem of minimizing $-x_j$ subject to $\mathbf{A}\mathbf{x} = \mathbf{b}$, $\mathbf{x} \geq \mathbf{0}$, and $-\mathbf{c}'\mathbf{x} \geq -d$, and form its dual.

(b) Show that there exist optimal solutions $\mathbf{x}$ and $\mathbf{p}$ to the primal and to the dual, respectively, such that for every j we have either $x_j > 0$ or $\mathbf{p}'\mathbf{A}_j < c_j$. *Hint:* Use part (a) for each j, and then take the average of the vectors obtained.

(c) Consider now the following linear programming problem and its dual:

$$
\begin{array}{llll}
\text{minimize} & \mathbf{c}'\mathbf{x} & \text{maximize} & \mathbf{p}'\mathbf{b} \\
\text{subject to} & \mathbf{A}\mathbf{x} \geq \mathbf{b} & \text{subject to} & \mathbf{p}'\mathbf{A} \leq \mathbf{c}' \\
& \mathbf{x} \geq \mathbf{0}, & & \mathbf{p} \geq \mathbf{0}.
\end{array}
$$

Assume that both problems have an optimal solution. Show that there exist optimal solutions to the primal and to the dual, respectively, that satisfy *strict complementary slackness*, that is:

(i) For every j we have either $x_j > 0$ or $\mathbf{p}'\mathbf{A}_j < c_j$.

(ii) For every i, we have either $\mathbf{a}_i'\mathbf{x} > b_i$ or $p_i > 0$. (Here, $\mathbf{a}_i'$ is the ith row of $\mathbf{A}$.) *Hint:* Convert the primal to standard form and apply part (b).

(d) Consider the linear programming problem

$$\begin{array}{ll}
\text{minimize} & 5x_1 + 5x_2 \\
\text{subject to} & x_1 + x_2 \geq 2 \\
& 2x_1 - x_2 \geq 0 \\
& x_1, x_2 \geq 0.
\end{array}$$

Does the optimal primal solution $(2/3, 4/3)$, together with the corresponding dual optimal solution, satisfy strict complementary slackness? Determine all primal and dual optimal solutions and identify the set of *all* strictly complementary pairs.

⋇ Exercise 4.21*   (Clark's theorem) Consider the following pair of linear programming problems:

$$\begin{array}{ll}
\text{minimize} & \mathbf{c}'\mathbf{x} \\
\text{subject to} & \mathbf{Ax} \geq \mathbf{b} \\
& \mathbf{x} \geq \mathbf{0},
\end{array}
\qquad\qquad
\begin{array}{ll}
\text{maximize} & \mathbf{p}'\mathbf{b} \\
\text{subject to} & \mathbf{p}'\mathbf{A} \leq \mathbf{c}' \\
& \mathbf{p} \geq \mathbf{0}.
\end{array}$$

Suppose that at least one of these two problems has a feasible solution. Prove that the set of feasible solutions to at least one of the two problems is unbounded. *Hint:* Interpret boundedness of a set in terms of the finiteness of the optimal cost of some linear programming problem.

Exercise 4.22 Consider the dual simplex method applied to a standard form problem with linearly independent rows. Suppose that we have a basis which is primal infeasible, but dual feasible, and let i be such that $x_{B(i)} < 0$. Suppose that all entries in the ith row in the tableau (other than $x_{B(i)}$) are nonnegative. Show that the optimal dual cost is $+\infty$.

Exercise 4.23 Describe in detail the mechanics of a revised dual simplex method that works in terms of the inverse basis matrix $\mathbf{B}^{-1}$ instead of the full simplex tableau.

Exercise 4.24 Consider the lexicographic pivoting rule for the dual simplex method and suppose that the algorithm is initialized with each column of the tableau being lexicographically positive. Prove that the dual simplex method does not cycle.

Exercise 4.25 This exercise shows that if we bring the dual problem into standard form and then apply the primal simplex method, the resulting algorithm is not identical to the dual simplex method.

Consider the following standard form problem and its dual.

$$\begin{array}{ll}
\text{minimize} & x_1 + x_2 \\
\text{subject to} & x_1 = 1 \\
& x_2 = 1 \\
& x_1, x_2 \geq 0
\end{array}
\qquad\qquad
\begin{array}{ll}
\text{maximize} & p_1 + p_2 \\
\text{subject to} & p_1 \leq 1 \\
& p_2 \leq 1.
\end{array}$$

Here, there is only one possible basis and the dual simplex method must terminate immediately. Show that if the dual problem is converted into standard form and the primal simplex method is applied to it, one or more changes of basis may be required.

Exercise 4.26 Let $\mathbf{A}$ be a given matrix. Show that exactly one of the following alternatives must hold.

(a) There exists some $\mathbf{x} \neq \mathbf{0}$ such that $\mathbf{Ax} = \mathbf{0}$, $\mathbf{x} \geq \mathbf{0}$.

(b) There exists some $\mathbf{p}$ such that $\mathbf{p}'\mathbf{A} > \mathbf{0}'$.

Exercise 4.27 Let $\mathbf{A}$ be a given matrix. Show that the following two statements are equivalent.

(a) Every vector such that $\mathbf{Ax} \geq \mathbf{0}$ and $\mathbf{x} \geq \mathbf{0}$ must satisfy $x_1 = 0$.

(b) There exists some $\mathbf{p}$ such that $\mathbf{p}'\mathbf{A} \leq \mathbf{0}$, $\mathbf{p} \geq \mathbf{0}$, and $\mathbf{p}'\mathbf{A}_1 < 0$, where $\mathbf{A}_1$ is the first column of $\mathbf{A}$.

Exercise 4.28 Let $\mathbf{a}$ and $\mathbf{a}_1, \ldots, \mathbf{a}_m$ be given vectors in $\Re^n$. Prove that the following two statements are equivalent:

(a) For all $\mathbf{x} \geq \mathbf{0}$, we have $\mathbf{a}'\mathbf{x} \leq \max_i \mathbf{a}_i'\mathbf{x}$.

(b) There exist nonnegative coefficients λ_i that sum to 1 and such that $\mathbf{a} \leq \sum_{i=1}^m \lambda_i \mathbf{a}_i$.

Exercise 4.29 (Inconsistent systems of linear inequalities) Let $\mathbf{a}_1, \ldots, \mathbf{a}_m$ be some vectors in $\Re^n$, with $m > n + 1$. Suppose that the system of inequalities $\mathbf{a}_i'\mathbf{x} \geq b_i$, $i = 1, \ldots, m$, does not have any solutions. Show that we can choose $n + 1$ of these inequalities, so that the resulting system of inequalities has no solutions.

Exercise 4.30 (Helly's theorem)

(a) Let $\mathcal{F}$ be a finite family of polyhedra in $\Re^n$ such that every $n+1$ polyhedra in $\mathcal{F}$ have a point in common. Prove that all polyhedra in $\mathcal{F}$ have a point in common. *Hint:* Use the result in Exercise 4.29.

(b) For $n = 2$, part (a) asserts that the polyhedra $P_1, P_2, \ldots, P_K$ $(K \geq 3)$ in the plane have a point in common if and only if every three of them have a point in common. Is the result still true with "three" replaced by "two"?

Exercise 4.31 (Unit eigenvectors of stochastic matrices) We say that an $n \times n$ matrix $\mathbf{P}$, with entries p_{ij}, is *stochastic* if all of its entries are nonnegative and

$$\sum_{j=1}^n p_{ij} = 1, \qquad \forall\, i,$$

that is, the sum of the entries of each row is equal to 1.

Use duality to show that if $\mathbf{P}$ is a stochastic matrix, then the system of equations

$$\mathbf{p}'\mathbf{P} = \mathbf{p}', \qquad \mathbf{p} \geq \mathbf{0},$$

has a nonzero solution. (Note that the vector $\mathbf{p}$ can be normalized so that its components sum to one. Then, the result in this exercise establishes that every finite state Markov chain has an invariant probability distribution.)

Exercise 4.32 * (Leontief systems and Samuelson's substitution theorem) A *Leontief matrix* is an $m \times n$ matrix $\mathbf{A}$ in which every column has at most one positive element. For an interpretation, each column $\mathbf{A}_j$ corresponds to a production process. If a_{ij} is negative, $|a_{ij}|$ represents the amount of goods of type i consumed by the process. If a_{ij} is positive, it represents the amount of goods of type i produced by the process. If x_j is the intensity with which process j is used, then $\mathbf{A}\mathbf{x}$ represents the net output of the different goods. The matrix $\mathbf{A}$ is called *productive* if there exists some $\mathbf{x} \geq \mathbf{0}$ such that $\mathbf{A}\mathbf{x} > \mathbf{0}$.

(a) Let $\mathbf{A}$ be a square productive Leontief matrix $(m = n)$. Show that every vector $\mathbf{z}$ that satisfies $\mathbf{A}\mathbf{z} \geq \mathbf{0}$ must be nonnegative. *Hint:* If $\mathbf{z}$ satisfies $\mathbf{A}\mathbf{z} \geq \mathbf{0}$ but has a negative component, consider the smallest nonnegative θ such that some component of $\mathbf{x} + \theta\mathbf{z}$ becomes zero, and derive a contradiction.

(b) Show that every square productive Leontief matrix is invertible and that all entries of the inverse matrix are nonnegative. *Hint:* Use the result in part (a).

(c) We now consider the general case where $n \geq m$, and we introduce a constraint of the form $\mathbf{e}'\mathbf{x} \leq 1$, where $\mathbf{e} = (1, \ldots, 1)$. (Such a constraint could capture, for example, a bottleneck due to the finiteness of the labor force.) An "output" vector $\mathbf{y} \in \Re^m$ is said to be *achievable* if $\mathbf{y} \geq \mathbf{0}$ and there exists some $\mathbf{x} \geq \mathbf{0}$ such that $\mathbf{A}\mathbf{x} = \mathbf{y}$ and $\mathbf{e}'\mathbf{y} \leq 1$. An achievable vector $\mathbf{y}$ is said to be *efficient* if there exists no achievable vector $\mathbf{z}$ such that $\mathbf{z} \geq \mathbf{y}$ and $\mathbf{z} \neq \mathbf{y}$. (Intuitively, an output vector $\mathbf{y}$ which is not efficient can be improved upon and is therefore uninteresting.) Suppose that $\mathbf{A}$ is productive. Show that there exists a positive efficient vector $\mathbf{y}$. *Hint:* Given a positive achievable vector $\mathbf{y}^*$, consider maximizing $\sum_i y_i$ over all achievable vectors $\mathbf{y}$ that are larger than $\mathbf{y}^*$.

(d) Suppose that $\mathbf{A}$ is productive. Show that there exists a set of m production processes that are capable of generating all possible efficient output vectors $\mathbf{y}$. That is, there exist indices $B(1), \ldots, B(m)$, such that every efficient output vector $\mathbf{y}$ can be expressed in the form $\mathbf{y} = \sum_{i=1}^{m} \mathbf{A}_{B(i)} x_{B(i)}$, for some nonnegative coefficients $x_{B(i)}$ whose sum is bounded by 1. *Hint:* Consider the problem of minimizing $\mathbf{e}'\mathbf{x}$ subject to $\mathbf{A}\mathbf{x} = \mathbf{y}$, $\mathbf{x} \geq \mathbf{0}$, and show that we can use the same optimal basis for all efficient vectors $\mathbf{y}$.

Exercise 4.33 (Options pricing) Consider a market that operates for a single period, and which involves three assets: a stock, a bond, and an option. Let S be the price of the stock, in the beginning of the period. Its price $\overline{S}$ at the end of the period is random and is assumed to be equal to either Su, with probability β, or Sd, with probability $1 - \beta$. Here u and d are scalars that satisfy $d < 1 < u$. Bonds are assumed riskless. Investing one dollar in a bond results in a payoff of r, at the end of the period. (Here, r is a scalar greater than 1.) Finally, the option gives us the right to purchase, at the end of the period, one stock at a fixed price of K. If the realized price $\overline{S}$ of the stock is greater than K, we exercise the option and then immediately sell the stock in the stock market, for a payoff of $\overline{S} - K$. If on the other hand we have $\overline{S} < K$, there is no advantage in exercising the option, and we receive zero payoff. Thus, the value of the option at the end of the period is equal to $\max\{0, \overline{S} - K\}$. Since the option is itself an asset, it should have a value in the beginning of the time period. Show that under the absence of arbitrage condition, the value of the option must be equal to

$$\gamma \max\{0, Su - K\} + \delta \max\{0, Sd - K\},$$

where γ and δ are a solution to the following system of linear equations:

$$u\gamma + d\delta = 1$$
$$\gamma + \delta = \frac{1}{r}.$$

Hint: Write down the payoff matrix **R** and use Theorem 4.8.

Exercise 4.34 (Finding separating hyperplanes) Consider a polyhedron P that has at least one extreme point.

(a) Suppose that we are given the extreme points $\mathbf{x}^i$ and a complete set of extreme rays $\mathbf{w}^j$ of P. Create a linear programming problem whose solution provides us with a separating hyperplane that separates P from the origin, or allows us to conclude that none exists.

(b) Suppose now that P is given to us in the form $P = \{\mathbf{x} \mid \mathbf{a}_i'\mathbf{x} \geq b_i, \ i = 1, \ldots, m\}$. Suppose that $\mathbf{0} \notin P$. Explain how a separating hyperplane can be found.

Exercise 4.35 (Separation of disjoint polyhedra) Consider two nonempty polyhedra $P = \{\mathbf{x} \in \Re^n \mid \mathbf{Ax} \leq \mathbf{b}\}$ and $Q = \{\mathbf{x} \in \Re^n \mid \mathbf{Dx} \leq \mathbf{d}\}$. We are interested in finding out whether the two polyhedra have a point in common.

(a) Devise a linear programming problem such that: if $P \cap Q$ is nonempty, it returns a point in $P \cap Q$; if $P \cap Q$ is empty, the linear programming problem is infeasible.

(b) Suppose that $P \cap Q$ is empty. Use the dual of the problem you have constructed in part (a) to show that there exists a vector $\mathbf{c}$ such that $\mathbf{c}'\mathbf{x} < \mathbf{c}'\mathbf{y}$ for all $\mathbf{x} \in P$ and $\mathbf{y} \in Q$.

Exercise 4.36 (Containment of polyhedra)

(a) Let P and Q be two polyhedra in $\Re^n$ described in terms of linear inequality constraints. Devise an algorithm that decides whether P is a subset of Q.

(b) Repeat part (a) if the polyhedra are described in terms of their extreme points and extreme rays.

Exercise 4.37 (Closedness of finitely generated cones) Let $\mathbf{A}_1, \ldots, \mathbf{A}_n$ be given vectors in $\Re^m$. Consider the cone $C = \left\{ \sum_{i=1}^n \mathbf{A}_i x_i \mid x_i \geq 0 \right\}$ and let $\mathbf{y}^k$, $k = 1, 2, \ldots$, be a sequence of elements of C that converges to some $\mathbf{y}$. Show that $\mathbf{y} \in C$ (and hence C is closed), using the following argument. With $\mathbf{y}$ fixed as above, consider the problem of minimizing $\|\mathbf{y} - \sum_{i=1}^n \mathbf{A}_i x_i\|_\infty$, subject to the constraints $x_1, \ldots, x_n \geq 0$. Here $\|\cdot\|_\infty$ stands for the maximum norm, defined by $\|\mathbf{x}\|_\infty = \max_i |x_i|$. Explain why the above minimization problem has an optimal solution, find the value of the optimal cost, and prove that $\mathbf{y} \in C$.

Exercise 4.38 (From Farkas' lemma to duality) Use Farkas' lemma to prove the duality theorem for a linear programming problem involving constraints of the form $a_i'x = b_i$, $a_i'x \geq b_i$, and nonnegativity constraints for some of the variables x_j. *Hint:* Start by deriving the form of the set of feasible directions at an optimal solution.

Exercise 4.39 (Extreme rays of cones) Let us define a nonzero element d of a pointed polyhedral cone C to be an *extreme ray* if it has the following property: if there exist vectors $f \in C$ and $g \in C$ and some $\lambda \in (0, 1)$ satisfying $d = f + g$, then both f and g are scalar multiples of d. Prove that this definition of extreme rays is equivalent to Definition 4.2.

Exercise 4.40 (Extreme rays of a cone are extreme points of its sections) Consider the cone $C = \{x \in \Re^n \mid a_i'x \geq 0, \ i = 1, \ldots, m\}$ and assume that the first n constraint vectors $a_1, \ldots, a_n$ are linearly independent. For any nonnegative scalar r, we define the polyhedron P_r by

$$P_r = \left\{ x \in C \ \Big| \ \sum_{i=1}^{n} a_i'x = r \right\}.$$

(a) Show that the polyhedron P_r is bounded for every $r \geq 0$.

(b) Let $r > 0$. Show that a vector $x \in P_r$ is an extreme point of P_r if and only if x is an extreme ray of the cone C.

Exercise 4.41 (Carathéodory's theorem) Show that every element x of a bounded polyhedron $P \subset \Re^n$ can be expressed as a convex combination of at most $n + 1$ extreme points of P. *Hint:* Consider an extreme point of the set of all possible representations of x.

Exercise 4.42 (Problems with side constraints) Consider the linear programming problem of minimizing $c'x$ over a bounded polyhedron $P \subset \Re^n$ and subject to additional constraints $a_i'x = b_i$, $i = 1, \ldots, L$. Assume that the problem has a feasible solution. Show that there exists an optimal solution which is a convex combination of $L + 1$ extreme points of P. *Hint:* Use the resolution theorem to represent P.

Exercise 4.43

(a) Consider the minimization of $c_1 x_1 + c_2 x_2$ subject to the constraints

$$x_2 - 3 \leq x_1 \leq 2x_2 + 2, \qquad x_1, x_2 \geq 0.$$

Find necessary and sufficient conditions on (c_1, c_2) for the optimal cost to be finite.

(b) For a general feasible linear programming problem, consider the set of all cost vectors for which the optimal cost is finite. Is it a polyhedron? Prove your answer.

Exercise 4.44

(a) Let $P = \{(x_1, x_2) \mid x_1 - x_2 = 0, \ x_1 + x_2 = 0\}$. What are the extreme points and the extreme rays of P?

(b) Let $P = \{(x_1, x_2) \mid 4x_1 + 2x_2 \geq 8, \ 2x_1 + x_2 \leq 8\}$. What are the extreme points and the extreme rays of P?

(c) For the polyhedron of part (b), is it possible to express each one of its elements as a convex combination of its extreme points plus a nonnegative linear combination of its extreme rays? Is this compatible with the resolution theorem?

Exercise 4.45 Let P be a polyhedron with at least one extreme point. Is it possible to express an arbitrary element of P as a convex combination of its extreme points plus a nonnegative multiple of a single extreme ray?

Exercise 4.46 (Resolution theorem for polyhedral cones) Let C be a nonempty polyhedral cone.

(a) Show that C can be expressed as the union of a finite number $C_1, \ldots, C_k$ of pointed polyhedral cones. *Hint:* Intersect with orthants.

(b) Show that an extreme ray of C must be an extreme ray of one of the cones $C_1, \ldots, C_k$.

(c) Show that there exists a finite number of elements $\mathbf{w}^1, \ldots, \mathbf{w}^r$ of C such that

$$C = \left\{ \sum_{i=1}^{r} \theta_i \mathbf{w}^i \ \middle| \ \theta_1, \ldots, \theta_r \geq 0 \right\}.$$

Exercise 4.47 (Resolution theorem for general polyhedra) Let P be a polyhedron. Show that there exist vectors $\mathbf{x}^1, \ldots, \mathbf{x}^k$ and $\mathbf{w}^1, \ldots, \mathbf{w}^r$ such that

$$P = \left\{ \sum_{i=1}^{k} \lambda_i \mathbf{x}^i + \sum_{j=1}^{r} \theta_j \mathbf{w}^j \ \middle| \ \lambda_i \geq 0, \ \theta_j \geq 0, \ \sum_{i=1}^{k} \lambda_i = 1 \right\}.$$

Hint: Generalize the steps in the preceding exercise.

Exercise 4.48 * (Polar, finitely generated, and polyhedral cones) For any cone C, we define its *polar* $C^\perp$ by

$$C^\perp = \left\{ \mathbf{p} \mid \mathbf{p}'\mathbf{x} \leq 0, \text{ for all } \mathbf{x} \in C \right\}.$$

(a) Let F be a finitely generated cone, of the form

$$F = \left\{ \sum_{i=1}^{r} \theta_i \mathbf{w}^i \ \middle| \ \theta_1, \ldots, \theta_r \geq 0 \right\}.$$

Show that $F^\perp = \{\mathbf{p} \mid \mathbf{p}'\mathbf{w}^i \leq 0, \ i = 1, \ldots, r\}$, which is a polyhedral cone.

(b) Show that the polar of $F^\perp$ is F and conclude that the polar of a polyhedral cone is finitely generated. *Hint:* Use Farkas' lemma.

(c) Show that a finitely generated pointed cone F is a polyhedron. *Hint:* Consider the polar of the polar.

(d) **(Polar cone theorem)** Let C be a closed, nonempty, and convex cone. Show that $(C^\perp)^\perp = C$. *Hint:* Mimic the derivation of Farkas' lemma using the separating hyperplane theorem (Section 4.7).

(e) Is the polar cone theorem true when C is the empty set?

Exercise 4.49 Consider a polyhedron, and let $\mathbf{x}$, $\mathbf{y}$ be two basic feasible solutions. If we are only allowed to make moves from any basic feasible solution to an adjacent one, show that we can go from $\mathbf{x}$ to $\mathbf{y}$ in a finite number of steps. *Hint:* Generalize the simplex method to nonstandard form problems: starting from a nonoptimal basic feasible solution, move along an extreme ray of the cone of feasible directions.

Exercise 4.50 We are interested in the problem of deciding whether a polyhedron

$$Q = \left\{ \mathbf{x} \in \Re^n \mid A\mathbf{x} \le \mathbf{b}, \ D\mathbf{x} \ge \mathbf{d}, \ \mathbf{x} \ge \mathbf{0} \right\}$$

is nonempty. We assume that the polyhedron $P = \{\mathbf{x} \in \Re^n \mid A\mathbf{x} \le \mathbf{b}, \ \mathbf{x} \ge \mathbf{0}\}$ is nonempty and bounded. For any vector $\mathbf{p}$, of the same dimension as $\mathbf{d}$, we define

$$g(\mathbf{p}) = -\mathbf{p}'\mathbf{d} + \max_{\mathbf{x} \in P} \mathbf{p}'D\mathbf{x}.$$

(a) Show that if Q is nonempty, then $g(\mathbf{p}) \ge 0$ for all $\mathbf{p} \ge \mathbf{0}$.

(b) Show that if Q is empty, then there exists some $\mathbf{p} \ge \mathbf{0}$, such that $g(\mathbf{p}) < 0$.

(c) If Q is empty, what is the minimum of $g(\mathbf{p})$ over all $\mathbf{p} \ge \mathbf{0}$?

4.13   Notes and sources

4.3. The duality theorem is due to von Neumann (1947), and Gale, Kuhn, and Tucker (1951).

4.6. Farkas' lemma is due to Farkas (1894) and Minkowski (1896). See Schrijver (1986) for a comprehensive presentation of related results. The connection between duality theory and arbitrage was developed by Ross (1976, 1978).

4.7. Weierstrass' Theorem and its proof can be found in most texts on real analysis; see, for example, Rudin (1976). While the simplex method is only relevant to linear programming problems with a finite number of variables, the approach based on the separating hyperplane theorem leads to a generalization of duality theory that covers more general convex optimization problems, as well as infinite-dimensional linear programming problems, that is, linear programming problems with infinitely many variables and constraints; see, e.g., Luenberger (1969) and Rockafellar (1970).

4.9. The resolution theorem and its converse are usually attributed to Farkas, Minkowski, and Weyl.

4.10. For extensions of duality theory to problems involving general convex functions and constraint sets, see Rockafellar (1970) and Bertsekas (1995b).

4.12 Exercises 4.6 and 4.7 are adapted from Boyd and Vandenberghe (1995). The result on strict complementary slackness (Exercise 4.20) was proved by Tucker (1956). The result in Exercise 4.21 is due to Clark (1961). The result in Exercise 4.30 is due to Helly (1923). Input-output macroeconomic models of the form considered in Exercise 4.32, have been introduced by Leontief, who was awarded the 1973 Nobel prize in economics. The result in Exercise 4.41 is due to Carathéodory (1907).

Chapter 5

Sensitivity analysis

Contents

Consider the standard form problem

$$\begin{array}{ll} \text{minimize} & \mathbf{c'x} \\ \text{subject to} & \mathbf{Ax} = \mathbf{b} \\ & \mathbf{x} \geq \mathbf{0}, \end{array}$$

and its dual

$$\begin{array}{ll} \text{maximize} & \mathbf{p'b} \\ \text{subject to} & \mathbf{p'A} \leq \mathbf{c'}. \end{array}$$

In this chapter, we study the dependence of the optimal cost and the optimal solution on the coefficient matrix $\mathbf{A}$, the requirement vector $\mathbf{b}$, and the cost vector $\mathbf{c}$. This is an important issue in practice because we often have incomplete knowledge of the problem data and we may wish to predict the effects of certain parameter changes.

In the first section of this chapter, we develop conditions under which the optimal basis remains the same despite a change in the problem data, and we examine the consequences on the optimal cost. We also discuss how to obtain an optimal solution if we add or delete some constraints. In subsequent sections, we allow larger changes in the problem data, resulting in a new optimal basis, and we develop a global perspective of the dependence of the optimal cost on the vectors $\mathbf{b}$ and $\mathbf{c}$. The chapter ends with a brief discussion of parametric programming, which is an extension of the simplex method tailored to the case where there is a single scalar unknown parameter.

Many of the results in this chapter can be extended to cover general linear programming problems. Nevertheless, and in order to simplify the presentation, our standing assumption throughout this chapter will be that we are dealing with a standard form problem and that the rows of the $m \times n$ matrix $\mathbf{A}$ are linearly independent.

5.1 Local sensitivity analysis

In this section, we develop a methodology for performing sensitivity analysis. We consider a linear programming problem, and we assume that we already have an optimal basis $\mathbf{B}$ and the associated optimal solution $\mathbf{x}^*$. We then assume that some entry of $\mathbf{A}$, $\mathbf{b}$, or $\mathbf{c}$ has been changed, or that a new constraint is added, or that a new variable is added. We first look for conditions under which the current basis is still optimal. If these conditions are violated, we look for an algorithm that finds a new optimal solution without having to solve the new problem from scratch. We will see that the simplex method can be quite useful in this respect.

Having assumed that $\mathbf{B}$ is an optimal basis for the original problem, the following two conditions are satisfied:

$$\mathbf{B}^{-1}\mathbf{b} \geq \mathbf{0}, \qquad \text{(feasibility)}$$

$$\mathbf{c}' - \mathbf{c}_B' \mathbf{B}^{-1} \mathbf{A} \geq \mathbf{0}', \qquad \text{(optimality)}.$$

When the problem is changed, we check to see how these conditions are affected. By insisting that both conditions (feasibility and optimality) hold for the modified problem, we obtain the conditions under which the basis matrix $\mathbf{B}$ remains optimal for the modified problem. In what follows, we apply this approach to several examples.

A new variable is added

Suppose that we introduce a new variable x_{n+1}, together with a corresponding column $\mathbf{A}_{n+1}$, and obtain the new problem

$$
\begin{array}{ll}
\text{minimize} & \mathbf{c}'\mathbf{x} + c_{n+1} x_{n+1} \\
\text{subject to} & \mathbf{A}\mathbf{x} + \mathbf{A}_{n+1} x_{n+1} = \mathbf{b} \\
& \mathbf{x} \geq \mathbf{0}.
\end{array}
$$

We wish to determine whether the current basis $\mathbf{B}$ is still optimal.

We note that $(\mathbf{x}, x_{n+1}) = (\mathbf{x}^*, 0)$ is a basic feasible solution to the new problem associated with the basis $\mathbf{B}$, and we only need to examine the optimality conditions. For the basis $\mathbf{B}$ to remain optimal, it is necessary and sufficient that the reduced cost of x_{n+1} be nonnegative, that is,

$$\bar{c}_{n+1} = c_{n+1} - \mathbf{c}_B' \mathbf{B}^{-1} \mathbf{A}_{n+1} \geq 0.$$

If this condition is satisfied, $(\mathbf{x}^*, 0)$ is an optimal solution to the new problem. If, however, $\bar{c}_{n+1} < 0$, then $(\mathbf{x}^*, 0)$ is not necessarily optimal. In order to find an optimal solution, we add a column to the simplex tableau, associated with the new variable, and apply the primal simplex algorithm starting from the current basis $\mathbf{B}$. Typically, an optimal solution to the new problem is obtained with a small number of iterations, and this approach is usually much faster than solving the new problem from scratch.

Example 5.1 Consider the problem

$$
\begin{array}{lrcrcrcrcl}
\text{minimize} & -5x_1 & - & x_2 & + & 12x_3 & & \\
\text{subject to} & 3x_1 & + & 2x_2 & + & x_3 & & & = & 10 \\
& 5x_1 & + & 3x_2 & & & + & x_4 & = & 16 \\
& & & & x_1, \ldots, x_4 \geq 0. & & & &
\end{array}
$$

An optimal solution to this problem is given by $\mathbf{x} = (2, 2, 0, 0)$ and the corresponding simplex tableau is given by

		x_1	x_2	x_3	x_4
	12	0	0	2	7
$x_1 =$	2	1	0	-3	2
$x_2 =$	2	0	1	5	-3

Note that $\mathbf{B}^{-1}$ is given by the last two columns of the tableau.

Let us now introduce a variable x_5 and consider the new problem

$$
\begin{array}{rl}
\text{minimize} & -5x_1 - x_2 + 12x_3 \quad\quad - x_5 \\
\text{subject to} & 3x_1 + 2x_2 + x_3 \quad\quad + x_5 = 10 \\
& 5x_1 + 3x_2 \quad\quad + x_4 + x_5 = 16 \\
& x_1, \ldots, x_5 \geq 0.
\end{array}
$$

We have $\mathbf{A}_5 = (1, 1)$ and

$$
\bar{c}_5 = c_5 - \mathbf{c}_B' \mathbf{B}^{-1} \mathbf{A}_5 = -1 - \begin{bmatrix} -5 & -1 \end{bmatrix} \begin{bmatrix} -3 & 2 \\ 5 & -3 \end{bmatrix} \begin{bmatrix} 1 \\ 1 \end{bmatrix} = -4.
$$

Since $\bar{c}_5$ is negative, introducing the new variable to the basis can be beneficial. We observe that $\mathbf{B}^{-1}\mathbf{A}_5 = (-1, 2)$ and augment the tableau by introducing a column associated with x_5:

		x_1	x_2	x_3	x_4	x_5
	12	0	0	2	7	-4
$x_1 =$	2	1	0	-3	2	-1
$x_2 =$	2	0	1	5	-3	2

We then bring x_5 into the basis; x_2 exits and we obtain the following tableau, which happens to be optimal:

		x_1	x_2	x_3	x_4	x_5
	16	0	2	12	1	0
$x_1 =$	3	1	0.5	-0.5	0.5	0
$x_5 =$	1	0	0.5	2.5	-1.5	1

An optimal solution is given by $\mathbf{x} = (3, 0, 0, 0, 1)$.

A new inequality constraint is added

Let us now introduce a new constraint $\mathbf{a}_{m+1}' \mathbf{x} \geq b_{m+1}$, where $\mathbf{a}_{m+1}$ and b_{m+1} are given. If the optimal solution $\mathbf{x}^*$ to the original problem satisfies this constraint, then $\mathbf{x}^*$ is an optimal solution to the new problem as well. If the new constraint is violated, we introduce a nonnegative slack variable x_{n+1}, and rewrite the new constraint in the form $\mathbf{a}_{m+1}' \mathbf{x} - x_{n+1} = b_{m+1}$. We obtain a problem in standard form, in which the matrix $\mathbf{A}$ is replaced by

$$
\begin{bmatrix} \mathbf{A} & \mathbf{0} \\ \mathbf{a}_{m+1}' & -1 \end{bmatrix}.
$$

Let **B** be an optimal basis for the original problem. We form a basis for the new problem by selecting the original basic variables together with x_{n+1}. The new basis matrix $\overline{\mathbf{B}}$ is of the form

$$\overline{\mathbf{B}} = \begin{bmatrix} \mathbf{B} & \mathbf{0} \\ \mathbf{a}' & -1 \end{bmatrix},$$

where the row vector $\mathbf{a}'$ contains those components of $\mathbf{a}'_{m+1}$ associated with the original basic columns. (The determinant of this matrix is the negative of the determinant of **B**, hence nonzero, and we therefore have a true basis matrix.) The basic solution associated with this basis is $(\mathbf{x}^*, \mathbf{a}'_{m+1}\mathbf{x}^* - b_{m+1})$, and is infeasible because of our assumption that $\mathbf{x}^*$ violates the new constraint. Note that the new inverse basis matrix is readily available because

$$\overline{\mathbf{B}}^{-1} = \begin{bmatrix} \mathbf{B}^{-1} & \mathbf{0} \\ \mathbf{a}'\mathbf{B}^{-1} & -1 \end{bmatrix}.$$

(To see this, note that the product $\overline{\mathbf{B}}^{-1}\overline{\mathbf{B}}$ is equal to the identity matrix.)

Let $\mathbf{c}_B$ be the m-dimensional vector with the costs of the basic variables in the original problem. Then, the vector of reduced costs associated with the basis $\overline{\mathbf{B}}$ for the new problem, is given by

$$\begin{bmatrix} \mathbf{c}' & 0 \end{bmatrix} - \begin{bmatrix} \mathbf{c}'_B & 0 \end{bmatrix} \begin{bmatrix} \mathbf{B}^{-1} & \mathbf{0} \\ \mathbf{a}'\mathbf{B}^{-1} & -1 \end{bmatrix} \begin{bmatrix} \mathbf{A} & \mathbf{0} \\ \mathbf{a}'_{m+1} & -1 \end{bmatrix} = \begin{bmatrix} \mathbf{c}' - \mathbf{c}'_B\mathbf{B}^{-1}\mathbf{A} & 0 \end{bmatrix},$$

and is nonnegative due to the optimality of **B** for the original problem. Hence, $\overline{\mathbf{B}}$ is a dual feasible basis and we are in a position to apply the dual simplex method to the new problem. Note that an initial simplex tableau for the new problem is readily constructed. For example, we have

$$\overline{\mathbf{B}}^{-1} \begin{bmatrix} \mathbf{A} & \mathbf{0} \\ \mathbf{a}'_{m+1} & -1 \end{bmatrix} = \begin{bmatrix} \mathbf{B}^{-1}\mathbf{A} & \mathbf{0} \\ \mathbf{a}'\mathbf{B}^{-1}\mathbf{A} - \mathbf{a}'_{m+1} & 1 \end{bmatrix},$$

where $\mathbf{B}^{-1}\mathbf{A}$ is available from the final simplex tableau for the original problem.

Example 5.2 Consider again the problem in Example 5.1:

$$\begin{array}{lrcrcrcrcl}
\text{minimize} & -5x_1 & - & x_2 & + & 12x_3 & & & \\
\text{subject to} & 3x_1 & + & 2x_2 & + & x_3 & & & = 10 \\
& 5x_1 & + & 3x_2 & & & + & x_4 & = 16 \\
& & & x_1, \ldots, x_4 & \geq & 0, & & &
\end{array}$$

and recall the optimal simplex tableau:

		x_1	x_2	x_3	x_4
	12	0	0	2	7
$x_1 =$	2	1	0	-3	2
$x_2 =$	2	0	1	5	-3

We introduce the additional constraint $x_1 + x_2 \geq 5$, which is violated by the optimal solution $\mathbf{x}^* = (2, 2, 0, 0)$. We have $\mathbf{a}_{m+1} = (1, 1, 0, 0)$, $b_{m+1} = 5$, and $\mathbf{a}'_{m+1}\mathbf{x}^* < b_{m+1}$. We form the standard form problem

$$
\begin{aligned}
\text{minimize} \quad & -5x_1 - x_2 + 12x_3 \\
\text{subject to} \quad & 3x_1 + 2x_2 + x_3 && = 10 \\
& 5x_1 + 3x_2 && + x_4 && = 16 \\
& x_1 + x_2 && - x_5 && = 5 \\
& x_1, \ldots, x_5 \geq 0.
\end{aligned}
$$

Let $\mathbf{a}$ consist of the components of $\mathbf{a}_{m+1}$ associated with the basic variables. We then have $\mathbf{a} = (1, 1)$ and

$$
\mathbf{a}'\mathbf{B}^{-1}\mathbf{A} - \mathbf{a}'_{m+1} = \begin{bmatrix} 1 & 1 \end{bmatrix} \begin{bmatrix} 1 & 0 & -3 & 2 \\ 0 & 1 & 5 & -3 \end{bmatrix} - \begin{bmatrix} 1 & 1 & 0 & 0 \end{bmatrix} = \begin{bmatrix} 0 & 0 & 2 & -1 \end{bmatrix}.
$$

The tableau for the new problem is of the form

		x_1	x_2	x_3	x_4	x_5
	12	0	0	2	7	0
$x_1 =$	2	1	0	-3	2	0
$x_2 =$	2	0	1	5	-3	0
$x_5 =$	-1	0	0	2	-1	1

We now have all the information necessary to apply the dual simplex method to the new problem.

Our discussion has been focused on the case where an inequality constraint is added to the primal problem. Suppose now that we introduce a new constraint $\mathbf{p}'\mathbf{A}_{n+1} \leq c_{n+1}$ in the dual. This is equivalent to introducing a new variable in the primal, and we are back to the case that was considered in the preceding subsection.

A new equality constraint is added

We now consider the case where the new constraint is of the form $\mathbf{a}'_{m+1}\mathbf{x} = b_{m+1}$, and we assume that this new constraint is violated by the optimal solution $\mathbf{x}^*$ to the original problem. The dual of the new problem is

$$
\text{maximize} \quad \mathbf{p}'\mathbf{b} + p_{m+1}b_{m+1}
$$

$$
\text{subject to} \quad \begin{bmatrix} \mathbf{p}' & p_{m+1} \end{bmatrix} \begin{bmatrix} \mathbf{A} \\ \mathbf{a}'_{m+1} \end{bmatrix} \leq \mathbf{c}',
$$

where p_{m+1} is a dual variable associated with the new constraint. Let $\mathbf{p}^*$ be an optimal basic feasible solution to the original dual problem. Then, $(\mathbf{p}^*, 0)$ is a feasible solution to the new dual problem.

Let m be the dimension of $\mathbf{p}$, which is the same as the original number of constraints. Since $\mathbf{p}^*$ is a basic feasible solution to the original dual problem, m of the constraints in $(\mathbf{p}^*)'\mathbf{A} \leq \mathbf{c}'$ are linearly independent and active. However, there is no guarantee that at $(\mathbf{p}^*, 0)$ we will have $m+1$ linearly independent active constraints of the new dual problem. In particular, $(\mathbf{p}^*, 0)$ need not be a basic feasible solution to the new dual problem and may not provide a convenient starting point for the dual simplex method on the new problem. While it may be possible to obtain a dual basic feasible solution by setting p_{m+1} to a suitably chosen nonzero value, we present here an alternative approach.

Let us assume, without loss of generality, that $\mathbf{a}'_{m+1}\mathbf{x}^* > b_{m+1}$. We introduce the auxiliary primal problem

$$
\begin{array}{llll}
\text{minimize} & \mathbf{c}'\mathbf{x} + Mx_{n+1} & & \\
\text{subject to} & \mathbf{A}\mathbf{x} & = \mathbf{b} \\
& \mathbf{a}'_{m+1}\mathbf{x} - & x_{n+1} = b_{m+1} \\
& \mathbf{x} \geq \mathbf{0}, \; x_{n+1} \geq 0,
\end{array}
$$

where M is a large positive constant. A primal feasible basis for the auxiliary problem is obtained by picking the basic variables of the optimal solution to the original problem, together with the variable x_{n+1}. The resulting basis matrix is the same as the matrix $\overline{\mathbf{B}}$ of the preceding subsection. There is a difference, however. In the preceding subsection, $\overline{\mathbf{B}}$ was a dual feasible basis, whereas here $\overline{\mathbf{B}}$ is a primal feasible basis. For this reason, the primal simplex method can now be used to solve the auxiliary problem to optimality.

Suppose that an optimal solution to the auxiliary problem satisfies $x_{n+1} = 0$; this will be the case if the new problem is feasible and the coefficient M is large enough. Then, the additional constraint $\mathbf{a}'_{m+1}\mathbf{x} = b_{m+1}$ has been satisfied and we have an optimal solution to the new problem.

Changes in the requirement vector b

Suppose that some component b_i of the requirement vector $\mathbf{b}$ is changed to $b_i + \delta$. Equivalently, the vector $\mathbf{b}$ is changed to $\mathbf{b} + \delta\mathbf{e}_i$, where $\mathbf{e}_i$ is the ith unit vector. We wish to determine the range of values of δ under which the current basis remains optimal. Note that the optimality conditions are not affected by the change in $\mathbf{b}$. We therefore need to examine only the feasibility condition

$$
\mathbf{B}^{-1}(\mathbf{b} + \delta\mathbf{e}_i) \geq \mathbf{0}. \tag{5.1}
$$

Let $\mathbf{g} = (\beta_{1i}, \beta_{2i}, \ldots, \beta_{mi})$ be the ith column of $\mathbf{B}^{-1}$. Equation (5.1) becomes

$$
\mathbf{x}_B + \delta\mathbf{g} \geq \mathbf{0},
$$

or,

$$
x_{B(j)} + \delta\beta_{ji} \geq 0, \qquad j = 1, \ldots, m.
$$

Equivalently,

$$\max_{\{j|\beta_{ji}>0\}}\left(-\frac{x_{B(j)}}{\beta_{ji}}\right) \le \delta \le \min_{\{j|\beta_{ji}<0\}}\left(-\frac{x_{B(j)}}{\beta_{ji}}\right).$$

For δ in this range, the optimal cost, as a function of δ, is given by $\mathbf{c}_B'\mathbf{B}^{-1}(\mathbf{b} + \delta\mathbf{e}_i) = \mathbf{p}'\mathbf{b} + \delta p_i$, where $\mathbf{p}' = \mathbf{c}_B'\mathbf{B}^{-1}$ is the (optimal) dual solution associated with the current basis $\mathbf{B}$.

　　If δ is outside the allowed range, the current solution satisfies the optimality (or dual feasibility) conditions, but is primal infeasible. In that case, we can apply the dual simplex algorithm starting from the current basis.

Example 5.3 Consider the optimal tableau

		x_1	x_2	x_3	x_4
	12	0	0	2	7
$x_1 =$	2	1	0	-3	2
$x_2 =$	2	0	1	5	-3

from Example 5.1.

　　Let us contemplate adding δ to b_1. We look at the first column of $\mathbf{B}^{-1}$ which is $(-3, 5)$. The basic variables under the same basis are $x_1 = 2 - 3\delta$ and $2 + 5\delta$. This basis will remain feasible as long as $2 - 3\delta \ge 0$ and $2 + 5\delta \ge 0$, that is, if $-2/5 \le \delta \le 2/3$. The rate of change of the optimal cost per unit change of δ is given by $\mathbf{c}_B'\mathbf{B}^{-1}\mathbf{e}_1 = (-5, -1)'(-3, 5) = 10$.

　　If δ is increased beyond $2/3$, then x_1 becomes negative. At this point, we can perform an iteration of the dual simplex method to remove x_1 from the basis, and x_3 enters the basis.

Changes in the cost vector c

Suppose now that some cost coefficient c_j becomes $c_j + \delta$. The primal feasibility condition is not affected. We therefore need to focus on the optimality condition

$$\mathbf{c}_B'\mathbf{B}^{-1}\mathbf{A} \le \mathbf{c}'.$$

If c_j is the cost coefficient of a nonbasic variable x_j, then $\mathbf{c}_B$ does not change, and the only inequality that is affected is the one for the reduced cost of x_j; we need

$$\mathbf{c}_B'\mathbf{B}^{-1}\mathbf{A}_j \le c_j + \delta,$$

or

$$\delta \ge -\bar{c}_j.$$

If this condition holds, the current basis remains optimal; otherwise, we can apply the primal simplex method starting from the current basic feasible solution.

If c_j is the cost coefficient of the ℓth basic variable, that is, if $j = B(\ell)$, then $\mathbf{c}_B$ becomes $\mathbf{c}_B + \delta \mathbf{e}_\ell$ and all of the optimality conditions will be affected. The optimality conditions for the new problem are

$$\left(\mathbf{c}_B + \delta \mathbf{e}_\ell\right)' \mathbf{B}^{-1} \mathbf{A}_i \leq c_i, \qquad \forall\, i \neq j.$$

(Since x_j is a basic variable, its reduced cost stays at zero and need not be examined.) Equivalently,

$$\delta q_{\ell i} \leq \bar{c}_i, \qquad \forall\, i \neq j,$$

where $q_{\ell i}$ is the ℓth entry of $\mathbf{B}^{-1}\mathbf{A}_i$, which can be obtained from the simplex tableau. These inequalities determine the range of δ for which the same basis remains optimal.

Example 5.4 We consider once more the problem in Example 5.1 and determine the range of changes δ_i of c_i, under which the same basis remains optimal. Since x_3 and x_4 are nonbasic variables, we obtain the conditions

$$\delta_3 \geq -\bar{c}_3 = -2,$$
$$\delta_4 \geq -\bar{c}_4 = -7.$$

Consider now adding δ_1 to c_1. From the simplex tableau, we obtain $q_{12} = 0$, $q_{13} = -3$, $q_{14} = 2$, and we are led to the conditions

$$\delta_1 \geq -2/3,$$
$$\delta_1 \leq 7/2.$$

Changes in a nonbasic column of A

Suppose that some entry a_{ij} in the jth column $\mathbf{A}_j$ of the matrix $\mathbf{A}$ is changed to $a_{ij} + \delta$. We wish to determine the range of values of δ for which the old optimal basis remains optimal.

If the column $\mathbf{A}_j$ is nonbasic, the basis matrix $\mathbf{B}$ does not change, and the primal feasibility condition is unaffected. Furthermore, only the reduced cost of the jth column is affected, leading to the condition

$$c_j - \mathbf{p}'\left(\mathbf{A}_j + \delta \mathbf{e}_i\right) \geq 0,$$

or,

$$\bar{c}_j - \delta p_i \geq 0,$$

where $\mathbf{p}' = \mathbf{c}_B' \mathbf{B}^{-1}$. If this condition is violated, the nonbasic column $\mathbf{A}_j$ can be brought into the basis, and we can continue with the primal simplex method.

Changes in a basic column of A

If one of the entries of a basic column $\mathbf{A}_j$ changes, then both the feasibility and optimality conditions are affected. This case is more complicated and we leave the full development for the exercises. As it turns out, the range of values of δ for which the same basis is optimal is again an interval (Exercise 5.3).

Suppose that the basic column $\mathbf{A}_j$ is changed to $\mathbf{A}_j + \delta\mathbf{e}_i$, where $\mathbf{e}_i$ is the ith unit vector. Assume that both the original problem and its dual have unique and nondegenerate optimal solutions $\mathbf{x}^*$ and $\mathbf{p}$, respectively. Let $\mathbf{x}^*(\delta)$ be an optimal solution to the modified problem, as a function of δ. It can be shown (Exercise 5.2) that for small δ we have

$$\mathbf{c}'\mathbf{x}^*(\delta) = \mathbf{c}'\mathbf{x}^* - \delta x_j^* p_i + O(\delta^2).$$

For an intuitive interpretation of this equation, let us consider the diet problem and recall that a_{ij} corresponds to the amount of the ith nutrient in the jth food. Given an optimal solution $\mathbf{x}^*$ to the original problem, an increase of a_{ij} by δ means that we are getting "for free" an additional amount δx_j^* of the ith nutrient. Since the dual variable p_i is the marginal cost per unit of the ith nutrient, we are getting for free something that is normally worth $\delta p_i x_j^*$, and this allows us to reduce our costs by that same amount.

Production planning revisited

In Section 1.2, we introduced a production planning problem that DEC had faced in the end of 1988. In this section, we answer some of the questions that we posed. Recall that there were two important choices, whether to use the constrained or the unconstrained mode of production for disk drives, and whether to use alternative memory boards. As discussed in Section 1.2, these four combinations of choices led to four different linear programming problems. We report the solution to these problems, as obtained from a linear programming package, in Table 5.1.

Table 5.1 indicates that revenues can substantially increase by using alternative memory boards, and the company should definitely do so. The decision of whether to use the constrained or the unconstrained mode of production for disk drives is less clear. In the constrained mode, the revenue is 248 million versus 213 million in the unconstrained mode. However, customer satisfaction and, therefore, future revenues might be affected, since in the constrained mode some customers will get a product different than the desired one. Moreover, these results are obtained assuming that the number of available 256K memory boards and disk drives were 8,000 and 3,000, respectively, which is the lowest value in the range that was estimated. We should therefore examine the sensitivity of the solution as the number of available 256K memory boards and disk drives increases.

Alt. boards	Mode	Revenue	x_1	x_2	x_3	x_4	x_5
no	constr.	145	0	2.5	0	0.5	2
yes	constr.	248	1.8	2	0	1	2
no	unconstr.	133	0.272	1.304	0.3	0.5	2.7
yes	unconstr.	213	1.8	1.035	0.3	0.5	2.7

Table 5.1: Optimal solutions to the four variants of the production planning problem. Revenue is in millions of dollars and the quantities x_i are in thousands.

With most linear programming packages, the output includes the values of the dual variables, as well as the range of parameter variations under which local sensitivity analysis is valid. Table 5.2 presents the values of the dual variables associated with the constraints on available disk drives and 256K memory boards. In addition, it provides the range of allowed changes on the number of disk drives and memory boards that would leave the dual variables unchanged. This information is provided for the two linear programming problems corresponding to constrained and unconstrained mode of production for disk drives, respectively, under the assumption that alternative memory boards will be used.

Mode	Constrained	Unconstrained
Revenue	248	213
Dual variable for 256K boards	15	0
Range for 256K boards	$[-1.5, 0.2]$	$[-1.62, \infty]$
Dual variable for disk drives	0	23.52
Range for disk drives	$[-0.2, 0.75]$	$[-0.91, 1.13]$

Table 5.2: Dual prices and ranges for the constraints corresponding to the availability of the number of 256K memory boards and disk drives.

In the constrained mode, increasing the number of available 256K boards by 0.2 thousand (the largest number in the allowed range) results in a revenue increase of $15 \times 0.2 = 3$ million. In the unconstrained mode, increasing the number of available 256K boards has no effect on revenues, because the dual variable is zero and the range extends upwards to infinity. In the constrained mode, increasing the number of available disk drives by up to 0.75 thousand (the largest number in the allowed range) has no effect on revenue. Finally, in the unconstrained mode, increasing the number of available disk drives by 1.13 thousand results in a revenue increase of $23.52 \times 1.13 = 26.57$ million.

In conclusion, in the constrained mode of production, it is important to aim at an increase of the number of available 256K memory boards, while in the unconstrained mode, increasing the number of disk drives is more important.

This example demonstrates that even a small linear programming problem (with five variables, in this case) can have an impact on a company's planning process. Moreover, the information provided by linear programming solvers (dual variables, ranges, etc.) can offer significant insights and can be a very useful aid to decision makers.

5.2   Global dependence on the right-hand side vector

In this section, we take a global view of the dependence of the optimal cost on the requirement vector $\mathbf{b}$.

Let

$$P(\mathbf{b}) = \left\{ \mathbf{x} \mid \mathbf{A}\mathbf{x} = \mathbf{b}, \ \mathbf{x} \geq \mathbf{0} \right\}$$

be the feasible set, and note that our notation makes the dependence on $\mathbf{b}$ explicit. Let

$$S = \left\{ \mathbf{b} \mid P(\mathbf{b}) \text{ is nonempty} \right\},$$

and observe that

$$S = \left\{ \mathbf{A}\mathbf{x} \mid \mathbf{x} \geq \mathbf{0} \right\};$$

in particular, S is a convex set. For any $\mathbf{b} \in S$, we define

$$F(\mathbf{b}) = \min_{\mathbf{x} \in P(\mathbf{b})} \mathbf{c}'\mathbf{x},$$

which is the optimal cost as a function of $\mathbf{b}$.

Throughout this section, we assume that the dual feasible set $\{\mathbf{p} \mid \mathbf{p}'\mathbf{A} \leq \mathbf{c}'\}$ is nonempty. Then, duality theory implies that the optimal primal cost $F(\mathbf{b})$ is finite for every $\mathbf{b} \in S$. Our goal is to understand the structure of the function $F(\mathbf{b})$, for $\mathbf{b} \in S$.

Let us fix a particular element $\mathbf{b}^*$ of S. Suppose that there exists a nondegenerate primal optimal basic feasible solution, and let $\mathbf{B}$ be the corresponding optimal basis matrix. The vector $\mathbf{x}_B$ of basic variables at that optimal solution is given by $\mathbf{x}_B = \mathbf{B}^{-1}\mathbf{b}^*$, and is positive by nondegeneracy. In addition, the vector of reduced costs is nonnegative. If we change $\mathbf{b}^*$ to $\mathbf{b}$ and if the difference $\mathbf{b} - \mathbf{b}^*$ is sufficiently small, $\mathbf{B}^{-1}\mathbf{b}$ remains positive and we still have a basic feasible solution. The reduced costs are not affected by the change from $\mathbf{b}^*$ to $\mathbf{b}$ and remain nonnegative. Therefore, $\mathbf{B}$ is an optimal basis for the new problem as well. The optimal cost $F(\mathbf{b})$ for the new problem is given by

$$F(\mathbf{b}) = \mathbf{c}_B'\mathbf{B}^{-1}\mathbf{b} = \mathbf{p}'\mathbf{b}, \qquad \text{for } \mathbf{b} \text{ close to } \mathbf{b}^*,$$

where $\mathbf{p}' = \mathbf{c}_B'\mathbf{B}^{-1}$ is the optimal solution to the dual problem. This establishes that in the vicinity of $\mathbf{b}^*$, $F(\mathbf{b})$ is a linear function of $\mathbf{b}$ and its gradient is given by $\mathbf{p}$.

We now turn to the global properties of $F(\mathbf{b})$.

Theorem 5.1 *The optimal cost* $F(\mathbf{b})$ *is a convex function of* $\mathbf{b}$ *on the set* S.

Proof.   Let $\mathbf{b}^1$ and $\mathbf{b}^2$ be two elements of S. For $i = 1, 2$, let $\mathbf{x}^i$ be an optimal solution to the problem of minimizing $\mathbf{c}'\mathbf{x}$ subject to $\mathbf{x} \geq \mathbf{0}$ and $\mathbf{A}\mathbf{x} = \mathbf{b}^i$. Thus, $F(\mathbf{b}^1) = \mathbf{c}'\mathbf{x}^1$ and $F(\mathbf{b}^2) = \mathbf{c}'\mathbf{x}^2$. Fix a scalar $\lambda \in [0, 1]$, and note that the vector $\mathbf{y} = \lambda\mathbf{x}^1 + (1 - \lambda)\mathbf{x}^2$ is nonnegative and satisfies $\mathbf{A}\mathbf{y} = \lambda\mathbf{b}^1 + (1 - \lambda)\mathbf{b}^2$. In particular, $\mathbf{y}$ is a feasible solution to the linear programming problem obtained when the requirement vector $\mathbf{b}$ is set to $\lambda\mathbf{b}^1 + (1 - \lambda)\mathbf{b}^2$. Therefore,

$$F\big(\lambda\mathbf{b}^1 + (1 - \lambda)\mathbf{b}^2\big) \leq \mathbf{c}'\mathbf{y} = \lambda\mathbf{c}'\mathbf{x}^1 + (1 - \lambda)\mathbf{c}'\mathbf{x}^2 = \lambda F(\mathbf{b}^1) + (1 - \lambda)F(\mathbf{b}^2),$$

establishing the convexity of F. $\square$

We now corroborate Theorem 5.1 by taking a different approach, involving the dual problem

$$\text{maximize} \quad \mathbf{p}'\mathbf{b}$$
$$\text{subject to} \quad \mathbf{p}'\mathbf{A} \leq \mathbf{c}',$$

which has been assumed feasible. For any $\mathbf{b} \in S$, $F(\mathbf{b})$ is finite and, by strong duality, is equal to the optimal value of the dual objective. Let $\mathbf{p}^1, \mathbf{p}^2, \ldots, \mathbf{p}^N$ be the extreme points of the dual feasible set. (Our standing assumption is that the matrix $\mathbf{A}$ has linearly independent rows; hence its columns span $\Re^m$. Equivalently, the rows of $\mathbf{A}'$ span $\Re^m$ and Theorem 2.6 in Section 2.5 implies that the dual feasible set must have at least one

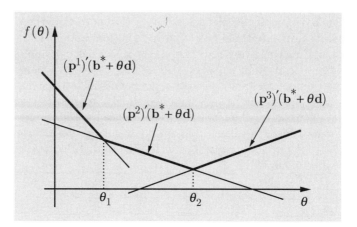

Figure 5.1: The optimal cost when the vector $\mathbf{b}$ is a function of a scalar parameter. Each linear piece is of the form $(\mathbf{p}^i)'(\mathbf{b}^* + \theta\mathbf{d})$, where $\mathbf{p}^i$ is the ith extreme point of the dual feasible set. In each one of the intervals $\theta < \theta_1$, $\theta_1 < \theta < \theta_2$, and $\theta > \theta_2$, we have different dual optimal solutions, namely, $\mathbf{p}^1$, $\mathbf{p}^2$, and $\mathbf{p}^3$, respectively. For $\theta = \theta_1$ or $\theta = \theta_2$, the dual problem has multiple optimal solutions.

extreme point.) Since the optimum of the dual must be attained at an extreme point, we obtain

$$F(\mathbf{b}) = \max_{i=1,\dots,N} (\mathbf{p}^i)'\mathbf{b}, \qquad \mathbf{b} \in S. \qquad (5.2)$$

In particular, F is equal to the maximum of a finite collection of linear functions. It is therefore a piecewise linear convex function, and we have a new proof of Theorem 5.1. In addition, within a region where F is linear, we have $F(\mathbf{b}) = (\mathbf{p}^i)'\mathbf{b}$, where $\mathbf{p}^i$ is a corresponding dual optimal solution, in agreement with our earlier discussion.

For those values of $\mathbf{b}$ for which F is not differentiable, that is, at the junction of two or more linear pieces, the dual problem does not have a unique optimal solution and this implies that every optimal basic feasible solution to the primal is degenerate. (This is because, as shown earlier in this section, the existence of a nondegenerate optimal basic feasible solution to the primal implies that F is locally linear.)

We now restrict attention to changes in $\mathbf{b}$ of a particular type, namely, $\mathbf{b} = \mathbf{b}^* + \theta\mathbf{d}$, where $\mathbf{b}^*$ and $\mathbf{d}$ are fixed vectors and θ is a scalar. Let $f(\theta) = F(\mathbf{b}^* + \theta\mathbf{d})$ be the optimal cost as a function of the scalar parameter θ. Using Eq. (5.2), we obtain

$$f(\theta) = \max_{i=1,\dots,N} (\mathbf{p}^i)'(\mathbf{b}^* + \theta\mathbf{d}), \qquad \mathbf{b}^* + \theta\mathbf{d} \in S.$$

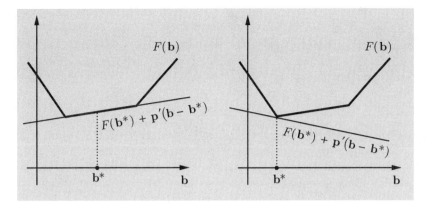

Figure 5.2: Illustration of subgradients of a function F at a point $\mathbf{b}^*$. A subgradient $\mathbf{p}$ is the gradient of a linear function $F(\mathbf{b}^*) + \mathbf{p}'(\mathbf{b} - \mathbf{b}^*)$ that lies below the function $F(\mathbf{b})$ and agrees with it for $\mathbf{b} = \mathbf{b}^*$.

This is essentially a "section" of the function F; it is again a piecewise linear convex function; see Figure 5.1. Once more, at breakpoints of this function, every optimal basic feasible solution to the primal must be degenerate.

5.3   The set of all dual optimal solutions*

We have seen that if the function F is defined, finite, and linear in the vicinity of a certain vector $\mathbf{b}^*$, then there is a unique optimal dual solution, equal to the gradient of F at that point, which leads to the interpretation of dual optimal solutions as marginal costs. We would like to extend this interpretation so that it remains valid at the breakpoints of F. This is indeed possible: we will show shortly that any dual optimal solution can be viewed as a "generalized gradient" of F. We first need the following definition, which is illustrated in Figure 5.2.

Definition 5.1 *Let F be a convex function defined on a convex set S. Let $\mathbf{b}^*$ be an element of S. We say that a vector $\mathbf{p}$ is a* **subgradient** *of F at $\mathbf{b}^*$ if*

$$F(\mathbf{b}^*) + \mathbf{p}'(\mathbf{b} - \mathbf{b}^*) \leq F(\mathbf{b}), \qquad \forall\, \mathbf{b} \in S.$$

Note that if $\mathbf{b}^*$ is a breakpoint of the function F, then there are several subgradients. On the other hand, if F is linear near $\mathbf{b}^*$, there is a unique subgradient, equal to the gradient of F.

Theorem 5.2 *Suppose that the linear programming problem of min-imizing $c'x$ subject to $Ax = b^*$ and $x \geq 0$ is feasible and that the optimal cost is finite. Then, a vector p is an optimal solution to the dual problem if and only if it is a subgradient of the optimal cost function F at the point b^*.*

Proof. Recall that the function F is defined on the set S, which is the set of vectors b for which the set $P(b)$ of feasible solutions to the primal problem is nonempty. Suppose that p is an optimal solution to the dual problem. Then, strong duality implies that $p'b^* = F(b^*)$. Consider now some arbitrary $b \in S$. For any feasible solution $x \in P(b)$, weak duality yields $p'b \leq c'x$. Taking the minimum over all $x \in P(b)$, we obtain $p'b \leq F(b)$. Hence, $p'b - p'b^* \leq F(b) - F(b^*)$, and we conclude that p is a subgradient of F at b^*.

We now prove the converse. Let p be a subgradient of F at b^*; that is,

$$F(b^*) + p'(b - b^*) \leq F(b), \qquad \forall \, b \in S. \qquad (5.3)$$

Pick some $x \geq 0$, let $b = Ax$, and note that $x \in P(b)$. In particular, $F(b) \leq c'x$. Using Eq. (5.3), we obtain

$$p'Ax = p'b \leq F(b) - F(b^*) + p'b^* \leq c'x - F(b^*) + p'b^*.$$

Since this is true for all $x \geq 0$, we must have $p'A \leq c'$, which shows that p is a dual feasible solution. Also, by letting $x = 0$, we obtain $F(b^*) \leq p'b^*$. Using weak duality, every dual feasible solution q must satisfy $q'b^* \leq F(b^*) \leq p'b^*$, which shows that p is a dual optimal solution. $\qquad \square$

5.4 Global dependence on the cost vector

In the last two sections, we fixed the matrix A and the vector c, and we considered the effect of changing the vector b. The key to our development was the fact that the set of dual feasible solutions remains the same as b varies. In this section, we study the case where A and b are fixed, but the vector c varies. In this case, the primal feasible set remains unaffected; our standing assumption will be that it is nonempty.

We define the dual feasible set

$$Q(c) = \{p \mid p'A \leq c\},$$

and let

$$T = \{c \mid Q(c) \text{ is nonempty}\}.$$

If $c^1 \in T$ and $c^2 \in T$, then there exist p^1 and p^2 such that $(p^1)'A \leq c'$ and $(p^2)'A \leq c'$. For any scalar $\lambda \in [0, 1]$, we have

$$\big(\lambda(p^1)' + (1 - \lambda)(p^2)'\big)A \leq \lambda c^1 + (1 - \lambda)c^2,$$

and this establishes that $\lambda \mathbf{c}^1 + (1 - \lambda)\mathbf{c}^2 \in T$. We have therefore shown that T is a convex set.

If $\mathbf{c} \notin T$, the infeasibility of the dual problem implies that the optimal primal cost is $-\infty$. On the other hand, if $\mathbf{c} \in T$, the optimal primal cost must be finite. Thus, the optimal primal cost, which we will denote by $G(\mathbf{c})$, is finite if and only if $\mathbf{c} \in T$.

Let $\mathbf{x}^1, \mathbf{x}^2, \ldots, \mathbf{x}^N$ be the basic feasible solutions in the primal feasible set; clearly, these do not depend on $\mathbf{c}$. Since an optimal solution to a standard form problem can always be found at an extreme point, we have

$$G(\mathbf{c}) = \min_{i=1,\ldots,N} \mathbf{c}'\mathbf{x}^i.$$

Thus, $G(\mathbf{c})$ is the minimum of a finite collection of linear functions and is a piecewise linear concave function. If for some value $\mathbf{c}^*$ of $\mathbf{c}$, the primal has a unique optimal solution $\mathbf{x}^i$, we have $(\mathbf{c}^*)'\mathbf{x}^i < (\mathbf{c}^*)'\mathbf{x}^j$, for all $j \neq i$. For $\mathbf{c}$ very close to $\mathbf{c}^*$, the inequalities $\mathbf{c}'\mathbf{x}^i < \mathbf{c}'\mathbf{x}^j$, $j \neq i$, continue to hold, implying that $\mathbf{x}^i$ is still a unique primal optimal solution with cost $\mathbf{c}'\mathbf{x}^i$. We conclude that, locally, $G(\mathbf{c}) = \mathbf{c}'\mathbf{x}^i$. On the other hand, at those values of $\mathbf{c}$ that lead to multiple primal optimal solutions, the function G has a breakpoint.

We summarize the main points of the preceding discussion.

Theorem 5.3 *Consider a feasible linear programming problem in standard form.*

(a) *The set T of all $\mathbf{c}$ for which the optimal cost is finite, is convex.*

(b) *The optimal cost $G(\mathbf{c})$ is a concave function of $\mathbf{c}$ on the set T.*

(c) *If for some value of $\mathbf{c}$ the primal problem has a unique optimal solution $\mathbf{x}^*$, then G is linear in the vicinity of $\mathbf{c}$ and its gradient is equal to $\mathbf{x}^*$.*

5.5 Parametric programming

Let us fix $\mathbf{A}$, $\mathbf{b}$, $\mathbf{c}$, and a vector $\mathbf{d}$ of the same dimension as $\mathbf{c}$. For any scalar θ, we consider the problem

$$\begin{aligned} \text{minimize} \quad & (\mathbf{c} + \theta\mathbf{d})'\mathbf{x} \\ \text{subject to} \quad & \mathbf{A}\mathbf{x} = \mathbf{b} \\ & \mathbf{x} \geq \mathbf{0}, \end{aligned}$$

and let $g(\theta)$ be the optimal cost as a function of θ. Naturally, we assume that the feasible set is nonempty. For those values of θ for which the optimal cost is finite, we have

$$g(\theta) = \min_{i=1,\ldots,N} (\mathbf{c} + \theta\mathbf{d})'\mathbf{x}^i,$$

where $\mathbf{x}^1, \ldots, \mathbf{x}^N$ are the extreme points of the feasible set; see Figure 5.3. In particular, $g(\theta)$ is a piecewise linear and concave function of the parameter θ. In this section, we discuss a systematic procedure, based on the simplex method, for obtaining $g(\theta)$ for all values of θ. We start with an example.

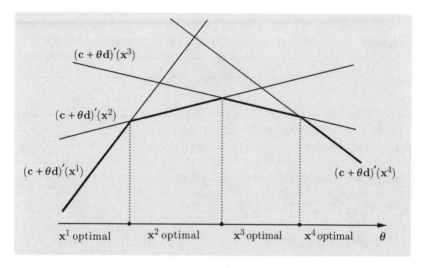

Figure 5.3: The optimal cost $g(\theta)$ as a function of θ.

Example 5.5 Consider the problem

$$
\begin{array}{rl}
\text{minimize} & (-3 + 2\theta)x_1 + (3 - \theta)x_2 + x_3 \\
\text{subject to} & x_1 + 2x_2 - 3x_3 \leq 5 \\
& 2x_1 + x_2 - 4x_3 \leq 7 \\
& x_1, x_2, x_3 \geq 0.
\end{array}
$$

We introduce slack variables in order to bring the problem into standard form, and then let the slack variables be the basic variables. This determines a basic feasible solution and leads to the following tableau.

		x_1	x_2	x_3	x_4	x_5
	0	$-3 + 2\theta$	$3 - \theta$	1	0	0
$x_4 =$	5	1	2	-3	1	0
$x_5 =$	7	2	1	-4	0	1

If $-3 + 2\theta \geq 0$ and $3 - \theta \geq 0$, all reduced costs are nonnegative and we have an optimal basic feasible solution. In particular,

$$
g(\theta) = 0, \qquad \text{if } \frac{3}{2} \leq \theta \leq 3.
$$

If θ is increased slightly above 3, the reduced cost of x_2 becomes negative and we no longer have an optimal basic feasible solution. We let x_2 enter the basis, x_4 exits, and we obtain the new tableau:

	x_1	x_2	x_3	x_4	x_5
	$-7.5 + 2.5\theta$	$-4.5 + 2.5\theta$	0	$5.5 - 1.5\theta$	$-1.5 + 0.5\theta$	0
$x_2 =$	2.5	0.5	1	-1.5	0.5	0
$x_5 =$	4.5	1.5	0	-2.5	-0.5	1

We note that all reduced costs are nonnegative if and only if $3 \le \theta \le 5.5/1.5$. The optimal cost for that range of values of θ is

$$g(\theta) = 7.5 - 2.5\theta, \qquad \text{if } 3 \le \theta \le \frac{5.5}{1.5}.$$

If θ is increased beyond $5.5/1.5$, the reduced cost of x_3 becomes negative. If we attempt to bring x_3 into the basis, we cannot find a positive pivot element in the third column of the tableau, and the problem is unbounded, with $g(\theta) = -\infty$.

Let us now go back to the original tableau and suppose that θ is decreased to a value slightly below $3/2$. Then, the reduced cost of x_1 becomes negative, we let x_1 enter the basis, and x_5 exits. The new tableau is:

	x_1	x_2	x_3	x_4	x_5
	$10.5 - 7\theta$	0	$4.5 - 2\theta$	$-5 + 4\theta$	0	$1.5 - \theta$
$x_4 =$	1.5	0	1.5	-1	1	-0.5
$x_1 =$	3.5	1	0.5	-2	0	0.5

We note that all of the reduced costs are nonnegative if and only if $5/4 \le \theta \le 3/2$. For these values of θ, we have an optimal solution, with an optimal cost of

$$g(\theta) = -10.5 + 7\theta, \qquad \text{if } \frac{5}{4} \le \theta \le \frac{3}{2}.$$

Finally, for $\theta < 5/4$, the reduced cost of x_3 is negative, but the optimal cost is equal to $-\infty$, because all entries in the third column of the tableau are negative. We plot the optimal cost in Figure 5.4.

We now generalize the steps in the preceding example, in order to obtain a broader methodology. The key observation is that once a basis is fixed, the reduced costs are affine (linear plus a constant) functions of θ. Then, if we require that all reduced costs be nonnegative, we force θ to belong to some interval. (The interval could be empty but if it is nonempty, its endpoints are also included.) We conclude that for any given basis, the set of θ for which this basis is optimal is a closed interval.

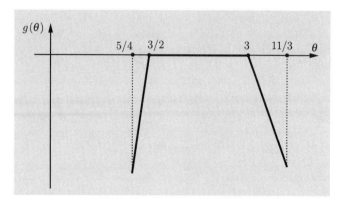

Figure 5.4: The optimal cost $g(\theta)$ as a function of θ, in Example 5.5. For θ outside the interval $[5/4, 11/3]$, $g(\theta)$ is equal to $-\infty$.

Let us now assume that we have chosen a basic feasible solution and an associated basis matrix $\mathbf{B}$, and suppose that this basis is optimal for θ satisfying $\theta_1 \le \theta \le \theta_2$. Let x_j be a variable whose reduced cost becomes negative for $\theta > \theta_2$. Since this reduced cost is nonnegative for $\theta_1 \le \theta \le \theta_2$, it must be equal to zero when $\theta = \theta_2$. We now attempt to bring x_j into the basis and consider separately the different cases that may arise.

Suppose that no entry of the jth column $\mathbf{B}^{-1}\mathbf{A}_j$ of the simplex tableau is positive. For $\theta > \theta_2$, the reduced cost of x_j is negative, and this implies that the optimal cost is $-\infty$ in that range.

If the jth column of the tableau has at least one positive element, we carry out a change of basis and obtain a new basis matrix $\overline{\mathbf{B}}$. For $\theta = \theta_2$, the reduced cost of the entering variable is zero and, therefore, the cost associated with the new basis is the same as the cost associated with the old basis. Since the old basis was optimal for $\theta = \theta_2$, the same must be true for the new basis. On the other hand, for $\theta < \theta_2$, the entering variable x_j had a positive reduced cost. According to the pivoting mechanics, and for $\theta < \theta_2$, a negative multiple of the pivot row is added to the pivot row, and this makes the reduced cost of the exiting variable negative. This implies that the new basis cannot be optimal for $\theta < \theta_2$. We conclude that the range of values of θ for which the new basis is optimal is of the form $\theta_2 \le \theta \le \theta_3$, for some θ_3. By continuing similarly, we obtain a sequence of bases, with the ith basis being optimal for $\theta_i \le \theta \le \theta_{i+1}$.

Note that a basis which is optimal for $\theta \in [\theta_i, \theta_{i+1}]$ cannot be optimal for values of θ greater than θ_{i+1}. Thus, if $\theta_{i+1} > \theta_i$ for all i, the same basis cannot be encountered more than once and the entire range of values of θ will be traced in a finite number of iterations, with each iteration leading to a new breakpoint of the optimal cost function $g(\theta)$. (The number of breakpoints may increase exponentially with the dimension of the problem.)

The situation is more complicated if for some basis we have $\theta_i = \theta_{i+1}$. In this case, it is possible that the algorithm keeps cycling between a finite number of different bases, all of which are optimal only for $\theta = \theta_i = \theta_{i+1}$. Such cycling can only happen in the presence of degeneracy in the primal problem (Exercise 5.17), but can be avoided if an appropriate anticycling rule is followed. In conclusion, the procedure we have outlined, together with an anticycling rule, partitions the range of possible values of θ into consecutive intervals and, for each interval, provides us with an optimal basis and the optimal cost function as a function of θ.

There is another variant of parametric programming that can be used when $\mathbf{c}$ is kept fixed but $\mathbf{b}$ is replaced by $\mathbf{b} + \theta\mathbf{d}$, where $\mathbf{d}$ is a given vector and θ is a scalar. In this case, the zeroth column of the tableau depends on θ. Whenever θ reaches a value at which some basic variable becomes negative, we apply the dual simplex method in order to recover primal feasibility.

5.6   Summary

In this chapter, we have studied the dependence of optimal solutions and of the optimal cost on the problem data, that is, on the entries of $\mathbf{A}$, $\mathbf{b}$, and $\mathbf{c}$. For many of the cases that we have examined, a common methodology was used. Subsequent to a change in the problem data, we first examine its effects on the feasibility and optimality conditions. If we wish the same basis to remain optimal, this leads us to certain limitations on the magnitude of the changes in the problem data. For larger changes, we no longer have an optimal basis and some remedial action (involving the primal or dual simplex method) is typically needed.

We close with a summary of our main results.

(a) If a new variable is added, we check its reduced cost and if it is negative, we add a new column to the tableau and proceed from there.

(b) If a new constraint is added, we check whether it is violated and if so, we form an auxiliary problem and its tableau, and proceed from there.

(c) If an entry of $\mathbf{b}$ or $\mathbf{c}$ is changed by δ, we obtain an interval of values of δ for which the same basis remains optimal.

(d) If an entry of $\mathbf{A}$ is changed by δ, a similar analysis is possible. However, this case is somewhat complicated if the change affects an entry of a basic column.

(e) Assuming that the dual problem is feasible, the optimal cost is a piecewise linear convex function of the vector $\mathbf{b}$ (for those $\mathbf{b}$ for which the primal is feasible). Furthermore, subgradients of the optimal cost function correspond to optimal solutions to the dual problem.

(f) Assuming that the primal problem is feasible, the optimal cost is a piecewise linear concave function of the vector $\mathbf{c}$ (for those $\mathbf{c}$ for which the primal has finite cost).

(g) If the cost vector is an affine function of a scalar parameter θ, there is a systematic procedure (parametric programming) for solving the problem for all values of θ. A similar procedure is possible if the vector $\mathbf{b}$ is an affine function of a scalar parameter.

5.7 Exercises

Exercise 5.1 Consider the same problem as in Example 5.1, for which we already have an optimal basis. Let us introduce the additional constraint $x_1 + x_2 = 3$. Form the auxiliary problem described in the text, and solve it using the primal simplex method. Whenever the "large" constant M is compared to another number, M should be treated as being the larger one.

Exercise 5.2 (Sensitivity with respect to changes in a basic column of A) In this problem (and the next two) we study the change in the value of the optimal cost when an entry of the matrix $\mathbf{A}$ is perturbed by a small amount. We consider a linear programming problem in standard form, under the usual assumption that $\mathbf{A}$ has linearly independent rows. Suppose that we have an optimal basis $\mathbf{B}$ that leads to a nondegenerate optimal solution $\mathbf{x}^*$, and a nondegenerate dual optimal solution $\mathbf{p}$. We assume that the first column is basic. We will now change the first entry of $\mathbf{A}_1$ from a_{11} to $a_{11} + \delta$, where δ is a small scalar. Let $\mathbf{E}$ be a matrix of dimensions $m \times m$ (where m is the number of rows of $\mathbf{A}$), whose entries are all zero except for the top left entry e_{11}, which is equal to 1.

(a) Show that if δ is small enough, $\mathbf{B} + \delta\mathbf{E}$ is a basis matrix for the new problem.

(b) Show that under the basis $\mathbf{B} + \delta\mathbf{E}$, the vector $\mathbf{x}_B$ of basic variables in the new problem is equal to $(\mathbf{I} + \delta\mathbf{B}^{-1}\mathbf{E})^{-1}\mathbf{B}^{-1}\mathbf{b}$.

(c) Show that if δ is sufficiently small, $\mathbf{B} + \delta\mathbf{E}$ is an optimal basis for the new problem.

(d) We use the symbol $\approx$ to denote equality when second order terms in δ are ignored. The following approximation is known to be true: $(\mathbf{I} + \delta\mathbf{B}^{-1}\mathbf{E})^{-1} \approx \mathbf{I} - \delta\mathbf{B}^{-1}\mathbf{E}$. Using this approximation, show that

$$\mathbf{c}'_B \mathbf{x}_B \approx \mathbf{c}'\mathbf{x}^* - \delta p_1 x_1^*,$$

where x_1^* (respectively, p_1) is the first component of the optimal solution to the original primal (respectively, dual) problem, and $\mathbf{x}_B$ has been defined in part (b).

Exercise 5.3 (Sensitivity with respect to changes in a basic column of A) Consider a linear programming problem in standard form under the usual assumption that the rows of the matrix $\mathbf{A}$ are linearly independent. Suppose that the columns $\mathbf{A}_1, \ldots, \mathbf{A}_m$ form an optimal basis. Let $\mathbf{A}_0$ be some vector and suppose that we change $\mathbf{A}_1$ to $\mathbf{A}_1 + \delta\mathbf{A}_0$. Consider the matrix $\mathbf{B}(\delta)$ consisting of the columns $A_0 + \delta A_1, A_2, \ldots, A_m$. Let $[\delta_1, \delta_2]$ be a closed interval of values of δ that contains zero and in which the determinant of $B(\delta)$ is nonzero. Show that the subset of $[\delta_1, \delta_2]$ for which $B(\delta)$ is an optimal basis is also a closed interval.

Exercise 5.4 Consider the problem in Example 5.1, with a_{11} changed from 3 to $3 + \delta$. Let us keep x_1 and x_2 as the basic variables and let $B(\delta)$ be the corresponding basis matrix, as a function of δ.

(a) Compute $B(\delta)^{-1}b$. For which values of δ is $B(\delta)$ a feasible basis?

(b) Compute $c'_B B(\delta)^{-1}$. For which values of δ is $B(\delta)$ an optimal basis?

(c) Determine the optimal cost, as a function of δ, when δ is restricted to those values for which $B(\delta)$ is an optimal basis matrix.

Exercise 5.5 While solving a standard form linear programming problem using the simplex method, we arrive at the following tableau:

	x_1	x_2	x_3	x_4	x_5
	0	0	$\bar{c}_3$	0	$\bar{c}_5$
$x_2 =$	1	0	1	-1	0	β
$x_4 =$	2	0	0	2	1	γ
$x_1 =$	3	1	0	4	0	δ

Suppose also that the last three columns of the matrix A form an identity matrix.

(a) Give necessary and sufficient conditions for the basis described by this tableau to be optimal (in terms of the coefficients in the tableau).

(b) Assume that this basis is optimal and that $\bar{c}_3 = 0$. Find an optimal basic feasible solution, other than the one described by this tableau.

(c) Suppose that $\gamma \geq 0$. Show that there exists an optimal basic feasible solution, regardless of the values of $\bar{c}_3$ and $\bar{c}_5$.

(d) Assume that the basis associated with this tableau is optimal. Suppose also that b_1 in the original problem is replaced by $b_1 + \epsilon$. Give upper and lower bounds on ϵ so that this basis remains optimal.

(e) Assume that the basis associated with this tableau is optimal. Suppose also that c_1 in the original problem is replaced by $c_1 + \epsilon$. Give upper and lower bounds on ϵ so that this basis remains optimal.

Exercise 5.6 Company A has agreed to supply the following quantities of special lamps to Company B during the next 4 months:

Month	January	February	March	April
Units	150	160	225	180

Company A can produce a maximum of 160 lamps per month at a cost of $35 per unit. Additional lamps can be purchased from Company C at a cost of $50 per lamp. Company A incurs an inventory holding cost of $5 per month for each lamp held in inventory.

(a) Formulate the problem that Company A is facing as a linear programming problem.

(b) Solve the problem using a linear programming package.

(c) Company A is considering some preventive maintenance during one of the first three months. If maintenance is scheduled for January, the company can manufacture only 151 units (instead of 160); similarly, the maximum possible production if maintenance is scheduled for February or March is 153 and 155 units, respectively. What maintenance schedule would you recommend and why?

(d) Company D has offered to supply up to 50 lamps (total) to Company A during either January, February or March. Company D charges $45 per lamp. Should Company A buy lamps from Company D? If yes, when and how many lamps should Company A purchase, and what is the impact of this decision on the total cost?

(e) Company C has offered to lower the price of units supplied to Company A during February. What is the maximum decrease that would make this offer attractive to Company A?

(f) Because of anticipated increases in interest rates, the holding cost per lamp is expected to increase to $8 per unit in February. How does this change affect the total cost and the optimal solution?

(g) Company B has just informed Company A that it requires only 90 units in January (instead of 150 requested previously). Calculate upper and lower bounds on the impact of this order on the optimal cost using information from the optimal solution to the original problem.

Exercise 5.7 A paper company manufactures three basic products: pads of paper, 5-packs of paper, and 20-packs of paper. The pad of paper consists of a single pad of 25 sheets of lined paper. The 5-pack consists of 5 pads of paper, together with a small notebook. The 20-pack of paper consists of 20 pads of paper, together with a large notebook. The small and large notebooks are not sold separately.

Production of each pad of paper requires 1 minute of paper-machine time, 1 minute of supervisory time, and $.10 in direct costs. Production of each small notebook takes 2 minutes of paper-machine time, 45 seconds of supervisory time, and $.20 in direct cost. Production of each large notebook takes 3 minutes of paper machine time, 30 seconds of supervisory time and $.30 in direct costs. To package the 5-pack takes 1 minute of packager's time and 1 minute of supervisory time. To package the 20-pack takes 3 minutes of packager's time and 2 minutes of supervisory time. The amounts of available paper-machine time, supervisory time, and packager's time are constants b_1, b_2, b_3, respectively. Any of the three products can be sold to retailers in any quantity at the prices $.30, $1.60, and $7.00, respectively.

Provide a linear programming formulation of the problem of determining an optimal mix of the three products. (You may ignore the constraint that only integer quantities can be produced.) Try to formulate the problem in such a way that the following questions can be answered by looking at a single dual variable or reduced cost in the final tableau. Also, for each question, give a brief explanation of why it can be answered by looking at just one dual price or reduced cost.

(a) What is the marginal value of an extra unit of supervisory time?

(b) What is the lowest price at which it is worthwhile to produce single pads of paper for sale?

(c) Suppose that part-time supervisors can be hired at $8 per hour. Is it worthwhile to hire any?

(d) Suppose that the direct cost of producing pads of paper increases from $.10 to $.12. What is the profit decrease?

Exercise 5.8 A pottery manufacturer can make four different types of dining room service sets: JJP English, Currier, Primrose, and Bluetail. Furthermore, Primrose can be made by two different methods. Each set uses clay, enamel, dry room time, and kiln time, and results in a profit shown in Table 5.3. (Here, lbs is the abbreviation for pounds).

Resources	E	C	P_1	P_2	B	Total
Clay (lbs)	10	15	10	10	20	130
Enamel (lbs)	1	2	2	1	1	13
Dry room (hours)	3	1	6	6	3	45
Kiln (hours)	2	4	2	5	3	23
Profit	51	102	66	66	89	

Table 5.3: The rightmost column in the table gives the manufacturer's resource availability for the remainder of the week. Notice that Primrose can be made by two different methods. They both use the same amount of clay (10 lbs.) and dry room time (6 hours). But the second method uses one pound less of enamel and three more hours in the kiln.

The manufacturer is currently committed to making the same amount of Primrose using methods 1 and 2. The formulation of the profit maximization problem is given below. The decision variables E, C, P_1, P_2, B are the number of sets of type English, Currier, Primrose Method 1, Primrose Method 2, and Bluetail, respectively. We assume, for the purposes of this problem, that the number of sets of each type can be fractional.

$$
\begin{array}{rl}
\text{maximize} & 51E + 102C + 66P_1 + 66P_2 + 89B \\
\text{subject to} & 10E + 15C + 10P_1 + 10P_2 + 20B \le 130 \\
& E + 2C + 2P_1 + P_2 + B \le 13 \\
& 3E + C + 6P_1 + 6P_2 + 3B \le 45 \\
& 2E + 4C + 2P_1 + 5P_2 + 3B \le 23 \\
& P_1 - P_2 = 0 \\
& E, C, P_1, P_2, B \ge 0.
\end{array}
$$

The optimal solution to the primal and the dual, respectively, together with sensitivity information, is given in Tables 5.4 and 5.5. Use this information to answer the questions that follow.

	Optimal Value	Reduced Cost	Objective Coefficient	Allowable Increase	Allowable Decrease
E	0	−3.571	51	3.571	∞
C	2	0	102	16.667	12.5
P_1	0	0	66	37.571	∞
P_2	0	−37.571	66	37.571	∞
B	5	0	89	47	12.5

Table 5.4: The optimal primal solution and its sensitivity with respect to changes in coefficients of the objective function. The last two columns describe the allowed changes in these coefficients for which the same solution remains optimal.

(a) What is the optimal quantity of each service set, and what is the total profit?

(b) Give an economic (not mathematical) interpretation of the optimal dual variables appearing in the sensitivity report, for each of the five constraints.

(c) Should the manufacturer buy an additional 20 lbs. of Clay at $1.1 per pound?

(d) Suppose that the number of hours available in the dry room decreases by 30. Give a bound for the decrease in the total profit.

(e) In the current model, the number of Primrose produced using method 1 was required to be the same as the number of Primrose produced by method 2. Consider a revision of the model in which this constraint is replaced by the constraint $P_1 - P_2 \ge 0$. In the reformulated problem would the amount of Primrose made by method 1 be positive?

Exercise 5.9 Using the notation of Section 5.2, show that for any positive scalar λ and any $\mathbf{b} \in S$, we have $F(\lambda \mathbf{b}) = \lambda F(\mathbf{b})$. Assume that the dual feasible set is nonempty, so that $F(\mathbf{b})$ is finite.

	Slack Value	Dual Variable	Constr. RHS	Allowable Increase	Allowable Decrease
Clay	130	1.429	130	23.33	43.75
Enamel	9	0	13	∞	4
Dry Rm.	17	0	45	∞	28
Kiln	23	20.143	23	5.60	3.50
Prim.	0	11.429	0	3.50	0

Table 5.5: The optimal dual solution and its sensitivity. The column labeled "slack value" gives us the optimal values of the slack variables associated with each of the primal constraints. The third column simply repeats the right-hand side vector **b**, while the last two columns describe the allowed changes in the components of **b** for which the optimal dual solution remains the same.

Exercise 5.10 Consider the linear programming problem:

$$\begin{aligned}
\text{minimize} \quad & x_1 + x_2 \\
\text{subject to} \quad & x_1 + 2x_2 = \theta, \\
& x_1, x_2 \geq 0.
\end{aligned}$$

(a) Find (by inspection) an optimal solution, as a function of θ.

(b) Draw a graph showing the optimal cost as a function of θ.

(c) Use the picture in part (b) to obtain the set of all dual optimal solutions, for every value of θ.

Exercise 5.11 Consider the function $g(\theta)$, as defined in the beginning of Section 5.5. Suppose that $g(\theta)$ is linear for $\theta \in [\theta_1, \theta_2]$. Is it true that there exists a unique optimal solution when $\theta_1 < \theta < \theta_2$? Prove or provide a counterexample.

Exercise 5.12 Consider the parametric programming problem discussed in Section 5.5.

(a) Suppose that for some value of θ, there are exactly two distinct basic feasible solutions that are optimal. Show that they must be adjacent.

(b) Let θ^* be a breakpoint of the function $g(\theta)$. Let $\mathbf{x}^1, \mathbf{x}^2, \mathbf{x}^3$ be basic feasible solutions, all of which are optimal for $\theta = \theta^*$. Suppose that $\mathbf{x}^1$ is a unique optimal solution for $\theta < \theta^*$, $\mathbf{x}^3$ is a unique optimal solution for $\theta > \theta^*$, and $\mathbf{x}^1, \mathbf{x}^2, \mathbf{x}^3$ are the only optimal basic feasible solutions for $\theta = \theta^*$. Provide an example to show that $\mathbf{x}^1$ and $\mathbf{x}^3$ need not be adjacent.

Exercise 5.13 Consider the following linear programming problem:

$$
\begin{array}{rrl}
\text{minimize} & 4x_1 & + 5x_3 \\
\text{subject to} & 2x_1 + x_2 - 5x_3 & = 1 \\
& -3x_1 \quad\quad + 4x_3 + x_4 & = 2 \\
& x_1, x_2, x_3, x_4 \geq 0.
\end{array}
$$

(a) Write down a simplex tableau and find an optimal solution. Is it unique?

(b) Write down the dual problem and find an optimal solution. Is it unique?

(c) Suppose now that we change the vector $\mathbf{b}$ from $\mathbf{b} = (1, 2)$ to $\mathbf{b} = (1 - 2\theta, 2 - 3\theta)$, where θ is a scalar parameter. Find an optimal solution and the value of the optimal cost, as a function of θ. (For all θ, both positive and negative.)

Exercise 5.14 Consider the problem

$$
\begin{array}{rl}
\text{minimize} & (\mathbf{c} + \theta \mathbf{d})'\mathbf{x} \\
\text{subject to} & \mathbf{Ax} = \mathbf{b} + \theta \mathbf{f} \\
& \mathbf{x} \geq \mathbf{0},
\end{array}
$$

where $\mathbf{A}$ is an $m \times n$ matrix with linearly independent rows. We assume that the problem is feasible and the optimal cost $f(\theta)$ is finite for all values of θ in some interval $[\theta_1, \theta_2]$.

(a) Suppose that a certain basis is optimal for $\theta = -10$ and for $\theta = 10$. Prove that the same basis is optimal for $\theta = 5$.

(b) Show that $f(\theta)$ is a piecewise quadratic function of θ. Give an upper bound on the number of "pieces."

(c) Let $\mathbf{b} = \mathbf{0}$ and $\mathbf{c} = \mathbf{0}$. Suppose that a certain basis is optimal for $\theta = 1$. For what other nonnegative values of θ is that same basis optimal?

(d) Is $f(\theta)$ convex, concave or neither?

Exercise 5.15 Consider the problem

$$
\begin{array}{rl}
\text{minimize} & \mathbf{c}'\mathbf{x} \\
\text{subject to} & \mathbf{Ax} = \mathbf{b} + \theta \mathbf{d} \\
& \mathbf{x} \geq \mathbf{0},
\end{array}
$$

and let $f(\theta)$ be the optimal cost, as a function of θ.

(a) Let $X(\theta)$ be the set of all optimal solutions, for a given value of θ. For any nonnegative scalar t, define $X(0, t)$ to be the union of the sets $X(\theta)$, $0 \leq \theta \leq t$. Is $X(0, t)$ a convex set? Provide a proof or a counterexample.

(b) Suppose that we remove the nonnegativity constraints $\mathbf{x} \geq \mathbf{0}$ from the problem under consideration. Is $X(0, t)$ a convex set? Provide a proof or a counterexample.

(c) Suppose that $\mathbf{x}^1$ and $\mathbf{x}^2$ belong to $X(0, t)$. Show that there is a continuous path from $\mathbf{x}^1$ to $\mathbf{x}^2$ that is contained within $X(0, t)$. That is, there exists a continuous function $g(\lambda)$ such that $g(\lambda_1) = \mathbf{x}^1$, $g(\lambda_2) = \mathbf{x}^2$, and $g(\lambda) \in X(0, t)$ for all $\lambda \in (\lambda_1, \lambda_2)$.

Exercise 5.16 Consider the parametric programming problem of Section 5.5. Suppose that some basic feasible solution is optimal if and only if θ is equal to some θ^*.

(a) Suppose that the feasible set is unbounded. Is it true that there exist at least three distinct basic feasible solutions that are optimal when $\theta = \theta^*$?

(b) Answer the question in part (a) for the case where the feasible set is bounded.

Exercise 5.17 Consider the parametric programming problem. Suppose that every basic solution encountered by the algorithm is nondegenerate. Prove that the algorithm does not cycle.

5.8   Notes and sources

The material in this chapter, with the exception of Section 5.3, is standard, and can be found in any text on linear programming.

5.1. A more detailed discussion of the results of the production planning case study can be found in Freund and Shannahan (1992).

5.3. The results in this section have beautiful generalizations to the case of nonlinear convex optimization; see, e.g., Rockafellar (1970).

5.5. Anticycling rules for parametric programming can be found in Murty (1983).

Chapter 6

Large scale optimization

Contents

In this chapter, we discuss methods for solving linear programming problems with a large number of variables or constraints. We present the idea of *delayed column generation* whereby we generate a column of the matrix $\mathbf{A}$ only after it has been determined that it can profitably enter the basis. The dual of this idea leads to the *cutting plane*, or *delayed constraint generation* method, in which the feasible set is approximated using only a subset of the constraints, with more constraints added if the resulting solution is infeasible. We illustrate the delayed column generation method by discussing a classical application, the *cutting-stock* problem. Another application is found in *Dantzig-Wolfe decomposition*, which is a method designed for linear programming problems with a special structure. We close with a discussion of stochastic programming, which deals with two-stage optimization problems involving uncertainty. We obtain a large scale linear programming formulation, and we present a decomposition method known as *Benders decomposition*.

6.1   Delayed column generation

Consider the standard form problem

$$\begin{aligned}
\text{minimize} \quad & \mathbf{c}'\mathbf{x} \\
\text{subject to} \quad & \mathbf{A}\mathbf{x} = \mathbf{b} \\
& \mathbf{x} \geq \mathbf{0},
\end{aligned}$$

with $\mathbf{x} \in \Re^n$ and $\mathbf{b} \in \Re^m$, under the usual assumption that the rows of $\mathbf{A}$ are linearly independent. Suppose that the number of columns is so large that it is impossible to generate and store the entire matrix $\mathbf{A}$ in memory. Experience with large problems indicates that, usually, most of the columns never enter the basis, and we can therefore afford not to ever generate these unused columns. This blends well with the revised simplex method which, at any given iteration, only requires the current basic columns and the column which is to enter the basis. There is only one difficulty that remains to be addressed; namely, we need a method for discovering variables x_i with negative reduced costs $\bar{c}_i$, without having to generate all columns. Sometimes, this can be accomplished by solving the problem

$$\text{minimize} \quad \bar{c}_i, \tag{6.1}$$

where the minimization is over all i. In many instances (e.g., for the formulations to be studied in Sections 6.2 and 6.4), this optimization problem has a special structure: a smallest $\bar{c}_i$ can be found efficiently without computing every $\bar{c}_i$. If the minimum in this optimization problem is greater than or equal to 0, all reduced costs are nonnegative and we have an optimal solution to the original linear programming problem. If on the other hand, the minimum is negative, the variable x_i corresponding to a minimizing index i has negative reduced cost, and the column $\mathbf{A}_i$ can enter the basis.

The key to the above outlined approach is our ability to solve the optimization problem (6.1) efficiently. We will see that in the Dantzig-Wolfe decomposition method, the problem (6.1) is a smaller auxiliary linear programming problem that can be solved using the simplex method. For the cutting-stock problem, the problem (6.1) is a certain discrete optimization problem that can be solved fairly efficiently using special purpose methods. Of course, there are also cases where the problem (6.1) has no special structure and the methodology described here cannot be applied.

A variant involving retained columns

In the delayed column generation method that we have just discussed, the columns that exit the basis are discarded from memory and do not enjoy any special status. In a variant of this method, the algorithm retains in memory all or some of the columns that have been generated in the past, and proceeds in terms of restricted linear programming problems that involve only the retained columns.

We describe the algorithm as a sequence of *master* iterations. At the beginning of a master iteration, we have a basic feasible solution to the original problem, and an associated basis matrix. We search for a variable with negative reduced cost, possibly by minimizing $\bar{c}_i$ over all i; if none is found, the algorithm terminates. Suppose that we have found some j such that $\bar{c}_j < 0$. We then form a collection of columns $\mathbf{A}_i$, $i \in I$, which contains all of the basic columns, the entering column $\mathbf{A}_j$, and possibly some other columns as well. Let us define the *restricted* problem

$$\begin{aligned} \text{minimize} \quad & \sum_{i \in I} c_i x_i \\ \text{subject to} \quad & \sum_{i \in I} \mathbf{A}_i x_i = \mathbf{b} \\ & \mathbf{x} \geq \mathbf{0}. \end{aligned} \tag{6.2}$$

Recall that the basic variables at the current basic feasible solution to the original problem are among the columns that have been kept in the restricted problem. We therefore have a basic feasible solution to the restricted problem, which can be used as a starting point for its solution. We then perform as many simplex iterations as needed, until the restricted problem is solved to optimality. At that point, we are ready to start with the next master iteration.

The method we have just described is a special case of the revised simplex method, in conjunction with some special rules for choosing the entering variable that give priority to the variables x_i, $i \in I$; it is only when the reduced costs of these variables are all nonnegative (which happens at an optimal solution to the restricted problem) that the algorithm examines the reduced costs of the remaining variables. The motivation is that we may wish to give priority to variables for which the corresponding columns have already been generated and stored in memory, or to variables that are more probable to have negative reduced cost. There are several variants of this method, depending on the manner that the set I is chosen at each iteration.

(a) At one extreme, I is just the set of indices of the current basic variables, together with the entering variable; a variable that exits the basis is immediately dropped from the set I. Since the restricted problem has $m + 1$ variables and m constraints, its feasible set is at most one-dimensional, and it gets solved in a single simplex iteration, that is, as soon as the column $\mathbf{A}_j$ enters the basis.

(b) At the other extreme, we let I be the set of indices of all variables that have become basic at some point in the past; equivalently, no variables are ever dropped, and each entering variable is added to I. If the number of master iterations is large, this option can be problematic because the set I keeps growing.

(c) Finally, there are intermediate options in which the set I is kept to a moderate size by dropping from I those variables that have exited the basis in the remote past and have not reentered since.

In the absence of degeneracy, all of the above variants are guaranteed to terminate because they are special cases of the revised simplex method. In the presence of degeneracy, cycling can be avoided by using the revised simplex method in conjunction with the lexicographic tie breaking rule.

6.2   The cutting stock problem

In this section, we discuss the cutting stock problem, which is a classical example of delayed column generation.

Consider a paper company that has a supply of large rolls of paper, of width W. (We assume that W is a positive integer.) However, customer demand is for smaller widths of paper; in particular b_i rolls of width w_i, $i = 1, 2, \ldots, m$, need to be produced. We assume that $w_i \leq W$ for each i, and that each w_i is an integer. Smaller rolls are obtained by slicing a large roll in a certain way, called a *pattern*. For example, a large roll of width 70 can be cut into three rolls of width $w_1 = 17$ and one roll of width $w_2 = 15$, with a waste of 4.

In general, a pattern, say the jth pattern, can be represented by a column vector $\mathbf{A}_j$ whose ith entry a_{ij} indicates how many rolls of width w_i are produced by that pattern. For example, the pattern described earlier is represented by the vector $(3, 1, 0, \ldots, 0)$. For a vector $(a_{1j}, \ldots, a_{mj})$ to be a representation of a feasible pattern, its components must be nonnegative integers and we must also have

$$\sum_{i=1}^{m} a_{ij} w_i \leq W. \tag{6.3}$$

Let n be the number of all feasible patterns and consider the $m \times n$ matrix $\mathbf{A}$ with columns $\mathbf{A}_j$, $j = 1, \ldots, n$. Note that n can be a very large number.

The goal of the company is to minimize the number of large rolls used while satisfying customer demand. Let x_j be the number of large rolls cut according to pattern j. Then, the problem under consideration is

$$
\begin{aligned}
\text{minimize} \quad & \sum_{j=1}^{n} x_j \\
\text{subject to} \quad & \sum_{j=1}^{n} a_{ij} x_j = b_i, \qquad i = 1, \ldots, m, \\
& x_j \geq 0, \qquad j = 1, \ldots, n.
\end{aligned}
\tag{6.4}
$$

Naturally, each x_j should be an integer and we have an integer programming problem. However, an optimal solution to the linear programming problem (6.4) often provides a feasible solution to the integer programming problem (by rounding or other ad hoc methods), which is fairly close to optimal, at least if the demands b_i are reasonably large (cf. Exercise 6.1).

Solving the linear programming problem (6.4) is a difficult computational task: even if m is comparatively small, the number of feasible patterns n can be huge, so that forming the coefficient matrix $\mathbf{A}$ in full is impractical. However, we will now show that the problem can be solved efficiently, by using the revised simplex method and by generating columns of $\mathbf{A}$ as needed rather than in advance.

Finding an initial basic feasible solution is easy for this problem. For $j = 1, \ldots, m$, we may let the jth pattern consist of one roll of width w_j and none of the other widths. Then, the first m columns of $\mathbf{A}$ form a basis that leads to a basic feasible solution. (In fact, the corresponding basis matrix is the identity.)

Suppose now that we have a basis matrix $\mathbf{B}$ and an associated basic feasible solution, and that we wish to carry out the next iteration of the revised simplex method. Because the cost coefficient of every variable x_j is unity, every component of the vector $\mathbf{c}_B$ is equal to 1. We compute the simplex multipliers $\mathbf{p}' = \mathbf{c}_B' \mathbf{B}^{-1}$. Next, instead of computing the reduced cost $\bar{c}_j = 1 - \mathbf{p}' \mathbf{A}_j$ associated with every column (pattern) $\mathbf{A}_j$, we consider the problem of minimizing $(1 - \mathbf{p}' \mathbf{A}_j)$ over all j. This is the same as maximizing $\mathbf{p}' \mathbf{A}_j$ over all j. If the maximum is less than or equal to 1, all reduced costs are nonnegative and we have an optimal solution. If on the other hand, the maximum is greater than 1, the column $\mathbf{A}_j$ corresponding to a maximizing j has negative reduced cost and enters the basis.

We are now left with the task of finding a pattern j that maximizes $\mathbf{p}' \mathbf{A}_j$. Given our earlier description of what constitutes an admissible pattern [cf. Eq. (6.3)], we are faced with the problem

$$\text{maximize} \quad \sum_{i=1}^{m} p_i a_i$$

$$\text{subject to} \quad \sum_{i=1}^{m} w_i a_i \leq W \tag{6.5}$$

$$a_i \geq 0, \qquad i = 1, \ldots, m,$$

$$a_i \text{ integer}, \qquad i = 1, \ldots, m.$$

This problem is called the *integer knapsack* problem. (Think of p_i as the value, and w_i as the weight of the ith item; we seek to fill a knapsack and maximize its value without the total weight exceeding W). Solving the knapsack problem requires some effort, but for the range of numbers that arise in the cutting stock problem, this can be done fairly efficiently.

One possible algorithm for solving the knapsack problem, based on *dynamic programming*, is as follows. Let $F(v)$ denote the optimal objective value in the problem (6.5), when W is replaced by v, and let us use the convention $F(v) = 0$ when $v < 0$. Let $w_{\min} = \min_i w_i$. If $v < w_{\min}$, then clearly $F(v) = 0$. For $v \geq w_{\min}$, we have the recursion

$$F(v) = \max_{i=1,\ldots,m} \left\{ F(v - w_i) + p_i \right\}. \tag{6.6}$$

For an interpretation of this recursion, note that a knapsack of weight at most v is obtained by first filling the knapsack with weight at most $v - w_i$, and then adding an item of weight w_i. The knapsack of weight at most $v - w_i$ should be filled so that we obtain the maximum value, which is $F(v - w_i)$, and the ith item should be chosen so that the total value $F(v - w_i) + p_i$ is maximized. Using the recursion (6.6), $F(v)$ can be computed for $v = w_{\min}, w_{\min} + 1, \ldots, W$. In addition, an optimal solution is obtained by backtracking if a record of the maximizing index i is kept at each step. The computational complexity of this procedure is $O(mW)$ because the recursion (6.6) is to be carried out for $O(W)$ different values of v, each time requiring $O(m)$ arithmetic operations.

The dynamic programming methodology is discussed in more generality in Section 11.3, where it is also applied to a somewhat different variant of the knapsack problem. The knapsack problem can also be solved using the branch and bound methodology, developed in Section 11.2.

6.3   Cutting plane methods

Delayed column generation methods, when viewed in terms of the dual variables, can be described as *delayed constraint generation*, or *cutting plane* methods. In this section, we develop this alternative perspective.

Consider the problem

$$\text{maximize} \quad \mathbf{p}'\mathbf{b} \tag{6.7}$$
$$\text{subject to} \quad \mathbf{p}'\mathbf{A}_i \leq c_i, \qquad i = 1, \ldots, n,$$

which is the dual of the standard form problem considered in Section 6.1. Once more, we assume that it is impossible to generate and store each one of the vectors $\mathbf{A}_i$, because the number n is very large. Instead of dealing with all n of the dual constraints, we consider a subset I of $\{1, \ldots, n\}$, and form the *relaxed dual* problem

$$\text{maximize} \quad \mathbf{p}'\mathbf{b} \tag{6.8}$$
$$\text{subject to} \quad \mathbf{p}'\mathbf{A}_i \leq c_i, \qquad i \in I,$$

which we solve to optimality. Let $\mathbf{p}^*$ be an optimal basic feasible solution to the relaxed dual problem. There are two possibilities.

(a) Suppose that $\mathbf{p}^*$ is a feasible solution to the original problem (6.7). Any other feasible solution $\mathbf{p}$ to the original problem (6.7) is also feasible for the relaxed problem (6.8), because the latter has fewer constraints. Therefore, by the optimality of $\mathbf{p}^*$ for the problem (6.8), we have $\mathbf{p}'\mathbf{b} \leq (\mathbf{p}^*)'\mathbf{b}$. Therefore, $\mathbf{p}^*$ is an optimal solution to the original problem (6.7), and we can terminate the algorithm.

(b) If $\mathbf{p}^*$ is infeasible for the problem (6.7), we find a violated constraint, add it to the constraints of the relaxed dual problem, and continue similarly. See Figure 6.1 for an illustration.

In order to carry out this algorithm, we need a method for checking whether a vector $\mathbf{p}^*$ is a feasible solution to the original dual problem (6.7). Second, if $\mathbf{p}^*$ is dual infeasible, we need an efficient method for identifying a violated constraint. (This is known as the *separation problem*, because it amounts to finding a hyperplane that separates $\mathbf{p}^*$ from the dual feasible set, and is discussed further in Section 8.5.) One possibility is to formulate and solve the optimization problem

$$\text{minimize} \quad c_i - (\mathbf{p}^*)'\mathbf{A}_i \tag{6.9}$$

over all i. If the optimal value in this problem is nonnegative, we have a feasible (and, therefore, optimal) solution to the original dual problem; if it is negative, then an optimizing i satisfies $c_i < (\mathbf{p}^*)'\mathbf{A}_i$, and we have identified a violated constraint. The success of this approach hinges on our ability to solve the problem (6.9) efficiently; fortunately, this is sometimes possible. In addition, there are cases where the optimization problem (6.9) is not easily solved but one can test for feasibility and identify violated constraints using other means. (See, e.g., Section 11.1 for applications of the cutting plane method to integer programming problems.)

It should be apparent at this point that applying the cutting plane method to the dual problem is identical to applying the delayed column

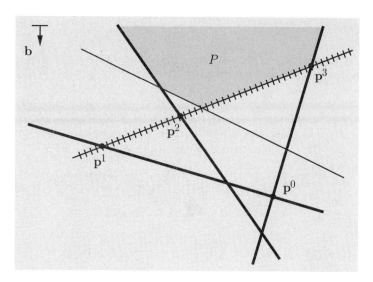

Figure 6.1: A polyhedron P defined in terms of several inequality constraints. Let the vector **b** point downwards, so that maximizing $\mathbf{p}'\mathbf{b}$ is the same as looking for the lowest point. We start with the constraints indicated by the thicker lines, and the optimal solution to the relaxed dual problem is $\mathbf{p}^0$. The vector $\mathbf{p}^0$ is infeasible and we identify the constraint indicated by a thatched line as a violated one. We incorporate this constraint in the relaxed dual problem, and solve the new relaxed dual problem to optimality, to arrive at the vector $\mathbf{p}^2$.

generation method to the primal. For example, minimizing $c_i - (\mathbf{p}^*)'\mathbf{A}_i$ in order to find a violated dual constraint is identical to minimizing $\bar{c}_i$ in order to find a primal variable with negative reduced cost. Furthermore, the relaxed dual problem (6.8) is simply the dual of the restricted primal problem (6.2) formed in Section 6.1.

The cutting plane method, as described here, corresponds to the variant of delayed column generation in which all columns generated by the algorithm are retained, and the set I grows with each iteration. As discussed in Section 6.1, a possible alternative is to drop some of the elements of I; for example, we could drop those constraints that have not been active for some time.

If we take the idea of dropping old dual constraints and carry it to the extreme, we obtain a variant of the cutting plane method whereby, at each stage, we add one violated constraint, move to a new $\mathbf{p}$ vector, and remove a constraint that has been rendered inactive at the new vector.

Example 6.1 Consider Figure 6.1 once more. We start at $\mathbf{p}^0$ and let I consist of the two constraints that are active at $\mathbf{p}^0$. The constraint corresponding to the thatched line is violated and we add it to the set I. At this point, the set I consists of three dual constraints, and the relaxed dual problem has exactly three basic solutions, namely the points $\mathbf{p}^0$, $\mathbf{p}^1$, and $\mathbf{p}^3$. We maximize $\mathbf{p}'\mathbf{b}$ subject to these three constraints, and the vector $\mathbf{p}^1$ is chosen. At this point, the constraint that goes through $\mathbf{p}^0$ and $\mathbf{p}^3$ is satisfied, but has been rendered inactive. We drop this constraint from I, which leaves us with the two constraints through the point $\mathbf{p}^1$. Since $\mathbf{p}^1$ is infeasible, we can now identify another violated constraint and continue similarly.

Since the cutting plane method is simply the delayed column generation method, viewed from a different angle, there is no need to provide implementation details. While the algorithm is easily visualized in terms of cutting planes and the dual problem, the computations can be carried out using the revised simplex method on the primal problem, in the standard fashion.

We close by noting that in some occasions, we may be faced with a primal problem (not in standard form) that has relatively few variables but a very large number of constraints. In that case, it makes sense to apply the cutting plane algorithm to the primal; equivalently, we can form the dual problem and solve it using delayed column generation.

6.4   Dantzig-Wolfe decomposition

Consider a linear programming problem of the form

$$
\begin{aligned}
\text{minimize} \quad & \mathbf{c}_1'\mathbf{x}_1 + \mathbf{c}_2'\mathbf{x}_2 \\
\text{subject to} \quad & \mathbf{D}_1\mathbf{x}_1 + \mathbf{D}_2\mathbf{x}_2 = \mathbf{b}_0 \\
& \mathbf{F}_1\mathbf{x}_1 = \mathbf{b}_1 \\
& \mathbf{F}_2\mathbf{x}_2 = \mathbf{b}_2 \\
& \mathbf{x}_1, \mathbf{x}_2 \geq \mathbf{0}.
\end{aligned}
\tag{6.10}
$$

Suppose that $\mathbf{x}_1$ and $\mathbf{x}_2$ are vectors of dimensions n_1 and n_2, respectively, and that $\mathbf{b}_0$, $\mathbf{b}_1$, $\mathbf{b}_2$ have dimensions m_0, m_1, m_2, respectively. Thus, besides nonnegativity constraints, $\mathbf{x}_1$ satisfies m_1 constraints, $\mathbf{x}_2$ satisfies m_2 constraints, and $\mathbf{x}_1, \mathbf{x}_2$ together satisfy m_0 coupling constraints. Here, $\mathbf{D}_1, \mathbf{D}_2, \mathbf{F}_1, \mathbf{F}_2$ are matrices of appropriate dimensions.

Problems with the structure we have just described arise in several applications. For example, $\mathbf{x}_1$ and $\mathbf{x}_2$ could be decision variables associated with two divisions of the same firm. There are constraints tied to each division, and there are also some coupling constraints representing shared resources, such as a total budget. Often, the number of coupling constraints is a small fraction of the total. We will now proceed to develop a decomposition method tailored to problems of this type.

Reformulation of the problem

Our first step is to introduce an equivalent problem, with fewer equality constraints, but many more variables.

For $i = 1, 2$, we define

$$P_i = \{\mathbf{x}_i \geq \mathbf{0} \mid \mathbf{F}_i \mathbf{x}_i = \mathbf{b}_i\},$$

and we assume that P_1 and P_2 are nonempty. Then, the problem can be rewritten as

$$\begin{aligned}
\text{minimize} \quad & \mathbf{c}_1' \mathbf{x}_1 + \mathbf{c}_2' \mathbf{x}_2 \\
\text{subject to} \quad & \mathbf{D}_1 \mathbf{x}_1 + \mathbf{D}_2 \mathbf{x}_2 = \mathbf{b}_0 \\
& \mathbf{x}_1 \in P_1 \\
& \mathbf{x}_2 \in P_2.
\end{aligned}$$

For $i = 1, 2$, let $\mathbf{x}_i^j$, $j \in J_i$, be the extreme points of P_i. Let also $\mathbf{w}_i^k$, $k \in K_i$, be a complete set of extreme rays of P_i. Using the resolution theorem (Theorem 4.15 in Section 4.9), any element $\mathbf{x}_i$ of P_i can be represented in the form

$$\mathbf{x}_i = \sum_{j \in J_i} \lambda_i^j \mathbf{x}_i^j + \sum_{k \in K_i} \theta_i^k \mathbf{w}_i^k,$$

where the coefficients λ_i^j and θ_i^k are nonnegative and satisfy

$$\sum_{j \in J_i} \lambda_i^j = 1, \qquad i = 1, 2.$$

The original problem (6.10) can be now reformulated as

$$\begin{aligned}
\text{minimize} \quad & \sum_{j \in J_1} \lambda_1^j \mathbf{c}_1' \mathbf{x}_1^j + \sum_{k \in K_1} \theta_1^k \mathbf{c}_1' \mathbf{w}_1^k + \sum_{j \in J_2} \lambda_2^j \mathbf{c}_2' \mathbf{x}_2^j + \sum_{k \in K_2} \theta_2^k \mathbf{c}_2' \mathbf{w}_2^k \\
\text{subject to} \quad & \sum_{j \in J_1} \lambda_1^j \mathbf{D}_1 \mathbf{x}_1^j + \sum_{k \in K_1} \theta_1^k \mathbf{D}_1 \mathbf{w}_1^k + \sum_{j \in J_2} \lambda_2^j \mathbf{D}_2 \mathbf{x}_2^j \\
& \hspace{4cm} + \sum_{k \in K_2} \theta_2^k \mathbf{D}_2 \mathbf{w}_2^k = \mathbf{b}_0 \quad (6.11)
\end{aligned}$$

$$\sum_{j \in J_1} \lambda_1^j = 1 \qquad\qquad\qquad (6.12)$$

$$\sum_{j \in J_2} \lambda_2^j = 1 \qquad\qquad\qquad (6.13)$$

$$\lambda_i^j \geq 0, \ \theta_i^k \geq 0, \qquad \forall \ i, j, k.$$

This problem will be called the *master* problem. It is equivalent to the original problem (6.10) and is a linear programming problem in standard form, with decision variables λ_i^j and θ_i^k. An alternative notation for the equality constraints (6.11)-(6.13) that shows more clearly the structure of the column associated with each variable is

$$\sum_{j\in J_1}\lambda_1^j\begin{bmatrix}\mathbf{D}_1\mathbf{x}_1^j\\1\\0\end{bmatrix}+\sum_{j\in J_2}\lambda_2^j\begin{bmatrix}\mathbf{D}_2\mathbf{x}_2^j\\0\\1\end{bmatrix}$$

$$+\sum_{k\in K_1}\theta_1^k\begin{bmatrix}\mathbf{D}_1\mathbf{w}_1^k\\0\\0\end{bmatrix}+\sum_{k\in K_2}\theta_2^k\begin{bmatrix}\mathbf{D}_2\mathbf{w}_2^k\\0\\0\end{bmatrix}=\begin{bmatrix}\mathbf{b}_0\\1\\1\end{bmatrix}.$$

The decomposition algorithm

In contrast to the original problem, which had $m_0 + m_1 + m_2$ equality constraints, the master problem has only $m_0 + 2$ equality constraints. On the other hand, the number of decision variables in the master problem could be astronomical, because the number of extreme points and rays is usually exponential in the number of variables and constraints. Because of the enormous number of variables in the master problem, we need to use the revised simplex method which, at any given iteration, involves only m_0+2 basic variables and a basis matrix of dimensions $(m_0+2)\times(m_0+2)$.

Suppose that we have a basic feasible solution to the master problem, associated with a basis matrix $\mathbf{B}$. We assume that the inverse basis matrix $\mathbf{B}^{-1}$ is available, as well as the dual vector $\mathbf{p}' = \mathbf{c}_B'\mathbf{B}^{-1}$. Since we have m_0+2 equality constraints, the vector $\mathbf{p}$ has dimension m_0+2. The first m_0 components of $\mathbf{p}$, to be denoted by $\mathbf{q}$, are the dual variables associated with the constraints (6.11). The last two components, to be denoted by r_1 and r_2, are the dual variables associated with the "convexity" constraints (6.12) and (6.13), respectively. In particular, $\mathbf{p} = (\mathbf{q}, r_1, r_2)$.

In order to decide whether the current basic feasible solution is optimal, we need to examine the reduced costs of the different variables and check whether any one of them is negative. The cost coefficient of a variable λ_1^j is $\mathbf{c}_1'\mathbf{x}_1^j$. Therefore, the reduced cost of the variable λ_1^j is given by

$$\mathbf{c}_1'\mathbf{x}_1^j-\begin{bmatrix}\mathbf{q}' & r_1 & r_2\end{bmatrix}\begin{bmatrix}\mathbf{D}_1\mathbf{x}_1^j\\1\\0\end{bmatrix}=(\mathbf{c}_1'-\mathbf{q}'\mathbf{D}_1)\mathbf{x}_1^j-r_1.$$

Similarly, the cost coefficient of the variable θ_1^k is $\mathbf{c}_1'\mathbf{w}_1^k$. Therefore, its reduced cost is

$$\mathbf{c}_1'\mathbf{w}_1^k-\begin{bmatrix}\mathbf{q}' & r_1 & r_2\end{bmatrix}\begin{bmatrix}\mathbf{D}_1\mathbf{w}_1^k\\0\\0\end{bmatrix}=(\mathbf{c}_1'-\mathbf{q}'\mathbf{D}_1)\mathbf{w}_1^k.$$

We now introduce the most critical idea in the decomposition algorithm. Instead of evaluating the reduced cost of every variable λ_1^j and θ_1^k, and checking its sign, we form the linear programming problem

$$\text{minimize} \quad (\mathbf{c}_1' - \mathbf{q}'\mathbf{D}_1)\mathbf{x}_1$$
$$\text{subject to} \quad \mathbf{x}_1 \in P_1,$$

called the first *subproblem*, which we solve by means of the simplex method. There are three possibilities to consider.

(a) If the optimal cost in the subproblem is $-\infty$, then, upon termination, the simplex method provides us with an extreme ray $\mathbf{w}_1^k$ that satisfies $(\mathbf{c}_1' - \mathbf{q}'\mathbf{D}_1)\mathbf{w}_1^k < 0$ (see the discussion at the end of Section 4.8). In this case, the reduced cost of the variable θ_1^k is negative. At this point, we can generate the column

$$\begin{bmatrix} \mathbf{D}_1\mathbf{w}_1^k \\ 0 \\ 0 \end{bmatrix}$$

associated with θ_1^k, and have it enter the basis in the master problem.

(b) If the optimal cost in the subproblem is finite and smaller than r_1, then, upon termination, the simplex method provides us with an extreme point $\mathbf{x}_1^j$ that satisfies $(\mathbf{c}_1' - \mathbf{q}'\mathbf{D}_1)\mathbf{x}_1^j < r_1$. In this case, the reduced cost of the variable λ_1^j is negative. At this point, we can generate the column

$$\begin{bmatrix} \mathbf{D}_1\mathbf{x}_1^j \\ 1 \\ 0 \end{bmatrix}$$

associated with λ_1^j, and have it enter the basis in the master problem.

(c) Finally, if the optimal cost in the subproblem is finite and no smaller than r_1, this implies that $(\mathbf{c}_1' - \mathbf{q}'\mathbf{D}_1)\mathbf{x}_1^j \geq r_1$ for all extreme points $\mathbf{x}_1^j$, and $(\mathbf{c}_1' - \mathbf{q}'\mathbf{D}_1)\mathbf{w}_1^k \geq 0$ for all extreme rays $\mathbf{w}_1^k$. In this case, the reduced cost of every variable λ_1^j or θ_1^k is nonnegative.

The same approach is followed for checking the reduced costs of the variables λ_2^j and θ_2^k: we form the second subproblem

$$\text{minimize} \quad (\mathbf{c}_2' - \mathbf{q}'\mathbf{D}_2)\mathbf{x}_2$$
$$\text{subject to} \quad \mathbf{x}_2 \in P_2,$$

and solve it using the simplex method. Either the optimal cost is greater than or equal to r_2 and all reduced costs are nonnegative, or we find a variable λ_2^j or θ_2^k whose reduced cost is negative and can enter the basis. The resulting algorithm is summarized below.

Dantzig-Wolfe decomposition algorithm

1. A typical iteration starts with a total of m_0+2 extreme points and extreme rays of P_1, P_2, which lead to a basic feasible solution to the master problem, the corresponding inverse basis matrix $\mathbf{B}^{-1}$, and the dual vector $\mathbf{p}' = (\mathbf{q}, r_1, r_2)' = \mathbf{c}_B' \mathbf{B}^{-1}$.

2. Form and solve the two subproblems. If the optimal cost in the first subproblem is no smaller than r_1 and the optimal cost in the second subproblem is no smaller than r_2, then all reduced costs in the master problem are nonnegative, we have an optimal solution, and the algorithm terminates.

3. If the optimal cost in the ith subproblem is $-\infty$, we obtain an extreme ray $\mathbf{w}_i^k$, associated with a variable θ_i^k whose reduced cost is negative; this variable can enter the basis in the master problem.

4. If the optimal cost in the ith subproblem is finite and less than r_i, we obtain an extreme point $\mathbf{x}_i^j$, associated with a variable λ_i^j whose reduced cost is negative; this variable can enter the basis in the master problem.

5. Having chosen a variable to enter the basis, generate the column associated with that variable, carry out an iteration of the revised simplex method for the master problem, and update $\mathbf{B}^{-1}$ and $\mathbf{p}$.

We recognize delayed column generation as the centerpiece of the decomposition algorithm. Even though the master problem can have a huge number of columns, a column is generated only after it is found to have negative reduced cost and is about to enter the basis. Note that the subproblems are smaller linear programming problems that are employed as an economical search method for discovering columns with negative reduced costs.

As discussed in Section 6.1, we can also use a variant whereby all columns that have been generated in the past are retained. In this case, Step 5 of the algorithm has to be modified. Instead of carrying out a single simplex iteration, we solve a restricted master problem to optimality. This restricted problem has the same structure as the master problem, except that it only involves the columns that have been generated so far.

Economic interpretation

We provide an appealing economic interpretation of the Dantzig-Wolfe decomposition method. We have an organization with two divisions that have to meet a common objective, reflected in the coupling constraint $\mathbf{D}_1\mathbf{x}_1 + \mathbf{D}_2\mathbf{x}_2 = \mathbf{b}_0$. A central planner assigns a value of $\mathbf{q}$ for each unit of contribution towards the common objective. Division i is interested in minimizing $c_i' x_i$ subject to its own constraints. However, any choice of x_i contributes $D_i x_i$ towards the common objective and has therefore a value of $q' D_i x_i$. This leads division i to minimize $(c_i' - q' D_i) x_i$ (cost minus value) subject to its local constraints. The optimal solution to the division's subproblem can be viewed as a proposal to the central planner. The central planner uses these proposals and combines them (optimally) with preexisting proposals to form a feasible solution for the overall problem. Based on this feasible solution (which is a basic feasible solution to the master problem), the values q are reassessed and the process is repeated.

Applicability of the method

It should be clear that there is nothing special about having exactly two subproblems in the Dantzig-Wolfe decomposition method. In particular, the method generalizes in a straightforward manner to problems of the form

$$
\begin{aligned}
\text{minimize} \quad & c_1' x_1 + c_2' x_2 + \cdots + c_t' x_t \\
\text{subject to} \quad & D_1 x_1 + D_2 x_2 + \cdots + D_t x_t = b_0 \\
& F_i x_i = b_i, \qquad\qquad i = 1, 2, \ldots, t, \\
& x_1, x_2, \ldots, x_t \geq 0.
\end{aligned}
$$

The only difference is that at each iteration of the revised simplex method for the master problem, we may have to solve t subproblems.

In fact, the method is applicable even if $t = 1$, as we now discuss. Consider the linear programming problem

$$
\begin{aligned}
\text{minimize} \quad & c' x \\
\text{subject to} \quad & Dx = b_0 \\
& Fx = b \\
& x \geq 0,
\end{aligned}
$$

in which the equality constraints have been partitioned into two sets, and define the polyhedron $P = \{x \geq 0 \mid Fx = b\}$. By expressing each element of P in terms of extreme points and extreme rays, we obtain a master problem with a large number of columns, but a smaller number of equality constraints. Searching for columns with negative reduced cost in the master problem is then accomplished by solving a single subproblem, which is a minimization over the set P. This approach can be useful if the subproblem has a special structure and can be solved very fast.

Throughout our development, we have been assuming that all constraints are in standard form and, in particular, the feasible sets P_i of the subproblems are also in standard form. This is hardly necessary. For example, if we assume that the sets P_i have at least one extreme point, the resolution theorem and the same line of development applies.

Examples

We now consider some examples and go through the details of the algorithm. In order to avoid excessive bookkeeping, our first example involves a single subproblem.

Example 6.2 Consider the problem

$$
\begin{array}{ll}
\text{minimize} & -4x_1 - x_2 - 6x_3 \\
\text{subject to} & 3x_1 + 2x_2 + 4x_3 = 17 \\
& 1 \le x_1 \le 2 \\
& 1 \le x_2 \le 2 \\
& 1 \le x_3 \le 2.
\end{array}
$$

We divide the constraints into two groups: the first group consists of the constraint $\mathbf{Dx} = \mathbf{b}_0$, where $\mathbf{D}$ is the 1×3 matrix $\mathbf{D} = [3 \ 2 \ 4]$, and where $\mathbf{b}_0 = 17$; the second group is the constraint $\mathbf{x} \in P$, where $P = \{\mathbf{x} \in \Re^3 \mid 1 \le x_i \le 2, \ i = 1, 2, 3\}$. Note that P has eight extreme points; furthermore, it is bounded and, therefore, has no extreme rays. The master problem has two equality constraints, namely

$$
\sum_{j=1}^{8} \lambda^j \mathbf{Dx}^j = 17,
$$

$$
\sum_{j=1}^{8} \lambda^j = 1,
$$

where $\mathbf{x}^j$ are the extreme points of P. The columns of the constraint matrix in the master problem are of the form $(\mathbf{Dx}^j, 1)$. Let us pick two of the extreme points of P, say, $\mathbf{x}^1 = (2, 2, 2)$ and $\mathbf{x}^2 = (1, 1, 2)$, and let the corresponding variables λ^1 and λ^2 be our initial basic variables. We have $\mathbf{Dx}^1 = 18$, $\mathbf{Dx}^2 = 13$, and, therefore, the corresponding basis matrix is

$$
\mathbf{B} = \begin{bmatrix} 18 & 13 \\ 1 & 1 \end{bmatrix};
$$

its inverse is

$$
\mathbf{B}^{-1} = \begin{bmatrix} 0.2 & -2.6 \\ -0.2 & 3.6 \end{bmatrix}.
$$

We form the product of $\mathbf{B}^{-1}$ with the vector $(17, 1)$. The result, which is $(0.8, 0.2)$, gives us the values of the basic variables λ^1, λ^2. Since these values are nonnegative, we have a basic feasible solution to the master problem.

   We now determine the simplex multipliers. Recalling that the cost of λ^j is $\mathbf{c}'\mathbf{x}^j$, we have

$$
c_{B(1)} = \mathbf{c}'\mathbf{x}^1 = \begin{bmatrix} -4 & -1 & -6 \end{bmatrix} \begin{bmatrix} 2 \\ 2 \\ 2 \end{bmatrix} = -22,
$$

and

$$c_{B(2)} = \mathbf{c}'\mathbf{x}^2 = \begin{bmatrix} -4 & -1 & -6 \end{bmatrix} \begin{bmatrix} 1 \\ 1 \\ 2 \end{bmatrix} = -17.$$

We therefore have

$$\mathbf{p}' = \begin{bmatrix} \mathbf{q}' & r \end{bmatrix} = \mathbf{c}'_B \mathbf{B}^{-1} = \begin{bmatrix} -22 & -17 \end{bmatrix} \mathbf{B}^{-1} = \begin{bmatrix} -1 & -4 \end{bmatrix}.$$

We now form the subproblem. We are to minimize $(\mathbf{c}' - \mathbf{q}'\mathbf{D})\mathbf{x}$ subject to $\mathbf{x} \in P$. We have

$$\mathbf{c}' - \mathbf{q}'\mathbf{D} = \begin{bmatrix} -4 & -1 & -6 \end{bmatrix} - (-1)\begin{bmatrix} 3 & 2 & 4 \end{bmatrix} = \begin{bmatrix} -1 & 1 & -2 \end{bmatrix},$$

and the optimal solution is $\mathbf{x} = (2, 1, 2)$. This is a new extreme point of P, which we will denote by $\mathbf{x}^3$. The optimal cost in the subproblem is -5, and is less than r, which is -4. It follows that the reduced cost of the variable λ^3 is negative, and this variable can enter the basis. At this point, we generate the column corresponding to λ^3. Since $\mathbf{D}\mathbf{x}^3 = 16$, the corresponding column, call it $\mathbf{g}$, is $(16, 1)$. We form the vector $\mathbf{u} = \mathbf{B}^{-1}\mathbf{g}$, which is found to be $(0.6, 0.4)$. In order to determine which variable exits the basis, we form the ratios $\lambda^1/u_1 = 0.8/0.6$ and $\lambda^2/u_2 = 0.2/0.4$. The second ratio is smaller and λ^2 exits the basis. We now have a new basis

$$\mathbf{B} = \begin{bmatrix} 18 & 16 \\ 1 & 1 \end{bmatrix};$$

its inverse is

$$\mathbf{B}^{-1} = \begin{bmatrix} 0.5 & -8 \\ -0.5 & 9 \end{bmatrix}.$$

We form the product of $\mathbf{B}^{-1}$ with the vector $(17, 1)$ and determine the values of the basic variables, which are $\lambda^1 = 0.5$ and $\lambda^3 = 0.5$. The new value of $c_{B(2)}$ is $\mathbf{c}'\mathbf{x}^3 = -21$. Once more, we compute $\begin{bmatrix} \mathbf{q}' & r \end{bmatrix} = \mathbf{c}'_B \mathbf{B}^{-1}$, which is $(-0.5, -13)'$.

We now go back to the subproblem. We have

$$\mathbf{c}' - \mathbf{q}'\mathbf{D} = \begin{bmatrix} -4 & -1 & -6 \end{bmatrix} - (-0.5)\begin{bmatrix} 3 & 2 & 4 \end{bmatrix} = \begin{bmatrix} -2.5 & 0 & -4 \end{bmatrix}.$$

We minimize $(\mathbf{c}' - \mathbf{q}'\mathbf{D})\mathbf{x}$ over P. We find that $(2, 2, 2)$ is an optimal solution, and the optimal cost is equal to -13. Since this is the same as the value of r, we conclude that the reduced cost of every λ^i is nonnegative, and we have an optimal solution to the master problem.

In terms of the variables x_i, the optimal solution is

$$\mathbf{x} = \frac{1}{2}\mathbf{x}^1 + \frac{1}{2}\mathbf{x}^3 = \begin{bmatrix} 2 \\ 1.5 \\ 2 \end{bmatrix}.$$

The progress of the algorithm is illustrated in Figure 6.2.

As shown in Figure 6.2, even though the optimal solution is an extreme point of the feasible set in $\mathbf{x}$-space, feasible solutions generated in the course of the algorithm (e.g., the point A) are not extreme points. Another illustration that conveys the same message is provided by Figure 6.3. Notice the similarity with our discussion of the column geometry in Section 3.6.

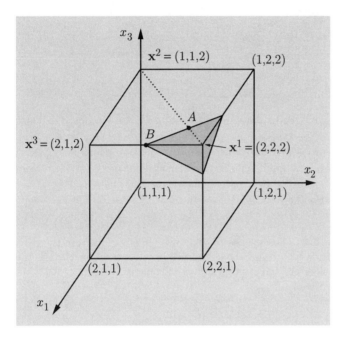

Figure 6.2: Illustration of Example 6.2, in terms of the variables x_i in the original problem. The cube shown is the set P. The feasible set is the intersection of the cube with the hyperplane $3x_1 + 2x_2 + 4x_3 = 17$, and corresponds to the shaded triangle. Under the first basis considered, we have a feasible solution which is a convex combination of the extreme points $\mathbf{x}^1$, $\mathbf{x}^2$, namely, point A. At the next step, the extreme point $\mathbf{x}^3$ is introduced. If λ^1 were to become nonbasic, we would be dealing with convex combinations of $\mathbf{x}^2$ and $\mathbf{x}^3$, and we would not be able to satisfy the constraint $3x_1 + 2x_2 + 4x_3 = 17$. This provides a geometric explanation of why λ^1 must stay and λ^2 must exit the basis. The new basic feasible solution corresponds to the point B, is a convex combination of $\mathbf{x}^1$ and $\mathbf{x}^3$, and was found to be optimal.

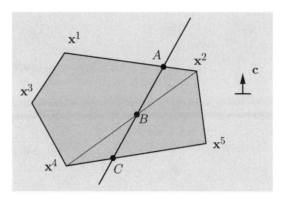

Figure 6.3: Another illustration of the geometry of Dantzig-Wolfe decomposition. Consider the case where there is a single subproblem whose feasible set has extreme points $\mathbf{x}^1, \ldots, \mathbf{x}^5$, and a single coupling equality constraint which corresponds to the line shown in the figure. The algorithm is initialized at point A and follows the path A, B, C, with point C being an optimal solution.

Example 6.3 The purpose of this example is to illustrate the behavior of the decomposition algorithm when the feasible set of a subproblem is unbounded.

Consider the linear programming problem

$$
\begin{aligned}
\text{minimize} \quad & -5x_1 + x_2 \\
\text{subject to} \quad & x_1 \qquad\quad \le 8 \\
& x_1 - x_2 \le 4 \\
& 2x_1 - x_2 \le 10 \\
& x_1, x_2 \ge 0.
\end{aligned}
$$

The feasible set is shown in Figure 6.4.

We associate a slack variable x_3 with the first constraint and obtain the problem

$$
\begin{aligned}
\text{minimize} \quad & -5x_1 + x_2 \\
\text{subject to} \quad & x_1 + x_3 = 8 \\
& x_1 - x_2 \le 4 \\
& 2x_1 - x_2 \le 10 \\
& x_1, x_2 \ge 0 \\
& x_3 \ge 0.
\end{aligned}
$$

We view the constraint $x_1 + x_3 = 8$ as a coupling constraint and let

$$
P_1 = \Big\{ (x_1, x_2) \ \Big| \ x_1 - x_2 \le 4, \ 2x_1 - x_2 \le 10, \ x_1, x_2 \ge 0 \Big\},
$$

$$
P_2 = \{ x_3 \mid x_3 \ge 0 \}.
$$

We therefore have two subproblems, although the second subproblem has a very simple feasible set.

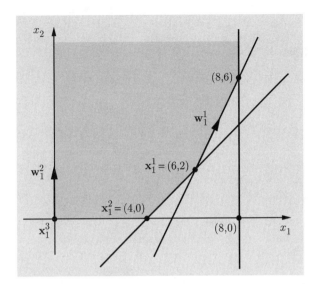

Figure 6.4: Illustration of Example 6.3. The algorithm starts at $(x_1, x_2) = (6, 2)$ and after one master iteration reaches point $(x_1, x_2) = (8, 6)$, which is an optimal solution.

The set P_1 is the same as the set shown in Figure 6.4, except that the constraint $x_1 \leq 8$ is absent. Thus, P_1 has three extreme points, namely, $\mathbf{x}_1^1 = (6, 2)$, $\mathbf{x}_1^2 = (4, 0)$, $\mathbf{x}_1^3 = (0, 0)$, and two extreme rays, namely, $\mathbf{w}_1^1 = (1, 2)$ and $\mathbf{w}_1^2 = (0, 1)$.

Because of the simple structure of the set P_2, instead of introducing an extreme ray $\mathbf{w}_2^1$ and an associated variable θ_2^1, we identify θ_2^1 with x_3, and keep x_3 as a variable in the master problem.

The master problem has two equality constraints, namely,

$$\sum_{j=1}^{3} \lambda_1^j \mathbf{x}_1^j + \sum_{k=1}^{2} \theta_1^k \mathbf{w}_1^k + x_3 = 8,$$

$$\sum_{j=1}^{3} \lambda_1^j = 1.$$

Accordingly, a basis consists of exactly two columns.

In this example, we have $\mathbf{D}_1 = [1 \ 0]$ and $\mathbf{D}_2 = 1$. Consider the variable λ_1^1 associated with the extreme point $\mathbf{x}_1^1 = (6, 2)$ of the first subproblem. The corresponding column is $(\mathbf{D}_1 \mathbf{x}_1^1, 1) = (6, 1)$. The column associated with x_3 is $(1, 0)$. If we choose λ_1^1 and x_3 as the basic variables, the basis matrix is

$$\mathbf{B} = \begin{bmatrix} 6 & 1 \\ 1 & 0 \end{bmatrix},$$

and its inverse is

$$\mathbf{B}^{-1} = \begin{bmatrix} 0 & 1 \\ 1 & -6 \end{bmatrix}.$$

We form the product of $\mathbf{B}^{-1}$ with the vector $(\mathbf{b}_0, 1) = (8, 1)$. The result, which is $(1, 2)$, gives us the values of the basic variables λ_1^1, x_3. Since these values are nonnegative, we have a basic feasible solution to the master problem, which corresponds to $(x_1, x_2) = \mathbf{x}_1^1 = (6, 2)$; see Figure 6.4.

We now determine the dual variables. We have $c_{B(1)} = (-5, 1)'\mathbf{x}_1^1 = -28$ and $c_{B(2)} = 0 \times 1 = 0$. We therefore have

$$\mathbf{p}' = \begin{bmatrix} q & r_1 \end{bmatrix} = \mathbf{c}_B'\mathbf{B}^{-1} = \begin{bmatrix} -28 & 0 \end{bmatrix}\mathbf{B}^{-1} = \begin{bmatrix} 0 & -28 \end{bmatrix}.$$

(Note that we use the notation q instead of $\mathbf{q}$, because $\mathbf{q}$ is one-dimensional. Furthermore, the dual variable r_2 is absent because there is no convexity constraint associated with the second subproblem.)

We form the first subproblem. We are to minimize $(\mathbf{c}_1' - \mathbf{q}'\mathbf{D}_1)\mathbf{x}_1$ subject to $\mathbf{x}_1 \in P_1$. Because $q = 0$, we have $\mathbf{c}_1' - q\mathbf{D}_1 = \mathbf{c}_1' = (-5, 1)'$. We are therefore minimizing $-5x_1 + x_2$ subject to $\mathbf{x}_1 \in P_1$ and the optimal cost is $-\infty$. In particular, we find that the extreme ray $\mathbf{w}_1^1 = (1, 2)$ has negative cost. The associated variable θ_1^1 is to enter the basis. At this point, we generate the column corresponding to θ_1^1. Since $\mathbf{D}_1\mathbf{w}_1^1 = 1$, the corresponding column, call it $\mathbf{g}$, is $(1, 0)$. We form the vector $\mathbf{u} = \mathbf{B}^{-1}\mathbf{g}$, which is found to be $(0, 1)$. The only positive entry is the second one and this is therefore the pivot element. It follows that the second basic variable, namely x_3, exits the basis. Because the column associated with the entering variable θ_1^1 is equal to the column associated with the exiting variable x_3, we still have the same basis matrix and, therefore, the same values of the basic variables, namely, $\lambda_1^1 = 1$, $\theta_1^1 = 2$. This takes us to the vector $\mathbf{x} = \mathbf{x}_1^1 + 2\mathbf{w}_1^1 = (8, 6)$; see Figure 6.4.

For the new basic variables, $c_{B(1)}$ is again -28 and

$$c_{B(2)} = \mathbf{c}_1'\mathbf{w}_1^1 = \begin{bmatrix} -5 & 1 \end{bmatrix}\begin{bmatrix} 1 \\ 2 \end{bmatrix} = -3.$$

We compute $(q, r_1)' = \mathbf{c}_B'\mathbf{B}^{-1}$, which is equal to $(-3, -10)'$.

We now go back to the first subproblem. Since $q = -3$, we have

$$\mathbf{c}_1' - q\mathbf{D}_1 = \begin{bmatrix} -5 & 1 \end{bmatrix} - (-3)\begin{bmatrix} 1 & 0 \end{bmatrix} = \begin{bmatrix} -2 & 1 \end{bmatrix}.$$

We minimize $-2x_1 + x_2$ over the set P_1. The optimal cost is -10 and is attained at $(x_1, x_2) = (8, 6)$. Because the optimal cost -10 is equal to r_1, all of the variables associated with the first subproblem have nonnegative reduced costs.

We next consider the second subproblem. We have $\mathbf{c}_2 = 0$, $q = -3$, and $\mathbf{D}_2 = 1$. Thus, the reduced cost of x_3 is equal to $\mathbf{c}_2' - q\mathbf{D}_2 = 3$. We conclude that all of the variables in the master problem have nonnegative reduced costs and we have an optimal solution.

Starting the algorithm

In order to start the decomposition algorithm, we need to find a basic feasible solution to the master problem. This can be done as follows. We first apply Phase I of the simplex method to each one of the polyhedra P_1 and P_2, separately, and find extreme points $\mathbf{x}_1^1$ and $\mathbf{x}_2^1$ of P_1 and P_2, respectively. By possibly multiplying both sides of some of the coupling constraints by -1, we can assume that $\mathbf{D}_1\mathbf{x}_1^1 + \mathbf{D}_2\mathbf{x}_2^1 \leq \mathbf{b}$. Let $\mathbf{y}$ be a vector of auxiliary variables of dimension m_0. We form the auxiliary master problem

$$\text{minimize} \quad \sum_{t=1}^{m_0} y_t$$

$$\text{subject to} \quad \sum_{i=1,2}\left(\sum_{j\in J_i}\lambda_i^j\mathbf{D}_i\mathbf{x}_i^j + \sum_{k\in K_i}\theta_i^k\mathbf{D}_i\mathbf{w}_i^k\right) + \mathbf{y} = \mathbf{b}_0$$

$$\sum_{j\in J_1}\lambda_1^j = 1$$

$$\sum_{j\in J_2}\lambda_2^j = 1$$

$$\lambda_i^j \geq 0, \ \theta_i^k \geq 0, \ y_t \geq 0, \qquad \forall \ i,j,k,t.$$

A basic feasible solution to the auxiliary problem is obtained by letting $\lambda_1^1 = \lambda_2^1 = 1$, $\lambda_i^j = 0$ for $j \neq 1$, $\theta_i^k = 0$ for all k, and $\mathbf{y} = \mathbf{b}_0 - \mathbf{D}_1\mathbf{x}_1^1 - \mathbf{D}_2\mathbf{x}_2^1$. Starting from here, we can use the decomposition algorithm to solve the auxiliary master problem. If the optimal cost is positive, then the master problem is infeasible. If the optimal cost is zero, an optimal solution to the auxiliary problem provides us with a basic feasible solution to the master problem.

Termination and computational experience

The decomposition algorithm is a special case of the revised simplex method and, therefore, inherits its termination properties. In particular, in the absence of degeneracy, it is guaranteed to terminate in a finite number of steps. In the presence of degeneracy, finite termination is ensured if an anticycling rule is used, although this is rarely done in practice. Note that Bland's rule cannot be applied in this context, because it is incompatible with the way that the decomposition algorithm chooses the entering variable. There is no such difficulty, in principle, with the lexicographic pivoting rule, provided that the inverse basis matrix is explicitly computed.

   A practical way of speeding up the solution of the subproblems is to start the simplex method on a subproblem using the optimal solution obtained the previous time that the subproblem was solved. As long as the objective function of the subproblem does not change too drastically between successive master iterations, one expects that this could lead to an optimal solution for the subproblem after a relatively small number of iterations.

   Practical experience suggests that the algorithm makes substantial progress in the beginning, but the cost improvement can become very slow later on. For this reason, the algorithm is sometimes terminated prematurely, yielding a suboptimal solution.

The available experience also suggests that the algorithm is usually no faster than the revised simplex method applied to the original problem. The true advantage of the decomposition algorithm lies in its storage requirements. Suppose that we have t subproblems, each one having the same number m_1 of equality constraints. The storage requirements of the revised simplex method for the original problem are $O\big((m_0+tm_1)^2\big)$, which is the size of the revised simplex tableau. In contrast, the storage requirements of the decomposition algorithm are $O\big((m_0+t)^2\big)$ for the tableau of the master problem, and t times $O(m_1^2)$ for the revised simplex tableaux of the subproblems. Furthermore, the decomposition algorithm needs to have only one tableau stored in main memory at any given time. For example, if $t = 10$ and if $m_0 = m_1$ is much larger than t, the main memory requirements of the decomposition algorithm are about 100 times smaller than those of the revised simplex method. With memory being a key bottleneck in handling very large linear programming problems, the decomposition approach can substantially enlarge the range of problems that can be practically solved.

Bounds on the optimal cost

As already discussed, the decomposition algorithm may take a long time to terminate, especially for very large problems. We will now show how to obtain upper and lower bounds for the optimal cost. Such bounds can be used to stop the algorithm once the cost gets acceptably close to the optimum.

Theorem 6.1 *Suppose that the master problem is feasible and its optimal cost z^* is finite. Let z be the cost of the feasible solution obtained at some intermediate stage of the decomposition algorithm. Also, let r_i be the value of the dual variable associated with the convexity constraint for the ith subproblem. Finally, let z_i be the optimal cost in the ith subproblem, assumed finite. Then,*

$$z + \sum_i (z_i - r_i) \le z^* \le z.$$

Proof. The inequality $z^* \le z$ is obvious, since z is the cost associated with a feasible solution to the original problem. It remains to prove the left-hand side inequality in the statement of the theorem.

We provide the proof for the case of two subproblems. The proof for the general case is similar. The dual of the master problem is

$$\text{maximize} \quad \mathbf{q}'\mathbf{b}_0 + r_1 + r_2$$

$$\text{subject to} \quad \begin{array}{llll}
\mathbf{q}'\mathbf{D}_1\mathbf{x}_1^j & + r_1 & \leq \mathbf{c}_1'\mathbf{x}_1^j, & \forall\, j \in J_1, \\
\mathbf{q}'\mathbf{D}_1\mathbf{w}_1^k & & \leq \mathbf{c}_1'\mathbf{w}_1^k, & \forall\, k \in K_1, \\
\mathbf{q}'\mathbf{D}_2\mathbf{x}_2^j & + r_2 & \leq \mathbf{c}_2'\mathbf{x}_2^j, & \forall\, j \in J_2, \\
\mathbf{q}'\mathbf{D}_2\mathbf{w}_2^k & & \leq \mathbf{c}_2'\mathbf{w}_2^k, & \forall\, k \in K_2.
\end{array} \quad (6.14)$$

Suppose that we have a basic feasible solution to the master problem, with cost z, and let $(\mathbf{q}, r_1, r_2)$ be the associated vector of simplex multipliers. This is a (generally infeasible) basic solution to the dual problem, with the same cost, that is,

$$\mathbf{q}'\mathbf{b}_0 + r_1 + r_2 = z. \tag{6.15}$$

Since the optimal cost z_1 in the first subproblem is finite, we have

$$\min_{j \in J_1}(\mathbf{c}_1'\mathbf{x}_1^j - \mathbf{q}'\mathbf{D}_1\mathbf{x}_1^j) = z_1,$$

$$\min_{k \in K_1}(\mathbf{c}_1'\mathbf{w}_1^k - \mathbf{q}'\mathbf{D}_1\mathbf{w}_1^k) \geq 0.$$

Thus, $\mathbf{q}$ together with z_1 in the place of r_1, satisfy the first two dual constraints. By a similar argument, $\mathbf{q}$ together with z_2 in the place of r_2, satisfy the last two dual constraints. Therefore, $(\mathbf{q}, z_1, z_2)$ is a feasible solution to the dual problem (6.14). Its cost is $\mathbf{q}'\mathbf{b}_0 + z_1 + z_2$ and, by weak duality, is no larger than the optimal cost z^*. Hence,

$$\begin{aligned}
z^* &\geq \mathbf{q}'\mathbf{b}_0 + z_1 + z_2 \\
&= \mathbf{q}'\mathbf{b}_0 + r_1 + r_2 + (z_1 - r_1) + (z_2 - r_2) \\
&= z + (z_1 - r_1) + (z_2 - r_2),
\end{aligned}$$

where the last equality follows from Eq. (6.15). $\square$

Note that if the optimal cost in one of the subproblems is $-\infty$, then Theorem 6.1 does not provide any useful bounds.

The proof of Theorem 6.1 is an instance of a general method for obtaining lower bounds on the optimal cost of linear programming problems, which is the following. Given a nonoptimal basic feasible solution to the primal, we consider the corresponding (infeasible) basic solution to the dual problem. If we can somehow modify this dual solution, to make it feasible, the weak duality theorem readily yields a lower bound. This was the approach taken in the proof of Theorem 6.1, where we started from the generally infeasible dual solution $(\mathbf{q}, r_1, r_2)$, moved to the dual feasible solution $(\mathbf{q}, z_1, z_2)$, and then invoked weak duality.

Example 6.4 Let us revisit Example 6.2 and consider the situation just before the first change of basis. We are at a basic feasible solution determined by

$(\lambda^1, \lambda^2) = (0.8, 0.2)$. Since $\mathbf{c}_B = (-22, -17)$, we have $z = (-22, -17)'(0.8, 0.2) = -21$. We also have $r = -4$. Finally, the optimal cost in the subproblem is $(-1, 1, -2)'(2, 1, 2) = -5$. It follows that $-21 \geq z^* \geq -21 + (-5) - (-4) = -22$. Indeed, the true value of z^* is -21.5.

6.5   Stochastic programming and Benders decomposition

In this section, we introduce and study two-stage stochastic linear programming problems. In this important class of problems, there are two sets of decisions that are made in consecutive stages. Furthermore, there are some exogenous parameters that influence the second stage of decision making, but whose values are uncertain, and only become known after the first set of decisions has been fixed. In order to address problems of this type, we develop a new decomposition algorithm, called Benders decomposition, which is based on delayed constraint generation (as opposed to delayed column generation).

Problem formulation

Consider a decision maker who has to act in two consecutive stages. The first stage involves the choice of a decision vector $\mathbf{x}$. Subsequently, some new information is obtained, and then, at the second stage, a new vector $\mathbf{y}$ of decisions is to be chosen. Regarding the nature of the obtained information, we assume that there are K possible scenarios, and that the true scenario is only revealed after $\mathbf{x}$ is chosen. We use ω to index the different scenarios, and we let α_ω stand for the probability of any particular scenario ω, which we assume to be positive. Since the second stage decisions are made after the true scenario ω becomes known, we allow the decision vector $\mathbf{y}$ to depend on ω, and we use the notation $\mathbf{y}_\omega$ to make this dependence explicit.

We now make more specific assumptions on the problem objectives and constraints. We are given cost vectors $\mathbf{c}$ and $\mathbf{f}$, associated with the decisions $\mathbf{x}$ and $\mathbf{y}_\omega$, respectively. The first stage decisions must satisfy the constraints

$$\mathbf{Ax} = \mathbf{b}$$
$$\mathbf{x} \geq \mathbf{0}.$$

In addition, the first and second stage decisions need to satisfy constraints of the form

$$\mathbf{B}_\omega \mathbf{x} + \mathbf{Dy}_\omega = \mathbf{d}_\omega$$
$$\mathbf{y}_\omega \geq \mathbf{0},$$

for all ω; in particular, every scenario may involve a different set of constraints. The objective is to choose $\mathbf{x}$ and $\mathbf{y}_1, \ldots, \mathbf{y}_K$ so that the "expected cost"

$$\mathbf{c'x} + \alpha_1 \mathbf{f'y}_1 + \cdots + \alpha_K \mathbf{f'y}_K$$

is minimized. We thus arrive at the problem

$$
\begin{array}{llll}
\text{minimize} & \mathbf{c'x} + \alpha_1 \mathbf{f'y}_1 + \alpha_2 \mathbf{f'y}_2 + \cdots + \alpha_K \mathbf{f'y}_K & \\
\text{subject to} & \mathbf{Ax} & = \mathbf{b} \\
& \mathbf{B}_1\mathbf{x} + \mathbf{Dy}_1 & = \mathbf{d}_1 \\
& \mathbf{B}_2\mathbf{x} \quad\quad + \mathbf{Dy}_2 & = \mathbf{d}_2 \\
& \quad\vdots \quad\quad\quad\quad\quad\ddots & \vdots \\
& \mathbf{B}_K\mathbf{x} \quad\quad\quad\quad\quad + \mathbf{Dy}_K & = \mathbf{d}_K \\
& \mathbf{x}, \mathbf{y}_1, \mathbf{y}_2, \ldots, \mathbf{y}_K \geq \mathbf{0},
\end{array}
$$

which will be referred to as the *master problem*. Notice that even if the number of possible scenarios K is moderate, this formulation can be a large linear programming problem. For this reason, a decomposition method is in order.

Example 6.5 (Electric power capacity expansion) An electric utility is installing two generators (indexed by $j = 1, 2$) with different fixed and operating costs, in order to meet the demand within its service region. Each day is divided into three parts of equal duration, indexed by $i = 1, 2, 3$. These correspond to parts of the day during which demand takes a base, medium, or peak value, respectively. The fixed cost per unit capacity of generator j is amortized over its lifetime and amounts to c_j per day. The operating cost of generator j during the ith part of the day is f_{ij}. If the demand during the ith part of the day cannot be served due to lack of capacity, additional capacity must be purchased at a cost of g_i. Finally, the capacity of each generator j is required to be at least b_j.

There are two sources of uncertainty, namely, the exact value of the demand d_i during each part of the day, and the availability a_j of generator j. The demand d_i can take one of four values $d_{i,1}, \ldots, d_{i,4}$, with probability $p_{i,1}, \ldots, p_{i,4}$, respectively. The availability of generator 1 is $a_{1,1}, \ldots, a_{1,4}$, with probability $q_{1,1}, \ldots, q_{1,4}$, respectively. Similarly, the availability of generator 2 is $a_{2,1}, \ldots, a_{2,5}$, with probability $q_{2,1}, \ldots, q_{2,5}$, respectively. If we enumerate all the possible events, we see that there is a total of $4^3 \times 4 \times 5 = 1280$ scenarios ω. Let us use d_i^ω and a_j^ω to denote the demands and availabilities, respectively, under scenario ω.

We introduce the first stage variables x_j, $j = 1, 2$, that represent the installed capacity of generator j. We also introduce the second stage variables y_{ij}^ω that denote the operating levels of generator j during the ith part of the day and under scenario ω. Finally y_i^ω is the capacity that needs to be purchased under scenario ω, in order to satisfy unmet demand during the ith part of the day. We interpret availability to mean that the operating level of generator j, at any given time, is at most $a_j x_j$. We then arrive at the following formulation:

$$\text{minimize} \quad \sum_{j=1}^{2} c_j x_j + E\left[\sum_{i=1}^{3}\left(\sum_{j=1}^{2} f_{ij} y_{ij}^{\omega} + g_i y_i^{\omega}\right)\right]$$

$$\text{subject to} \quad x_j \geq b_j, \qquad\qquad\qquad \forall\, j,$$

$$y_{ij}^{\omega} \leq a_j^{\omega} x_j, \qquad\qquad\quad \forall\, i, j, \omega,$$

$$\sum_{j=1}^{2} y_{ij}^{\omega} + y_i^{\omega} \geq d_i^{\omega}, \qquad\quad \forall\, i, \omega,$$

$$x_j, y_{ij}^{\omega}, y_i^{\omega} \geq 0, \qquad\qquad \forall\, i, j, \omega.$$

(Here, $E[\cdot]$ stands for mathematical expectation, that is the average over all scenarios ω, weighted according to their probabilities.) The full model involves 11522 variables and 11522 constraints (not counting nonnegativity constraints).

Reformulation of the problem

Consider a vector $\mathbf{x}$ such that $\mathbf{Ax} = \mathbf{b}$ and $\mathbf{x} \geq \mathbf{0}$, and suppose that this is our choice for the first stage decisions. Once $\mathbf{x}$ is fixed, the optimal second stage decisions $\mathbf{y}_\omega$ can be determined separately from each other, by solving for each ω the problem

$$\text{minimize} \quad \mathbf{f}'\mathbf{y}_\omega$$

$$\text{subject to} \quad \mathbf{B}_\omega \mathbf{x} + \mathbf{D}\mathbf{y}_\omega = \mathbf{d}_\omega \qquad (6.16)$$

$$\mathbf{y}_\omega \geq \mathbf{0}.$$

Let $z_\omega(\mathbf{x})$ be the optimal cost of the problem (6.16), together with the convention $z_\omega(\mathbf{x}) = \infty$ if the problem is infeasible. If we now go back to the optimization of $\mathbf{x}$, we are faced with the problem

$$\text{minimize} \quad \mathbf{c}'\mathbf{x} + \sum_{\omega=1}^{K} \alpha_\omega z_\omega(\mathbf{x})$$

$$\text{subject to} \quad \mathbf{Ax} = \mathbf{b} \qquad\qquad (6.17)$$

$$\mathbf{x} \geq \mathbf{0}.$$

Of course, in solving this problem, we should only consider those $\mathbf{x}$ for which none of the $z_\omega(\mathbf{x})$ are equal to infinity.

We will approach problem (6.16) by forming its dual, which is

$$\text{maximize} \quad \mathbf{p}'_\omega(\mathbf{d}_\omega - \mathbf{B}_\omega \mathbf{x})$$

$$\text{subject to} \quad \mathbf{p}'_\omega \mathbf{D} \leq \mathbf{f}'. \qquad (6.18)$$

Let

$$P = \{\mathbf{p} \mid \mathbf{p}'\mathbf{D} \leq \mathbf{f}'\}.$$

We assume that P is nonempty and has at least one extreme point. Let $\mathbf{p}^i$, $i = 1, \ldots, I$, be the extreme points, and let $\mathbf{w}^j$, $j = 1, \ldots, J$, be a complete set of extreme rays of P.

Under our assumption that the set P is nonempty, either the dual problem (6.18) has an optimal solution and $z_\omega(\mathbf{x})$ is finite, or the optimal dual cost is infinite, the primal problem (6.16) is infeasible, and $z_\omega(\mathbf{x}) = \infty$. In particular, $z_\omega(\mathbf{x}) < \infty$ if and only if

$$(\mathbf{w}^j)'(\mathbf{d}_\omega - \mathbf{B}_\omega \mathbf{x}) \le 0, \qquad \forall \, j. \tag{6.19}$$

Whenever $z_\omega(\mathbf{x})$ is finite, it is the optimal cost of the problem (6.18), and the optimum must be attained at an extreme point of the set P; in particular,

$$z_\omega(\mathbf{x}) = \max_{i=1,\dots,I} (\mathbf{p}^i)'(\mathbf{d}_\omega - \mathbf{B}_\omega \mathbf{x}).$$

Alternatively, $z_\omega(\mathbf{x})$ is the smallest number z_ω such that

$$(\mathbf{p}^i)'(\mathbf{d}_\omega - \mathbf{B}_\omega \mathbf{x}) \le z_\omega, \qquad \forall \, i.$$

We use this characterization of $z_\omega(\mathbf{x})$ in the original problem (6.17), and also take into account the condition (6.19), which is required for $z_\omega(\mathbf{x})$ to be finite, and we conclude that the master problem (6.17) can be put in the form

$$
\begin{aligned}
\text{minimize} \quad & \mathbf{c}'\mathbf{x} + \sum_{\omega=1}^{K} \alpha_\omega z_\omega \\
\text{subject to} \quad & \mathbf{A}\mathbf{x} = \mathbf{b} \\
& (\mathbf{p}^i)'(\mathbf{d}_\omega - \mathbf{B}_\omega \mathbf{x}) \le z_\omega, \qquad \forall \, i, \omega, \\
& (\mathbf{w}^j)'(\mathbf{d}_\omega - \mathbf{B}_\omega \mathbf{x}) \le 0, \qquad \forall \, j, \omega, \\
& \mathbf{x} \ge \mathbf{0}.
\end{aligned}
\tag{6.20}
$$

With this reformulation, the number of variables has been reduced substantially. The number of constraints can be extremely large, but this obstacle can be overcome using the cutting plane method. In particular, we will only generate constraints that we find to be violated by the current solution.

Delayed constraint generation

At a typical iteration of the algorithm, we consider the *relaxed master problem*, which has the same objective as the problem (6.20), but involves only a subset of the constraints. We assume that we have an optimal solution to the relaxed master problem, consisting of a vector $\mathbf{x}^*$ and a vector $\mathbf{z}^* = (z_1^*, \dots, z_K^*)$. In the spirit of the cutting plane method, we need to check whether $(\mathbf{x}^*, \mathbf{z}^*)$ is also a feasible solution to the full master problem. However, instead of individually checking all of the constraints, we proceed by solving some auxiliary subproblems.

For $\omega = 1, \ldots, K$, we consider the subproblem

$$\begin{array}{ll} \text{minimize} & \mathbf{f}'\mathbf{y}_\omega \\ \text{subject to} & \mathbf{D}\mathbf{y}_\omega = \mathbf{d}_\omega - \mathbf{B}_\omega \mathbf{x}^* \\ & \mathbf{y}_\omega \geq \mathbf{0}, \end{array}$$

which we solve to optimality. Notice that the subproblems encountered at different iterations, or for different values of ω, differ only in the right-hand side vector $\mathbf{d}_\omega - \mathbf{B}_\omega \mathbf{x}^*$. In particular, the corresponding dual problems always have the same feasible set, namely, P. For this reason, it is natural to assume that the subproblems are solved by means of the dual simplex method.

There are a few different possibilities to consider:

(a) If the dual simplex method indicates that a (primal) subproblem is infeasible, it provides us with an extreme ray $\mathbf{w}^{j(\omega)}$ of the dual feasible set P, such that

$$(\mathbf{w}^{j(\omega)})'(\mathbf{d}_\omega - \mathbf{B}_\omega \mathbf{x}^*) > 0.$$

We have then identified a violated constraint, which can be added to the relaxed master problem.

(b) If a primal subproblem is feasible, then the dual simplex method terminates, and provides us with a dual optimal basic feasible solution $\mathbf{p}^{i(\omega)}$. If we have

$$(\mathbf{p}^{i(\omega)})'(\mathbf{d}_\omega - \mathbf{B}_\omega \mathbf{x}^*) > z^*_\omega,$$

we have again identified a violated constraint, which can be added to the relaxed master problem.

(c) Finally, if the primal subproblems are all feasible and we have

$$(\mathbf{p}^{i(\omega)})'(\mathbf{d}_\omega - \mathbf{B}_\omega \mathbf{x}^*) \leq z^*_\omega,$$

for all ω, then, by the optimality of $\mathbf{p}^{i(\omega)}$, we obtain

$$(\mathbf{p}^i)'(\mathbf{d}_\omega - \mathbf{B}_\omega \mathbf{x}^*) \leq z^*_\omega,$$

for all extreme points $\mathbf{p}^i$. In addition,

$$(\mathbf{w}^j)'(\mathbf{d}_\omega - \mathbf{B}_\omega \mathbf{x}^*) \leq 0,$$

for all extreme rays $\mathbf{w}^j$, and no constraint is violated. We then have an optimal solution to the master problem (6.20), and the algorithm terminates.

The resulting algorithm is summarized below.

Benders decomposition for two-stage problems

1. A typical iteration starts with a relaxed master problem, in which only some of the constraints of the master problem (6.20) are included. An optimal solution $(\mathbf{x}^*, \mathbf{z}^*)$ to the relaxed master problem is calculated.

2. For every ω, we solve the subproblem

$$\text{minimize} \quad \mathbf{f}'\mathbf{y}_\omega$$
$$\text{subject to} \quad \mathbf{D}\mathbf{y}_\omega = \mathbf{d}_\omega - \mathbf{B}_\omega\mathbf{x}^*$$
$$\mathbf{y}_\omega \geq \mathbf{0},$$

using the dual simplex method.

3. If for every ω, the corresponding subproblem is feasible and the optimal cost is less than or equal to z_ω^*, all constraints are satisfied, we have an optimal solution to the master problem, and the algorithm terminates.

4. If the subproblem corresponding to some ω has an optimal solution whose cost is greater than z_ω^*, an optimal basic feasible solution $\mathbf{p}^{i(\omega)}$ to the dual of the subproblem is identified, and the constraint

$$(\mathbf{p}^{i(\omega)})'(\mathbf{d}_\omega - \mathbf{B}_\omega\mathbf{x}) \leq z_\omega$$

is added to the relaxed master problem.

5. If the subproblem corresponding to some ω is infeasible, its dual has infinite cost, and a positive cost extreme ray $\mathbf{w}^{j(\omega)}$ is identified. Then, the constraint

$$(\mathbf{w}^{j(\omega)})'(\mathbf{d}_\omega - \mathbf{B}_\omega\mathbf{x}) \leq 0$$

is added to the relaxed master problem.

Benders decomposition uses delayed constraint generation and the cutting plane method, and should be contrasted with Dantzig-Wolfe decomposition, which is based on column generation. Nevertheless, the two methods are almost identical, with Benders decomposition being essentially the same as Dantzig-Wolfe decomposition applied to the dual. Let us also note, consistently with our discussion in Section 6.3, that we have the option of discarding all or some of the constraints in the relaxed primal that have become inactive.

One of the principal practical difficulties with stochastic programming, is that the number K of possible scenarios is often large, leading to a large number of subproblems. This is even more so for stochastic programming problems involving more than two stages, where similar methods can be in principle applied. A number of remedies have been proposed, including the use of random sampling to generate only a representative set of scenarios. With the use of parallel computers and sophisticated sampling methods, the solution of some extremely large problems may become possible.

6.6 Summary

The main ideas developed in this chapter are the following:

(a) In a problem with an excessive number of columns, we need to generate a column only if its reduced cost is negative, and that column is to enter the basis (delayed column generation). A method of this type requires an efficient subroutine for identifying a variable with negative reduced cost.

(b) In a problem with an excessive number of constraints, a constraint needs to be taken into account only if it is violated by the current solution (delayed constraint generation). A method of this type (cutting plane method) requires an efficient subroutine for identifying violated constraints.

We have noted that delayed column generation methods applied to the primal coincide with cutting plane methods applied to the dual. Furthermore, we noted that there are several variants depending on whether we retain or discard from memory previously generated columns or constraints.

For a problem consisting of a number of subproblems linked by coupling constraints, the delayed column generation method applied to a suitably reformulated problem, results in the Dantzig-Wolfe decomposition method. Loosely speaking, Benders decomposition is the "dual" of Dantzig-Wolfe decomposition, and is based on delayed constraint generation. Stochastic programming is an important class of problems where Benders decomposition can be applied.

6.7 Exercises

Exercise 6.1 Consider the cutting stock problem. Use an optimal solution to the linear programming problem (6.4) to construct a feasible solution for the corresponding integer programming problem, whose cost differs from the optimal cost by no more than m.

Exercise 6.2 This problem is a variation of the diet problem. There are n foods and m nutrients. We are given an $m \times n$ matrix $\mathbf{A}$, with a_{ij} specifying the amount of nutrient i per unit of the jth food. Consider a parent with two children. Let $\mathbf{b}^1$ and $\mathbf{b}^2$ be the minimal nutritional requirements of the two children, respectively. Finally, let $\mathbf{c}$ be the cost vector with the prices of the different foods. Assume that $a_{ij} \geq 0$ and $c_i > 0$ for all i and j.

The parent has to buy food to satisfy the children's needs, at minimum cost. To avoid jealousy, there is the additional constraint that the amount to be spent for each child is the same.

(a) Provide a standard form formulation of this problem. What are the dimensions of the constraint matrix?

(b) If the Dantzig-Wolfe method is used to solve the problem in part (a), construct the subproblems solved during a typical iteration of the master problem.

(c) Suggest a direct approach for solving this problem based on the solution of two single-child diet problems.

Exercise 6.3 Consider the following linear programming problem:

$$
\begin{array}{llll}
\text{maximize} & x_{12} & + x_{22} + x_{23} \\
\text{subject to} & x_{11} + x_{12} + x_{13} & = 20 \\
& x_{21} + x_{22} + x_{23} = 20 \\
& -x_{11} \quad\qquad - x_{21} = -20 \\
& \quad - x_{12} \quad\qquad - x_{22} = -10 \\
& \qquad - x_{13} \quad\qquad - x_{23} = -10 \\
& x_{11} \quad\qquad + x_{23} \leq 15 \\
& x_{ij} \geq 0, \quad \text{for all } i, j.
\end{array}
$$

We wish to solve this problem using Dantzig-Wolfe decomposition, where the constraint $x_{11} + x_{23} \leq 15$ is the only "coupling" constraint and the remaining constraints define a single subproblem.

(a) Consider the following two feasible solutions for the subproblem:

$$\mathbf{x}^1 = (x_{11}, x_{12}, x_{13}, x_{21}, x_{22}, x_{23}) = (20, 0, 0, 0, 10, 10),$$

and

$$\mathbf{x}^2 = (x_{11}, x_{12}, x_{13}, x_{21}, x_{22}, x_{23}) = (0, 10, 10, 20, 0, 0).$$

Construct a restricted master problem in which $\mathbf{x}$ is constrained to be a convex combination of $\mathbf{x}^1$ and $\mathbf{x}^2$. Find the optimal solution and the optimal simplex multipliers for the restricted master problem.

(b) Using the simplex multipliers calculated in part (a), formulate the subproblem and solve it by inspection.

(c) What is the reduced cost of the variable λ_i associated with the optimal extreme point $\mathbf{x}^i$ obtained from the subproblem solved in part (b)?

(d) Compute an upper bound on the optimal cost.

Exercise 6.4 Consider a linear programming problem of the form

$$
\text{minimize} \quad \mathbf{c}_1'\mathbf{x}_1 + \mathbf{c}_2'\mathbf{x}_2 + \mathbf{c}_0'\mathbf{y}
$$

$$
\text{subject to} \quad
\begin{bmatrix}
\mathbf{D}_1 & \mathbf{0} & \mathbf{F}_1 \\
\mathbf{0} & \mathbf{D}_2 & \mathbf{F}_2
\end{bmatrix}
\begin{bmatrix}
\mathbf{x}_1 \\
\mathbf{x}_2 \\
\mathbf{y}
\end{bmatrix}
\geq
\begin{bmatrix}
\mathbf{b}_1 \\
\mathbf{b}_2
\end{bmatrix}
$$

$$
\mathbf{x}_1, \mathbf{x}_2 \geq \mathbf{0}.
$$

We will develop two different ways of decomposing this problem.

  (a) Form the dual problem and explain how Dantzig-Wolfe decomposition can be applied to it. What is the structure of the subproblems solved during a typical iteration?

  (b) Rewrite the first set of constraints in the form $\mathbf{D}_1\mathbf{x}_1 + \mathbf{F}_1\mathbf{y}_1 \geq \mathbf{b}_1$ and $\mathbf{D}_2\mathbf{x}_2 + \mathbf{F}_2\mathbf{y}_2 \geq \mathbf{b}_2$, together with a constraint relating $\mathbf{y}_1$ to $\mathbf{y}_2$. Discuss how to apply Dantzig-Wolfe decomposition and describe the structure of the subproblems solved during a typical iteration.

Exercise 6.5 Consider a linear programming problem of the form

$$\begin{array}{ll} \text{minimize} & \mathbf{c}'\mathbf{x} + \mathbf{d}'\mathbf{y} \\ \text{subject to} & \mathbf{Ax} + \mathbf{Dy} \leq \mathbf{b} \\ & \mathbf{Fx} \leq \mathbf{f} \\ & \mathbf{y} \geq \mathbf{0}. \end{array}$$

  (a) Suppose that we have access to a very fast subroutine for solving problems of the form

$$\begin{array}{ll} \text{minimize} & \mathbf{h}'\mathbf{x} \\ \text{subject to} & \mathbf{Fx} \leq \mathbf{f}, \end{array}$$

for arbitrary cost vectors $\mathbf{h}$. How would you go about decomposing the problem?

  (b) Suppose that we have access to a very fast subroutine for solving problems of the form

$$\begin{array}{ll} \text{minimize} & \mathbf{d}'\mathbf{y} \\ \text{subject to} & \mathbf{Dy} \leq \mathbf{h} \\ & \mathbf{y} \geq \mathbf{0}, \end{array}$$

for arbitrary right-hand side vectors $\mathbf{h}$. How would you go about decomposing the problem?

Exercise 6.6 Consider a linear programming problem in standard form in which the matrix $\mathbf{A}$ has the following structure:

$$\mathbf{A} = \begin{bmatrix} \mathbf{A}_{00} & \mathbf{A}_{01} & \cdots & \cdots & \mathbf{A}_{0n} \\ \mathbf{A}_{10} & \mathbf{A}_{11} & & & \\ \vdots & & \mathbf{A}_{22} & & \\ \vdots & & & \ddots & \\ \mathbf{A}_{n0} & & & & \mathbf{A}_{nn} \end{bmatrix}.$$

(All submatrices other than those indicated are zero.) Show how a decomposition method can be applied to a problem with this structure. Do not provide details, as long as you clearly indicate the master problem and the subproblems. *Hint:* Decompose twice.

Exercise 6.7 Consider a linear programming problem in standard form. Let us treat the equality constraints as the "coupling" constraints and use the Dantzig-Wolfe decomposition method, for the case of a single subproblem. Show that the resulting master problem is identical to the problem that we started with.

Exercise 6.8 Consider the Dantzig-Wolfe decomposition method and suppose that we are at a basic feasible solution to the master problem.

(a) Show that at least one of the variables λ_1^j must be a basic variable.

(b) Let r_1 be the current value of the simplex multiplier associated with the first convexity constraint (6.12), and let z_1 be the optimal cost in the first subproblem. Show that $z_1 \leq r_1$.

Exercise 6.9 Consider a problem of the form

$$\text{minimize} \quad \max_{i=1,\ldots,m} \; (\mathbf{a}_i'\mathbf{x} - b_i),$$

subject to no constraints, where $\mathbf{a}_i$, b_i are given vectors and scalars, respectively.

(a) Describe a cutting plane method for problems of this form.

(b) Let $\mathbf{x}$ be an optimal solution to a relaxed problem in which only some of the terms $\mathbf{a}_i'\mathbf{x} - b_i$ have been retained. Describe a simple method for obtaining lower and upper bounds on the optimal cost in the original problem.

Exercise 6.10 In this exercise, we develop an alternative proof of Theorem 6.1.

(a) Suppose that $\mathbf{x}$ is a basic feasible solution to a standard form problem, and let $\bar{\mathbf{c}}$ be the corresponding vector of reduced costs. Let $\mathbf{y}$ be any other feasible solution. Show that $\mathbf{c}'\mathbf{y} = \bar{\mathbf{c}}'\mathbf{y} + \mathbf{c}'\mathbf{x}$.

(b) Consider a basic feasible solution to the master problem whose cost is equal to z. Write down a lower bound on the reduced cost of any variable λ_i^j and θ_i^k, in terms of r_i and z_i. Then, use the result of part (a) to provide a proof of Theorem 6.1.

Exercise 6.11 (The relation between Dantzig-Wolfe and Benders decomposition) Consider the two-stage stochastic linear programming problem treated in Section 6.5.

(a) Show that the dual problem has a form which is amenable to Dantzig-Wolfe decomposition.

(b) Describe the Dantzig-Wolfe decomposition algorithm, as applied to the dual, and identify differences and similarities with Benders decomposition.

Exercise 6.12 (Bounds in Benders decomposition) For the two-stage stochastic linear programming problem of Section 6.5, derive upper and lower bounds on the optimal cost of the master problem, based on the information provided by the solutions to the subproblems.

6.8 Notes and sources

6.2. The delayed column generation approach to the cutting stock problem was put forth by Gilmore and Gomory (1961, 1963).

6.3. Cutting plane methods are often employed in linear programming approaches to integer programming problems, and will be discussed in Section 11.1. The same idea can also be applied to more general convex optimization problems; see, e.g., Bertsekas (1995b).

6.4. Dantzig-Wolfe decomposition was developed by Dantzig and Wolfe (1960). Example 6.2 is adapted from Bradley, Hax, and Magnanti (1977).

6.5. Stochastic programming began with work by Dantzig in the 1950's and has been extensively studied since then. Some books on this subject are Kall and Wallace (1994), and Infanger (1993); Example 6.5 is adapted from the latter reference. The Benders decomposition method was developed by Benders (1962). It finds applications in other contexts as well, such as discrete optimization; see, e.g., Schrijver (1986), and Nemhauser and Wosley (1988).

Chapter 7

Network flow problems

Network flow problems (also known as *transshipment* problems) are the most frequently solved linear programming problems. They include as special cases, the assignment, transportation, maximum flow, and shortest path problems, and they arise naturally in the analysis and design of communication, transportation, and logistics networks, as well as in many other contexts.

The network flow problem is a special case of linear programming, and any algorithm for linear programming can be directly applied. On the other hand, network flow problems have a special structure which results in substantial simplification of general methods (e.g., of the simplex method), as well as in new, special purpose, methods.

From a high level point of view, most of the available algorithms for network flow problems fall into one of three categories:

(a) **Primal methods.** These methods maintain and keep improving a primal feasible solution. The primal *simplex method*, presented in Section 7.3, is an important representative. An alternative algorithm is derived from first principles in Section 7.4.

(b) **Dual ascent methods.** These methods, which are discussed in Section 7.7, maintain a dual feasible solution and an auxiliary primal (usually infeasible) solution that satisfy complementary slackness. The dual variables are updated so as to increase the value of the dual objective and reduce the infeasibility of the complementary primal solution. The *Hungarian, primal-dual, relaxation*, and *dual simplex* methods fall in this general category.

(c) **Approximate dual ascent methods.** These methods are similar in spirit to the dual ascent methods, except that small decreases in the dual objective are allowed to occur and the complementary slackness conditions are only approximately enforced. The *auction* algorithm, which is discussed in Section 7.8, as well as the *ε-relaxation* and *preflow-push* methods, are of this type.

In this chapter, all three of the above mentioned algorithm types will be encountered. The chapter begins with a brief introduction to graphs (Section 7.1), that provides us with the language for studying network flow problems, and with a problem formulation (Section 7.2). We develop a number of general methods, but we also pay attention to special cases whose structure can be further exploited, such as the maximum flow problem (Section 7.5), the assignment problem (Section 7.8), and the shortest path problem (Section 7.9). We also discuss the minimum spanning tree problem (Section 7.10), which is not a network flow problem, but has a similar underlying graph structure. Throughout this chapter, our focus is on major algorithmic ideas, rather than on the refinements that can lead to better complexity estimates.

7.1   Graphs

Network flow problems are defined on graphs. In this section, we introduce graphs formally and provide a number of elementary definitions and properties.

Undirected graphs

An *undirected graph* $G = (\mathcal{N}, \mathcal{E})$ consists of a set $\mathcal{N}$ of *nodes* and a set $\mathcal{E}$ of *(undirected) arcs* or *edges*, where an edge e is an *unordered pair* of distinct nodes, that is, a two-element subset $\{i, j\}$ of $\mathcal{N}$; see Figure 7.1. Note that

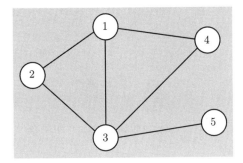

Figure 7.1:   An undirected graph $G = (\mathcal{N}, \mathcal{E})$ with $\mathcal{N} = \{1, 2, 3, 4, 5\}$ and $\mathcal{E} = \big\{\{1, 2\}, \{1, 3\}, \{2, 3\}, \{1, 4\}, \{3, 4\}, \{3, 5\}\big\}$.

an undirected arc $\{i, j\}$ is one and the same object as the undirected arc $\{j, i\}$. Furthermore, "self-arcs" like $\{i, i\}$ are not allowed. We say that the arc $\{i, j\}$ is *incident* to nodes i and j, and these nodes are called the *endpoints* of the arc.

The *degree* of a node in an undirected graph is the number of arcs incident to that node. The degree of an undirected graph is defined as the maximum of the degrees of its nodes.

A *walk* from node i_1 to node i_t in an undirected graph is defined as a finite sequence of nodes $i_1, i_2, \ldots, i_t$ such that $\{i_k, i_{k+1}\} \in \mathcal{E}$, $k = 1, 2, \ldots, t-1$. A walk is called a *path* if it has no repeated nodes. A *cycle* is defined as a walk $i_1, i_2, \ldots, i_t$ such that the nodes $i_1, \ldots, i_{t-1}$ are distinct (and hence form a path) and $i_t = i_1$. In addition, we require the number $t-1$ of distinct nodes to be at least 3. This is in order to exclude a walk of the form i, j, i, where the same arc $\{i, j\}$ is traversed back and forth. An undirected graph is said to be *connected* if for every two distinct nodes $i, j \in \mathcal{N}$, there exists a path from i to j.

As an example, the graph in Figure 7.1 is connected. The sequence 1,2,3,1,4 is a walk but not a path. The sequence 1,2,3,1 is a cycle, and the sequence 1,3,5 is a path.

For undirected graphs, we will often denote the number of nodes by $|\mathcal{N}|$ or n, and the number of edges by $|\mathcal{E}|$ or m.

Directed graphs

A *directed graph* $G = (\mathcal{N}, \mathcal{A})$ consists of a set $\mathcal{N}$ of *nodes* and a set $\mathcal{A}$ of *(directed) arcs*, where a directed arc is an *ordered pair* (i, j) of distinct nodes; see Figure 7.2. Our definition allows for both (i, j) and (j, i) to be

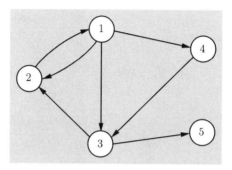

Figure 7.2: A directed graph $G = (\mathcal{N}, \mathcal{A})$ with $\mathcal{N} = \{1, 2, 3, 4, 5\}$ and $\mathcal{A} = \{(1, 2),\ (2, 1),\ (1, 3),\ (3, 2),\ (1, 4),\ (4, 3),\ (3, 5)\}$.

elements of the arc set $\mathcal{A}$, but self-arcs like (i, i) are not allowed.

For any arc (i, j), we say that i is the *start node* and j is the *end node*. The arc (i, j) is said to be *outgoing* from node i, *incoming* to node j, and *incident* to both i and j. We define $I(i)$ and $O(i)$ as the set of start nodes (respectively, end nodes) of arcs that are incoming to (respectively, outgoing from) node i. That is,

$$I(i) = \{j \in \mathcal{N} \mid (j, i) \in \mathcal{A}\},$$

and

$$O(i) = \{j \in \mathcal{N} \mid (i, j) \in \mathcal{A}\}.$$

Starting from a directed graph, we can construct a corresponding undirected graph by ignoring the direction of the arcs and by deleting repeated arcs; for example, the directed graph in Figure 7.2 leads to the undirected graph in Figure 7.1. Under one possible interpretation, flow or movement in a directed arc is permitted only from the start node to the end node, whereas in an undirected arc, flow or movement is permitted in both directions. We say that a directed graph is *connected* if the resulting undirected graph is connected.

We now present a definition of walks in directed graphs; it is important to note that this definition allows us to traverse an arc in either direction, irrespective of the arc's direction. More specifically, a *walk* is defined as a sequence $i_1, \ldots, i_t$ of nodes, together with an associated sequence $a_1, \ldots, a_{t-1}$ of arcs such that for $k = 1, \ldots, t-1$, we have either $a_k = (i_k, i_{k+1})$ (in which case we say that a_k is a *forward* arc) or $a_k = (i_{k+1}, i_k)$ (in which case we say that a_k is a *backward* arc). Note that if i_k and i_{k+1} are consecutive nodes in a walk and if (i_k, i_{k+1}) and (i_{k+1}, i_k) are both arcs of the underlying directed graph, then either arc can be used in the walk. The reason for including the arcs a_k in the definition of a walk is precisely to avoid such ambiguities.

A walk is said to be a *path* if all of its nodes $i_1, \ldots, i_t$ are distinct, and a *cycle* if the nodes $i_1, \ldots, i_{t-1}$ are distinct and $i_t = i_1$. Note that we allow a cycle to consist of only two distinct nodes (in contrast to our definition for the case of undirected graphs). Thus, a sequence $i, (i, j), j, (j, i), i$ is a bona fide cycle. Finally, a walk, path, or cycle is said to be *directed* if it only contains forward arcs.

For the graph shown in Figure 7.2, the sequence $1, (1, 3), 3, (3, 2), 2,$ $(1, 2), 1, (1, 4), 4$ is a walk, but not a directed walk, because $(1, 2)$ is a backward arc. The sequence $1, (1, 3), 3, (3, 2), 2, (2, 1), 1$ is a directed cycle. The sequence $1, (1, 2), 2, (2, 1), 1$ is also a directed cycle. The sequence $4, (4, 3), 3, (1, 3), 1, (1, 2), 2$ is a path, but not a directed path, because $(1, 3)$ is a backward arc.

For directed graphs, we will often denote the number of nodes by $|\mathcal{N}|$ or n, and the number of arcs by $|\mathcal{A}|$ or m.

Trees

An undirected graph $G = (\mathcal{N}, \mathcal{E})$ is called a *tree* if it is connected and has no cycles. If a node of a tree has degree equal to 1, it is called a *leaf*. See Figure 7.3 for an illustration.

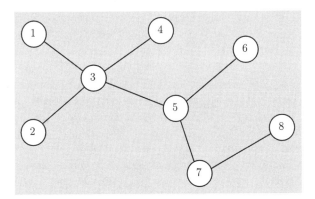

Figure 7.3: A tree with 8 nodes, 7 arcs, and 5 leaves. Note that if we were to add the arc $\{2, 7\}$, a single cycle would be created, namely, 2,3,5,7,2.

We now present some important properties of trees that will be of use later on (e.g., in the development of the simplex method, in Section 7.3).

Theorem 7.1

(a) *Every tree with more than one node has at least one leaf.*

(b) *An undirected graph is a tree if and only if it is connected and has $|\mathcal{N}| - 1$ arcs.*

(c) *For any two distinct nodes i and j in a tree, there exists a unique path from i to j.*

(d) *If we start with a tree and add a new arc, the resulting graph contains exactly one cycle (as long as we do not distinguish between cycles involving the same set of nodes).*

Proof.

(a) Consider a tree with more than one node and suppose that there are no leaves. Then, every node has degree greater than 1. (If the degree of a node were 1, that node would be a leaf, and if it were 0, the graph would not be connected.) Therefore, given a node and an arc through which we enter the node, we can find a different arc through which we can exit. By repeating such a process, we must eventually visit the same node twice, which implies that there exists a cycle, contradicting the definition of a tree.

(b) We first prove that every tree has $|\mathcal{N}| - 1$ arcs. This is trivially true if the tree has a single node. Consider now a tree that has more than one node. Such a tree must have at least one leaf, by part (a). We delete that leaf together with the single arc incident to that node. The resulting graph is again a tree, because the deletion of a leaf cannot create a cycle or cause a graph to become disconnected. This process can be carried out $|\mathcal{N}| - 1$ times, until we are left with a single node and, therefore, no arcs. Since at each stage there was exactly one arc deletion, we conclude that the original tree had $|\mathcal{N}| - 1$ arcs.

In order to prove the converse statement, let us consider a connected graph with $|\mathcal{N}| - 1$ arcs. If this graph contains a cycle, we can delete one of the arcs in the cycle and still maintain connectivity. We repeat this process as many times as needed, until we are left with a connected graph without any cycles, that is, a tree. We have already proved that a tree with $|\mathcal{N}|$ nodes must have $|\mathcal{N}| - 1$ arcs, and this shows that the final tree has as many arcs as the original graph. It follows that no arc was deleted and the original graph was a tree to start with.

(c) Suppose that there exist two different paths joining the same nodes i and j. By joining these two paths and by deleting any arcs that are

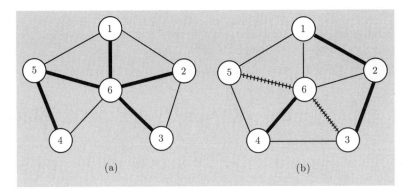

Figure 7.4: (a) An undirected graph. The thicker arcs form a spanning tree. (b) Another undirected graph. The arcs $\{1,2\}$, $\{2,3\}$, $\{4,6\}$ do not form any cycle. They can be augmented to form a spanning tree, e.g., by adding arcs $\{3,6\}$ and $\{5,6\}$.

common to both, we are left with one or more cycles, contradicting the definition of a tree.

(d) Consider a tree, and let us add an undirected arc $\{i,j\}$. Using part (b), the resulting graph must have $|\mathcal{N}|$ arcs. Therefore, it cannot be a tree, and must have a cycle. Any cycle created by this addition consists of the arc $\{i,j\}$ and a path from i to j. Since there exists a unique path from i to j [part (c)], it follows that a unique cycle has been created.   □

Spanning trees

Given a connected undirected graph $G = (\mathcal{N}, \mathcal{E})$, let $\mathcal{E}_1$ be a subset of $\mathcal{E}$ such that $T = (\mathcal{N}, \mathcal{E}_1)$ is a tree. Such a tree is called a *spanning tree*. The following result will be used later on (in Sections 7.3 and 7.10) and is illustrated in Figure 7.4.

Theorem 7.2 *Let $G = (\mathcal{N}, \mathcal{E})$ be a connected undirected graph and let $\mathcal{E}_0$ be some subset of the set $\mathcal{E}$ of arcs. Suppose that the arcs in $\mathcal{E}_0$ do not form any cycles. Then, the set $\mathcal{E}_0$ can be augmented to a set $\mathcal{E}_1 \supset \mathcal{E}_0$ so that $(\mathcal{N}, \mathcal{E}_1)$ is a spanning tree.*

Proof. Let $G = (\mathcal{N}, \mathcal{E})$ be a connected undirected graph. Suppose that $\mathcal{E}_0 \subset \mathcal{E}$, and that the arcs in $\mathcal{E}_0$ do not form any cycles. If G is a tree, we may let $\mathcal{E}_1 = \mathcal{E}$ and we are done. Otherwise, G contains at least one cycle. A cycle cannot consist exclusively of arcs in $\mathcal{E}_0$, because of our assumption on $\mathcal{E}_0$. Let us choose and delete an arc that lies on a cycle and that does not belong to $\mathcal{E}_0$. The resulting graph is still connected. By repeating this process as many times as needed, we end up with a connected graph $(\mathcal{N}, \mathcal{E}_1)$ without any cycles, hence a tree. In addition, since the arcs in $\mathcal{E}_0$ are never deleted, we have $\mathcal{E}_0 \subset \mathcal{E}_1$.   □

7.2   Formulation of the network flow problem

A *network* is a directed graph $G = (\mathcal{N}, \mathcal{A})$ together with some additional numerical information, such as numbers b_i representing the external *supply* to each node $i \in \mathcal{N}$, nonnegative (possibly infinite) numbers u_{ij} representing the *capacity* of each arc $(i, j) \in \mathcal{A}$, and numbers c_{ij} representing the cost per unit of flow along arc (i, j).

We visualize a network by thinking of some material that flows on each arc. We use f_{ij} to denote the amount of flow through arc (i, j). The supply b_i is interpreted as the amount of flow that enters the network from the outside, at node i. In particular, node i is called a *source* if $b_i > 0$, and a *sink* if $b_i < 0$. If node i is a sink, the quantity $|b_i|$ is sometimes called the *demand* at node i. We impose the following conditions on the flow variables $f_{ij}, (i, j) \in \mathcal{A}$:

$$b_i + \sum_{j \in I(i)} f_{ji} = \sum_{j \in O(i)} f_{ij}, \qquad \forall\, i \in \mathcal{N}, \qquad (7.1)$$

$$0 \le f_{ij} \le u_{ij}, \qquad \forall\, (i, j) \in \mathcal{A}. \qquad (7.2)$$

Equation (7.1) is a flow conservation law: it states that the amount of flow into a node i must be equal to the total flow out of that node. Equation (7.2) simply requires that the flow through an arc must be nonnegative and cannot exceed the capacity of the arc. Any vector with components f_{ij}, $(i, j) \in \mathcal{A}$, will be called a *flow*. If it also satisfies the constraints (7.1)-(7.2), it will be called a *feasible flow*.

By summing both sides of Eq. (7.1) over all $i \in \mathcal{N}$, we obtain

$$\sum_{i \in \mathcal{N}} b_i = 0,$$

which means that the total flow from the environment into the network (at the sources) must be equal to the total flow from the network (at the sinks) to the environment. From now on, we will always assume that the condition $\sum_{i \in \mathcal{N}} b_i = 0$ holds, because otherwise no flow vector could satisfy the flow conservation constraints, and we would have an infeasible problem.

The general minimum cost network flow problem deals with the minimization of a linear cost function of the form

$$\sum_{(i,j) \in \mathcal{A}} c_{ij} f_{ij},$$

over all feasible flows. We observe that this is a linear programming problem. If $u_{ij} = \infty$ for all $(i, j) \in \mathcal{A}$, we say that the problem is *uncapacitated*; otherwise, we say that it is *capacitated*. Note that in the uncapacitated case, we only have equality and nonnegativity constraints, and the problem is in standard form.

We now provide an overview of important special cases of the network flow problem; most of them will be studied later in this chapter.

The shortest path problem

For any directed path in a network, we define its *length* as the sum of the costs of all arcs on the path. We wish to find a *shortest path*, that is, a directed path from a given origin node to a given destination node whose length is smallest. This problem is studied in Section 7.9, where we show that it can be formulated as a network flow problem, under a certain assumption on the arc lengths.

The maximum flow problem

In the maximum flow problem, we wish to determine the largest possible amount of flow that can be sent from a given source node to a given sink node, without exceeding the arc capacities. This problem is studied in Section 7.5.

The transportation problem

Let there be m suppliers and n consumers. The ith supplier can provide s_i units of a certain good and the jth consumer has a demand for d_j units. We assume that the total supply $\sum_{i=1}^{m} s_i$ is equal to the total demand $\sum_{j=1}^{n} d_j$. Finally, we assume that the transportation of goods from the ith supplier to the jth consumer carries a cost of c_{ij} per unit of goods transported. The problem is to transport the goods from the suppliers to the consumers at minimum cost. Let f_{ij} be the amount of goods transported from the ith supplier to the jth consumer. We then have the following problem:

$$
\begin{aligned}
\text{minimize} \quad & \sum_{i=1}^{m} \sum_{j=1}^{n} c_{ij} f_{ij} \\
\text{subject to} \quad & \sum_{i=1}^{m} f_{ij} = d_j, \qquad j = 1, \dots, n, \\
& \sum_{j=1}^{n} f_{ij} = s_i, \qquad i = 1, \dots, m, \\
& f_{ij} \geq 0, \qquad \forall\, i, j.
\end{aligned}
$$

The first equality constraint specifies that the demand d_j of each consumer must be met; the second equality constraint requires that the entire supply s_i of each supplier must be shipped. This is a special case of the uncapacitated network flow problem, where the underlying graph has a special structure; see Figure 7.5. It turns out that every network flow problem can

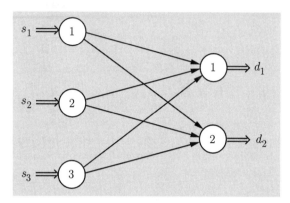

Figure 7.5: A network corresponding to a transportation problem with three suppliers and two consumers.

be transformed into an equivalent transportation problem (Exercises 7.5 and 7.6). Consequently, any algorithm for the transportation problem can be adapted and can be used to solve general network flow problems. For this reason, the initial development and testing of new algorithms is often carried out for the special case of transportation problems.

The assignment problem

The assignment problem is a special case of the transportation problem, where the number of suppliers is equal to the number of consumers, each supplier has unit supply, and each consumer has unit demand. As will be proved later in this chapter, one can always find an optimal solution in which every f_{ij} is either 0 or 1. This means that for each i there will be a unique and distinct j for which $f_{ij} = 1$, and we can say that the ith supplier is *assigned* to the jth consumer; this justifies the name of this problem.

Variants of the network flow problem

There are several variants of the network flow problem all of which can be shown to be equivalent to each other. For example, we have already mentioned that every network flow problem is equivalent to a transportation problem. We now discuss some more examples.

(a) *Every network flow problem can be reduced to one with exactly one source and exactly one sink node.* This is illustrated in Figure 7.6.

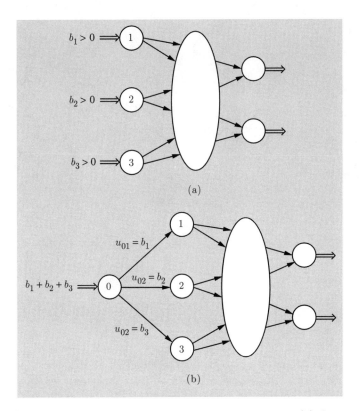

Figure 7.6: (a) A network with three source nodes. (b) A network with only one source node. The costs of the new arcs are zero. Because of the way that the arc capacities u_{0i} are chosen ($u_{0i} = b_i$, $i = 1, 2, 3$), exactly b_i units must flow on each arc $(0, i)$, $i = 1, 2, 3$. The reduction to a network with a single sink node is similar.

(b) *Every network flow problem can be reduced to one without sources or sinks.* (Problems in which all of the supplies are zero are called *circulation* problems.) Consider, without loss of generality, a network with a single source s and a single sink t. We introduce a new arc (t, s) whose capacity u_{ts} is equal to b_s and whose unit cost is $c_{ts} = -M$, where M is a large number; see Figure 7.7. Since M is large, an optimal solution to the circulation problem will try to set f_{ts} to b_s, which has the same effect as having a supply of b_s at node s. If an optimal solution to the circulation problem does not succeed in setting f_{ts} to b_s, this means that there is no way of shipping b_s units of flow from s to t, and the original problem is infeasible.

(c) *Node capacities.* Suppose that we have an upper bound of g_i on the total flow that can enter a given node i; for example, if i is a source

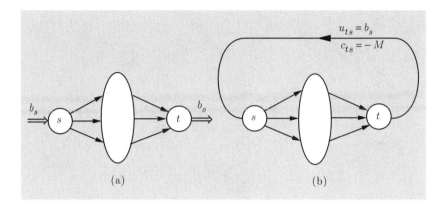

Figure 7.7: (a) A network. (b) An equivalent circulation problem.

node, we may have a constraint

$$b_i + \sum_{j \in I(i)} f_{ji} \le g_i.$$

By splitting node i into two nodes i and i', and by letting g_i be the capacity of arc (i, i'), we are back to the case where we only have arc capacities; see Figure 7.8.

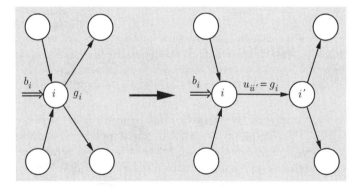

Figure 7.8: Transformation of a node capacity into an arc capacity.

(d) *Lower bounds on the arc flows.* Suppose that we add constraints of the form $f_{ij} \ge d_{ij}$, where d_{ij} are given scalars. The resulting problem can be reduced to an equivalent problem in which every d_{ij} is equal to zero. Exercise 7.7 provides some guidance as to how this can be accomplished.

A concise formulation

We now discuss how to rewrite the network flow problem, and especially the flow conservation constraint, in more economical matrix-vector notation. We assume that $\mathcal{N} = \{1, \ldots, n\}$ and we let m be the number of arcs. Let us fix a particular ordering of the arcs, and let $\mathbf{f}$ be the vector of flows that results when the components f_{ij} are ordered accordingly. We define the *node-arc incidence matrix* $\mathbf{A}$ as follows: its dimensions are $n \times m$ (each row corresponds to a node and each column to an arc) and its (i, k)th entry a_{ik} is associated with the ith node and the kth arc. We let

$$
a_{ik} = \begin{cases}
1, & \text{if } i \text{ is the start node of the } k\text{th arc,} \\
-1, & \text{if } i \text{ is the end node of the } k\text{th arc,} \\
0, & \text{otherwise.}
\end{cases}
$$

Thus, every column of $\mathbf{A}$ has exactly two nonzero entries, one equal to $+1$, and one equal to -1, indicating the start and the end node of the corresponding arc.

Example 7.1 Consider the directed graph of Figure 7.2 and let us use the following ordering of the arcs: $(1, 2), (2, 1), (3, 2), (4, 3), (1, 4), (1, 3), (3, 5)$. The corresponding node-arc incidence matrix is

$$
\mathbf{A} = \begin{bmatrix}
1 & -1 & 0 & 0 & 1 & 1 & 0 \\
-1 & 1 & -1 & 0 & 0 & 0 & 0 \\
0 & 0 & 1 & -1 & 0 & -1 & 1 \\
0 & 0 & 0 & 1 & -1 & 0 & 0 \\
0 & 0 & 0 & 0 & 0 & 0 & -1
\end{bmatrix}.
$$

Let us now focus on the ith row of $\mathbf{A}$, denoted by $\mathbf{a}'_i$ (this is the row associated with node i). Nonzero entries indicate the arcs that are incident to node i; such entries are $+1$ or -1 depending on whether the arc is outgoing or incoming, respectively. Thus,

$$
\mathbf{a}'_i \mathbf{f} = \sum_{j \in O(i)} f_{ij} - \sum_{j \in I(i)} f_{ji},
$$

and the flow conservation constraint at node i [cf. Eq. (7.1)] can be written as

$$
\mathbf{a}'_i \mathbf{f} = b_i,
$$

or, in matrix notation,

$$
\mathbf{A} \mathbf{f} = \mathbf{b},
$$

where $\mathbf{b}$ is the vector $(b_1, \ldots, b_n)$.

We observe that the sum of the rows of $\mathbf{A}$ is equal to the zero vector; in particular, the rows of $\mathbf{A}$ are linearly dependent. Thus, the matrix $\mathbf{A}$ violates one of the basic assumptions underlying our development of the simplex method. As discussed in Chapter 2 (cf. Theorem 2.5 in Section 2.3), either the problem is infeasible or we can remove some of the equality constraints, without affecting the feasible set, so that the remaining constraints are linearly independent. We revisit this issue in the next section.

Circulations

We close by introducing some elementary concepts that are central to many network flow algorithms.

Any flow vector $\mathbf{f}$ (feasible or infeasible) that satisfies

$$\mathbf{Af} = \mathbf{0},$$

is called a *circulation*. Intuitively, we have flow conservation within the network and zero external supply or demand, which means that the flow "circulates" inside the network.

Let us now consider a cycle C. We let F and B be the set of forward and backward arcs of the cycle, respectively. The flow vector $\mathbf{h}^C$ with components

$$h_{ij}^C = \begin{cases} 1, & \text{if } (i,j) \in F, \\ -1, & \text{if } (i,j) \in B, \\ 0, & \text{otherwise.} \end{cases}$$

is called the *simple circulation* associated with the cycle C. It is easily seen that $\mathbf{h}^C$ satisfies

$$\mathbf{Ah}^C = \mathbf{0}, \tag{7.3}$$

and is indeed a circulation. The reason is that any two consecutive arcs on the cycle are either similarly oriented and carry the same amount of flow, or they have the opposite orientation and the sum of the flows that they carry is equal to 0; in either case, the net inflow to any node is zero; see Figure 7.9. We finally define the *cost of a cycle* C to be equal to

$$\mathbf{c}'\mathbf{h}^C = \sum_{(i,j)\in F} c_{ij} - \sum_{(i,j)\in B} c_{ij}.$$

If $\mathbf{f}$ is a flow vector, C is a cycle, and θ is a scalar, we say that the flow vector $\mathbf{f} + \theta\mathbf{h}^C$ is obtained from $\mathbf{f}$ by *pushing* θ units of flow around the cycle C. Note that the resulting cost change is θ times the cost $\mathbf{c}'\mathbf{h}^C$ of the cycle C.

7.3 The network simplex algorithm

In this section, we develop the details of the simplex method, as applied to the uncapacitated network flow problem

$$\begin{array}{ll} \text{minimize} & \mathbf{c}'\mathbf{f} \\ \text{subject to} & \mathbf{Af} = \mathbf{b} \\ & \mathbf{f} \geq \mathbf{0}, \end{array}$$

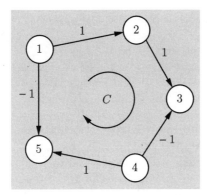

Figure 7.9: A cycle and the corresponding simple circulation. Arcs $(4, 3)$ and $(1, 5)$ are backward arcs and carry a flow of -1. Note that flow is conserved at each node.

where $\mathbf{A}$ is the node-arc incidence matrix of a directed graph $G = (\mathcal{N}, \mathcal{A})$. (Capacitated problems are briefly discussed at the end of this section.) The network simplex algorithm is widely used in practice, and is included in many commercial optimization codes, due to its simplicity and efficiency. In particular, it tends to run an order of magnitude faster than a general purpose simplex code applied to a network flow problem.

Due to our restriction to uncapacitated problems, we are dealing with a linear programming problem in standard form. We let m and n be the number of arcs and nodes, respectively. We therefore have m flow variables and n equality constraints which, unfortunately, is the exact opposite of the notational conventions used in earlier chapters.

There are two different ways of developing the network simplex method. The first is to go through the mechanics of the general simplex method and specialize each step to the present context. The second is to develop the algorithm from first principles and then to point out that it is a special case of the simplex method. We take a middle ground that proceeds along two parallel tracks; each step is justified from first principles, but its relation to the simplex method is also explained. The end result is an algorithm with a fairly intuitive structure.

Throughout this section, the following assumption will be in effect.

Assumption 7.1

   (a) *We have $\sum_{i \in \mathcal{N}} b_i = 0$.*

   (b) *The graph G is connected.*

Part (a) of this assumption is natural, because otherwise the problem is infeasible. Part (b) is also natural, because if the graph is not connected, then the problem can be decomposed into subproblems that can be treated independently.

As noted in Section 7.2, the rows of the matrix $\mathbf{A}$ sum to the zero vector and are therefore linearly dependent. In fact, the last constraint (flow conservation at node n) is a consequence of the flow conservation constraints at the other nodes, and can be omitted without affecting the feasible set. Let us define the *truncated node-arc incidence matrix* $\tilde{\mathbf{A}}$ to be the matrix of dimensions $(n-1) \times m$, which consists of the first $n-1$ rows of the matrix $\mathbf{A}$. Any column of $\tilde{\mathbf{A}}$ that corresponds to an arc of the form (i, n) has a single nonzero entry, equal to 1, at the ith row. Similarly, any column of $\tilde{\mathbf{A}}$ that corresponds to an arc of the form (n, i) has a single nonzero entry, equal to -1, at the ith row. All other columns of $\tilde{\mathbf{A}}$ have two nonzero entries. Let $\tilde{\mathbf{b}} = (b_1, \ldots, b_{n-1})$. We replace the original equality constraint $\mathbf{A}\mathbf{f} = \mathbf{b}$ by the constraint $\tilde{\mathbf{A}}\mathbf{f} = \tilde{\mathbf{b}}$. We will see shortly that under Assumption 7.1, the matrix $\tilde{\mathbf{A}}$ has linearly independent rows.

Example 7.2 Consider the node-arc incidence matrix $\mathbf{A}$ in Example 7.1. The associated matrix $\tilde{\mathbf{A}}$ is given by

$$\tilde{\mathbf{A}} = \begin{bmatrix} 1 & -1 & 0 & 0 & 1 & 1 & 0 \\ -1 & 1 & -1 & 0 & 0 & 0 & 0 \\ 0 & 0 & 1 & -1 & 0 & -1 & 1 \\ 0 & 0 & 0 & 1 & -1 & 0 & 0 \end{bmatrix}.$$

It can be verified that the matrix $\tilde{\mathbf{A}}$ has full rank. For example, the third, fourth, sixth, and seventh columns are linearly independent.

Trees and basic feasible solutions

We now introduce an important definition.

Definition 7.1 A flow vector $\mathbf{f}$ is called a **tree solution** if it can be constructed by the following procedure.

(a) Pick a set $T \subset \mathcal{A}$ of $n-1$ arcs that form a tree when their direction is ignored.

(b) Let $f_{ij} = 0$ for every $(i, j) \notin T$.

(c) Use the flow conservation equation $\tilde{\mathbf{A}}\mathbf{f} = \tilde{\mathbf{b}}$ to determine the flow variables f_{ij}, for $(i, j) \in T$.

A tree solution that also satisfies $\mathbf{f} \geq \mathbf{0}$, is called a **feasible tree solution**.

Step (c) in the above definition can be carried out using the following systematic procedure, illustrated in Figure 7.10:

(a) Call node n the *root* of the tree.

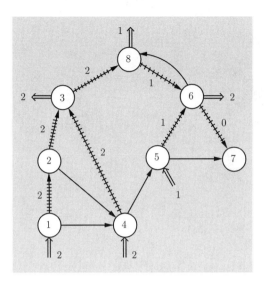

Figure 7.10: A network and a set of $n-1$ arcs (indicated by thatched lines) that form a tree. By setting the arc flows outside the tree to zero, we obtain $f_{12} = 2$, $f_{23} = 2$ and $f_{43} = 2$. We then use conservation of flow at node 3, to obtain $f_{38} = 2$. We also have $f_{56} = 1$ and $f_{67} = 0$. Using conservation of flow at node 6, we obtain $f_{86} = 1$. Note that this is a feasible tree solution.

(b)   Use the flow conservation equations to determine the flows on the arcs incident to the leaves, and continue by proceeding from the leaves towards the root.

It should be pretty obvious from Figure 7.10 that once a tree is fixed, a corresponding tree solution is uniquely determined. Nevertheless, we provide a rigorous proof.

> **Theorem 7.3** *Let $T \subset \mathcal{A}$ be a set of $n-1$ arcs that form a tree when their direction is ignored. Then, the system of linear equations $\tilde{\mathbf{A}}\mathbf{f} = \tilde{\mathbf{b}}$, and $f_{ij} = 0$ for all $(i,j) \notin T$, has a unique solution.*

Proof. Let $\mathbf{B}$ be the $(n-1) \times (n-1)$ matrix that results if we only keep those $n-1$ columns of $\tilde{\mathbf{A}}$ that correspond to the arcs in T. Let $\mathbf{f}_T$ be the subvector of $\mathbf{f}$, of dimension $n-1$, whose entries are the flow variables f_{ij}, $(i,j) \in T$. We need to show that the linear system $\mathbf{B}\mathbf{f}_T = \tilde{\mathbf{b}}$ has a unique solution. For this, it suffices to show that the matrix $\mathbf{B}$ is nonsingular.

Let us assume that the nodes have been renumbered so that numbers increase along any path from a leaf to the root node n. Let us also assign

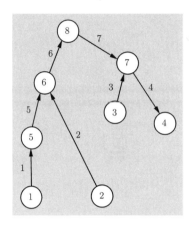

$$\begin{bmatrix} 1 & 0 & 0 & 0 & 0 & 0 & 0 \\ 0 & 1 & 0 & 0 & 0 & 0 & 0 \\ 0 & 0 & 1 & 0 & 0 & 0 & 0 \\ 0 & 0 & 0 & -1 & 0 & 0 & 0 \\ -1 & 0 & 0 & 0 & 1 & 0 & 0 \\ 0 & -1 & 0 & 0 & -1 & 1 & 0 \\ 0 & 0 & -1 & 1 & 0 & 0 & -1 \end{bmatrix}$$

Figure 7.11: A numbering of the nodes and arcs of a tree, and the corresponding **B** matrix.

to every arc $(i, j) \in T$, the number $\min\{i, j\}$; see Figure 7.11. Such a renumbering of nodes and arcs amounts to a reordering of the rows and columns of **B** but does not affect whether **B** is singular or not.

With the above numbering, the ith column of **B** corresponds to the ith arc, which is an arc of the form (i, j) or (j, i), with $j > i$. Thus, any nonzero entries in the ith column will be in row i or j. Since $j > i$, no nonzero entry can be found above the diagonal. We conclude that **B** is lower triangular and has nonzero diagonal entries. This implies that **B** has nonzero determinant and is nonsingular, which completes the proof.   □

We note an important corollary of the proof of the previous theorem.

Corollary 7.1 *If the graph G is connected, then the matrix $\tilde{\mathbf{A}}$ has linearly independent rows.*

Proof. If the graph G is connected, then there exists a set of arcs $T \subset \mathcal{A}$ that form a tree, when their orientation is ignored (cf. Theorem 7.2). Let us pick such a set T and form the corresponding matrix **B**, as in the proof of Theorem 7.3. Since the $(n-1) \times (n-1)$ matrix **B** is nonsingular, it has linearly independent columns. Hence, the matrix $\tilde{\mathbf{A}}$ has $n-1$ linearly independent columns and, therefore, has $n-1$ linearly independent rows. □

With our construction of a tree solution, the columns of **B** are the columns of $\tilde{\mathbf{A}}$ corresponding to the variables f_{ij}, for $(i, j) \in T$, and are linearly independent. In general linear programming terminology, **B** is a basis matrix. Since the remaining variables f_{ij}, $(i,j) \notin T$, are set to zero, the resulting flow vector $\mathbf{f}$ is the basic solution corresponding to this basis. Thus, a tree solution is a basic solution, and a feasible tree solution is a basic feasible solution. In fact, the converse is also true.

Theorem 7.4 *A flow vector is a basic solution if and only if it is a tree solution.*

Proof. We have already argued that a tree solution is a basic solution. Suppose now that a flow vector $\mathbf{f}$ is not a tree solution. We will show that it is not a basic solution. Note that if $\mathbf{Af} \neq \mathbf{b}$, then $\mathbf{f}$ is not a basic solution, by definition. Thus, we only need to consider the case where $\mathbf{Af} = \mathbf{b}$.

Let $S = \{(i,j) \in \mathcal{A} \mid f_{ij} \neq 0\}$. If the arcs in the set S do not form a cycle, then there exists a set T of $n-1$ arcs such that $S \subset T$, and such that the arcs in T form a tree [cf. Assumption 7.1(b) and Theorem 7.2]. Since $f_{ij} = 0$ for all $(i,j) \notin T$, the flow vector $\mathbf{f}$ is the tree solution associated with T, which is a contradiction.

Let us now assume that the set S contains a cycle C and let $\mathbf{h}^C$ be the simple circulation associated with C. Consider the flow vector $\mathbf{f} + \mathbf{h}^C$. We have $\mathbf{Af} = \mathbf{b}$ and $\mathbf{Ah}^C = \mathbf{0}$, which implies that $\mathbf{A}(\mathbf{f} + \mathbf{h}^C) = \mathbf{b}$. Furthermore, whenever $f_{ij} = 0$, the arc (i,j) does not belong to the cycle C, and we have $h_{ij}^C = 0$. We see that all constraints that are active at the vector $\mathbf{f}$ are also active at the vector $\mathbf{f} + \mathbf{h}^C$. Thus, the constraints that are active at $\mathbf{f}$ do not have a unique solution, and $\mathbf{f}$ is not a basic solution (cf. Theorem 2.2 and Definition 2.9 in Section 2.2). See Figure 7.12 for an illustration. $\qquad\qquad\square$

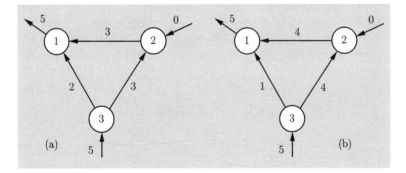

Figure 7.12: (a) Part of a flow vector that satisfies $\mathbf{Af} = \mathbf{b}$. This flow vector is not a tree solution because the arcs $(2,1)$, $(3,1)$, and $(3,2)$ form a cycle C and carry nonzero flow. (b) The flow vector $\mathbf{f} + \mathbf{h}^C$. Active constraints (arcs that carry zero flow) under $\mathbf{f}$ remain active under $\mathbf{f} + \mathbf{h}^C$.

To summarize our conclusions so far, we have established the following:

(a) Basic (feasible) solutions are (feasible) tree solutions and vice versa.

(b) Every basis matrix is triangular when its rows and columns are suitably reordered.

(c) Given a basis matrix $\mathbf{B}$, the vector of basic variables $\mathbf{B}^{-1}\tilde{\mathbf{b}}$ can be easily computed, without the need to maintain $\mathbf{B}^{-1}$ in a tableau.

As in the case of general linear programming problems, a basic feasible solution can be degenerate. This happens if the flow on some arc $(i,j) \in T$ turns out to be 0. In this case, the same basic feasible solution may correspond to several trees. For example, the tree shown in Figure 7.10 leads to a degenerate basic feasible solution, because $f_{67} = 0$. A different tree that would yield the same basic feasible solution is obtained by replacing arc $(6,7)$ by arc $(5,7)$.

Change of basis

We will now develop the mechanics of a change of basis. Recall that in a general linear programming problem, we first choose a nonbasic variable that enters the basis, find how to adjust the basic variables in order to maintain the equality constraints, and increase the value of the entering variable until one of the old basic variables is about to become negative. We specialize this procedure to the network case. Picking a nonbasic variable is the same as choosing an arc (i,j) that does not belong to T. Then, the arc (i,j) together with some of the arcs in T form a cycle. Let us choose the orientation of the cycle so that (i,j) is a forward arc. Let F and B be the sets of forward and backward arcs in the cycle, respectively. If we are to increase the value of the nonbasic variable f_{ij} to some θ, the old basic variables need to be adjusted in order not to violate the flow conservation constraints. This can be accomplished by pushing θ units of flow around the cycle. More precisely, $f_{k\ell}$ is increased (decreased) by θ for all forward (backward) arcs of the cycle. The new flow variables $\hat{f}_{k\ell}$ are given by

$$\hat{f}_{k\ell} = \begin{cases} f_{k\ell} + \theta, & \text{if } (k,\ell) \in F, \\ f_{k\ell} - \theta, & \text{if } (k,\ell) \in B, \\ f_{k\ell}, & \text{otherwise.} \end{cases} \tag{7.4}$$

We set θ as large as possible, provided that all arc flows remain nonnegative. It is clear that the largest possible value of θ is equal to

$$\theta^* = \min_{(k,\ell) \in B} f_{k\ell}, \tag{7.5}$$

except if B is empty, in which case we let $\theta^* = \infty$. A variable $f_{k\ell}$ that attains the minimum in Eq. (7.5) is set to zero and exits the basis. If $f_{k\ell} = 0$ for some arc $(k,\ell) \in B$ (which can happen if we start with a degenerate basic feasible solution), then the change of basis occurs without any change of the arc flows. (For the example shown in Figure 7.10, if f_{57} enters the basis, f_{67} exits the basis and $\theta^* = 0$.)

Calculation of the cost change

The cost change resulting from the above described change of basis, is equal to

$$\theta^* \cdot \left(\sum_{(k,\ell) \in F} c_{k\ell} - \sum_{(k,\ell) \in B} c_{k\ell} \right). \tag{7.6}$$

Naturally, the variable f_{ij} should enter the basis only if the value of the expression (7.6) is negative.

From the development of the simplex method for general linear programming problems, we know that if the variable that enters the basis takes the value θ^*, then the cost changes by θ^* times the reduced cost of the entering variable. Comparing with Eq. (7.6), we see that the reduced cost $\bar{c}_{ij}$ of a nonbasic variable f_{ij} is given by

$$\bar{c}_{ij} = \sum_{(k,\ell) \in F} c_{k\ell} - \sum_{(k,\ell) \in B} c_{k\ell}, \tag{7.7}$$

which is simply the cost of the cycle around which flow is being pushed.

We will now derive an alternative formula for the reduced costs that allows for more efficient computation. Recall the general formula $\bar{\mathbf{c}}' = \mathbf{c}' - \mathbf{p}'\tilde{\mathbf{A}}$ for determining the reduced costs, where $\mathbf{p}$ is the dual vector given by $\mathbf{p}' = \mathbf{c}'_B \mathbf{B}^{-1}$, $\mathbf{B}$ is the current basis matrix, and $\mathbf{c}_B$ is the vector with the costs of the basic variables. The dimension of $\mathbf{p}$ is equal to the number of rows of $\tilde{\mathbf{A}}$, which is $n - 1$, and we have one dual variable p_i associated with each node $i \neq n$. Suppose that (i, j) is the kth arc of the graph. Then, the kth entry of the vectors $\bar{\mathbf{c}}$ and $\mathbf{c}$ is equal to $\bar{c}_{ij}$ and c_{ij}, respectively. The kth entry of $\mathbf{p}'\tilde{\mathbf{A}}$ is equal to the inner product of $\mathbf{p}$ with the kth column of $\tilde{\mathbf{A}}$. From the definition of the node-arc incidence matrix, the kth column of $\tilde{\mathbf{A}}$ has an entry equal to 1 at the ith row (if $i < n$), and an entry equal to -1 at the jth row (if $j < n$). We conclude that

$$\bar{c}_{ij} = \begin{cases} c_{ij} - (p_i - p_j), & \text{if } i, j \neq n, \\ c_{ij} - p_i, & \text{if } j = n, \\ c_{ij} + p_j, & \text{if } i = n. \end{cases} \tag{7.8}$$

Equation (7.8) can be written more concisely if we define $p_n = 0$, in which case we have

$$\bar{c}_{ij} = c_{ij} - (p_i - p_j), \qquad \forall \, (i, j) \in \mathcal{A}. \tag{7.9}$$

It remains to compute the dual vector $\mathbf{p}' = \mathbf{c}'_B \mathbf{B}^{-1}$ associated with the current basis. Since the reduced cost of every basic variable must be equal to zero, Eq. (7.9) yields

$$p_i - p_j = c_{ij}, \qquad \forall\, (i,j) \in T,$$
$$p_n = 0. \qquad\qquad\qquad\qquad (7.10)$$

The system of equations (7.10) is easily solved using the following procedure. We view node n as the root of the tree and set $p_n = 0$. We then go down the tree, proceeding from the root towards the leaves, with a new component of $\mathbf{p}$ being evaluated at each step; see Figure 7.13.

Overview of the algorithm

We start with a summary of the network simplex algorithm and then proceed to discuss some issues related to initialization and termination.

The simplex method for uncapacitated network flow problems

1. A typical iteration starts with a basic feasible solution $\mathbf{f}$ associated with a tree T.

2. To compute the dual vector $\mathbf{p}$, solve the system of equations (7.10), by proceeding from the root towards the leaves.

3. Compute the reduced costs $\bar{c}_{ij} = c_{ij} - (p_i - p_j)$ of all arcs $(i,j) \notin T$. If they are all nonnegative, the current basic feasible solution is optimal and the algorithm terminates; else, choose some (i,j) with $\bar{c}_{ij} < 0$ to be brought into the basis.

4. The entering arc (i,j) and the arcs in T form a unique cycle. If all arcs in the cycle are oriented the same way as (i,j), then the optimal cost is $-\infty$ and the algorithm terminates.

5. Let B be the set of arcs in the cycle that are oriented in the opposite direction from (i,j). Let $\theta^* = \min_{(k,\ell) \in B} f_{k\ell}$, and push θ^* units of flow around the cycle. A new flow vector is determined according to Eq. (7.4). Remove from the basis one of the old basic variables whose new value is equal to zero.

In the case where finding an initial basic feasible solution is difficult, we may need to form and solve an auxiliary problem. For example, for each pair of source and sink nodes, we may introduce an auxiliary arc; finding a basic feasible solution in the presence of these arcs is straightforward. Furthermore, if the unit costs c_{ij} of the auxiliary arcs are chosen large enough, solving the auxiliary problem is equivalent to solving the original problem.

The network simplex algorithm is similar to the naive implementation described in Section 3.3. Because of the special structure of the basis matrix $\mathbf{B}$, the system $\mathbf{c}'_B = \mathbf{p}'\mathbf{B}$ can be solved on the fly, without the need to maintain a simplex tableau or the inverse basis matrix $\mathbf{B}^{-1}$. For a rough

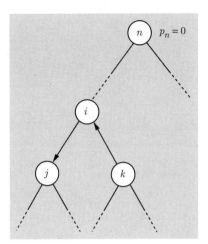

Figure 7.13: Once p_i is computed, p_j and p_k can also be computed, because we have $p_i - p_j = c_{ij}$ and $p_k - p_i = c_{ki}$. Starting from the root and continuing in this fashion, all dual variables can be computed.

count of the computational requirements of each iteration, we need $O(n)$ computations to evaluate the dual vector $\mathbf{p}$, $O(m)$ computations to evaluate all of the reduced costs, and another $O(n)$ computations to effect the change of basis. Given that $m \geq n - 1$, the total is $O(m)$, which compares favorably with the $O(mn)$ computational requirements of an iteration of the simplex method for general linear programming problems. In practice, the running time of the network simplex algorithm is improved further by using a somewhat more clever way of updating the dual variables, and by using suitable data structures to organize the computation.

All of the theory in Chapters 3 and 4 applies to the network simplex method. In particular, in the absence of degeneracy, the algorithm is guaranteed to terminate after a finite number of steps. In the presence of degeneracy, the algorithm may cycle. Cycling can be avoided by using either a general purpose anticycling rule or special methods. If the optimal cost is $-\infty$, the algorithm terminates with a negative cost directed cycle. (The simple circulation $\mathbf{h}^C$ associated with that cycle is an extreme ray of the feasible set, and $\mathbf{c}'\mathbf{h}^C < 0$.) If the optimal cost is finite, the algorithm terminates with an optimal flow vector $\mathbf{f}$ and an optimal dual vector $\mathbf{p}$. In practice, the number of iterations is often $O(m)$, but there exist examples involving an exponential number of basis changes.

Example 7.3 Consider the uncapacitated network problem shown in Figure 7.14(a); the numbers next to each arc are the corresponding costs. Figure 7.14(b) shows a tree and a corresponding feasible tree solution. Arc $(4, 3)$ forms a cycle consisting of nodes 4, 3, and 5. The reduced cost $\bar{c}_{43}$ of f_{43} is equal to the cost of

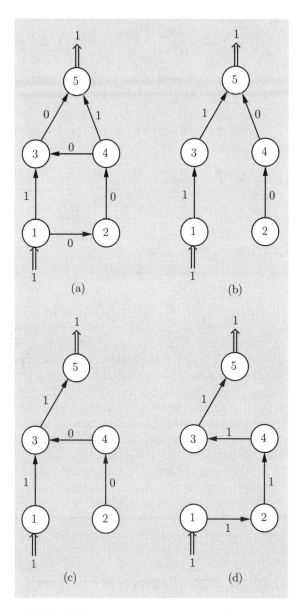

Figure 7.14: (a) An uncapacitated network flow problem. Arc costs are indicated next to each arc. (b) An initial feasible tree solution. The arc flows are indicated next to each arc. (c)-(d) Feasible tree solutions obtained after the first and the second change of basis, respectively.

that cycle, which is $c_{43} + c_{35} - c_{45} = -1$. We let arc $(4, 3)$ enter the tree. Pushing flow along the cycle attempts to reduce the flow along the arc $(4, 5)$. Since this was zero to start with (degeneracy), we have $\theta^* = 0$; the arc $(4, 5)$ leaves the tree and we obtain the feasible tree solution indicated in Figure 7.14(c). The reduced cost associated with arc $(1, 2)$ is $c_{12} + c_{24} + c_{43} - c_{13} = -1$, and we let that arc enter the tree. We can push up to one unit of flow along the cycle 1,2,4,3,1, that is, until the flow along arc $(1, 3)$ is set to zero. Thus, $\theta^* = 1$, the arc $(1, 3)$ leaves the tree, and we obtain the feasible tree solution indicated in Figure 7.14(d). It is not hard to verify that all reduced costs are nonnegative and we have an optimal solution.

Integrality of optimal solutions

An important feature of network flow problems is that when the problem data are integer, most quantities of interest are also integer and the simplex method can be implemented using integer (as opposed to floating point) arithmetic. This allows for faster computation and, equally important, the issues of finite precision and truncation error disappear. The theorem that follows provides a summary of integrality properties.

Theorem 7.5 *Consider an uncapacitated network flow problem and assume that the underlying graph is connected.*

(a) *For every basis matrix* $\mathbf{B}$, *the matrix* $\mathbf{B}^{-1}$ *has integer entries.*

(b) *If the supplies* b_i *are integer, then every basic solution has integer coordinates.*

(c) *If the cost coefficients* c_{ij} *are integer, then every dual basic solution has integer coordinates.*

Proof.

(a) As shown in the proof of Theorem 7.3, we can reorder the rows and columns of a basis matrix $\mathbf{B}$ so that it becomes lower triangular and its diagonal entries are either 1 or -1. Therefore, the determinant of $\mathbf{B}$ is equal to 1 or -1. By Cramer's rule, $\mathbf{B}^{-1}$ has integer entries.

(b) This follows by inspecting the nature of the algorithm that determines the values of the basic variables (see the proof of Theorem 7.3), or from the formula $\mathbf{f}_T = \mathbf{B}^{-1}\tilde{\mathbf{b}}$.

(c) This follows by inspecting the nature of the algorithm that determines the values of the dual variables, or from the formula $\mathbf{p}' = \mathbf{c}'_B\mathbf{B}^{-1}$. $\quad\square$

We now have the following important corollary of Theorem 7.5.

Corollary 7.2 *Consider an uncapacitated network flow problem, and assume that the optimal cost is finite.*

(a) *If all supplies b_i are integer, there exists an integer optimal flow vector.*

(b) *If all cost coefficients c_{ij} are integer, there exists an integer optimal solution to the dual problem.*

The simplex method for capacitated problems

We will now generalize the simplex method to the case where some of the arc capacities are finite and we have constraints of the form

$$d_{ij} \leq f_{ij} \leq u_{ij}, \qquad (i,j) \in \mathcal{A}.$$

There are only some minor differences from the discussion earlier in this section. For this reason, our development will be less formal.

Consider a set $T \subset \mathcal{A}$ of $n-1$ arcs that form a tree when their direction is ignored. We partition the remaining arcs into two disjoint subsets D and U. We let $f_{ij} = d_{ij}$ for every $(i,j) \in D$, $f_{ij} = u_{ij}$ for every $(i,j) \in U$, and then solve the flow conservation equations for the remaining variables f_{ij}, $(i,j) \in T$. The resulting flow vector is easily shown to be a basic solution, and all basic solutions can be obtained in this manner; the argument is similar to the proofs of Theorems 7.3 and 7.4.

Given a basic feasible solution associated with the sets T, D, and U, we evaluate the vector of reduced costs using the same formulae as before, and then examine the arcs outside T. If we find an arc $(i,j) \in D$ whose reduced cost is negative, we push as much flow as possible around the cycle created by that arc. (This is the same as in our previous development.) Alternatively, if we can find an arc $(i,j) \in U$ with positive reduced cost, we push as much flow as possible around the cycle created by that arc, but in the opposite direction. In either case, we are dealing with a direction of cost decrease. Determining how much flow can be pushed is done as follows. Let F be the set of arcs whose flow is to increase due to the contemplated flow push; let B be the set of arcs whose flow is to decrease. Then, the flow increment is limited by θ^*, defined as follows:

$$\theta^* = \min \left\{ \min_{(k,\ell) \in B} \{f_{k\ell} - d_{k\ell}\}, \ \min_{(k,\ell) \in F} \{u_{k\ell} - f_{k\ell}\} \right\}. \qquad (7.11)$$

By pushing θ^* units of flow around the cycle, there will be at least one arc (k,ℓ) whose flow is set to either $d_{k\ell}$ or $u_{k\ell}$. If the arc (k,ℓ) belongs to T, it is removed from the tree and is replaced by (i,j). The other possibility is that $(k,\ell) = (i,j)$. (For example, pushing flow around the cycle may result in f_{ij} being reduced from u_{ij} to d_{ij}.) In that case, the set T remains the same, but (i, j) is moved from U to D, or vice versa. In any case, we obtain a new basic feasible solution. (In the presence of degeneracy, it is possible that the new basic feasible solution coincides with the old one, and only the sets T, D, or U change.) To summarize, the network simplex algorithm for capacitated problems is as follows.

The simplex method for capacitated network flow problems

1. A typical iteration starts with a basic feasible solution **f** associated with a tree T, and a partition of the remaining arcs into two sets D, U, such that $f_{ij} = d_{ij}$ for $(i, j) \in D$, and $f_{ij} = u_{ij}$ for $(i, j) \in U$.

2. Solve the system of equations (7.10) for $p_1, \ldots, p_n$, by proceeding from the root towards the leaves.

3. Compute the reduced costs $\bar{c}_{ij} = c_{ij} - (p_i - p_j)$ of all arcs $(i, j) \notin T$. If $\bar{c}_{ij} \geq 0$ for all $(i, j) \in D$, and $\bar{c}_{ij} \leq 0$ for all $(i, j) \in U$, the current basic feasible solution is optimal and the algorithm terminates.

4. Let (i, j) be an arc such that $\bar{c}_{ij} < 0$ and $(i, j) \in D$, or such that $\bar{c}_{ij} > 0$ and $(i, j) \in U$. This arc (i, j) together with the tree T forms a unique cycle. Choose the orientation of the cycle as follows. If $(i, j) \in D$, then (i, j) should be a forward arc. If $(i, j) \in U$, then (i, j) should be a backward arc.

5. Let F and B be the forward and backward arcs, respectively, in the cycle. Determine θ^* according to Eq. (7.11). Compute a new flow vector, with components $\hat{f}_{k\ell}$, by letting

$$\hat{f}_{k\ell} = \begin{cases} f_{k\ell} + \theta^*, & \text{if } (k, \ell) \in F, \\ f_{k\ell} - \theta^*, & \text{if } (k, \ell) \in B, \\ f_{k\ell}, & \text{otherwise.} \end{cases}$$

Finally, update the sets T, D, U.

7.4   The negative cost cycle algorithm

The network simplex algorithm incorporates a basic idea, which is present in practically every primal method for network flow problems: given a current primal feasible solution, find an improved one by identifying a negative cost cycle along which flow can be pushed. One advantage of the simplex method is that it searches for negative cost cycles using a streamlined and efficient mechanism. A potential disadvantage is that a change of basis can be degenerate, with no flow being pushed, and without any cost improvement.

In this section, we present a related, but different, algorithm, where every iteration aims at a nonzero cost improvement. In particular, at every

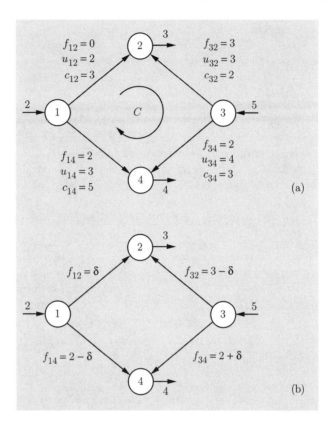

Figure 7.15: (a) A portion of a network, together with the values of some of the flow variables. (b) The new arc flows after pushing δ units of flow around the cycle C.

iteration we push some flow around a negative cost cycle. The algorithm terminates when no profitable cycle can be identified. The method is justified by a key result that relates the absence of profitable cycles with optimality.

Motivation

Consider the portion of a network shown in Figure 7.15(a). Could the flow vector $\mathbf{f}$ given in the figure be optimal? The answer is no, for the following reason. Suppose that we push δ units of flow along the indicated cycle, where δ is a positive scalar. Taking into account the direction of the arcs, the new flow variables take the values indicated in Figure 7.15(b). In particular, the flow on every forward arc is increased by δ and the flow on every backward arc is reduced by δ. Flow conservation is preserved, and as long as $\delta \leq 2$, the constraints $0 \leq f_{ij} \leq u_{ij}$ are respected, and the new flow is feasible. The change in costs is

$$c_{12}\delta + c_{32}(-\delta) + c_{34}\delta + c_{14}(-\delta) = -\delta,$$

which is negative, and $\mathbf{f}$ cannot be optimal. As this example illustrates, a flow $\mathbf{f}$ can be improved if we can identify a cycle along which flow can be profitably pushed.

Description of the algorithm

In this subsection, we present the algorithm of interest after developing some of its elements. We assume that we have a network described by a directed graph $G = (\mathcal{N}, \mathcal{A})$, supplies b_i, arc capacities u_{ij}, and cost coefficients c_{ij}. Let C be a cycle, and let F and B be the sets of forward and backward arcs of the cycle, respectively. Let $\mathbf{h}^C$ be the simple circulation associated with this cycle; that is,

$$h_{ij}^C = \begin{cases} 1, & \text{if } (i,j) \in F, \\ -1, & \text{if } (i,j) \in B, \\ 0, & \text{otherwise.} \end{cases}$$

Let $\mathbf{f}$ be a feasible flow vector and let δ be a nonnegative scalar. If we change $\mathbf{f}$ to $\mathbf{f} + \delta\mathbf{h}^C$, we say that we are *pushing δ units of flow along the cycle C*. Since $\mathbf{f}$ is feasible, we have $\mathbf{Af} = \mathbf{b}$; since $\mathbf{Ah}^C = \mathbf{0}$, we obtain $\mathbf{A}(\mathbf{f} + \delta\mathbf{h}^C) = \mathbf{b}$, and the flow conservation constraint is still satisfied. In order to maintain feasibility, we also need

$$0 \le f_{ij} + \delta h_{ij}^C \le u_{ij},$$

that is,

$$0 \le f_{ij} + \delta \le u_{ij}, \qquad \text{if } (i,j) \in F,$$
$$0 \le f_{ij} - \delta \le u_{ij}, \qquad \text{if } (i,j) \in B.$$

Since $\delta \ge 0$ and $0 \le f_{ij} \le u_{ij}$, this is equivalent to

$$\delta \le u_{ij} - f_{ij}, \qquad \text{if } (i,j) \in F,$$
$$\delta \le f_{ij}, \qquad \text{if } (i,j) \in B.$$

Thus, the maximum amount of flow that can be pushed along the cycle, which we denote by $\delta(C)$, is given by

$$\delta(C) = \min \left\{ \min_{(i,j) \in F} (u_{ij} - f_{ij}), \min_{(i,j) \in B} f_{ij} \right\}. \tag{7.12}$$

If the set B is empty and if $u_{ij} = \infty$ for every arc in the cycle, then there are no restrictions on δ, and we set $\delta(C) = \infty$. If $f_{ij} < u_{ij}$ for all forward arcs and $f_{ij} > 0$ for all backward arcs, then $\delta(C) > 0$, and we say that the cycle is *unsaturated*. For the cycle considered in Figure 7.15(a), we have $\delta(C) = 2$.

We now calculate the cost change when we push a unit of flow along a cycle C. Using the definition of $\mathbf{h}^C$, the cost change is

$$\mathbf{c}'\mathbf{h}^C = \sum_{(i,j)\in F} c_{ij} - \sum_{(i,j)\in B} c_{ij},$$

the *cost of cycle C*.

We can now propose an algorithm which at each iteration looks for a negative cost unsaturated cycle and pushes as much flow as possible along that cycle.

Negative cost cycle algorithm

1. Start with a feasible flow $\mathbf{f}$.

2. Search for an unsaturated cycle with negative cost.

3. If no unsaturated cycle with negative cost can be found, the algorithm terminates.

4. If a negative cost unsaturated cycle C is found, then:

    (a) If $\delta(C) < \infty$, construct the new feasible flow $\mathbf{f} + \delta(C)\mathbf{h}^C$, and go to Step 2.

    (b) If $\delta(C) = \infty$, the algorithm terminates and the optimal cost is $-\infty$.

There are a few different issues that need to be discussed:

(a) How do we start the algorithm?

(b) How do we search for an unsaturated cycle with negative cost?

(c) If the algorithm terminates, does it provide us with an optimal solution?

(d) Is the algorithm guaranteed to terminate?

These issues are addressed, one at a time, in the subsections that follow.

Starting the algorithm

As discussed in Section 7.2, every network flow problem can be converted into an equivalent problem with no sources or sinks. For the latter problem, the zero flow is a feasible solution that provides a starting point. As an alternative, a feasible flow (if one exists) can be constructed by solving a suitable maximum flow problem (Exercise 7.21).

The residual network

Suppose that we have a network $G = (\mathcal{N}, \mathcal{A})$ and a feasible flow **f**. The *residual network* is an auxiliary network $\tilde{G} = (\mathcal{N}, \tilde{\mathcal{A}})$ with the same set of nodes, but with different arcs and arc capacities. It is a convenient device to keep track of the amount of flow that can be pushed along the arcs of the original network.

Consider an arc (i, j), with capacity u_{ij}, and let f_{ij} be the current flow through that arc. Then, f_{ij} can be increased by up to $u_{ij} - f_{ij}$, or can be decreased by up to f_{ij}. We represent these options in the residual network by introducing an arc (i, j) with capacity $u_{ij} - f_{ij}$, and an arc (j, i), with capacity f_{ij}. Any flow on the arc (j, i) in the residual network is to be interpreted as a corresponding reduction of the flow on the arc (i, j) of the original network.

We assign costs to the arcs of the residual network in a way that reflects the cost changes in the original network. In particular, we associate a cost of c_{ij} with the arc (i, j) of the residual network, and a cost of $-c_{ij}$ with the arc (j, i) of the residual network. [This is because a unit of flow on the arc (j, i) corresponds to a unit reduction of the flow on the arc (i, j) of the original network, and a cost change of $-c_{ij}$.] All supplies in the residual network are set to zero, which implies that every feasible flow is a circulation. Finally, we delete those arcs of the residual network that have zero capacity.

The construction of the residual network is shown in Figure 7.16. As seen in the figure, the residual network may contain two arcs with the same start node and the same end node. In particular, the presence of two arcs from i to j indicates that we can push flow from i to j either by increasing the value of f_{ij} or by decreasing the value of f_{ji}. Strictly speaking, this violates our original definition of a graph, but this turns out not to be a problem.

Let **f** be a feasible flow in the original network and let $\mathbf{f} + \bar{\mathbf{f}}$ be another feasible flow in the original network. The flow increment $\bar{\mathbf{f}}$ can be associated with a flow vector $\tilde{\mathbf{f}}$ in the residual network as follows.

(a) If $\bar{f}_{ij} > 0$, we let the flow $\tilde{f}_{ij}$ on the corresponding arc (i, j) in the residual network be equal to $\bar{f}_{ij}$. Feasibility in the original network implies that $\bar{f}_{ij} \leq u_{ij} - f_{ij}$, and $\tilde{f}_{ij}$ satisfies the capacity constraint in the residual network.

(b) If $\bar{f}_{ij} < 0$, we let the flow $\tilde{f}_{ji}$ on the corresponding arc (j, i) in the residual network be equal to $-\bar{f}_{ij}$. Feasibility in the original network implies that $-\bar{f}_{ij} \leq f_{ij}$ and therefore $\tilde{f}_{ji}$ satisfies the capacity constraint in the residual network.

All variables $\tilde{f}_{ij}$ that are not set by either (a) or (b) above are left at zero value. See Figure 7.17 for an illustration.

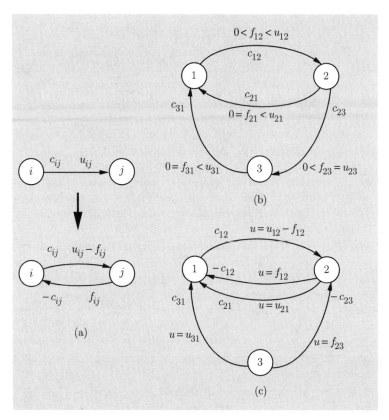

Figure 7.16: (a) Each arc of the original network leads to two arcs in the residual network. (b) A network and an associated feasible flow. (c) The corresponding residual network. Note that zero capacity arcs have been deleted.

We make the following observations:

(a) We have $\tilde{f}_{ij} \geq 0$ for all arcs in the residual network.

(b) The flow $\tilde{\mathbf{f}}$ in the residual network is a circulation. This is because in the original network, we have $\mathbf{Af} = \mathbf{b} = \mathbf{A}(\mathbf{f} + \bar{\mathbf{f}})$. Hence, $\mathbf{A}\bar{\mathbf{f}} = \mathbf{0}$, which means that with the flow vector $\bar{\mathbf{f}}$, the net flow into any node i is zero. Because of the way $\tilde{\mathbf{f}}$ was constructed, the net flow into any node of the residual network must also be zero.

(c) The cost of $\tilde{\mathbf{f}}$ in the residual network is equal to $\sum_{(i,j)} c_{ij} \bar{f}_{ij}$, which is the cost of $\bar{\mathbf{f}}$ in the original network. This is because for each arc with $\bar{f}_{ij} > 0$, we have an equal flow $\tilde{f}_{ij}$ in a corresponding arc (i, j) in the residual network, and the latter arc has unit cost c_{ij}. Furthermore, for each arc with $\bar{f}_{ij} < 0$ in the original network, we have a flow $\tilde{f}_{ji} = -\bar{f}_{ij}$ in a corresponding arc (j, i) in the residual network, and

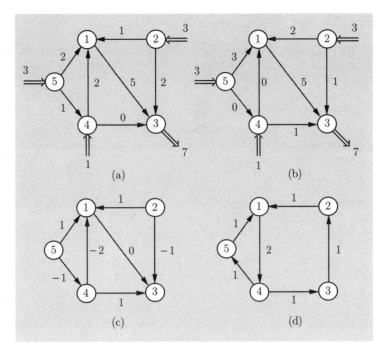

Figure 7.17: In this figure, the numbers next to each arc indicate arc flows. (a) A feasible flow $\mathbf{f}$ in a network. (b) Another feasible flow $\mathbf{f} + \overline{\mathbf{f}}$. (c) The flow increment $\overline{\mathbf{f}}$. Note that it is a circulation. (d) The flow $\tilde{\mathbf{f}}$ in the residual network (only arcs with nonzero flows are shown).

the latter arc has unit cost $-c_{ij}$. Since $(-c_{ij})\tilde{f}_{ji} = c_{ij}\overline{f}_{ij}$, we see that $\overline{f}_{ij}$ and $\tilde{f}_{ji}$ incur the same cost.

The preceding arguments can be reversed. That is, if we start with a feasible circulation $\tilde{\mathbf{f}}$ in the residual network, we can construct a circulation $\overline{\mathbf{f}}$ in the original network such that $\mathbf{f} + \overline{\mathbf{f}}$ is feasible and such that $\mathbf{c}'\overline{\mathbf{f}}$ is equal to the cost of $\tilde{\mathbf{f}}$ in the residual network.

We finally note that every unsaturated cycle in the original network corresponds to a directed cycle in the residual network in which all arcs have positive capacity and vice versa. Furthermore, the costs of these cycles in their respective networks are equal. We conclude that the search for negative cost unsaturated cycles in the original network can be accomplished by searching for a negative cost directed cycle in the residual network. In Section 7.9, we show that the problem of finding negative cost directed cycles in a graph can be solved in time $O(n^3)$; hence, the computational requirements of each iteration of the negative cost cycle algorithm are also $O(n^3)$.

Optimality conditions

We now investigate what happens at termination of the negative cost cycle algorithm. If the algorithm terminates because it discovered a negative cost cycle with $\delta(C) = \infty$, then the optimal cost is $-\infty$. In particular, the flow $\mathbf{f} + \delta \mathbf{h}^C$ is feasible for every $\delta > 0$, and by letting δ become arbitrarily large, the cost of such feasible solutions is unbounded below.

The algorithm may also terminate because no unsaturated negative cost cycle can be found. In that case, we have an optimal solution, as shown by the next result.

Theorem 7.6 *A feasible flow* $\mathbf{f}$ *is optimal if and only if there is no unsaturated cycle with negative cost.*

Proof. One direction is easy. If C is an unsaturated cycle with negative cost, then $\mathbf{f} + \delta(C)\mathbf{h}^C$ is a feasible flow whose cost is less than the cost of $\mathbf{f}$, and so $\mathbf{f}$ is not optimal.

For the converse, we argue by contradiction. Suppose that $\mathbf{f}$ is a feasible flow that is not optimal. Then, there exists another feasible flow $\mathbf{f} + \bar{\mathbf{f}}$ whose cost is less, and in particular, $\mathbf{c}'\bar{\mathbf{f}} < 0$. As discussed in the preceding subsection, it follows that there exists a feasible (in particular, nonnegative) circulation $\tilde{\mathbf{f}}$ in the residual network whose cost is negative. To prove that this circulation implies the existence of a negative cost directed cycle in the residual network, we need the following important result.

Lemma 7.1 (Flow decomposition theorem) *Let* $\mathbf{f} \geq \mathbf{0}$ *be a nonzero circulation. Then, there exist simple circulations* $\mathbf{f}^1, \ldots, \mathbf{f}^k$, *involving only forward arcs, and positive scalars* $a_1, \ldots, a_k$, *such that*

$$\mathbf{f} = \sum_{i=1}^{k} a_i \mathbf{f}^i.$$

Furthermore, if $\mathbf{f}$ *is an integer vector, then each* a_i *can be chosen to be an integer.*

Proof. (See Figure 7.18 for an illustration.) If $\mathbf{f}$ is the zero vector, the result is trivially true, with $k = 0$. Suppose that $\mathbf{f}$ is nonzero. Then, there exists some arc (i, j) for which $f_{ij} > 0$. Let us traverse arc (i, j). Because of flow conservation at node j, there exists some arc (j, k) for which $f_{jk} > 0$. We then traverse arc (j, k) and keep repeating the same process. Since there are finitely many nodes, some node will be eventually visited for a second time. At that point, we have found a directed cycle with each arc in the cycle carrying a positive amount of flow. Let $\mathbf{f}^1$ be the simple circulation

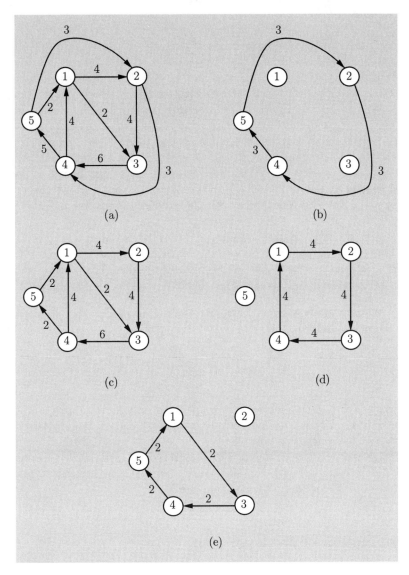

Figure 7.18: Illustration of the flow decomposition theorem. The numbers next to each arc indicate the value of the corresponding arc flows. Arcs with zero flow are not shown. (a) A nonnegative circulation $\mathbf{f}$. (b) The circulation $a_1\mathbf{f}^1$. (c) The remaining flow $\mathbf{f} - a_1\mathbf{f}^1$. (d) The circulation $a_2\mathbf{f}^2$. (e) The remaining flow $\mathbf{f} - a_1\mathbf{f}^1 - a_2\mathbf{f}^2$ is a simple circulation and we let $a_3\mathbf{f}^3$ be equal to it.

corresponding to that cycle. Let a_1 be the minimum value of f_{ij}, where the minimum is taken over all arcs in the cycle, and consider the vector $\hat{\mathbf{f}} = \mathbf{f} - a_1\mathbf{f}^1$. This vector is nonnegative because of the way that a_1 was chosen. In addition, we have $\mathbf{Af} = \mathbf{0}$ and $\mathbf{Af}^1 = \mathbf{0}$, which implies that $\mathbf{A}\hat{\mathbf{f}} = \mathbf{0}$ and $\hat{\mathbf{f}}$ is a circulation. By the definition of a_1, there exists some arc (k, ℓ) on the cycle for which $f_{k\ell} = a_1$ and $\hat{f}_{k\ell} = 0$. Therefore, the number of positive components of $\hat{\mathbf{f}}$ is smaller than the number of positive components of $\mathbf{f}$. We can now apply the same procedure to $\hat{\mathbf{f}}$, to obtain a new simple circulation $\mathbf{f}^2$, and continue similarly. Each time, the number of arcs that carry positive flow is reduced by at least one. Thus, after repeating this procedure a finite number of times, we end up with the zero flow. When this happens, we have succeeded in decomposing $\mathbf{f}$ as a nonnegative linear combination of simple circulations. Furthermore, since all of the cycles constructed were directed, these simple circulations involve only forward arcs.

If $\mathbf{f}$ is integer, then a_1 is integer, and $\hat{\mathbf{f}}$ is also an integer vector. It follows, by induction, that if we start with an integer flow vector $\mathbf{f}$, all flows produced in the course of the above procedure are integer, and all coefficients a_i are also integer. This concludes the proof of Lemma 7.1. $\square$

We now apply Lemma 7.1 to the residual network. The circulation $\tilde{\mathbf{f}}$ can be decomposed in the form

$$\tilde{\mathbf{f}} = \sum_i a_i \tilde{\mathbf{f}}^i,$$

where each $\tilde{\mathbf{f}}^i$ is a simple circulation involving only forward arcs, and each a_i is positive. Since $\tilde{\mathbf{f}}$ has negative cost, at least one of the circulations $\tilde{\mathbf{f}}^i$ must also have negative cost; hence, the residual network has a negative cost directed cycle. As discussed in the preceding subsection, this implies that the original network contains a negative cost unsaturated cycle, and the proof of Theorem 7.6 is now complete. $\square$

Termination of the algorithm

Before concluding that the algorithm is correct, we need a guarantee that it will eventually terminate. This is the subject of our next theorem.

Theorem 7.7 *Suppose that all arc capacities u_{ij} are integer or infinite, and that the negative cost cycle algorithm is initialized with an integer feasible flow. Then, the arc flow variables remain integer throughout the algorithm and, if the optimal cost is finite, the algorithm terminates with an integer optimal solution.*

Proof. If the current flow $\mathbf{f}$ is integer, then $\delta(C)$ is integer or infinite, for every cycle C. Hence, the flow obtained after one iteration of the algorithm must also be integer, and integrality is preserved.

At each iteration, before the algorithm terminates, we have a cost reduction of $\delta(C)|\mathbf{c}'\mathbf{h}^C|$, where C is the negative cost cycle along which flow is pushed. Since $\delta(C) \geq 1$, this is no smaller than $v = \min_D |\mathbf{c}'\mathbf{h}^D|$, where the minimum is taken over all negative cost cycles D. Thus, each iteration of the algorithm reduces the cost by at least v, which is positive. It follows that if the optimal cost is finite, the algorithm must terminate after a finite number of iterations. $\qquad\square$

Note that Theorem 7.7 establishes an integrality property of optimal solutions. This is the same conclusion that was reached in Corollary 7.2(a), for standard form problems.

Surprisingly, and unlike the simplex method, if the arc capacities are not integer, the algorithm is not guaranteed to terminate, even if the optimal cost is finite. One possibility is that the algorithm makes an infinite number of steps, each step results in lower costs, but the cost reductions become smaller and smaller, and the cost of the current flow does not converge to the optimal cost. It turns out that finite termination can be guaranteed under special rules for choosing between negative cost cycles. Two possible rules that are known to lead to finite termination are the following:

(a) **Largest improvement rule:** Choose a negative cost cycle for which the cost improvement $\delta(C)|\mathbf{c}'\mathbf{h}^C|$ is largest. Unfortunately, finding such a cycle is difficult. See Exercise 7.16 for an upper bound on the number of iterations.

(b) **Mean cost rule:** Choose a negative cost cycle for which $|\mathbf{c}'\mathbf{h}^C|/k(C)$ is largest, where $k(C)$ is the number of arcs in cycle C. It turns out that the search for such a cycle is not too difficult (Exercise 7.37).

When the optimal cost is $-\infty$, the algorithm may fail to terminate after a finite number of iterations, even if the arc capacities are integer. For this reason, one should verify that the optimal cost is finite before starting the algorithm; a simple criterion is developed in Exercise 7.17.

7.5   The maximum flow problem

In the maximum flow problem, we are given a directed graph $G = (\mathcal{N}, \mathcal{A})$ and an arc capacity bound $u_{ij} \in [0, \infty]$ for each arc $(i, j) \in A$. Let s and t be two special nodes, called the source and sink node, respectively. The problem is to find the largest possible amount of flow that can be sent through the network, from s to t. We will see shortly that this is a special case of the general network flow problem. On the other hand, special purpose algorithms are possible, because of the simple structure of the problem. The maximum flow problem arises in a variety of applications. Some are rather obvious (e.g., maximizing throughput in a logistics network), while others are less expected; see the example that follows.

Example 7.4 (Preemptive scheduling) We are given m identical machines and n jobs. Each job j must be processed for a total of p_j periods. (We assume that each p_j is an integer.) However, we allow *preemption*. That is, the processing of a job can be broken down and can be carried out by different machines in different periods. Each machine can only process one job at a time, and a job can only be processed by a single machine at a time. In addition, each job j is associated with a release time r_j and a deadline d_j: processing cannot start before period r_j, and must be completed before period d_j. Naturally, we assume that $r_j + p_j \leq d_j$ for all jobs j. We wish to determine a schedule whereby all jobs are processed, without violating the release times and deadlines, or show that no such schedule exists.

We will now construct a maximum flow formulation of the problem. The first step is to rank all the release times and deadlines in ascending order. The resulting ordered list of numbers divides the time horizon into a number of nonoverlapping intervals. Let T_{kl} be the interval that starts in the beginning of period k and ends in the beginning of period l. Note that during each interval T_{kl}, the set of jobs that can be processed does not change. In particular, we can process any job j that has been released ($r_j \leq k$) and its deadline has not yet been reached ($l \leq d_j$). For a concrete example, suppose that we have four jobs with release times 3, 1, 3, 5, and deadlines 5, 4, 7, 9. The ascending list of release times and deadlines is $1, 3, 4, 5, 7, 9$. We then obtain five intervals, namely, T_{13}, T_{34}, T_{45}, T_{57}, and T_{79}.

We construct a network involving a source node s, a sink node t, a node corresponding to each job j, and a node corresponding to each interval T_{kl}. The arcs and their capacities are as follows. For every job j, we have an arc (s, j), with capacity p_j. We interpret the flow along this arc as the number of periods of processing that job j receives. For every node T_{kl}, we introduce an arc (T_{kl}, t), with capacity $m(l - k)$. The flow along this arc represents the total number of machine-periods of processing during the interval T_{kl}. Finally, if a job j is available for processing during the interval T_{kl}, that is, if $r_j \leq k \leq l \leq d_j$, we introduce an arc (j, T_{kl}), with capacity $l - k$. The flow along this arc represents the number of periods that job j is processed during this interval. See Figure 7.19 for an illustration. It is not hard to show that every feasible schedule corresponds to a flow through this network, with value $\sum_{j=1}^{n} p_j$, and conversely. Therefore, the scheduling problem can be solved by solving a maximum flow problem, and checking whether the resulting maximum flow value is equal to $\sum_{j=1}^{n} p_j$.

Mathematically, the maximum flow problem can be formulated as follows:

$$
\begin{array}{ll}
\text{maximize} & b_s \\
\text{subject to} & \mathbf{Af} = \mathbf{b} \\
& b_t = -b_s \\
& b_i = 0, \qquad \forall\, i \neq s, t, \\
& 0 \leq f_{ij} \leq u_{ij}, \qquad \forall\, (i, j) \in \mathcal{A}.
\end{array}
$$

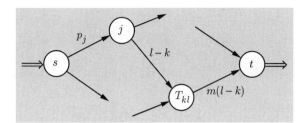

Figure 7.19: The structure of the network associated with the preemptive scheduling problem. The number next to each arc indicates its capacity. The arc from node j to node (k, l) is present only if $r_j \le k \le l \le d_j$.

Note that, in contrast to the network flow problems considered earlier, b_s is a variable to be optimized. Any flow vector $\mathbf{f}$ satisfying the above constraints is called a feasible flow and the corresponding value of b_s is called the *value* of that flow.

The maximum flow problem can be reformulated as a network flow problem, as follows (see Figure 7.20 for an illustration). We let the cost of every arc be equal to zero and we introduce a new infinite capacity arc (t, s), with cost $c_{ts} = -1$. Minimizing $\sum_{(i,j)} c_{ij} f_{ij}$ in the new network is the same as maximizing the flow f_{ts} on the new arc. Since the flow on the arc (t, s) must return from s to t through the original network, maximizing f_{ts} is the same as solving the original maximum flow problem.

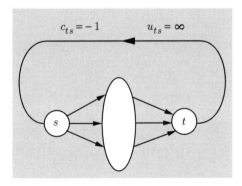

Figure 7.20: Reformulation of the maximum flow problem as a network flow problem.

Once the maximum flow problem is formulated as a network flow problem, the negative cost cycle algorithm of Section 7.4 can be applied, and this is one way of deriving the main algorithm in this section (Exercise 7.18). However, our derivation will be self-contained.

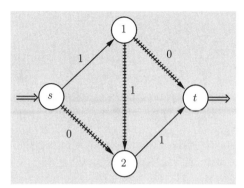

Figure 7.21: Let all arc capacities be equal to 1. The numbers next to each arc indicate the values of the arc flows. Note that up to one unit of additional flow can be pushed along the path indicated by thatched arcs.

Consider the flow illustrated in Figure 7.21. Its value can be increased by pushing additional flow along the path consisting of the arcs $(s, 2)$, $(1, 2)$, $(1, t)$. Note that arc $(1, 2)$ is a backward arc of that path; pushing δ units of flow along the path, reduces the flow along arc $(1, 2)$ by δ. The definition that follows deals with paths of this type, through which additional flow can be pushed.

Definition 7.2 *Let* **f** *be a feasible flow vector. An* **augmenting path** *is a path from s to t such that $f_{ij} < u_{ij}$ for all forward arcs, and $f_{ij} > 0$ for all backward arcs on the path.*

Suppose that we have a feasible flow and that we have found an augmenting path P. We can then increase the flow along every forward arc, decrease the flow along every backward arc by the same amount, and still satisfy all of the problem constraints; we then say that we are *pushing flow along the path P*, or that we have a *flow augmentation*. The amount of flow pushed along P can be no more than $\delta(P)$, defined by

$$\delta(P) = \min\left\{ \min_{(i,j)\in F} (u_{ij} - f_{ij}), \ \min_{(i,j)\in B} f_{ij} \right\}, \qquad (7.13)$$

where F and B are the sets of forward and backward arcs, respectively, in the augmenting path. If the augmenting path consists exclusively of forward arcs, and if all arcs on the path have infinite capacity, then there is no limit on the amount of flow that can be pushed, and we have $\delta(P) = \infty$. For the example in Figure 7.21, we have $\delta(P) = 1$.

We now introduce a natural algorithm for the maximum flow problem.

The Ford-Fulkerson algorithm

1. Start with a feasible flow **f**.

2. Search for an augmenting path.

3. If no augmenting path can be found, the algorithm terminates.

4. If an augmenting path P is found, then:

    (a) If $\delta(P) < \infty$, push $\delta(P)$ units of flow along P, and go to Step 2.

    (b) If $\delta(P) = \infty$, the algorithm terminates.

If the algorithm terminates because $\delta(P) = \infty$, we have found an augmenting path without capacity limitations and, using that path, an arbitrarily large amount of flow can be sent to the sink.

We now address the termination properties of the algorithm.

Theorem 7.8 *Suppose that all arc capacities u_{ij} are integer or infinite, and that the Ford-Fulkerson algorithm is initialized with an integer flow vector. Then, the arc flow variables remain integer throughout the algorithm and, if the optimal value is finite, the algorithm terminates after a finite number of steps.*

Proof. This result can be derived as a corollary of Theorem 7.7 in Section 7.4. For a self-contained proof, note that if we have an integer feasible flow, and if all arc capacities are integer or infinite, then $\delta(P)$ is integer or infinite. Thus, integrality of flows is maintained throughout the algorithm. Every iteration of the algorithm increases the value of the flow by at least 1 [since $\delta(P)$ is integer]. Hence, either the value of the flow increases to infinity, or the algorithm must terminate. $\square$

Example 7.5 Consider the network shown in Figure 7.22(a) and let us start with the zero flow. The path consisting of the thatched arcs in Figure 7.22(b) is an augmenting path, with $\delta(P) = 1$. After a flow augmentation, we obtain the flow indicated. The path consisting of the thatched arcs in Figure 7.22(c) is an augmenting path, with $\delta(P) = 1$. By continuing similarly, and after a total of four flow augmentations, we obtain the flow shown in Figure 7.22(e), whose value is equal to 6. At this point, no augmenting path can be found. In fact, this flow must be optimal because the total capacity of the arcs leaving node s is equal to 6, and this is a bottleneck that cannot be overcome.

If the arc capacities are rational numbers, the algorithm is again guaranteed to terminate after a finite number of iterations. This is because we can multiply all arc capacities by their least common denominator, and

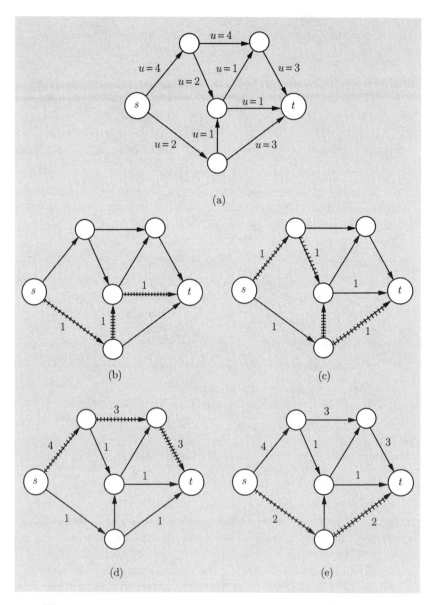

Figure 7.22: Illustration of the Ford-Fulkerson algorithm. The numbers next to the arcs in part (a) are arc capacities. We start with the zero flow. (b)-(e) In each case, we identify the augmenting indicated in the figure, and push as much flow as possible. The numbers next to the arcs correspond to the arc flows after the flow augmentation. The flow indicated in part (e) is optimal.

obtain an equivalent problem with integer arc capacities. However, if the arc capacities are not rational, there exist examples for which the algorithm never terminates. In particular, even though the value of the flow is monotonically increasing, its limit can be strictly less than the optimal.

For the non-rational case, the Ford-Fulkerson algorithm can be made to terminate after a finite number of iterations, if one uses special methods for choosing an augmenting path. For example, if one looks for an augmenting path with the least possible number of arcs, then the algorithm can be shown to terminate after $O(|\mathcal{A}| \cdot |\mathcal{N}|)$ iterations.

If the algorithm does terminate, it provides us with an optimal solution. This fact can be obtained as a corollary of the optimality conditions in Section 7.4. A self-contained proof using different ideas will be provided shortly. However, we will first discuss some issues related to the search for an augmenting path.

Searching for an augmenting path

The search for an augmenting path can be carried out in a fairly simple manner, using a method known as the *labeling algorithm*.

Suppose that we have a feasible flow **f**. Consider a path from the source s to some node k, such that $f_{ij} < u_{ij}$ for all forward arcs on the path, and $f_{ij} > 0$ for all backward arcs on the path; we say that this is an *unsaturated* path from s to k. Such a path can be used to push additional flow from node s to node k, without violating the capacity constraints. Note that an unsaturated path from s to t is the same as an augmenting path.

Let us say that a node i is *labeled* if we have determined that there exists an unsaturated path from s to i.

(a) Suppose that node i is labeled, that we have an unsaturated path P from s to i, and that (i, j) is an arc for which $f_{ij} < u_{ij}$. We may then append arc (i, j) to the path P, and obtain an unsaturated path from s to j. Thus, node j can also be labeled.

(b) Similarly, if we have an unsaturated path P from s to i, and if (j, i) is an arc for which $f_{ji} > 0$, we may append arc (j, i) to P (as a backward arc), and obtain an unsaturated path from s to j. Then, node j can be labeled.

The process of examining all nodes j neighboring a given labeled node i, to determine whether they can also be labeled, is called *scanning* node i. We now have the following algorithm, where I is the set of nodes that have been labeled but not yet scanned.

The labeling algorithm

1. The algorithm is initialized with $I = \{s\}$, and with s being the only labeled node.

2. A typical iteration starts with a set I of labeled, but not yet scanned nodes. If $t \in I$ or if $I = \emptyset$, the algorithm terminates. Otherwise, choose a node $i \in I$ to be scanned, and remove it from the set I. Examine all arcs of the form (i, j) or (j, i).

3. If $(i, j) \in \mathcal{A}$, $f_{ij} < u_{ij}$, and j is unlabeled, then label j, and add j to the set I.

4. If $(j, i) \in \mathcal{A}$, $f_{ji} > 0$, and j is unlabeled, then label j, and add j to the set I.

Note that a node enters the set I only if it changes from unlabeled to labeled. Therefore, a node can enter the set I at most once. Since each iteration removes a node from the set I, the algorithm must eventually terminate. We distinguish between two different possibilities.

(a) Suppose that the algorithm terminates because node t has been labeled. Then, there exists an unsaturated path from s to t, that is, an augmenting path. That path can be easily recovered if we do some extra bookkeeping in the course of the labeling algorithm, as follows. Whenever a node j is labeled while scanning a previously labeled node i, we record node i as the *parent* of j. At the end of the algorithm, we may start at node t, go to its parent, then to its parent's parent, etc., until we reach node s; the resulting path is an augmenting path from s to t.

(b) The second possibility is that the algorithm terminates because the set I is empty. We will now argue that this implies that there exists no augmenting path. Let S be the set of labeled nodes at termination, and suppose that there exists an augmenting path. Since $s \in S$ and $t \notin S$, it follows that there exist two consecutive nodes i and j on the augmenting path, such that $i \in S$ and $j \notin S$. Since i and j are consecutive nodes of an augmenting path, we have either $(i, j) \in \mathcal{A}$ and $f_{ij} < u_{ij}$, or $(j, i) \in \mathcal{A}$ and $f_{ji} > 0$. In either case, we see that node j should have been labeled at the time that node i was scanned. This is a contradiction and shows that no augmenting path exists.

Example 7.6 Consider the network shown in Figure 7.23. The labeling algorithm operates as follows:

1. $I = \{s\}$. Node s is scanned. Nodes 1, 2 are labeled.

2. $I = \{1, 2\}$. Node 1 is scanned. Node 4 is labeled.

3. $I = \{2, 4\}$. Node 4 is scanned. No node is labeled.

4. $I = \{2\}$. Node 2 is scanned. Node 3 is labeled.

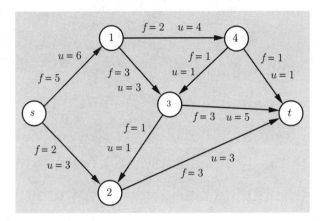

Figure 7.23: The network in Example 7.6 together, with a feasible flow.

5. $I = \{3\}$. Node 3 is scanned. Node t is labeled.

Since node t is labeled, we conclude that there exists an augmenting path, which can be obtained by backtracking, as follows. Node t was labeled while scanning node 3. Node 3 was labeled while scanning node 2. Node 2 was labeled while scanning node s. This leads us to the augmenting path $s, 2, 3, t$.

We conclude our analysis of the labeling algorithm with a brief discussion of its complexity. Every node is scanned at most once, and every arc is examined only when one of its end nodes is scanned. Thus, each arc is examined at most twice. Examining an arc entails only a constant (and small) number of arithmetic operations. We conclude that the computational complexity of the algorithm is proportional to the number of arcs.

We now formally record our conclusions so far.

Theorem 7.9 *The labeling algorithm runs in time $O(|\mathcal{A}|)$. At termination, the node t is labeled if and only if there exists an augmenting path.*

Cuts

We define an *s-t cut* as a subset S of the set of nodes $\mathcal{N}$, such that $s \in S$ and $t \notin S$. In our context, the nodes s and t are fixed, and we refer to S as simply a *cut*. We define the *capacity* $C(S)$ of a cut S as the sum of the capacities of the arcs that cross from S to its complement, that is,

$$C(S) = \sum_{\{(i,j) \in \mathcal{A} \mid i \in S, \, j \notin S\}} u_{ij}$$

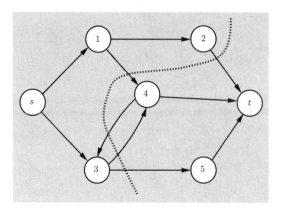

Figure 7.24: The set $S = \{s, 1, 2, 3\}$ is a cut. The capacity of this cut is $u_{2t} + u_{14} + u_{34} + u_{35}$.

(see Figure 7.24). Any flow from s to t must at some point cross an arc (i, j) with $i \in S$ and $j \notin S$. For this reason, the value v of any feasible flow satisfies

$$v \leq C(S), \tag{7.14}$$

for every cut. In essence, each cut provides a potential bottleneck for the maximum flow. Our next result shows that the value of the maximum flow is equal to the tightest of these bottlenecks.

Theorem 7.10

(a) *If the Ford-Fulkerson algorithm terminates because no augmenting path can be found, then the current flow is optimal.*

(b) **(Max-flow min-cut theorem)** *The value of the maximum flow is equal to the minimum cut capacity.*

Proof. (a) Suppose that the Ford-Fulkerson algorithm has terminated because it failed to find an augmenting path. Let S be the set of labeled nodes at termination. These are the nodes i for which there exists an unsaturated path from s to i. Since the search for an augmenting path starts by labeling node s, we have $s \in S$. On the other hand, since no augmenting path was found, node t is not labeled. Therefore, the set S is a cut. For every arc $(i, j) \in \mathcal{A}$, with $i \in S$ and $j \notin S$, we must have $f_{ij} = u_{ij}$. (Otherwise, node j would have been labeled by the labeling algorithm.) Thus, the total amount of flow that exits the set S is equal to $C(S)$. In addition, if $(i, j) \in \mathcal{A}$, with $i \notin S$ and $j \in S$, then $f_{ij} = 0$. (Otherwise, node i would have been labeled by the labeling algorithm.) Thus, the flow crossing from S to its complement cannot return to S, and must exit at the sink node t; see Figure 7.25. This establishes that the value of the

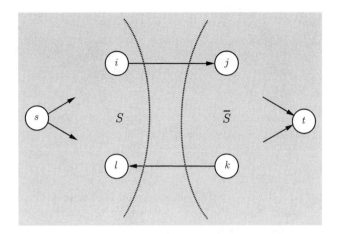

Figure 7.25: Let S and $\overline{S}$ be the sets of labeled and unlabeled nodes, respectively, at termination of the Ford-Fulkerson algorithm. Since j is not labeled, we must have $f_{ij} = u_{ij}$. Since k is not labeled, we must have $f_{kl} = 0$. In particular, all flow moves from s to the rest of S, then to nodes in $\overline{S}$, and finally exits at t.

flow from s to t, when the Ford-Fulkerson algorithm terminates, is equal to $C(S)$. Since the value of the maximum flow can be no higher than $C(S)$ [cf. Eq. (7.14)], we conclude that at termination of the Ford-Fulkerson algorithm, an optimal flow is obtained.

(b) If the optimal value of the flow is infinite, it is not hard to see that there must exist a directed path P from s to t (consisting only of forward arcs), such that every arc in P has infinite capacity. For every cut S, there is an arc (i, j) on the path P such that $i \in S$ and $j \notin S$. Since that arc has infinite capacity, we conclude that $C(S) = \infty$. Since this is true for every cut, we conclude that the minimum cut capacity is infinite and equal to the maximum flow value.

Suppose now that the optimal value, denoted by v^*, is finite. This implies that there exists an optimal solution, that is, a flow whose value is v^*. Let us apply the Ford-Fulkerson algorithm, starting with an optimal flow. Due to optimality of the initial flow, no flow augmentation is possible, and the algorithm terminates with the first iteration. Let S be the set of labeled nodes at termination, as in part (a). From the argument in the proof of part (a), it follows that $C(S) = v^*$. On the other hand, we have $v^* \leq C(S')$ for every cut S'. It follows that $C(S)$ is the minimum cut capacity and is equal to the value of a maximum flow.   □

The proof of the max-flow min-cut theorem did rely on the details of the Ford-Fulkerson algorithm. On the other hand, since this theorem relates the optimal values of two optimization problems, one being a minimization and the other being a maximization problem, it is reminiscent of the duality theorem. Indeed, the max-flow min-cut theorem can be proved by constructing a suitable pair of linear programming problems, dual to each other, and then appealing to the duality theorem (Exercise 7.20).

The complexity of the Ford-Fulkerson algorithm

We close with a discussion of the computational complexity of the Ford-Fulkerson algorithm. We assume that every arc capacity is either integer or infinite, and that the maximum flow value is finite. Let U be the largest of those arc capacities that are finite. The capacity of any cut is either infinite or bounded above by $|\mathcal{A}| \cdot U$. If the maximum flow value is finite, there exists at least one cut with finite capacity, and the value is bounded above by $|\mathcal{A}| \cdot U$. Therefore, there can be at most $|\mathcal{A}| \cdot U$ flow augmentations. Since each flow augmentation involves $O(|\mathcal{A}|)$ computations (to run the labeling algorithm), the overall complexity of the algorithm is $O(|\mathcal{A}|^2 \cdot U)$. Under the stronger assumption that all arcs outgoing from node s have finite capacity, the maximum flow value can be bounded above by $|\mathcal{N}| \cdot U$, by focusing on these arcs. The complexity bound then becomes $O(|\mathcal{A}| \cdot |\mathcal{N}| \cdot U)$.

The linear dependence of our complexity estimate on U is unappealing, especially if U is a large number. Exercise 7.25 develops a related algorithm whose complexity is proportional to the *logarithm* of U. The key idea is to *scale* the arc capacities, leading to a new problem with smaller arc capacities, which is easier to solve, and whose optimal solution provides a near-optimal solution to the original problem.

There is an alternative method that eliminates the dependence on U altogether. As mentioned earlier, if we always choose an augmenting path with the least possible number of arcs, the number of iterations is $O(|\mathcal{A}| \cdot |\mathcal{N}|)$, which implies that the complexity is $O(|\mathcal{A}|^2 \cdot |\mathcal{N}|)$. With proper implementation, this complexity estimate can be further reduced.

7.6 Duality in network flow problems

In this section, we examine the structure of the dual of the network flow problem. For simplicity, we restrict ourselves to the uncapacitated case. We provide interpretations of the dual variables, of complementary slackness, and of the duality theorem. Throughout this section, we let Assumption 7.1 be in effect; that is, the network is assumed to be connected and the supplies satisfy $\sum_{i \in \mathcal{N}} b_i = 0$.

The dual problem

The dual of the uncapacitated network flow problem is

$$\text{maximize} \quad \mathbf{p}'\mathbf{b}$$
$$\text{subject to} \quad \mathbf{p}'\mathbf{A} \leq \mathbf{c}'.$$

Due to the structure of $\mathbf{A}$, the dual constraints are of the form

$$p_i - p_j \leq c_{ij}, \qquad (i,j) \in \mathcal{A}.$$

Suppose that $(p_1, \ldots, p_n)$ is a dual feasible solution. Let θ be some scalar and consider the vector $(p_1 + \theta, \ldots, p_n + \theta)$. It is clear that this is also a dual feasible solution. Furthermore, using the equality $\sum_{i \in \mathcal{N}} b_i = 0$, we have

$$\sum_{i=1}^{n}(p_i + \theta)b_i = \sum_{i=1}^{n}p_i b_i + \theta \sum_{i=1}^{n} b_i = \sum_{i=1}^{n}p_i b_i.$$

Thus, adding a constant to all components of a dual vector is of no consequence as far as dual feasibility or the dual objective is concerned. For this reason, we can and will assume throughout this section that p_n has been set to zero. Note that this is equivalent to eliminating the (redundant) flow conservation constraint for node n.

According to the duality theorem in Chapter 4, if the original problem has an optimal solution, so does the dual, and the optimal value of the objective function is the same for both problems. The example that follows provides an interpretation of the duality theorem in the network context.

Example 7.7 Suppose that we are running a business and that we need to transport a quantity $b_i > 0$ of goods from each node $i = 1, \ldots, n - 1$, to node n through our private network. The solution to the corresponding network flow problem provides us with the best way of transporting these goods.

Consider now a transportation services company that offers to transport goods from any node i to node n, at a unit price of p_i. If (i,j) is an arc in our private network, we can always transport some goods from i to j, at a cost of c_{ij} and then give them to the transportation services company to transport them to node n. This would cost us $c_{ij} + p_j$ per unit of goods. The transportation services company knows $\mathbf{b}$ and $\mathbf{c}$. It wants to take over all of our transportation business, and it sets its prices so that we have no incentive of using arc (i,j). In particular, prices are set so that $p_i \leq c_{ij} + p_j$, and $p_n = 0$. Having ensured that its prices are competitive, it now tries to maximize its total revenue $\sum_{i=1}^{n-1} p_i b_i$. The duality theorem asserts that its optimal revenue is the same as our optimal cost if we were to use our private network. In other words, when the prices are set right, the new options opened up by the transportation services company will not result in any savings on our part.

Sensitivity

We now provide a sensitivity interpretation of the dual variables. In order to establish a connection with the theory of Chapter 5, we assume that we have eliminated the flow conservation constraint associated with node n, and that the remaining equality constraints are linearly independent.

Suppose that $\mathbf{f}$ is a nondegenerate optimal basic feasible solution, associated with a certain tree, and let $\mathbf{p}$ be the optimal solution to the dual.

Consider some node $i \neq n$ and let p_i be the associated dual variable. Let us change the supply b_i to $b_i + \epsilon$, where ϵ is a small positive number, while keeping the supplies $b_2, \ldots, b_{n-1}$ unchanged. The condition $\sum_{i=1}^{n} b_i = 0$ then requires that b_n be changed to $b_n - \epsilon$, but this only affects the nth equality constraint which has already been omitted. As long as we insist on keeping the same basis, the only available option is to route the supply increment ϵ from node i to the root node n, along the unique path determined by the tree. Because of the way that dual variables are calculated [cf. Eq. (7.10) in Section 7.3], the resulting cost change is precisely ϵp_i. This is in agreement with the discussion in Chapters 4 and 5, where we saw that a dual variable is the sensitivity of the cost with respect to changes in the right-hand side of the equality constraints.

By following a similar reasoning, we see that if we increase b_i by ϵ, decrease b_j by ϵ, keep all other supplies unchanged, and use the same basis, the resulting cost change is exactly $\epsilon(p_i - p_j)$, in the absence of degeneracy, and for small ϵ. We conclude that, in the absence of degeneracy, $p_i - p_j$ is the marginal cost of shipping an additional unit of flow from node i to node j.

Complementary slackness

The complementary slackness conditions for the minimum cost network flow problem are the following:

(a) If $p_i \neq 0$, then $[\mathbf{A}\mathbf{f}]_i = b_i$. This condition is automatically satisfied by any feasible flow $\mathbf{f}$.

(b) If $f_{ij} > 0$, then $p_i - p_j = c_{ij}$. This condition is interpreted as follows. We have $p_i - p_j \leq c_{ij}$, by dual feasibility. If $p_i - p_j < c_{ij}$, then there is a way of sending flow from i to j, which is less expensive than using arc (i, j). Hence, that arc should not carry any flow.

From Theorem 4.5 in Section 4.3, we know that $\mathbf{f}$ is primal optimal and $\mathbf{p}$ is dual optimal if and only if $\mathbf{f}$ is primal feasible, $\mathbf{p}$ is dual feasible, and complementary slackness holds. Consider now Figure 7.26, which captures the dual feasibility constraint $p_i - p_j \leq c_{ij}$, the nonnegativity constraint $f_{ij} \geq 0$, and the second complementary slackness condition. We then obtain the following result.

Theorem 7.11 *For any uncapacitated network flow problem, the following are equivalent.*

(a) *The vectors $\mathbf{f}$ and $\mathbf{p}$ are optimal solutions to the primal and the dual problem, respectively.*

(b) *The vector $\mathbf{f}$ satisfies the flow conservation equation $\mathbf{A}\mathbf{f} = \mathbf{b}$, and for every arc (i, j), the pair $(p_i - p_j, f_{ij})$ satisfies the relations indicated by Figure 7.26.*

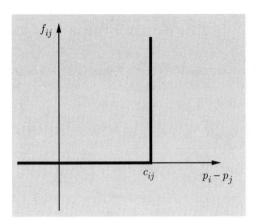

Figure 7.26: Illustration of the complementary slackness conditions. For any arc (i, j), the pair $(p_i - p_j, f_{ij})$ must lie on the heavy line.

A circuit analogy

We now draw an analogy between networks, as defined in this chapter, and electrical circuits. We visualize each node in the network as a place where several "wires" meet, and each arc as a two-terminal circuit element through which current may flow. Let us think of f_{ij} as the current on arc (i, j), and let b_i be the current pumped into the circuit at node i, by means of a current source. Then, the flow conservation equation $\mathbf{Af} = \mathbf{b}$ amounts to Kirchoff's current law. Let us view p_i as an electric potential. In these terms, Figure 7.26 specifies a relation between the "potential difference" $p_i - p_j$ across arc (i, j) and the current through that same arc. Such a relation is very much in the spirit of Ohm's law (potential difference equals current times resistance) except that here the relation between the potential difference and the current is a bit more complicated.

In circuit terms, Theorem 7.11 can be restated as follows. The vectors $\mathbf{f}$ and $\mathbf{p}$ are optimal solutions to the primal and dual problem, respectively, if and only if they are equal to an equilibrium state of an electrical circuit, where each circuit element is described by the relation specified by Figure 7.26. If circuit elements with the properties indicated by Figure 7.26 were easy to assemble and calibrate, we could build a circuit, drive it with current sources, and let it come to equilibrium. This would be an analog device that solves the network flow problem. While such devices do not seem promising at present, the conceptual connections with circuit theory are quite deep, and are valid in greater generality (e.g., in network flow problems with a convex nonlinear cost function).

7.7   Dual ascent methods*

In this section, we introduce a second major class of algorithms for the
network flow problem, based on dual ascent. These algorithms maintain
at all times a dual feasible solution which, at each iteration, is updated in
a direction of increase of the dual objective (such a direction is called a
dual ascent direction), until the algorithm terminates with a dual optimal
solution. Algorithms of this type seem to be among the fastest available.
In this section, we only consider the special case where all arc capacities are
infinite; the reader is referred to the literature for extensions to the general
case.

Recall that the dual of the network flow problem takes the form

$$\text{maximize} \quad \sum_{i=1}^{n} p_i b_i$$
$$\text{subject to} \quad p_i \leq c_{ij} + p_j, \qquad (i,j) \in \mathcal{A}.$$

Given a dual feasible vector $\mathbf{p}$, we are interested in changing $\mathbf{p}$ to a new
feasible vector $\mathbf{p} + \theta \mathbf{d}$, where θ is a positive scalar, and where $\mathbf{d}$ satisfies
$\mathbf{d}'\mathbf{b} > 0$ (which makes $\mathbf{d}$ a dual ascent direction).

Let S be some subset of the set $\mathcal{N} = \{1, \dots, n\}$ of nodes. The *elementary direction* $\mathbf{d}^S$ associated with S is defined as the vector with components

$$d_i^S = \begin{cases} 1, & \text{if } i \in S, \\ 0, & \text{if } i \notin S. \end{cases}$$

Moving along an elementary direction is the same as picking a set S of nodes
and raising the "price" p_i of each one of these nodes by the same amount.
A remarkable property of network flow problems is that the search for a
feasible ascent direction can be confined to the set of elementary directions,
as we now show.

Theorem 7.12 *Let $\mathbf{p}$ be a feasible solution to the dual problem.
Then, either $\mathbf{p}$ is dual optimal or there exists some $S \subset \mathcal{N}$ and some
$\theta > 0$, such that $\mathbf{p} + \theta \mathbf{d}^S$ is dual feasible and $(\mathbf{d}^S)'\mathbf{b} > 0$.*

Proof.   Let $S \subset \mathcal{N}$ and consider the vector $\mathbf{d}^S$. We start by deriving
conditions under which $\mathbf{p} + \theta \mathbf{d}^S$ is feasible for some $\theta > 0$. We only need to
check whether any active dual constraints are violated by moving along $\mathbf{d}^S$.
Note that the dual constraint corresponding to an arc $(i,j) \in \mathcal{A}$ is active
if and only if $p_i = c_{ij} + p_j$, in which case we say that the arc is *balanced*.
Clearly, if (i,j) is a balanced arc and if $i \in S$, raising the value of p_i will
violate the constraint $p_i \leq c_{ij} + p_j$, unless the value of p_j is also raised. We
conclude that dual feasibility of $\mathbf{p} + \theta \mathbf{d}^S$, for some $\theta > 0$, amounts to the

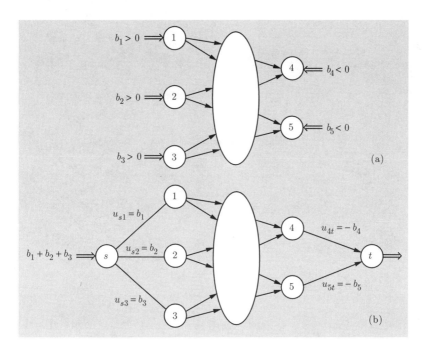

Figure 7.27: (a) A network with some source nodes and some sink nodes, and in which we have only kept the balanced arcs. (b) A corresponding maximum flow problem; all arcs have infinite capacity with the exception of the arcs (s, i) and (j, t), where i is a source and j is a sink in the original network. There is a feasible solution to the problem in (a) if and only if the optimal value in the maximum flow problem in (b) is equal to $V = b_1 + b_2 + b_3$.

following requirement:

$$\text{if } i \in S \text{ and } (i, j) \text{ is balanced,} \quad \text{then } j \in S. \tag{7.15}$$

Let $Q_+ = \{i \in \mathcal{N} \mid b_i > 0\}$ be the set of source nodes and let $Q_- = \{i \in \mathcal{N} \mid b_i < 0\}$ be the set of sink nodes. Let $V = \sum_{i \in Q_+} b_i$ be the total amount of flow that has to be routed from the sources to the sinks. Our first step is to determine whether the entire supply can be routed to the sinks using *only balanced arcs*. This is accomplished by solving a maximum flow problem of the type shown in Figure 7.27.

Let us run the labeling algorithm, starting from a maximum flow **f**. Since we already have a maximum flow, no augmenting path is found and node t remains unlabeled. We partition the set $\{1, \ldots, n\}$ of original nodes into sets S and $\overline{S}$ of labeled and unlabeled nodes, respectively. Then, the situation is as shown in Figure 7.28(a).

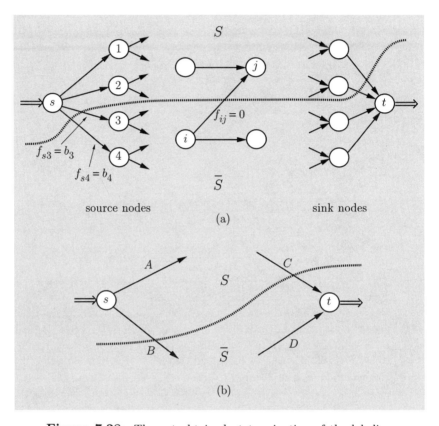

Figure 7.28: The cut obtained at termination of the labeling algorithm, for the network involving only balanced arcs. (a) If a source node i is not labeled, we must have $f_{si} = b_i$ and arc (s, i) is saturated. If a sink node j is labeled, we must have $f_{jt} = |b_j|$ and arc (j, t) is saturated, because otherwise node t would also be labeled. If (i, j) is a balanced arc and if $i \in S$, then we must also have $j \in S$, because otherwise node j would have been labeled (recall that arc capacities are infinite). If (i, j) is a balanced arc and i is not in S, j can be either in S or outside S; if $j \in S$, we must have $f_{ij} = 0$, because otherwise node i would have been labeled. (b) Interpretation of the variables A, B, C, D.

Let

$$A = \sum_{i \in Q_+ \cap S} f_{si}, \qquad\qquad C = \sum_{j \in Q_- \cap S} f_{jt},$$

$$B = \sum_{i \in Q_+ \cap \overline{S}} f_{si}, \qquad\qquad D = \sum_{j \in Q_- \cap \overline{S}} f_{jt};$$

see Figure 7.28(b) for an interpretation. The total flow F that leaves node s is equal to $A + B$. On the other hand, all of the flow must at some point traverse an arc that starts in $\{s\} \cup S$ and ends in $\{t\} \cup \overline{S}$. By adding the flow of all such arcs, we obtain $F = B + C$. We conclude that $A = C$, or

$$\sum_{i \in Q_+ \cap S} f_{si} = \sum_{j \in Q_- \cap S} f_{jt}.$$

For every labeled sink node $j \in Q_- \cap S$, we have $f_{jt} = |b_j| = -b_j$, because otherwise node t would have been labeled, which shows that

$$\sum_{i \in Q_+ \cap S} f_{si} = \sum_{j \in Q_- \cap S} |b_j|.$$

We finally note that

$$(\mathbf{d}^S)'\mathbf{b} = \sum_{i \in S} b_i = \sum_{i \in Q_+ \cap S} b_i - \sum_{j \in Q_- \cap S} |b_j| \geq \sum_{i \in Q_+ \cap S} f_{si} - \sum_{j \in Q_- \cap S} |b_j| = 0.$$

We distinguish between two cases. If $(\mathbf{d}^S)'\mathbf{b} > 0$, we have a dual ascent direction, as desired. On the other hand, if $(\mathbf{d}^S)'\mathbf{b} = 0$, we must have $f_{si} = b_i$ for every $i \in Q_+ \cap S$. Since we also have $f_{si} = b_i$ for every $i \in Q_+ \cap \overline{S}$, it follows that the value of the maximum flow is equal to $V = \sum_{i \in Q_+} b_i$, and we have a feasible solution to the original (primal) network flow problem. In addition, since positive flow is only carried by the balanced arcs, complementary slackness holds, and we have an optimal solution to the primal and the dual problem.   □

Theorem 7.12 leads to a general class of algorithms for the network flow problem.

Dual ascent algorithm

1. A typical iteration starts with a dual feasible solution **p**.
2. Search for a set $S \subset \mathcal{N}$ with the property

    $$\text{if } i \in S \text{ and } (i,j) \text{ is balanced, then } j \in S,$$

    and such that $\sum_{i \in S} b_i > 0$. If no such set S exists, **p** is dual optimal and the algorithm terminates.
3. Update **p** to $\mathbf{p} + \theta^* \mathbf{d}^S$, where θ^* is the largest value for which $\mathbf{p} + \theta \mathbf{d}^S$ is dual feasible. If $\theta^* = \infty$, the algorithm terminates; otherwise, go back to Step 2.

The value of θ^* in the dual ascent algorithm is easily determined, as follows. We consider each constraint $p_i \leq c_{ij} + p_j$. The possibility that $\mathbf{p} + \theta \mathbf{d}^S$ may violate this constraint arises only if $i \in S$ and $j \notin S$. For such pairs (i,j), we need $p_i + \theta \leq c_{ij} + p_j$, and we obtain

$$\theta^* = \min_{\{(i,j) \in \mathcal{A} \mid i \in S \ j \notin S\}} (c_{ij} + p_j - p_i). \tag{7.16}$$

If there is no (i,j) for which $i \in S$ and $j \notin S$, then θ can be taken arbitrarily large, and we let $\theta^* = \infty$. Since we are moving in a direction of dual cost increase, this implies that the optimal dual cost is $+\infty$ and, in particular, the primal problem is infeasible.

Our next results deals with the finite termination of the algorithm.

Theorem 7.13 *Suppose that the optimal cost is finite. If the cost coefficients c_{ij} are all integer, and if the dual ascent algorithm is initialized with an integer dual feasible vector, it terminates in a finite number of steps with a dual optimal solution.*

Proof. Suppose that the algorithm is initialized with an integer vector **p**. Then, the value of θ^* is integer. (It cannot be infinite, because the dual optimal cost would also be infinite, which we assumed not to be the case.) Let $v = \min_S (\mathbf{d}^S)' \mathbf{b}$, where the minimum is taken over all S for which $(\mathbf{d}^S)' \mathbf{b} > 0$. Clearly, v is positive. Since θ^* is integer, every iteration increases the dual objective by at least v. It follows that the algorithm must terminate after a finite number of steps.   □

There are several variations of the dual ascent algorithm which differ primarily in the method that they use to search for an elementary dual ascent direction. If the set S is chosen as in the proof of Theorem 7.12, we have the so-called *primal-dual* method. (When specialized to the assignment problem, it is also known as the *Hungarian* method.) It can be verified that the primal-dual method uses a "steepest" ascent direction, that is, an elementary ascent direction that maximizes $(\mathbf{d}^S)'\mathbf{b}$ (Exercise 7.30). On the other hand, the so-called *relaxation* method tries to discover an elementary ascent direction $\mathbf{d}^S$ as quickly as possible. In one implementation, a one-element set S is tried first. If it cannot provide a direction of ascent, the set is progressively enlarged until an ascent direction is found. In practice, a greedy search of this type pays off and the relaxation method is one of the fastest available methods for linear network flow problems.

In all of the available dual ascent methods, the search for an elementary ascent direction is streamlined and organized by maintaining a nonnegative vector $\mathbf{f}$ of primal flow variables. Throughout the algorithm, the vectors $\mathbf{f}$ and $\mathbf{p}$ are such that the complementary slackness condition $(c_{ij} + p_j - p_i)f_{ij} = 0$ is enforced. (That is, flow is only carried by balanced arcs.) If such a complementary vector $\mathbf{f}$ is primal feasible, we have an optimal solution to both the primal and the dual. For this reason, dual ascent algorithms can be alternatively described by focusing on the vector $\mathbf{f}$, and by interpreting the different steps as an effort to attain primal feasibility. (This is also the historical reason for the term "primal-dual.")

The primal-dual method

In this subsection, we consider in greater depth the primal-dual method. We do that in order to develop a complexity estimate, and also to illustrate how a network algorithm can be made more efficient by suitable refinements.

The primal-dual method is the special case of the dual ascent algorithm, where the set S is chosen exactly as in the proof of Theorem 7.12. In particular, given a dual feasible vector $\mathbf{p}$, we form a maximum flow problem, in which only the balanced arcs are retained, and we let S be the set of nodes in $\{1, \ldots, n\}$ that are labeled at termination of the maximum flow algorithm. We then update the price vector from $\mathbf{p}$ to $\mathbf{p} + \theta^* \mathbf{d}^S$, form a new maximum flow problem, and continue similarly.

We provide some observations that form the basis of efficient implementations of the algorithm.

(a) *The maximum flow and the current dual vector satisfy the complementary slackness condition* $(c_{ij} + p_j - p_i)f_{ij} = 0$. This is because in the maximum flow problem, we only allow flow on balanced arcs.

(b) *If we determine a maximum flow and then perform a dual update, the complementary slackness condition* $(c_{ij} + p_j - p_i)f_{ij} = 0$ *is preserved.* Suppose that an arc (i, j) carries positive flow in the solution to the maximum flow problem under the old prices. In particular, (i, j) must have been a balanced arc before the dual update. Note that $i \in S$ if and only if $j \in S$. (If $i \in S$, then j gets labeled because the arc capacity is infinite; if $j \in S$, then i gets labeled because $f_{ij} > 0$.) This implies that p_i and p_j are changed by the same amount, the arc (i, j) remains balanced, and complementary slackness is preserved.

(c) An important consequence of observation (b) is that subsequent to a dual update, we do not need to solve a new maximum flow problem from scratch. Instead, we use the maximum flow under the old prices as an initial feasible solution to the maximum flow problem under the new prices. Furthermore, the nodes that were labeled at termination of the maximum flow algorithm under the old prices, will be labeled at the first pass of the labeling algorithm under the new prices. [This is because if node j got its label from a node i through a balanced arc (i,j) or (j,i), then p_i and p_j get raised by the same amount, the arc (i,j) or (j,i) remains balanced, and that arc can be used to label j under the new prices.] Our conclusion is that subsequent to a dual update and given the current flow, we do not need to start the labeling algorithm from scratch, but we can readily assign a label to all nodes that were previously labeled.

(d) *A dual update (with $\theta^* < \infty$) results in at least one unlabeled node becoming labeled.* Consider an arc (i,j) with $i \in S$, $j \notin S$, and such that $\theta^* = c_{ij} + p_j - p_i$. Such an arc exists by the definition of θ^*. Subsequent to the dual update, this arc becomes balanced. At the first pass of the labeling algorithm, node j will inherit a label from node i.

The preceding observations lead to a new perspective of the primal-dual method. Instead of viewing the algorithm as a sequence of dual updates, with maximum flow problems solved in between, we can view it as a sequence of applications of the labeling algorithm, resulting in flow augmentations, interrupted by dual updates that create new labeled nodes.

At the beginning of a typical iteration, we have a price vector, a flow vector that only uses balanced arcs, and a set of labeled nodes; these are nodes to which additional flow can be sent, using only balanced arcs. We distinguish two cases:

(a) If node t is labeled, we have discovered an augmenting path and we are not yet at an optimal solution to the maximum flow problem. We push as much flow as possible along the augmenting path. At this point, we delete all labels and start another round of the labeling algorithm, to see whether further flow augmentation is possible.

(b) If node t is not labeled, we have a maximum flow and we perform a dual update. Right after the dual update, we resume with the labeling algorithm, but without erasing the old labels. Recall that a dual update results in at least one new balanced arc (i,j), with node i previously labeled and node j previously unlabeled. Node i remains labeled and j will now become labeled. Since every dual update results in an additional node being labeled, node t will become labeled after at most n dual updates, and a flow augmentation will take place.

We can now get an upper bound on the running time of the algorithm.

Let, as before, V be the sum of the supplies at the source nodes. Assuming that all supplies are integer, there can be at most V flow augmentations. Since there can be at most n dual updates between any two successive flow augmentations, the algorithm terminates after at most nV dual updates. If at each dual update we determine θ^* using Eq. (7.16), we need $O(m)$ arithmetic operations per dual update, and the running time of the algorithm is $O(mnV) = O(n^4 B)$, where $B = \max_i |b_i|$. With a more clever way of computing θ^*, the running time can be brought down to $O(n^3 B)$ (Exercise 7.28). For the assignment problem, we have $B = 1$, and we obtain the so-called Hungarian method, which runs in time $O(n^3)$.

Example 7.8 We go through an example of the primal-dual method. Consider the network shown in Figure 7.29(a), and let us start with the dual vector $\mathbf{p} = (1, 1, 1, 1, 0)$. It is easily checked that we have $p_i \leq c_{ij} + p_j$ for all arcs (i, j), and we therefore have a dual feasible solution. The balanced arcs are $(1, 4)$, $(2, 4)$, $(3, 5)$. In Figure 7.29(b), we form a maximum flow problem involving only the balanced arcs. We solve this problem using the Ford-Fulkerson algorithm. At termination, we obtain the labels and the flows shown in Figure 7.29(c). (Node 2 inherits a label from node 4.) The set of labeled nodes is $S = \{1, 2, 4\}$ and the corresponding elementary direction is $\mathbf{d}^S = (1, 1, 0, 1, 0)$. The only arc (i, j) with $i \in S$, $j \notin S$, is the arc $(2, 5)$, and Eq. (7.16) yields $\theta^* = 2$. The new dual vector is $\mathbf{p} + \theta^* \mathbf{d}^S = (3, 3, 1, 3, 0)$. The arc $(2, 5)$ has now become balanced and all nodes that were labeled remain labeled. Since node 2 is labeled, and arc $(2, 5)$ has become balanced, node 5 gets labeled. Finally, because arc $(5, t)$ is unsaturated ($f_{5t} = 2 < 3 = |b_5|$), node t also gets labeled. At this point, we have identified a path through which additional flow can be shipped, namely the path $s, 1, 4, 2, 5, t$. By shipping one unit of flow along this path, the value of the flow becomes 8. We now have a feasible solution to the original primal problem, which satisfies complementary slackness, and is therefore optimal. If primal feasibility had not been attained, we would erase all labels and rerun the labeling algorithm, in an attempt to discover a new augmenting path.

Comparison with the dual simplex method

Network flow problems (like all linear programming problems) can be solved by the dual simplex method. This is also a dual ascent method, in the sense that it maintains a dual feasible solution and keeps increasing the dual objective. Furthermore, it can be verified that dual updates in the dual simplex method only take place along elementary directions (Exercise 7.31). On the other hand, the dual simplex method can only visit basic feasible solutions in the dual feasible set. In contrast, the methods considered in this section, have more directions to choose from and do not always move along the edges of the dual feasible set.

A key difference between the dual simplex method and the dual ascent methods of this section is in the nature of the auxiliary flow information

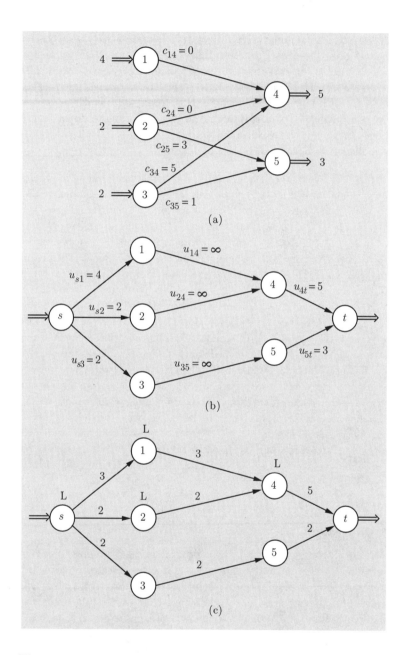

Figure 7.29: Illustration of the primal-dual method in Example 7.8.

that they employ. In the dual simplex method, we maintain a basic solution to the primal; in particular, the flow conservation constraints are always satisfied. If the basic solution is infeasible, it is only because some of the nonnegativity constraints are violated. In contrast, with the dual ascent methods of this section, auxiliary flow variables are always nonnegative, but we allow the flow conservation equations to be violated.

7.8   The assignment problem and the auction algorithm

The auction algorithm, which is the subject of this section, is a method that can be used to solve general network flow problems. We restrict ourselves to a special case, the assignment problem, because it results in a simpler and more intuitive form of the algorithm. The auction algorithm resembles dual ascent methods, except that it only changes the price of a single node at a time. Given a nonoptimal feasible solution to the dual, it is sometimes impossible to find a dual ascent direction involving a single node. For this reason, a typical iteration may result in a temporary deterioration (i.e., decrease) of the dual objective. As long as this deterioration is kept small, the algorithm is guaranteed to make progress in the long run, and can be viewed as an approximate dual ascent method. Our presentation bypasses this approximate dual ascent interpretation, for which the reader is referred to the literature.

The problem

$$\text{minimize} \quad \sum_{i=1}^{n}\sum_{j=1}^{n} c_{ij} f_{ij}$$

$$\text{subject to} \quad \sum_{i=1}^{n} f_{ij} = 1, \qquad j = 1, \ldots, n,$$

$$\sum_{j=1}^{n} f_{ij} = 1, \qquad i = 1, \ldots, n,$$

$$f_{ij} \geq 0, \qquad \forall \, i, j.$$

is known as the *assignment* problem. One interpretation is that there are n persons and n projects and that we wish to assign a different person to each project while minimizing a linear cost function of the form $\sum_{(i,j)} c_{ij} f_{ij}$, where $f_{ij} = 1$ if the ith person is assigned to the jth project, and $f_{ij} = 0$ otherwise. With this interpretation, it would be natural to introduce the additional constraint $f_{ij} \in \{0, 1\}$. However, this is unnecessary for the following reasons. First, the constraint $f_{ij} \leq 1$ is implied by the constraints that we already have. Second, Corollary 7.2 implies that the assignment problem always has an integer optimal solution. In particular, if we solve the assignment problem using the simplex method or the negative cost cycle algorithm, the optimal value obtained for each variable f_{ij} will be zero or one.

Let us now digress to mention an interesting special case of the assignment problem. Suppose that the cost coefficients c_{ij} are either zero or one. The resulting problem is called the *bipartite matching* problem and has the following interpretation. We have $c_{ij} = 0$ if and only if person i is compatible with project j and we are interested in finding as many compatible person-project pairs as possible. If the optimal value turns out to be 0, we say that there exists a *perfect matching*. Besides being an assignment problem, the bipartite matching problem is also a special case of the max-flow problem (send as much flow as possible from persons to projects using only zero cost arcs) and as such it can be also solved using maximum flow algorithms. There are even better special purpose algorithms, which can be found in the literature.

Duality and complementary slackness

We form the dual of the assignment problem. We associate a dual variable r_i with each constraint $\sum_{j=1}^{n} f_{ij} = 1$, and a dual variable p_j to each constraint $\sum_{i=1}^{n} f_{ij} = 1$. Then, the dual problem takes the form

$$\text{maximize} \quad \sum_{i=1}^{n} r_i + \sum_{j=1}^{n} p_j$$
$$\text{subject to} \quad r_i + p_j \leq c_{ij}, \qquad \forall \ i, j.$$

It is clear from the form of the dual constraints that once the values of $p_1, \ldots, p_n$ are determined, $\sum_{i=1}^{n} r_i$ is maximized if we set each r_i to the largest value allowed by the constraints $r_i + p_j \leq c_{ij}$, which is

$$r_i = \min_{j=1,\ldots,n} \{c_{ij} - p_j\}. \tag{7.17}$$

This leads to the following equivalent dual problem:

$$\text{maximize} \quad \sum_{j=1}^{n} p_j + \sum_{i=1}^{n} \min_{j} \{c_{ij} - p_j\}. \tag{7.18}$$

Note that this is an unconstrained problem with a piecewise linear concave objective function.

We now consider the complementary slackness conditions for the assignment problem, which are the following:

(a) flow must be conserved;

(b) if $f_{ij} > 0$, then $r_i + p_j = c_{ij}$.

Using Eq. (7.17) to eliminate r_i, the second complementary slackness condition is equivalent to

$$\text{if } f_{ij} > 0, \quad \text{then } p_j - c_{ij} = -r_i = \max_k \{p_k - c_{ik}\}. \qquad (7.19)$$

Condition (7.19) admits the following interpretation: each project k carries a reward p_k and if person i is assigned to it, there is a cost c_{ik}. The difference $p_k - c_{ik}$ is viewed as the profit to person i derived from carrying out project k. Condition (7.19) then states that each person should be assigned to a most profitable project.

Auction mechanisms

We recall that a pair of primal and dual solutions is optimal if and only if we have primal and dual feasibility, and complementary slackness. Having defined r_i according to Eq. (7.17), dual feasibility holds automatically. Thus, the problem boils down to finding a set of prices p_j and a feasible assignment, for which the condition (7.19) holds. This motivates a bidding mechanism whereby persons bid for the most profitable projects. It can be visualized by thinking about a set of contractors who compete for the same projects and therefore keep lowering the price (or reward) they are willing to accept for any given project.

Naive auction algorithm

1. *Bidding phase.* Given a set of prices $p_1, \ldots, p_n$ for the different projects, and a partial assignment of persons to projects, each unassigned person finds a best project j, that maximizes the profit $p_j - c_{ij}$, and "bids" for it, by accepting a lower price. In particular, the price is lowered by

   (profit of the best project) − (profit of the second best project).

   This is the maximum amount by which the price could be lowered before the best project ceases to be the best one.

2. Following the bidding phase, there is an assignment phase during which every project is assigned to the lowest bidder (if any). The new price of each project is set to the value of the lowest bid. The old holder of the project (if any) now becomes unassigned.

Example 7.9 Consider an assignment problem involving three persons and three objects; see Figure 7.30. Suppose that all p_i are equal to one, that person 1 is assigned to project 1, person 2 is assigned to object 2, and person 3 is unassigned.

Person 3 computes the profits of the different projects; they are $1 - 0 = 1$ for the first and second project, and $1 - 1 = 0$ for the third project. Person 3 bids for the second object. The bid for project 2 cannot be lower than one, because that would make project 2 less profitable than project 1. Hence, the bid is equal to one. Person 3, as the sole bidder, is assigned project 2, and person 2 becomes unassigned. However, there is no price change. In the next iteration, person 2 who is unassigned goes through a similar process, and bids for project 2. The price is again unchanged, and we end up in exactly the same situation as when the algorithm was started.

As Example 7.9 shows, the naive auction algorithm does not always work. The reason is that if there are two equally profitable projects, a bidder cannot lower the price of either, and the algorithm gets deadlocked. However, the algorithm works properly after a simple modification. Let us fix a positive number ϵ. The bid placed for a project is lower by ϵ than what it would have been if we wished that project to remain the best one; as a result, the project comes short, by ϵ, of being the most profitable one. A complete description of the algorithm is given below.

The auction algorithm

1. A typical iteration starts with a set of prices $p_1, \ldots, p_n$ for the different projects, a set S of assigned persons, and a project j_i assigned to each person $i \in S$ (that is, $f_{ij_i} = 1$, $i \in S$). (At the beginning of the algorithm, the set S is empty.)

2. Each unassigned person $i \notin S$ finds a best project k_i by maximizing the profit $p_k - c_{ik}$ over all k. Let k_i' be a second best project, that is,

$$p_{k_i'} - c_{ik_i'} \geq p_k - c_{ik}, \qquad \text{for all } k \neq k_i.$$

   Let
$$\Delta_{k_i} = (p_{k_i} - c_{ik_i}) - (p_{k_i'} - c_{ik_i'}).$$
   Person i "bids" $p_{k_i} - \Delta_{k_i} - \epsilon$ for project i.

3. Every project for which there is at least one bid is assigned to a lowest bidder; the old holder of the project (if any) becomes unassigned. The new price p_i of each project that has received at least one bid is set to the value of the lowest bid.

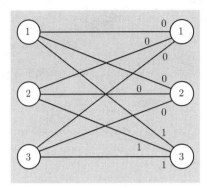

Figure 7.30: An assignment problem. The costs c_{i1} and c_{i2} for the first two projects are zero, for every i. The costs c_{i3} for the third project are equal to one, for every i.

Example 7.10 We apply the auction algorithm to the problem considered in Example 7.9. Once more, we assume that persons 1 and 2 are assigned to projects 1 and 2, respectively, and the initial prices are all equal to 1. Person 3 chooses to bid for project 2 and decreases its price to $1-\epsilon$. Person 2 becomes unassigned and computes the profits of the different projects; they are: $1-0 = 1$, $(1-\epsilon)-0 = 1-\epsilon$, and $1 - 1 = 0$, respectively. Project 1 is the most profitable. Its price is to be brought down so that its profit becomes equal to the profit of the second best project, minus ϵ. Therefore, the bid is equal to $1 - 2\epsilon$.

At the next iteration, person 1, who is unassigned, bids for project 2 and brings its price down to $1 - 3\epsilon$. The same process is then repeated. At each iteration, projects 1 and 2 have prices that are within ϵ of each other. An unassigned person always bids for the one that has the larger price, and brings its price down by 2ϵ. After a certain number of iterations, the prices of projects 1 and 2 become negative. At that point, project 3 finally becomes profitable, receives a bid, becomes assigned, and the algorithm terminates.

Note that a bid pushes the price of a project below the level at which that project would be the most profitable. For this reason, persons will not, in general, be assigned to their most profitable project, and the complementary slackness conditions fail to hold. On the other hand, since persons may underbid only by ϵ, the complementary slackness conditions are close to being satisfied. This motivates our next definition.

Definition 7.3 *Consider a set of prices p_j and a partial assignment where each assigned person $i \in S$ is assigned a project j_i. We say that the ϵ-**complementary slackness** condition holds if we have*

$$p_{j_i} - c_{ij_i} \geq \max_k \{p_k - c_{ik}\} - \epsilon, \qquad \forall\, i \in S.$$

The following result deals with a key property of the auction algorithm.

> **Theorem 7.14** *Throughout the auction algorithm, the ϵ-complementary slackness condition is satisfied.*

Proof. The condition is satisfied initially, before any person is assigned. Whenever a person i is assigned a project j_i, the price is chosen so that the profit $p_{j_i} - c_{ij_i}$ cannot be smaller than the profit of any other project by more than ϵ, assuming the other prices do not change. If the prices of some other projects do change, they can only go down, and project j_i is again guaranteed to be within ϵ of being most profitable. As long as a person holds the same project, the price of that project cannot change, and its profit stays constant. In the meantime, the prices of any other projects can only go down, thus reducing their profits, which means that the person still holds a project whose profit is within ϵ of the maximum profit. □

We also have the following result that ensures the finite termination of the algorithm.

> **Theorem 7.15** *The auction algorithm terminates after a finite number of stages with a feasible assignment.*

Proof. The proof rests on the following observations:

(a) Once a project receives a bid, it gets assigned to some person. Once a project is assigned, it may be later reassigned to another person, but it will never become unassigned. Thus, if all projects have received at least one bid, then all projects are assigned and, consequently, all persons are also assigned.

(b) If all persons are assigned, no person bids and the algorithm terminates.

(c) If the algorithm does not terminate, then some project never gets assigned. Such a project has never received a bid and its price is fixed at its initial value.

(d) If the algorithm does not terminate, some project receives an infinite number of bids. Since every successive bid lowers its price by at least ϵ, the price of such a project decreases to $-\infty$.

Using observations (c) and (d), a project that has never received a bid must eventually become more profitable than any project that receives an infinite number of bids. On the other hand, for a project to receive an infinite number of bids, it must remain more profitable than any project that has not received any bids. This is a contradiction, which establishes that every project will eventually receive a bid. Using observations (a) and (b), the algorithm must eventually terminate with all persons assigned to projects.   □

The preceding proof generalizes to the case where some assignments are not allowed, which is the same as setting some of the coefficients c_{ij} to infinity. However, a slightly more involved argument is needed (see Exercise 7.32).

At termination of the auction algorithm, we have:

(a) primal feasibility (all persons are assigned a project);

(b) dual feasibility (if we define $r_i = \max_k \{p_k - c_{ik}\}$, we have a dual feasible solution);

(c) ϵ-complementary slackness (Theorem 7.14).

If we had complementary slackness instead of ϵ-complementary slackness, linear programming theory would imply that we have an optimal solution. As it turns out, because of the special structure of the problem, ϵ-complementary slackness is enough, when ϵ is sufficiently small.

Theorem 7.16 *If the cost coefficients c_{ij} are integer and if*

$$0 < \epsilon < 1/n,$$

the auction algorithm terminates with an optimal solution.

Proof. Let j_i be the project assigned to person i when the algorithm terminates. Using ϵ-complementary slackness, we have

$$p_{j_i} - c_{ij_i} \geq \max_j \{p_j - c_{ij}\} - \epsilon, \qquad \forall\, i.$$

By adding these inequalities over all i, and rearranging, we obtain

$$\sum_{i=1}^{n} c_{ij_i} \leq \sum_{i=1}^{n} \left(p_{j_i} - \max_j \{p_j - c_{ij}\} \right) + n\epsilon$$

$$= \sum_{i=1}^{n} \left(p_{j_i} + \min_j \{c_{ij} - p_j\} \right) + n\epsilon.$$

Let z be the cost of an optimal assignment. The sum in the right-hand side of the above equation is the same as the dual objective function [cf. Eq. (7.18)] and by weak duality, it is bounded above by the optimal cost z. This implies that

$$\sum_{i=1}^{n} c_{ij_i} \leq z + n\epsilon < z + 1.$$

On the other hand

$$\sum_{i=1}^{n} c_{ij_i} \geq z,$$

by the definition of z. Since z and all c_{ij_i} are integer, we conclude that

$$\sum_{i=1}^{n} c_{ij_i} = z,$$

and optimality has been established. □

Discussion

Let us assume, for simplicity, that $c_{ij} \geq 0$ for all i, j, and let $C = \max_{i,j} c_{ij}$. Suppose that the algorithm is initialized with all projects having the same prices. If some project has received C/ϵ or more bids, then its price is lower than the price of any project that has not received any bids, by at least C. (This is because each bid lowers the price by at least ϵ.) At that point, a project that has not received any bids would become more profitable. We conclude that every project receives at most C/ϵ bids. The total number of bids is at most nC/ϵ. Since there is at least one bid at each iteration, this is also a bound on the number of iterations. Finally, the computational effort per iteration is easily seen to be $O(n^2)$. If we let ϵ be slightly smaller than $1/n$, the version of the auction algorithm that we have described here runs in time $O(n^4 C)$.

The auction algorithm can be sped up using the idea of ϵ-*scaling*. One first uses a relatively large value of ϵ, and obtains a solution which is optimal within $n\epsilon$. (The proof is the same as the proof of Theorem 7.16.) Then, the obtained prices are used to start another solution phase, with a smaller value of ϵ, etc. This device leads to better theoretical running time estimates and also to improved performance in practice.

7.9 The shortest path problem

The shortest path problem is an important problem that arises in a multitude of applications in transportation networks, communication networks, optimal control, as well as a subproblem of more complex problems. As will be seen shortly, it can be posed as a network flow problem. However, practical methods for solving the shortest path problem do not rely on the network flow formulation. Instead, they are centered around a set of optimality conditions, known as Bellman's equation, which are intimately related to the subject of dynamic programming (see Section 11.3). We will use duality to derive Bellman's equation, and we will then proceed to develop a suite of algorithms. Some of these algorithms are of a somewhat ad hoc nature, but they are quite efficient in practice.

Throughout this section, the words walk, path, and cycle will always mean *directed* walk, path, and cycle, respectively; that is, all arcs are traversed in the forward direction. This should not lead to any confusion, because in this section we never need to consider walks, paths, or cycles that are not directed.

Formulation

We are given a directed graph $G = (\mathcal{N}, \mathcal{A})$ with n nodes and m arcs. For each arc $(i,j) \in \mathcal{A}$, we are also given a cost or *length* c_{ij}; in general, the numbers c_{ij} are allowed to be negative. The *length* of a walk, path, or cycle is defined as the sum of the lengths of its arcs. A path from a certain node to another is said to be *shortest* if it has minimum length among all possible paths with the same origin and destination. A *shortest walk* from a node to another is defined similarly. A shortest walk and a shortest path from one node to another are not necessarily the same. In particular, if there exists a cycle with negative length, we can construct walks whose length converges to $-\infty$ (we can traverse the cycle several times before reaching the destination). On the other hand, the length of any path is bounded below by $-nC$, where $C = \max_{(i,j) \in \mathcal{A}} |c_{ij}|$. If all cycles have nonnegative length, there is no incentive to go around a cycle and, for this reason, a shortest path is also a shortest walk. Conversely, any cycles contained in a shortest walk must have zero length; by removing such cycles, we obtain a shortest path.

The shortest path problem can be posed in a few different ways; for example, we might be interested in a shortest path from a given origin to a given destination, or we might be interested in shortest paths from each of a number of selected origins to each of several destinations. We will focus on the problem of finding a shortest path from all possible origins to a particular destination node, which is called the *all-to-one shortest path* problem, as well as on the problem of finding shortest paths for all possible origin destination pairs, which is called the *all-pairs shortest path* problem.

Before continuing, we introduce two more concepts that will prove useful. Consider a tree, and suppose that all arcs are assigned directions so that we have a (directed) path from every node $i \neq n$ to node n. Such a directed graph will be called an *intree rooted at node* n; see Figure 7.31. If it happens that for every $i \neq n$, the path from i to n along the tree is a shortest path, we say that we have a *tree of shortest paths*.

Relation to the network flow problem

We consider here the all-to-one shortest path problem. For concreteness, we assume that node n is the destination node. We also assume that there exists at least one path from every node $i \neq n$ to node n, which means that the all-to-one shortest path problem is feasible. Finally, and without loss of

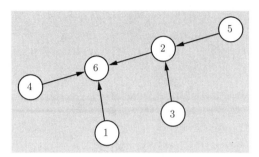

Figure 7.31: An intree rooted at node 6.

generality, we assume that there are no outgoing arcs from node n. These assumptions will remain in effect throughout this section.

We view the graph G as a network of infinite capacity arcs. Suppose that each one of the nodes $1, \ldots, n-1$ is a source node, with unit supply, and that node n is the only sink node, with a demand of $n-1$. If we pose the problem of minimizing $\sum_{(i,j) \in \mathcal{A}} c_{ij} f_{ij}$ over all feasible flow vectors, it should be clear that for every node i other than n, one unit of flow should be shipped from node i to node n, at least cost. As long as there are no negative length cycles, this should be done along a shortest path. If on the other hand, there are negative length cycles, the optimal cost in the network flow problem is $-\infty$, because we could "push" an arbitrarily large amount of flow around such a cycle. This discussion is refined in the following theorem.

Theorem 7.17 *Consider the shortest path problem in a directed graph with n nodes and the associated network flow problem. We assume that there is a path to node n from every other node, and that node n has no outgoing arcs.*

(a) *If there exists a negative length cycle, the optimal cost in the network flow problem is $-\infty$.*

(b) *Suppose that all cycles have nonnegative length. If a feasible tree solution is optimal, then the corresponding tree is a tree of shortest paths.*

(c) *Suppose that all cycles have nonnegative length. If we fix p_n to zero, the dual problem has a unique solution $\mathbf{p}^*$, and p_i^* is the shortest path length from node i.*

Proof. Part (a) is trivial. For part (b), we first note that in a feasible tree solution, all arcs in the tree must be oriented from the leaves towards the root and therefore form an intree rooted at node n. This is because if some arc (i, j) in the tree is pointing away from the root, the flow on that arc must be negative, contradicting feasibility. If for some node i there exists a path from i to n whose length is smaller than that of the path on the tree, the feasible tree solution is not optimal, because some flow could be redirected to that path. Thus, an optimal feasible tree solution provides us with a tree of shortest paths and this proves part (b).

Let $p_n^* = 0$ and let $(p_1^*, \ldots, p_{n-1}^*)$ be the vector of dual variables associated with an optimal feasible tree solution. For each arc on the tree, we have $p_i^* = c_{ij} + p_j^*$. Since all arcs are oriented towards the root, we can add the equalities $p_i^* = c_{ij} + p_j^*$ along a path contained in the tree, and conclude that p_i^* is the length of the path from node i to node n. Note that this is a shortest path, since we are dealing with an optimal feasible tree solution. Thus, p_i^* is the shortest path length.

We finally note that every feasible tree solution is nondegenerate. This is because any arc (i, j) on the tree must carry the supply at node i. It follows that the dual problem has a unique solution.   □

The connection between shortest paths, network flows, and linear programming duality is illustrated by our next example, which arises in practical context.

Example 7.11 (Project management) A project consists of a set of jobs and a set of *precedence relations*. In particular, we are given a set $\mathcal{A}$ of job pairs (i, j) indicating that job i cannot start before job j is completed. Let c_i be the duration of job i. We wish to identify the least possible duration of the project. We will show that this can be accomplished by solving a shortest path problem.

In addition to the original jobs, we introduce two artificial jobs s and t, of zero duration, that signify the beginning and the completion of the project. We augment the set $\mathcal{A}$ by introducing the additional precedence relations (s, i) and (i, t) for all jobs i. Let p_i be the time that job i begins. A precedence relation $(i, j) \in \mathcal{A}$ leads to a constraint $p_j \geq p_i + c_i$, that is, project j cannot begin before the completion time $p_i + c_i$ of project i. The project duration is $p_t - p_s$ and the minimal project duration is obtained by solving the following problem:

$$\begin{aligned} \text{minimize} \quad & p_t - p_s \\ \text{subject to} \quad & p_j - p_i \geq c_i, \qquad \forall \, (i, j) \in \mathcal{A}. \end{aligned}$$

The dual of this problem is

$$\begin{aligned} \text{maximize} \quad & \sum_{(i,j) \in \mathcal{A}} c_i f_{ij} \\ \text{subject to} \quad & \sum_{\{j \mid (j,i) \in \mathcal{A}\}} f_{ji} - \sum_{\{j \mid (i,j) \in \mathcal{A}\}} f_{ij} = b_i, \qquad \forall \, i, \\ & f_{ij} \geq 0, \qquad\qquad\qquad\qquad\qquad\quad \forall \, (i, j) \in \mathcal{A}. \end{aligned}$$

Here, $b_s = -1$, $b_t = 1$, and $b_i = 0$ for $i \neq s, t$. This is a shortest path problem, where each precedence relation $(i, j) \in \mathcal{A}$ corresponds to an arc with cost of $-c_i$. It is natural to assume that the set of arcs $\mathcal{A}$ does not contain any cycles, because otherwise the project cannot be completed. In that case, the network is guaranteed to have no negative cost cycles.

Bellman's equation

Recall that $b_1 = \cdots = b_{n-1} = 1$. Under the convention $p_n = 0$, the dual problem is of the form

$$\text{maximize} \quad \sum_{i=1}^{n-1} p_i$$
$$\text{subject to} \quad p_i \leq c_{ij} + p_j, \qquad \forall \, (i,j) \in \mathcal{A}.$$

It is evident that if all components of $\mathbf{p}$, except for p_i, are fixed to some values, the remaining component p_i should be set to the largest value allowed by the constraints, that is, $\min_{k \in O(i)} \{c_{ik} + p_k\}$. [Recall that $O(i)$ is the set of endpoints of arcs that are outgoing from node i.] We conclude that the optimal solution $\mathbf{p}^*$ to the dual problem, which is the same as the vector of shortest path lengths, satisfies

$$p_i^* = \min_{k \in O(i)} \{c_{ik} + p_k^*\}, \qquad i = 1, \ldots, n-1, \tag{7.20}$$

where $p_n^* = 0$. This is a system of $n-1$ nonlinear equations in $n-1$ unknowns, and is known as *Bellman's equation*. It has a rather intuitive interpretation: suppose that we are interested in paths that start at node i, but that we also impose the additional constraint that the path must start with the arc (i,k). Then, the best we can do is to find a shortest path from node k to n, for a total length of $c_{ik} + p_k^*$. However, since the first node k is of our own choosing, we should make an optimal choice of k, and therefore the length of a shortest path is $\min_{k \in O(i)} \{c_{ik} + p_k^*\}$. The key idea behind Bellman's equation is the so-called *principle of optimality*: if a shortest path from i to n goes through an intermediate node k, then the portion of the path from k to n is also a shortest path.

    We have argued that the shortest path lengths satisfy Bellman's equation. Thus, one possible method of computing shortest path distances is by trying to solve Bellman's equation directly. However, some care is needed, because Bellman's equation may have several solutions, and only one of them will give us the correct shortest path lengths; an example is given in Figure 7.32. It turns out that the shortest path lengths are the unique solution to Bellman's equation if all cycles have positive lengths. If all cycles have nonnegative length, we can only assert that the shortest path lengths are the *largest* solution to Bellman's equation (Exercise 7.33).

The Bellman-Ford algorithm

A common method for solving a system of equations of the form $\mathbf{x} = \mathbf{F}(\mathbf{x})$ is to use the iteration $\mathbf{x} := \mathbf{F}(\mathbf{x})$. If we attempt to solve Bellman's equation

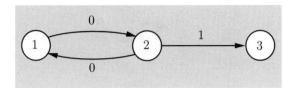

Figure 7.32: Consider a graph with three nodes and let the arc lengths be as indicated. The shortest path lengths to node 3 are $p_1^* = p_2^* = 1$. Bellman's equation is of the form $p_1 = p_2$ and $p_2 = \min\{p_1, 1\}$. It is easily seen that $p_1 = p_2 = \beta$ is a solution to Bellman's equation for every $\beta \leq 1$. Note that the shortest path lengths are the largest solution to Bellman's equation.

in this fashion, we obtain the Bellman-Ford algorithm. In the discussion that follows, we again assume that node n has no outgoing arcs.

Let $p_i(t)$ be the length of a shortest walk from node i to node n that uses at most t arcs; we let $p_i(t) = \infty$ if no such walk exists. We use the convention $p_n(t) = 0$ for all t, and $p_i(0) = \infty$ for all $i \neq n$. Note that $p_i(t+1) \leq p_i(t)$ for all i and t, because as t increases, there are more walks to choose from. A shortest walk from node i to node n that uses at most $t+1$ arcs, consists of an initial arc (i, k) and a walk from node k to node n that consists of at most t arcs. Of course, the latter walk should be chosen as short as possible and its length is therefore $p_k(t)$. Since node k should also be chosen in the most profitable fashion, we have

$$p_i(t+1) = \min_{k \in O(i)} \{c_{ik} + p_k(t)\}, \qquad i = 1, \ldots, n-1,$$

and this equation defines the Bellman-Ford algorithm. We now discuss the termination properties of the algorithm.

(a) Suppose that there are no negative length cycles. Then, there exists a shortest walk, which is also a shortest path, and has at most $n-1$ arcs. In particular, $p_i(n-1) = p_i^*$. Allowing for a walk with n or more arcs cannot reduce the total length, and we have $p_i(n) = p_i(n-1)$ for all nodes.

(b) Suppose that there exists a negative length cycle. Suppose for a moment, that we also have $\mathbf{p}(n) = \mathbf{p}(n-1)$. This implies that $\mathbf{p}(t) = \mathbf{p}(n)$ for all $t \geq n$ and the length of any walk is bounded below. However, in the presence of negative length cycles, there exist walks whose length tends to $-\infty$. This is a contradiction and proves that $\mathbf{p}(n) \neq \mathbf{p}(n-1)$.

By comparing the two cases just discussed, we see that no more than n iterations are needed. If $\mathbf{p}(n) = \mathbf{p}(n-1)$, then $\mathbf{p}(n)$ is the vector of shortest path lengths. (An example is given in Figure 7.33.) If on the other hand $\mathbf{p}(n) \neq \mathbf{p}(n-1)$, we conclude that there exists a negative length cycle.

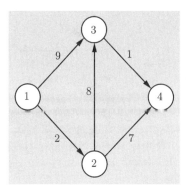

Figure 7.33: We apply the Bellman-Ford algorithm to the graph shown. Node 4 is the destination node. We have $p_4(t) = 0$ for all t, and

$$
\begin{aligned}
p_1(0) &= \infty, & p_1(1) &= \infty, & p_1(2) &= 9, & p_1(3) &= 9, \\
p_2(0) &= \infty, & p_2(1) &= 7, & p_2(2) &= 7, & p_2(3) &= 7, \\
p_3(0) &= \infty, & p_3(1) &= 1, & p_3(2) &= 1, & p_3(3) &= 1.
\end{aligned}
$$

We observe that $\mathbf{p}(3) = \mathbf{p}(2)$ and, therefore, $\mathbf{p}(2)$ is equal to the shortest path length vector $\mathbf{p}^*$.

The computational complexity of the algorithm is $O(mn)$ because there are at most n iterations and at each iteration, each arc is only examined once.

We have focused so far on the computation of the shortest path lengths rather than the shortest paths. The reason is that once the shortest path lengths are available, shortest paths can be determined fairly easily (Exercise 7.34). The task of finding shortest paths is made even easier if in the course of the algorithm, we maintain some information that allows us to backtrack and recover a shortest path. This is done as follows. For every node i, we keep a record of a *successor* node $s(i)$, chosen as the first node in a path whose total length is equal to the current estimate $p_i(t)$ available at node i. Determining a successor node with such a property is simple: whenever we have $p_i(t+1) < p_i(t)$, we delete the old successor of i, if any, and let $s(i)$ be such that $p_i(t+1) = c_{is(i)} + p_{s(i)}(t)$.

As noted earlier, the Bellman-Ford algorithm provides us with a method for checking whether there are any negative length cycles. Besides detecting the existence of a negative length cycle, some applications such as the negative cost cycle algorithm of Section 7.4, require the construction of a negative length cycle. This can be accomplished as follows. Consider a node i for which $p_i(n) < p_i(n-1)$. By starting at node i and going from each node to its successor, we obtain a walk with n arcs whose length is $p_i(n)$. Since there are only n nodes in the graph, this walk must contain a cycle. Suppose that this cycle has nonnegative length. Let us delete the arcs on the cycle and we are left with a walk with fewer than n arcs whose length is no greater than $p_i(n)$. This contradicts the inequality $p_i(n) < p_i(n-1)$. We conclude that by tracing the successors of node i, we will discover a negative length cycle.

Label correcting methods

Label correcting methods are a general class of shortest path algorithms, that have proved to be very efficient in practice. They are similar in spirit to the Bellman-Ford algorithm, but they are more flexible, hence the potential for improved performance.

The key idea is to maintain at each node j, a label p_j equal to the length of the shortest walk from j to n discovered thus far. Given a walk from j to n, of length p_j, there exists a walk from i to n of length $c_{ij} + p_j$. Thus, each time that p_j is revised downwards ("corrected"), we also have an opportunity to revise downwards the labels of all nodes i that have an outgoing arc to node j (the *predecessors* of j). The algorithm maintains a *list* S of all nodes whose labels have been revised downwards, and such that the revision has not yet been propagated to their predecessors. (The list S plays a role similar to the list of labeled but not yet scanned nodes in the labeling algorithm of Section 7.5.)

Label correcting algorithm

The algorithm is initialized with $S = \{n\}$, $p_n = 0$, and $p_i = \infty$ for every $i \neq n$. A typical iteration is as follows.

1. Remove a node j from S.

2. For every node $i \neq n$ such that (i, j) is an arc, do the following. Let $p_i := \min\{p_i, c_{ij} + p_j\}$. If the new value of p_i is smaller, add node i to the set S.

3. If S is empty, the algorithm terminates. Otherwise, go back to Step 1.

The label of a node is always equal to the length of some walk to node n. (Except when the label is infinite, indicating that a path has not yet been discovered.) This is easily shown by induction. Indeed, assuming this to be true before an update, the new label $\min\{p_i, c_{ij} + p_j\}$ is either equal to the length p_i of a previously identified walk, or is equal to the length $c_{ij} + p_j$ of a walk that starts with arc (i, j) and follows a previously identified walk from j to n.

We now establish the finite termination of the algorithm. We assume that all cycles have nonnegative length. Let p_i^0 be the first finite label assigned to node i. Any walk from i to n whose length is less than p_i^0, consists of a path from i to n, an arbitrary number of zero length cycles, and a bounded number of positive length cycles. Since zero length cycles have no effect on the length of the walk, the possible values of p_i that are smaller than p_i^0, are finitely many. This implies that there can only be finitely many downward revisions of each label. After some point, there will be no more revisions, and each iteration will only result in the removal of some node from S. It follows that S eventually becomes empty and the algorithm terminates.

We conclude our analysis, by analyzing the correctness of the algorithm.

Theorem 7.18 *Suppose that there exists a path from every node to node n, and that all cycles have nonnegative length. Then, the label correcting algorithm eventually terminates with the label p_i of each node equal to the shortest path length p_i^*.*

Proof. Consider a shortest path $i_1, i_2, \ldots, i_t = n$ from some node i_1 to n. By the definition of the algorithm, we have $p_n = 0 = p_n^*$, at all times. At the first iteration of the algorithm, we have $S = \{n\}$, the predecessors of n are examined, and we set $p_{i_{t-1}} = c_{i_{t-1}n}$, which is equal to $p_{i_{t-1}}^*$. (This is because the last arc of a shortest path is itself a shortest path.)

Consider now an intermediate node i_k in the path, and suppose that the final label p_{i_k} is equal to $p_{i_k}^*$. Since p_{i_k} was initially infinite, its label has changed at least once. The last time that p_{i_k} was changed, and was set to $p_{i_k}^*$, node i_k entered the set S. When at some later iteration, i_k exited S, $p_{i_{k-1}}$ was set to $\min\{p_{i_{k-1}}, c_{i_{k-1}i_k} + p_{i_k}^*\}$. This is less than or equal to $c_{i_{k-1}i_k} + p_{i_k}^* = p_{i_{k-1}}^*$. On the other hand, $p_{i_{k-1}}$ is the length of some walk, and can be no smaller than $p_{i_{k-1}}^*$. We have therefore completed an inductive proof that $p_{i_k} = p_{i_k}^*$ for all k.   □

The practical efficiency of label correcting methods is highly dependent on the rule used to select a node from the list S. It is interesting to note that for certain rules, including some that have been very successful in practice, the worst-case complexity is exponential in n. The reader is referred to the literature for a more detailed discussion.

Dijkstra's algorithm

Dijkstra's algorithm is an alternative to the Bellman-Ford algorithm and label correcting methods. We will see shortly that Dijkstra's algorithm is more efficient, but can only be applied if all arc lengths are nonnegative, which will be assumed throughout this section. The key idea in Dijkstra's algorithm is to identify the nodes in the order of the corresponding shortest path lengths, starting with a node for which the shortest path length is smallest. In order to simplify the presentation, we assume that c_{ij} is defined for every pair (i, j) of distinct nodes (with $i \neq n$), but may be equal to infinity for some pairs.

Our first step is to show that a node ℓ with a smallest shortest path length is easy to find. Nonnegativity of the arc lengths is crucial here.

Theorem 7.19 *Suppose that $c_{ij} \geq 0$ for all i, j. Let $\ell \neq n$ be such that*

$$c_{\ell n} = \min_{i \neq n} c_{in}.$$

Then, $p_\ell^* = c_{\ell n}$ and $p_\ell^* \leq p_k^*$ for all $k \neq n$.

Proof. Any path to node n has a last arc (i, n) whose length c_{in} is at least $c_{\ell n}$. Thus, $p_k^* \geq c_{\ell n}$ for all $k \neq n$. For node ℓ, we also have $p_\ell^* \leq c_{\ell n}$. We conclude that $p_\ell^* = c_{\ell n} \leq p_k^*$ for all $k \neq n$. $\qquad\square$

Suppose that ℓ and p_ℓ^* have been determined as in Theorem 7.19, and consider an arbitrary node i. One of the options available at that node is to traverse the arc (i, ℓ) and visit node ℓ. Once at node ℓ, we should traverse arc (ℓ, n), because this is a shortest path from ℓ to n. Thus, once an arc (i, ℓ) is traversed, the traversal of arc (ℓ, n) can be assumed to be automatic. We can therefore replace the two arcs (i, ℓ) and (ℓ, n) by a single arc $(i, n)'$ of length $c_{i\ell} + c_{\ell n}$; once we do that for every $i \neq \ell, n$, node ℓ can be taken out of the picture. Note that a node i may now have two direct arcs to node n, the original arc (i, n) as well as the new artificial arc $(i, n)'$. Naturally, any shortest path would only use the least expensive of the two. We therefore remove $(i, n)'$ and replace c_{in} by

$$\min\{c_{in}, c_{i\ell} + c_{\ell n}\}.$$

We are left with a new shortest path problem with one node less. We apply the same process to the new shortest path problem. Each iteration evaluates the shortest path length for one more node and, therefore, after $n - 1$ iterations, the algorithm terminates.

The resulting algorithm is summarized next.

Dijkstra's algorithm

1. Find a node $\ell \neq n$ such that $c_{\ell n} \leq c_{in}$ for all $i \neq n$. Set $p_\ell^* = c_{\ell n}$.
2. For every node $i \neq \ell, n$, set

$$c_{in} := \min\{c_{in}, c_{i\ell} + c_{\ell n}\}.$$

3. Remove node ℓ from the graph and apply the same steps to the new graph.

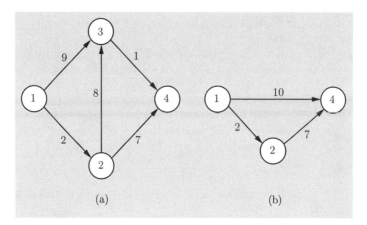

Figure 7.34: (a) A graph with arc lengths. The arcs that are not shown have infinite length. (b) The graph obtained after one iteration of Dijkstra's algorithm.

Example 7.12 We apply Dijkstra's algorithm to graph shown in Figure 7.34(a), with node $n = 4$ being the destination node. We have $\ell = 3$ and $p_3^* = 1$. The following arc lengths are modified: $c_{14} := \min\{\infty, 9 + 1\} = 10$ and $c_{24} := \min\{7, 8 + 1\} = 7$. We now eliminate node 3 and obtain the graph shown in Figure 7.34(b). We obtain $\ell = 2$ and $p_2^* = 7$. The arc length c_{14} is modified by $c_{14} := \min\{10, 2 + 7\} = 9$. Node 2 is eliminated. Since node 1 is the only nonterminal node left, p_1^* is equal to the current value of c_{14}, which is 9.

We now estimate the computational complexity of the Dijkstra algorithm. A typical iteration starts by comparing the coefficients c_{in} and this takes $O(n)$ time. Having determined ℓ, we need to update c_{in} for each node i. We conclude that there are only $O(n)$ arithmetic operations per iteration. The overall complexity is $O(n^2)$, which is one order of magnitude better than the Bellman-Ford algorithm. For a dense graph with $\Omega(n^2)$ arcs, any shortest path algorithm needs $\Omega(n^2)$ arithmetic operations because, in general, every arc has to be examined at least once. Thus, for dense graphs, Dijkstra's algorithm is the best possible.

For sparse graphs, that is, when m is much smaller than n, the computational complexity of Dijkstra's algorithm can be brought down to $O(m \log n)$. Doing so requires keeping the coefficients c_{in} in a suitable data structure that allows us to obtain the smallest such coefficient with minimal work.

Reduction to the case of nonnegative arc lengths and the all-pairs problem

Suppose that some of the arc lengths are negative, but that all cycles have nonnegative length. Let p_i^* be the shortest path length from node i to node

n. From Bellman's equation, we have

$$p_i^* \leq c_{ij} + p_j^*, \qquad (7.21)$$

for all arcs (i, j). Let us now construct a new shortest path problem in which the arc lengths c_{ij} are replaced by new arc lengths $\bar{c}_{ij}$, defined by

$$\bar{c}_{ij} = c_{ij} + p_j^* - p_i^*.$$

Using Eq. (7.21), we have $\bar{c}_{ij} \geq 0$ for all $(i, j) \in \mathcal{A}$. Under the new arc lengths, the length of any path $i_1, \ldots, i_t$ from some node i_1 to some other node i_t is given by

$$\sum_{\tau=1}^{t-1} \bar{c}_{i_\tau i_{\tau+1}} = \sum_{\tau=1}^{t-1} (c_{i_\tau i_{\tau+1}} + p_{i_{\tau+1}}^* - p_{i_\tau}^*) = p_{i_t}^* - p_{i_1}^* + \sum_{\tau=1}^{t-1} c_{i_\tau i_{\tau+1}}.$$

In particular, for any given pair of nodes, a shortest path under the new arc lengths is a shortest path under the old arc lengths, and conversely. Since the new arc lengths are nonnegative, we are in a position to apply Dijkstra's algorithm.

If we are only interested in a single destination, the transformation that we have just described is of no particular use. On the other hand, if we are interested in the all-pairs problem, we can solve a single all-to-one problem, using the Bellman-Ford algorithm, transform the arc lengths, and finally solve $n - 1$ additional all-to-one problems (one problem for every possible destination) using Dijkstra's algorithm. The overall complexity is $O(n^3) + (n - 1) \cdot O(n^2) = O(n^3)$. This is much better than applying the Bellman-Ford algorithm n times, which would require $O(n^4)$ time. For sparse graphs, the running time can be brought down to $O(nm \log n)$ by using an efficient implementation of Dijkstra's algorithm. An alternative $O(n^3)$ algorithm for the all-pairs problem is developed in Exercise 7.38.

7.10   The minimum spanning tree problem

We are given a connected *undirected* graph $G = (\mathcal{N}, \mathcal{E})$, with n nodes. For each edge $e \in \mathcal{E}$, we are also given a cost coefficient c_e. (Recall that an edge in an undirected graph is an unordered pair $e = \{i, j\}$ of distinct nodes in $\mathcal{N}$.) A *minimum spanning tree* (MST) is defined as a spanning tree such that the sum of the costs of its edges is as small as possible.

The minimum spanning tree problem arises naturally in many applications. For example, if edges correspond to communication links, a spanning tree is a set of links that allows every node to communicate (possibly, indirectly) to every other node. Then, a minimum spanning tree is a communication network that provides this type of connectivity, and whose cost is the smallest possible. The minimum spanning tree problem also arises as a subproblem of more complex, seemingly unrelated, problems. An example will be seen in Section 11.5, where it forms a basis for a heuristic for the traveling salesman problem.

Even though the MST problem is not a network flow problem, we include it in this chapter, because of its graph-theoretic structure. We will see that it can be solved by means of a simple *greedy* algorithm. A greedy algorithm is one consisting of a sequence of choices that appear to be best in the short run. For certain problems, like the MST, short run optimal decisions turn out to be optimal in the long run as well. The algorithm that we describe builds an MST by progressively adding edges to a current tree. At any stage, we have a tree and we add a least expensive edge that connects a node in the tree with a node outside the tree.

Greedy algorithm for the minimum spanning tree problem

1. The input to the algorithm is a connected undirected graph $G = (\mathcal{N}, \mathcal{E})$ and a coefficient c_e for each edge $e \in \mathcal{E}$. The algorithm is initialized with a tree $(\mathcal{N}_1, \mathcal{E}_1)$ that has a single node and no edges ($\mathcal{E}_1$ is empty).

2. Once $(\mathcal{N}_k, \mathcal{E}_k)$ is available, and if $k < n$, we consider all edges $\{i, j\} \in \mathcal{E}$ such that $i \in \mathcal{N}_k$ and $j \notin \mathcal{N}_k$. Choose an edge $e^* = \{i, j\}$ of this type whose cost is smallest. Let

$$\mathcal{N}_{k+1} = \mathcal{N}_k \cup \{j\}, \qquad \mathcal{E}_{k+1} = \mathcal{E}_k \cup \{e^*\}.$$

Since at each stage we connect a node in the current tree with a node outside the tree, no cycles are ever formed, and we always have a tree. The set $\mathcal{N}_n$ has n elements and, therefore, $(\mathcal{N}_n, \mathcal{E}_n)$ is a spanning tree. It remains to show that it is a minimum spanning tree. This is accomplished by showing a somewhat stronger property.

Theorem 7.20 *For $k = 1, \dots, n$, the tree $(\mathcal{N}_k, \mathcal{E}_k)$ is part of some MST. That is, there exists an MST $(\mathcal{N}, \overline{\mathcal{E}}_k)$ such that $\mathcal{E}_k \subset \overline{\mathcal{E}}_k$.*

Proof. The proof uses induction on k. The result is trivially true for $k = 1$, because the empty set $\mathcal{E}_1$ is a subset of the edge set of any spanning tree.

Suppose now that $k < n$, and that $\mathcal{E}_k$ is a subset of some MST $\overline{\mathcal{E}}_k$. [We are slightly abusing terminology by referring to $\overline{\mathcal{E}}_k$, instead of $(\mathcal{N}, \overline{\mathcal{E}}_k)$, as a spanning tree.] Let $e^* = \{i, j\}$ be the edge added to $\mathcal{E}_k$; that is, $i \in \mathcal{N}_k$, $j \notin \mathcal{N}_k$, and $\mathcal{E}_{k+1} = \mathcal{E}_k \cup \{e^*\}$. If $e^* \in \overline{\mathcal{E}}_k$, then $\mathcal{E}_{k+1}$ is also a subset of $\overline{\mathcal{E}}_k$, and the induction hypothesis is verified for $k + 1$, with $\overline{\mathcal{E}}_{k+1} = \overline{\mathcal{E}}_k$.

Suppose now that $e^* \notin \overline{\mathcal{E}}_k$. Then, e^*, together with $\overline{\mathcal{E}}_k$, forms a unique cycle [Theorem 7.1(d)]. This cycle must contain a second edge (call it $\overline{e}$) with one endpoint in $\mathcal{N}_k$ and another outside $\mathcal{N}_k$; see Figure 7.35. Since

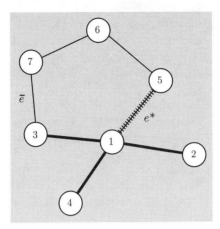

Figure 7.35: The thicker edges correspond to a tree $(\mathcal{N}_4, \mathcal{E}_4)$ involving 4 nodes. This is assumed to be part of an MST $\overline{\mathcal{E}}_4$, which consists of all edges shown, with the exception of e^*. If the algorithm selects e^*, its cost can be no greater than the cost of $\overline{e}$, and $\mathcal{E}_4 \cup \{e^*\}$ is part of an alternative MST, in which $\overline{e}$ is replaced by e^*.

the algorithm selected e^* rather than $\overline{e}$ to be added to $\mathcal{E}_k$, we must have $c_{e^*} \leq c_{\overline{e}}$. Let us now take the MST $\overline{\mathcal{E}}_k$, delete edge $\overline{e}$, and replace it by e^*. We obtain a new spanning tree, call it $\overline{\mathcal{E}}_{k+1}$, and the cost change is $c_{e^*} - c_{\overline{e}} \leq 0$. By the optimality of $\overline{\mathcal{E}}_k$, we must have $c_{e^*} = c_{\overline{e}}$, and both spanning trees are optimal. We now note that $\mathcal{E}_{k+1}$ is a subset of the MST $\overline{\mathcal{E}}_{k+1}$, and the induction is complete. $\qquad\square$

Having proved the correctness of the algorithm, we now discuss its computational complexity. We have $n - 1$ iterations. At each iteration, we need to examine each edge to see whether it is eligible for becoming part of the tree, and we then need to find the least expensive one, which can all be done in time $O(n^2)$. Thus, the overall complexity is $O(n^3)$. With a more clever implementation, it can be brought down to $O(n^2)$; see Exercise 7.39.

7.11 Summary

In this chapter, we provided an overview of a broad range of topics related to network flow problems, and we have covered most of the major available methodologies.

Network flow problems are special cases of linear programming problems, and can be solved by applying general purpose methods, suitably tuned to exploit the network structure. For example, the primal or the dual simplex method can be used. As we have pointed out, the underlying network structure allows for simple and efficient rules for updating the basic variables and the reduced costs. In addition, when the problem data are integer, integer arithmetic can also be employed.

An important property of network flow problems that we discovered in the course of our development, relates to integrality of basic solutions. Assuming that problem data are integer, we have shown that basic solutions to the primal and the dual have integer coordinates. The key reason behind this property is that the determinant of any basis matrix $\mathbf{B}$ has unit magnitude. Unfortunately, there are only precious few classes of linear programming problems that have such remarkable properties.

Besides fine tuning the simplex method, we also developed some algorithms that are specially tailored to network flow problems. These include the negative cost cycle algorithm of Section 7.4 and the dual ascent methods of Section 7.7. These two methods are dual to each other in many ways that can be made mathematically precise, but which are beyond our scope. Nevertheless, it is important to point out a common feature. In both methods, a direction of improvement is identified by examining only a finite number of possible directions, which are independent of the numerical values of the input data. (In the negative cost cycle algorithm, the directions considered correspond to simple circulations. In dual ascent methods, the directions considered correspond to subsets of the set of nodes.)

Both the negative cost cycle algorithm and the dual ascent methods can be described at a high level of generality, while leaving a lot of freedom on how to choose a cycle or a dual ascent direction. By making some more specific choices, the worst-case number of iterations can be reduced. Furthermore, the search for a direction of cost improvement, carried out in the course of each iteration, usually has a lot of room for increased efficiency. (An example of this is our development of the primal-dual method, where the search for an ascent direction is implemented by means of an auxiliary maximum flow problem and the labeling algorithm.) Such refinements lead to improved worst-case complexity bounds. It should be kept in mind, however, that worst-case complexity bounds may not accurately reflect the performance of an algorithm in practice.

The network flow problem contains some important special cases that can be solved by suitable special purpose algorithms. We saw the Ford-Fulkerson algorithm for the maximum flow problem, the auction algorithm for the assignment problem, and a number of (somewhat ad hoc) methods for the shortest path problem. Auction algorithms can also be developed for the general network flow problem, but this is a direction that we did not pursue.

The minimum spanning tree problem is somewhat disjoint from the rest of the chapter. It was included because of its importance, and also because it shares an underlying graph-theoretic structure.

7.12   Exercises

Exercise 7.1 (The caterer problem) A catering company must provide to a client r_i tablecloths on each of N consecutive days. The catering company can buy new tablecloths at a price of p dollars each, or launder the used ones. Laundering can be done at a fast service facility that makes the tablecloths unavailable for the next n days and costs f dollars per tablecloth, or at a slower facility that makes tablecloths unavailable for the next m days (with $m > n$) at a cost of g dollars per tablecloth ($g < f$). The caterer's problem is to decide how to meet the client's demand at minimum cost, starting with no tablecloths and under the assumption that any leftover tablecloths have no value.

(a) Show that the problem can be formulated as a network flow problem. *Hint:* Use a node corresponding to clean tablecloths and a node corresponding to dirty tablecloths for each day; more nodes may also be needed.

(b) Show explicitly the form of the network if $N = 5$, $n = 1$, $m = 3$.

Exercise 7.2 Consider a wood product company that owns M forest units and wants to find an optimal cutting schedule over a period of K years. Forest unit i is predicted to have a_{ij} tons of wood available for harvesting during period j. The company wants to meet a demand of d_j tons during year j. However, due to capacity limitations, it can only harvest up to u_j tons during that year. Wood harvested in past years can be stored and used to meet demand in subsequent years, but there is a cost of c_j for storing one ton of wood between year $j - 1$ and j. We also assume that wood that is available but not harvested during a year remains available for harvesting in later years. Formulate the problem of determining a minimum cost harvesting schedule that meets the demand as a network flow problem.

Exercise 7.3 (The tournament problem) Each of n teams plays against every other team a total of k games. Assume that every game ends in a win or a loss (no draws) and let x_i be the number of wins of team i. Let X be the set of all possible outcome vectors $(x_1, \ldots, x_n)$. Given an arbitrary vector $(x_1, \ldots, x_n)$, we would like to determine whether it belongs to X, that is, whether it is a possible tournament outcome vector. Provide a network flow formulation of this problem.

Exercise 7.4 (Piecewise linear convex costs)

(a) Consider the capacitated network flow problem except that the cost at each arc is a piecewise linear convex function of the flow on that arc. Show that the problem can be reduced to one with linear costs, but in which we allow multiple arcs with the same start node and end node.

(b) Show that a capacitated problem in which we have multiple arcs with the same start node and end node can be reduced to a problem without any such multiple arcs.

Exercise 7.5 (Equivalence of uncapacitated network flow and transportation problems) Consider an uncapacitated network flow problem and assume that $c_{ij} \geq 0$ for all arcs. Let S_+ and S_- be the sets of source and sink nodes, respectively. Let d_{ij} be the length of a shortest directed path from node $i \in S_+$ to node $j \in S_-$. We construct a transportation problem with the same source and sink nodes, and the same values for the supplies and the demands. For every source node i and every sink node j, we introduce a direct link with cost d_{ij}. Show that the two problems have the same optimal cost.

Exercise 7.6 (Equivalence of capacitated network flow and transportation problems) Consider a capacitated network flow problem defined by a graph $G = (\mathcal{N}, \mathcal{A})$ and the data u_{ij}, c_{ij}, b_i. Assume that the capacity u_{ij} of every arc is finite. We construct a related transportation problem as follows. For every arc $(i, j) \in \mathcal{A}$, we form a source node in the transportation problem with supply u_{ij}. For every node $i \in \mathcal{N}$, we construct a sink node with demand $\sum_{\{k|(i,k)\in\mathcal{A}\}} u_{ik} - b_i$. At every supply node (i, j) there are two outgoing infinite capacity arcs: one goes to demand node i, and its cost coefficient is 0; the other goes to demand node j and its cost coefficient is c_{ij}. See Figure 7.36 for an illustration.

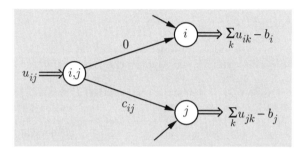

Figure 7.36: The transportation problem in Exercise 7.6.

Show that that there is a one-to-one correspondence between feasible flows in the two problems and that the cost of the two corresponding flows is the same.

Exercise 7.7 (Lower bounds on arc flows) Consider a network flow problem in which we impose an additional constraint $f_{ij} \geq d_{ij}$ for every arc (i, j). Construct an equivalent network flow problem in which there are no nonzero lower bounds on the arc costs. *Hint:* Let $\overline{f}_{ij} = f_{ij} - d_{ij}$ and construct a new network for the arc flows $\overline{f}_{ij}$. How should b_i be changed?

Exercise 7.8 Consider a transportation problem in which all cost coefficients c_{ij} are positive. Suppose that we increase the supply at some source nodes and the demand at some sink nodes. (In order to maintain feasibility, we assume that the increases are such that total demand is equal to total supply.) Is it true that the value of the optimal cost will also increase? Prove or provide a counterexample.

Exercise 7.9 Consider the uncapacitated network flow problem shown in Figure 7.37. The label next to each arc is its cost.

(a) What is the matrix $\mathbf{A}$ corresponding to this problem?

(b) Solve the problem using the network simplex algorithm. Start with the tree indicated by the dashed arcs in the figure.

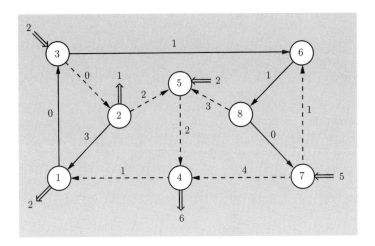

Figure 7.37: The network flow problem in Exercise 7.9.

Exercise 7.10 Consider the uncapacitated network flow problem shown in Figure 7.38. The label next to each arc is its cost. Consider the spanning tree indicated by the dashed arcs in the figure and the associated basic solution.

(a) What are the values of the arc flows corresponding to this basic solution? Is this a basic feasible solution?

(b) For this basic solution, find the reduced cost of each arc in the network.

(c) Is this basic solution optimal?

(d) Does there exist a nondegenerate basic feasible solution?

(e) Find an optimal dual solution.

(f) By how much can we increase c_{56} [the cost of arc $(5,6)$] and still have the same optimal basic feasible solution?

(g) If we increase the supply at node 1 and the demand at node 9 by a small positive amount δ, what is the change in the value of the optimal cost?

(h) Does this problem have a special structure that makes it simpler than the general uncapacitated network flow problem?

Exercise 7.11 (Degeneracy in a transportation problem) Consider a transportation problem with two source nodes s_1, s_2, and n demand nodes $1, \ldots, n$. All arcs (s_i, j) are assumed to be present and to have infinite capacity. Let $D = \sum_{i=1}^{n} d_i$ be the total demand. Let the supply at each source node be equal to $D/2$.

(a) How many basic variables are there in a basic feasible solution?

(b) Show that there exists a degenerate basic feasible solution if and only if there exists some set $S \subset \{1, \ldots, n\}$ such that $\sum_{i \in S} d_i = D/2$.

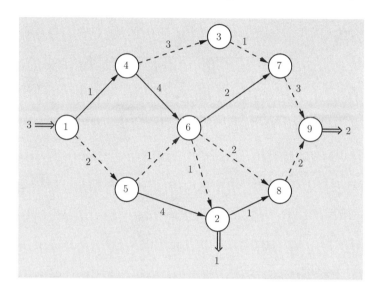

Figure 7.38: The network flow problem in Exercise 7.10.

Exercise 7.12 * (Degeneracy in the assignment problem) Consider the polyhedron $P \subset \Re^{k^2}$ defined by the constraints

$$\sum_{i=1}^{k} f_{ij} = 1, \qquad j = 1, \ldots, k,$$

$$\sum_{j=1}^{k} f_{ij} = 1, \qquad i = 1, \ldots, k,$$

$$f_{ij} \geq 0, \qquad i, j = 1, \ldots, k.$$

(a) Show that P has $k!$ basic feasible solutions and that if $k > 1$, every basic feasible solution is degenerate.

(b) Show that there are $2^{k-1}k^{k-2}$ different bases that lead to any given basic feasible solution.

Exercise 7.13 Suppose that we are given a noninteger optimal solution to an uncapacitated network flow problem with integer data.

(a) Show that there exists a cycle with every arc on the cycle carrying a positive flow. What can you say about the cost of such a cycle?

(b) Suggest a method for constructing an integer optimal solution, without solving the problem from scratch. *Hint:* Remove cycles.

Exercise 7.14 (Decomposition of circulations) Let **A** be the node-arc incidence matrix associated with a directed graph with m arcs. Suppose that a vector $\mathbf{f}$ satisfies $\mathbf{Af} = \mathbf{0}$. Show that there exists a nonnegative integer k (with $k \le m$), cycles $C_1, \ldots, C_k$, and nonnegative scalars $a_1, \ldots, a_k$, such that:

(i) $\mathbf{f} = \sum_{i=1}^{k} a_i \mathbf{h}^{C_i}$,

(ii)   for every arc (k, ℓ) on a cycle C_i, $h_{k\ell}^{C_i}$ and $f_{k\ell}$ have the same sign.

Furthermore, show that if $\mathbf{f}$ is an integer vector, then the coefficients $a_1, \ldots, a_k$ can be chosen to be integer. *Hint:* Reverse the arcs that carry negative flow and apply Lemma 7.1.

Exercise 7.15 (Flow decomposition theorem) State and prove a result analogous to the flow decomposition theorem in Exercise 7.14, for the case of a flow vector $\mathbf{f}$ that satisfies $\mathbf{Af} = \mathbf{b}$. *Hint:* Besides cycles, use paths as well.

Exercise 7.16 * (Negative cost cycle algorithm under the largest improvement rule) Consider the variant of the negative cost cycle algorithm in which we always choose a cycle C with the largest value of $\delta(C)|\mathbf{c}'\mathbf{h}^C|$. Let $\mathbf{f}$ be the current flow and let $\mathbf{f}^*$ be an optimal flow.

(a) Show that $\mathbf{f}^* - \mathbf{f}$ is equal to a nonnegative linear combination of at most m simple circulations, where m is the number of arcs. Furthermore, each such simple circulation is associated with an unsaturated cycle. *Hint:* Use the result in Exercise 7.14.

(b) Show that under the largest improvement rule, the cost improvement at each iteration is at least $(\mathbf{c}'\mathbf{f} - \mathbf{c}'\mathbf{f}^*)/m$.

(c) Assuming that all problem data are integer, show that the algorithm terminates after $O\big(m\log(mCU)\big)$ iterations, where C and U are upper bounds for $|c_{ij}|$ and u_{ij}, respectively.

Exercise 7.17 Consider a network flow problem and assume that there exists at least one feasible solution. We wish to show that the optimal cost is $-\infty$ if and only if there exists a negative cost directed cycle such that every arc on the cycle has infinite capacity.

(a) Provide a proof based on the flow decomposition theorem.

(b) For uncapacitated problems, provide a proof based on the network simplex method.

Exercise 7.18 Show that there is a one-to-one correspondence between augmenting paths in the maximum flow algorithm and negative cost unsaturated cycles in the network flow formulation of the maximum flow problem.

Exercise 7.19 Consider the maximum flow problem. Describe an algorithm with $O(|\mathcal{A}|)$ running time that determines whether the value of the maximum flow is infinite.

Exercise 7.20 (Duality and the max-flow min-cut theorem) Consider the maximum flow problem.

(a) Let p_i be a price variable associated with the flow conservation constraint at node i. Let q_{ij} be a price variable associated with the capacity constraint at arc (i, j). Write down a minimization problem, with variables p_i and q_{ij}, whose dual is the maximum flow problem.

(b) Show that the optimal value in the minimization problem is equal to the minimum cut capacity, and prove the max-flow min-cut theorem.

Exercise 7.21 (Finding a feasible solution) Show that a feasible solution to a capacitated network problem (if one exists) can be found by solving a maximum flow problem.

Exercise 7.22 (Connectivity and vulnerability) Consider a directed graph, and let us fix an origin node s and a destination node t. We define the *connectivity* of the graph as the maximum number of directed paths from s to t that do not share any nodes. We define the *vulnerability* of the graph as the minimum number of nodes (besides s and t) that need to be removed so that there exists no directed path from s to t. Prove that connectivity is equal to vulnerability. *Hint:* Convert the connectivity problem to a maximum flow problem.

Exercise 7.23 (The marriage problem) A small village has n unmarried men, n unmarried women, and m marriage brokers. Each broker knows a subset of the men and women and can arrange up to b_i marriages between any pair of men and women that she knows. Assuming that marriages are heterosexual and that each person can get married at most once, we are interested in determining the maximum number of marriages that are possible. Show that the answer can be found by solving a maximum flow problem.

Exercise 7.24 * (König-Egerváry theorem) Consider an $m \times n$ matrix whose entries are zero or one. We refer to a row or a column as a *line*. We say that a set of lines is a *cover* if every unit entry lies on one of the lines in the set. A set of unit entries are called *independent* if no two of them lie on the same line. Prove that the maximum cardinality of an independent set is equal to the smallest cardinality of a cover. *Hint:* Formulate an appropriate maximum flow problem.

Exercise 7.25 (The scaling method for the maximum flow problem) This exercise illustrates the *scaling method*, a common technique for reducing the complexity of network flow algorithms.

Consider a maximum flow problem Π. Let n be the number of nodes, let u_{ij} be the capacity of arc (i, j), assumed integer, and let v be the value of a maximum flow. We construct a scaled problem Π_s in which the capacity of each arc (i, j) is $\lfloor u_{ij}/2 \rfloor$, and we let v_s be the corresponding optimal value. (The notation $\lfloor a \rfloor$ stands for the largest integer k that satisfies $k \leq a$.)

(a) Consider an optimal flow for the problem Π_s, and multiply it by 2. Show that the result is a feasible flow for the original problem Π.

(b) Show that $2v_s \leq v \leq 2v_s + n^2$.

(c) Consider running the Ford-Fulkerson algorithm on problem Π, starting with the feasible flow described in (a). How many flow augmentations will be needed, and what is the total computational effort?

(d) Show how to solve the maximum flow problem with a total of $O(n^4 \log U)$ arithmetic operations, where U is an upper bound on the capacities u_{ij}.

Exercise 7.26 * (**Birkhoff-von Neumann theorem**) A square matrix $\mathbf{A}$ is called *doubly stochastic* if $\sum_{i=1}^{n} a_{ij} = 1$ for all j, $\sum_{j=1}^{n} a_{ij} = 1$ for all i, and all entries are nonnegative. A matrix $\mathbf{P}$ is called a *permutation matrix* if each row and each column has exactly one nonzero entry, which is equal to 1.

(a) Let $\mathbf{P}_1, \ldots, \mathbf{P}_k$ be permutation matrices, and let $\lambda_1, \ldots, \lambda_k$ be nonnegative scalars that sum to 1. Show that $\sum_{i=1}^{k} \lambda_i \mathbf{P}_i$ is doubly stochastic.

(b) Let $\mathbf{A}$ be a doubly stochastic matrix. Show that there exist permutation matrices $\mathbf{P}_1, \ldots, \mathbf{P}_k$, and nonnegative scalars $\lambda_1, \ldots, \lambda_k$ that sum to 1, such that $\mathbf{A} = \sum_{i=1}^{k} \lambda_i \mathbf{P}_i$. *Hint:* Consider the assignment problem.

Exercise 7.27 Consider the transportation problem shown in Figure 7.39, and solve it using the primal-dual method. Use $\mathbf{p} = (1, 1, 0, 0)$ to start the algorithm.

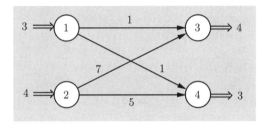

Figure 7.39: The transportation problem in Exercise 7.27. Arc costs are shown next to each arc.

Exercise 7.28 This exercise develops a more efficient method for computing θ^* in the primal-dual method. Let S be the set of nodes whose prices are to increase, as in the description of the general dual ascent algorithm. For every $j \notin S$, let

$$\theta_j^* = \min_{\{i \in S \mid (i,j) \in \mathcal{A}\}} (c_{ij} + p_j - p_i).$$

(a) Show that $\theta^* = \min_{j \notin S} \theta_j^*$.

(b) Suppose that some node $k \notin S$ satisfies $\theta_k^* = \theta^*$, so that node k enters the set S subsequent to the price increase. Let

$$\bar{\theta}_j = \min_{\{i \in S \cup \{k\} \mid (i,j) \in \mathcal{A}\}} (c_{ij} + p_j - p_i), \qquad j \notin S \cup \{k\}.$$

Show that $\bar{\theta}_j = \min\{\theta_j^*, c_{kj} + p_j - p_k\}$.

(c) Explain how to carry out each dual update in time proportional to n times the number of previously unlabeled nodes that become labeled.

(d) Show that the primal-dual method can be implemented so that it runs in time $O(n^3 B)$, where $B = \max_i |b_i|$.

Exercise 7.29 Consider a bipartite matching problem and suppose that every node has the same degree d. Show that there exists a perfect matching. *Hint:* Convert to a maximum flow problem and use the max-flow min-cut theorem.

Exercise 7.30* (The primal-dual method as steepest dual ascent) Consider the dual ascent algorithm. Show that the choice of the set S in the primal-dual method maximizes $(\mathbf{d}^S)'\mathbf{b}$ over all sets S for which $\mathbf{d}^S$ is a feasible direction.

Exercise 7.31 (Dual simplex method for network flow problems) Consider the uncapacitated network flow problem.

(a) Show that every spanning tree determines a basic solution to the dual problem.

(b) Given a basic feasible solution to the dual problem, associated with a certain tree, show that it is optimal if and only if the corresponding tree solution to the primal is feasible.

(c) If the tree solution in part (b) is infeasible, remove an arc that carries negative flow. Given that we wish to maintain dual feasibility, how should an arc be chosen to enter the tree?

(d) Note that the entering arc divides the tree into two parts. Consider the dual variables following a dual simplex update. Show that the dual variables in one part of the tree remain unchanged and in the other part of the tree, they are all changed by the same amount.

Exercise 7.32 (Termination of the auction algorithm) Consider a variation of the assignment problem in which we are given a subset $\mathcal{A}$ of the set of person-project pairs, and we allow f_{ij} to be nonzero only if $(i, j) \in \mathcal{A}$. We modify the bidding phase of the auction algorithm as follows. A person i takes into consideration only the profits $p_k - c_{ik}$ of those projects k for which $(i, k) \in \mathcal{A}$. Suppose that this form of the auction algorithm fails to terminate. Let I be the set of persons that bid an infinite number of times. Let J be the set of projects that receive an infinite number of bids.

(a) Show that if $i \in I$ and $(i, j) \in \mathcal{A}$, then $j \in J$.

(b) Show that the cardinality of I is strictly larger than the cardinality of J.

(c) Show the problem must be infeasible.

Exercise 7.33 (Shortest path lengths and Bellman's equation) Consider the all-to-one shortest path problem, and let $\mathbf{p}^*$ be the vector of shortest path lengths.

(a) Show that if every (directed) cycle has positive length, then Bellman's equation has a unique solution, equal to the shortest path lengths.

(b) Show that if every (directed) cycle has nonnegative length, and if $\mathbf{p}$ is a solution to Bellman's equation, then $\mathbf{p} \leq \mathbf{p}^*$. *Hint:* Consider $\max\{p_i, p_i^*\}$.

Exercise 7.34 (From shortest path lengths to shortest paths) Suppose that all directed cycles in a directed graph have nonnegative costs. Furthermore, suppose that the shortest path length p_i^* from any node to node n is known. Provide an algorithm that uses this information to determine a shortest path from node 1 to node n.

Exercise 7.35 (Convergence of the Bellman-Ford algorithm) This exercise develops an alternative proof of the convergence of the Bellman-Ford algorithm. Assume that the length of every cycle is nonnegative.

(a) Prove that $\mathbf{p}(t+1) \leq \mathbf{p}(t)$ for all t.

(b) Prove that $\mathbf{p}(t) \geq \mathbf{p}^*$ for all t, and conclude that $\mathbf{p}(t)$ has a limit.

(c) Prove that $\mathbf{p}(t)$ can take only a finite number of values and therefore converges.

(d) Prove that the limit satisfies Bellman's equation.

(e) Prove that the algorithm converges to $\mathbf{p}^*$.

Exercise 7.36 (Minimization of the mean cost of a cycle using linear programming) Consider a directed graph in which each arc is associated with a cost c_{ij}. For any directed cycle, we define its mean cost as the sum of the costs of its arcs, divided by the number of arcs. We are interested in a directed cycle whose mean cost is minimal. We assume that there exists at least one directed cycle.

Consider the linear programming problem

$$\text{maximize} \quad \lambda$$
$$\text{subject to} \quad p_i + \lambda \leq p_j + c_{ij}, \qquad \text{for all arcs } (i, j).$$

(a) Show that this maximization problem is feasible.

(b) Show that if $(\lambda, \mathbf{p})$ is a feasible solution to the maximization problem, then the mean cost of every directed cycle is at least λ.

(c) Show that the maximization problem has an optimal solution.

(d) Show how an optimal solution to the maximization problem can be used to construct a directed cycle with minimal mean cost.

Exercise 7.37 (Minimization of the mean cost of a cycle using the Bellman-Ford algorithm) Consider a directed graph in which each arc is associated with a cost c_{ij}. For any directed cycle, we define its mean cost as the sum of the costs of its arcs, divided by the number of arcs. We are interested in a directed cycle whose mean cost is minimal. We assume that there exists at least one directed cycle.

(a) Consider the algorithm

$$p_i(t+1) = \min_{j \in O(i)} \{c_{ij} + p_j(t)\}, \qquad \text{for all } i,$$

initialized with $p_i(0) = 0$ for all i. Show that $p_i(t)$ is equal to the length of a shortest walk that starts at i and and traverses t arcs.

(b) Prove that the optimal mean cycle cost λ satisfies

$$\lambda = \min_{i=1,\dots,n} \max_{0 \leq k \leq n-1} \left(\frac{p_i(n) - p_i(k)}{n - k} \right),$$

where n is the number of nodes.

Exercise 7.38 (Floyd-Warshall all-pairs shortest path algorithm) Consider the all-pairs shortest path problem and assume that there are no negative cost cycles. Let d_{ij}^k be the length of a shortest path from node i to node j using only nodes in $\{1, \dots, k\}$ as intermediate nodes. Let

$$d_{ij}^0 = \begin{cases} c_{ij}, & \text{if } (i,j) \in \mathcal{A}, \\ \infty, & \text{otherwise.} \end{cases}$$

Show that

$$d_{ij}^{k+1} = \min\left\{d_{ij}^k, d_{i,k+1}^k + d_{k+1,j}^k\right\}, \qquad \text{for } i \neq j.$$

Exercise 7.39 (Complexity of the greedy MST algorithm) Consider the greedy algorithm for the MST problem. For a given node $j \notin \mathcal{N}_k$, we examine all nodes $i \in \mathcal{N}_k$, and let $v_k(j)$ be that node $i \in \mathcal{N}_k$ for which the cost $c_{\{i,j\}}$ is smallest. Let us assume that $v_k(j)$ is available for every $j \notin \mathcal{N}_k$.

(a) Show that the node selected to enter the tree can be determined in time $O(n)$.

(b) For each $j \notin \mathcal{N}_{k+1}$, show that $v_{k+1}(j)$ can be determined in time $O(1)$.

(c) Show that the MST algorithm can be implemented in time $O(n^2)$.

7.13 Notes and sources

Network flow problems are discussed in several textbooks, starting with the classic book by Ford and Fulkerson (1962). Some subsequent books are Hu (1969), Lawler (1976), Bertsekas (1991), Ahuja, Magnanti, and Orlin (1993). The last one is rather comprehensive, containing a wealth of methods and applications, and can be consulted for further information on most of the subjects that were introduced in this chapter. In addition, most textbooks on linear programming cover the subject of network flow problems to some degree. A somewhat different view of the subject, that relies heavily on duality, is provided by Rockafellar (1984). Sophisticated data structures are an important element of efficient network flow algorithms. Suitable data structures are discussed by Cormen et al. (1990), and Ahuja et al. (1993).

7.1. The material in this section is a standard part of all books dealing with combinatorial algorithms.

7.2. Numerous applications of network flow problems can be found in Ahuja et al. (1993).

7.3. The simplex method for uncapacitated network flow problems was developed by Dantzig (1951), as a special case of the general simplex method. The theory in Section 7.3 was obtained as a byproduct. The capacitated case was addressed a little later, and these developments are discussed in Dantzig's (1963) book. The simplex method has also been extensively studied for special cases, such as the maximum flow, assignment, and shortest path problems; see Ahuja et al. (1993) for an overview.

Practical experience has indicated that network flow problems tend to be highly degenerate, and that most of the pivots are also degenerate. A special purpose anticycling rule for the network simplex algorithm, based on "strongly feasible" trees, was proposed by Cunningham (1976), and also by Barr, Glover, and Klingman (1977) for the assignment problem. Still, network simplex can take an exponential number of iterations, in the worst case. Tardos (1985) has devised a *strongly polynomial* algorithm for network flow problems, in which the number of arithmetic operations is bounded by a polynomial function of the number of nodes and arcs, independent of the numerical values of the problem data. This raises the question whether the same can be accomplished by the simplex method. At present, a version of the simplex method that requires a number of iterations polynomial in n is not available. However, this objective has been attained by variants of the dual simplex method; see Orlin (1984), and Plotkin and Tardos (1990).

Network flow problems have an important property known as *total unimodularity*, which is reflected in the integrality of the inverse basis matrix $\mathbf{B}^{-1}$. See Schrijver (1986) for a discussion of this topic.

7.4. The negative cost cycle algorithm is attributed to Klein (1967). The maximum improvement rule was proposed by Weintraub (1974), and was further studied by Barahona and Tardos (1989). The mean cost rule was studied by Goldberg and Tarjan (1989), who show that it leads to a polynomial time algorithm.

7.5. Example 7.4 on preemptive scheduling is due to Federgruen and Groenevelt (1986). The Ford-Fulkerson and labeling algorithms are due to Ford and Fulkerson (1956a). The max-flow min-cut theorem is due to Fulkerson and Dantzig (1955), Ford and Fulkerson (1956a), and Elias, Feinstein, and Shannon (1956). A nonterminating example, for the case of irrational capacities, can be found in Ford and Fulkerson (1962), and is also included in many textbooks. Edmonds and Karp (1972) have shown that the number of flow augmentations is $O(|\mathcal{N}| \cdot |\mathcal{A}|)$, when an augmenting path with the least number of arcs is used. For other polynomial time algorithms for the maximum flow problem, and an overview of the literature, see Ahuja et al. (1993).

7.6. For capacitated problems, the most natural form of the dual is obtained if dual variables are associated with the flow conservation constraints, but not with the capacity constraints. (This goes along the lines discussed in Section 4.10.) See Rockafellar (1984), Bertsekas (1991), and Ahuja et al. (1993). The relation between network flow theory and electrical circuits is discussed in Recski (1989).

7.7. Our presentation of dual ascent methods is in the spirit of Rockafellar (1984), and Bertsekas (1991). The primal-dual method was first developed for the assignment problem by Kuhn (1955). Kuhn named it the Hungarian method, because it was inspired by the work of two Hungarian mathematicians, König and Egerváry. A historical account is provided by Kuhn's article in Lenstra, Rinnooy Kan, and Schrijver (1991). The extension to general network flow problems was carried out by Ford and Fulkerson (1956b). Using the scaling ideas of Edmonds and Karp (1972), the complexity of the algorithm can be made proportional to the logarithm of B. The relaxation algorithm, which uses a different method for selecting ascent directions, was proposed by Bertsekas (1981) for the assignment problem, and it was subsequently extended to general network flow problems; see Bertsekas (1991), and Bertsekas and Tsitsiklis (1989), for textbook expositions. The dual network simplex method is discussed in Section 11.9 of Ahuja et al. (1993).

7.8. Algorithms for bipartite matching can be found in Papadimitriou and Steiglitz (1982), and Ahuja et al. (1993). The auction algorithm is due to Bertsekas (1979), has been extended to general network flow problems, and is also known as ϵ-relaxation; see Bertsekas (1991), and Bertsekas and Tsitsiklis (1989), for textbook presentations. The preflow-push algorithms of Goldberg and Tarjan (1988), for the maximum flow problem, are closely related and have also been extended to the general network case.

7.9. The Bellman-Ford algorithm goes back to the work of Ford (1956) and Bellman (1958), and is a special case of dynamic programming methods, to be discussed further in Section 11.3. Dijkstra's algorithm is from Dijkstra (1959). The literature on shortest path problems is extensive and the reader is referred to Ahuja et al. (1993) for an overview.

7.10. The minimum spanning tree algorithm that we have presented is attributed to Prim (1957) and Dijkstra (1959). For other algorithms, see Papadimitriou and Steiglitz (1981), Cormen et al. (1990), and Ahuja et al. (1993).

7.12. The transformation of a network flow problem to a transportation problem (Exercise 7.6) is attributed to Wagner (1959). The scaling idea used in Exercise 7.25 is due to Edmonds and Karp (1972) who applied it to general network flow problems, and obtained algorithms whose running time is proportional to the logarithm of the numerical values of the input data. The mean cost cycle algorithm developed in Exercise 7.37 is due to Karp (1978). The all-pairs algorithm in Exercise 7.38 is from Floyd (1962) and Warshall (1962).

Chapter 8

Complexity of linear programming and the ellipsoid method

The simplex method described in previous chapters has been very effective over the years in solving linear programming problems arising in applications. For specially constructed problems, however, the simplex method can take an exponential number of iterations, as we have seen in Section 3.7. These examples motivate the discussion in Section 8.1 regarding computational complexity and efficient algorithms. In Sections 8.2-8.4, we address the question of whether linear programming can be solved efficiently and show that the ellipsoid method, an algorithm developed in the Soviet literature, is indeed theoretically efficient. In Section 8.5, we demonstrate its applications to linear programming problems with a large (even exponential) number of constraints.

The ellipsoid method did not lead to a practical algorithm for solving linear programming problems. Rather, it demonstrated that linear programming is efficiently solvable from a theoretical point of view. This is important, because once a problem is shown to be efficiently solvable, usually more efficient and practical algorithms follow. Indeed a new class of algorithms, known as interior point methods, that are both practical and theoretically efficient have been proposed, and are the subject of the next chapter.

8.1 Efficient algorithms and computational complexity

In Section 1.6, we have discussed the notion of an efficient algorithm for a computational problem. In this section we refine that discussion with particular emphasis on linear programming problems.

In Section 3.7, we introduced a linear programming problem with n variables and $2n$ inequality constraints, for which the simplex method with a particular pivoting rule, requires $2^n - 1$ iterations to find an optimal solution. On the other hand, there is strong empirical evidence suggesting that the simplex method "typically" takes $O(m)$ iterations to find an optimal solution to standard form problems with m equality constraints.

This discussion raises the question: should we consider the simplex method an efficient algorithm for linear programming? More generally, what are the criteria for calling an algorithm efficient?

Before answering these questions, it is useful to draw a distinction between a *problem* and an *instance* of a problem. For example, "linear programming" is a problem, whereas

$$\begin{array}{ll} \text{minimize} & 2x + 3y \\ \text{subject to} & x + y \leq 1 \\ & x, y \geq 0, \end{array}$$

is an instance of the linear programming problem. We define these terms more generally, as follows.

> **Definition 8.1** *An* **instance** *of an optimization problem consists of a feasible set F and a cost function $c : F \mapsto \Re$ [the objective is to minimize $c(\mathbf{x})$ over all $\mathbf{x} \in F$]. An optimization* **problem** *is defined as a collection of instances.*

Instances of a problem need to be described according to a common format. For example, instances of linear programming in standard form can be described by listing the entries of $\mathbf{A}$, $\mathbf{b}$, and $\mathbf{c}$.

Note that some instances are "larger" than others, and it is convenient to define the notion of the "size" of an instance. While several definitions are possible, the definition given below applies to all problems in a uniform fashion. In addition, this definition is geared towards digital computers in which information is represented by binary numbers.

> **Definition 8.2** *The* **size** *of an instance is defined as the number of bits used to describe the instance, according to a prespecified format.*

Given that arbitrary real numbers cannot be represented in binary, this definition is geared towards instances involving integer (or rational) numbers. Note that any nonnegative integer r smaller than or equal to U can be written in binary as follows:

$$r = a_k 2^k + a_{k-1} 2^{k-1} + \cdots + a_1 2^1 + a_0,$$

where the scalars $a_0, \ldots, a_k$, are 0 or 1. The number k is clearly at most $\lfloor \log_2 U \rfloor$, since $r \leq U$. We can then represent r by the binary vector $(a_0, a_1, \ldots, a_k)$. With an extra bit for the sign, we can also represent negative numbers. In other words, we can represent any integer with absolute value less than or equal to U using at most $\lfloor \log_2 U \rfloor + 2$ bits.

Consider now an instance of a linear programming problem in standard form, i.e., an $m \times n$ matrix $\mathbf{A}$, an m-vector $\mathbf{b}$, and an n-vector $\mathbf{c}$, and assume that the magnitude of the largest element of $\mathbf{A}$, $\mathbf{b}$, $\mathbf{c}$ is equal to U. Since there are $(mn + m + n)$ entries in $\mathbf{A}$, $\mathbf{b}$, and $\mathbf{c}$, the size of such an instance is at most

$$(mn + m + n)\bigl(\lfloor \log_2 U \rfloor + 2\bigr).$$

In fact, this count is not exactly correct: more bits will be needed to encode "flags" that indicate where a number ends, and another starts. However, our count is right as far as the order of magnitude is concerned. To avoid details of this kind, we will be using instead the order-of-magnitude notation, and we will simply say that the size of such an instance is $O(mn \log U)$.

Optimization problems are solved by *algorithms*. Note at this point a very important distinction. Algorithms are designed for problems (e.g., the simplex method is an algorithm for linear programming), but are applied to individual instances. We say that an algorithm solves a problem if it terminates in finite time and produces the correct answer for all instances of the problem. Of course, it is to be expected that when the algorithm is applied to instances of larger size, it may take longer to terminate. For this reason, the running time of an algorithm is usually expressed as a function of the size of the instance to which it is applied. In order to make this discussion precise, we need to define exactly what an algorithm is, how running time is counted, etc. While this can be done with absolute rigor, a rough description is sufficient for our purposes.

As we mentioned in Section 1.6, an algorithm is a finite set of instructions of the type used in common programming languages (arithmetic operations, conditional statements, read and write statements, etc.). The running time of an algorithm is then the total number of steps involved in carrying out these instructions until a termination statement is reached. In the simplest of circumstances, we can assume that each instruction (including arithmetic operations) takes unit time; we call this the *arithmetic* model.

In an alternative model, the *bit* model, each instruction is decomposed into a set of elementary instructions that operate on single-bit numbers, and each such elementary instruction is assumed to take unit time. This latter model is more natural and can capture the fact that the time to add two numbers increases with the size of these numbers. On the other hand, it complicates the calculation of running time.

The running time of an algorithm will, in general, depend on the instance to which it is applied. Let $T(n)$ be the *worst-case* running time of some algorithm over all instances of size n, under the bit model. In other words, out of all instances of size n, we consider an instance on which the algorithm takes the longest.

We next give a very important definition.

Definition 8.3 *An algorithm runs in* **polynomial time** *if there exists an integer k such that $T(n) = O(n^k)$.*

Given that it is easier to count time using the arithmetic model, the following fact is often useful.

Fact: Suppose that an algorithm takes polynomial time under the arithmetic model. Furthermore, suppose that on instances of size n, any integer produced in the course of the execution of the algorithm has size bounded by a polynomial in n. Then, the algorithm runs in polynomial time under the bit model as well.

The essential reason that makes this fact true is that arithmetic operations can be carried out by subroutines that take polynomial time under the bit model. (Think of the algorithms taught in elementary school!)

Matrix inversion can serve to illustrate these issues. As mentioned in Section 1.6, an $n \times n$ matrix can be inverted using $O(n^3)$ arithmetic operations, by means of the Gaussian elimination algorithm. However, to assert that matrix inversion can be performed in polynomial time (under the bit model) requires the additional fact that the algorithm only produces numbers whose size is bounded by a polynomial in n and in the size of the entries in the matrix to be inverted. Fortunately, this turns out to be the case.

In order to make the discussion in this section fully rigorous, we would need to be much more specific regarding our choice of programming language, instruction set, and model of computation. Could an algorithm be polynomial under some set of choices and non-polynomial under another? In principle, this is indeed possible. However, it has been observed that polynomiality is a fairly "stable" property; that is, the set of polynomial time algorithms is essentially the same under all reasonable models of digital computation that have been studied.

As we mentioned in Section 1.6, an algorithm is considered efficient if its running time grows polynomially with the size of the input; otherwise, it is usually considered inefficient. Clearly, this view of algorithmic complexity has its problems. In our counting of the running time we consider the worst-case running time. Therefore, it only takes one instance to pronounce an algorithm inefficient, while the algorithm might be very fast in the vast majority of instances. Thus, this view of worst-case efficiency, although insightful, may not always reflect reality. The simplex method is a case in point. As discussed earlier in the book, it solves routinely large scale problems fast, even though it takes exponential time in the worst case.

8.2   The key geometric result behind the ellipsoid method

In this section, we prepare the ground for a new algorithm for linear programming, called the ellipsoid method, by developing its key geometric elements.

The ellipsoid method can be used to decide whether a polyhedron

$$P = \left\{ \mathbf{x} \in \Re^n \mid \mathbf{A}\mathbf{x} \geq \mathbf{b} \right\}$$

is empty or not. Later in this chapter, we provide an extension that solves the problem

$$\begin{array}{ll} \text{minimize} & \mathbf{c}'\mathbf{x} \\ \text{subject to} & \mathbf{A}\mathbf{x} \geq \mathbf{b}. \end{array}$$

We first give some definitions.

Definition 8.4 *An $n \times n$ symmetric matrix $\mathbf{D}$ is called* **positive definite** *if $\mathbf{x}'\mathbf{D}\mathbf{x} > 0$ for all nonzero vectors $\mathbf{x} \in \Re^n$.*

A positive definite matrix $\mathbf{D}$ has only real and positive eigenvalues, and is nonsingular. Moreover, $\mathbf{D}^{-1}$ is also positive definite. We now define ellipsoids, which are higher dimensional generalizations of the familiar two–dimensional ellipses.

Definition 8.5 *A set E of vectors in $\Re^n$ of the form*

$$E = E(\mathbf{z}, \mathbf{D}) = \left\{\mathbf{x} \in \Re^n \mid (\mathbf{x} - \mathbf{z})'\mathbf{D}^{-1}(\mathbf{x} - \mathbf{z}) \leq 1\right\},$$

where $\mathbf{D}$ is an $n \times n$ positive definite symmetric matrix, is called an **ellipsoid** *with center $\mathbf{z} \in \Re^n$.*

For any $r > 0$, the ellipsoid

$$
\begin{aligned}
E(\mathbf{z}, r^2\mathbf{I}) &= \left\{\mathbf{x} \in \Re^n \mid (\mathbf{x} - \mathbf{z})'(\mathbf{x} - \mathbf{z}) \leq r^2\right\} \\
&= \left\{\mathbf{x} \in \Re^n \mid \|\mathbf{x} - \mathbf{z}\| \leq r\right\}
\end{aligned}
$$

is called a *ball* centered at $\mathbf{z}$, of radius r.

Definition 8.6 *If $\mathbf{D}$ is an $n \times n$ nonsingular matrix and $\mathbf{b} \in \Re^n$, then the mapping $S : \Re^n \mapsto \Re^n$ defined by $S(\mathbf{x}) = \mathbf{D}\mathbf{x} + \mathbf{b}$, is called an* **affine transformation.**

Note that an affine transformation is always invertible, since the matrix $\mathbf{D}$ is nonsingular. If L is any subset of $\Re^n$, we define the *image* of L under the affine transformation $S(\cdot)$ as

$$S(L) = \left\{\mathbf{y} \in \Re^n \mid \mathbf{y} = \mathbf{D}\mathbf{x} + \mathbf{b}, \text{ for some } \mathbf{x} \in L\right\}.$$

The *volume* of a set $L \subset \Re^n$, which is denoted by $\mathrm{Vol}(L)$, is defined as

$$\mathrm{Vol}(L) = \int_{\mathbf{x} \in L} d\mathbf{x}.$$

In the sequel, we will use the following property of affine transformations.

Lemma 8.1 If $S(\mathbf{x}) = \mathbf{D}\mathbf{x} + \mathbf{b}$, then $\text{Vol}\big(S(L)\big) = \big|\det(\mathbf{D})\big|\text{Vol}(L)$.

Proof. The volume of $S(L)$ is given by

$$\text{Vol}\big(S(L)\big) = \int_{\mathbf{y} \in S(L)} d\mathbf{y}.$$

If we change variables in the above multivariable integral, using the transformation $\mathbf{y} = \mathbf{D}\mathbf{x} + \mathbf{b}$, we obtain

$$\text{Vol}\big(S(L)\big) = \int_{\mathbf{x} \in L} \big|\det\big(J(\mathbf{x})\big)\big|\, d\mathbf{x}.$$

Here, $J(\mathbf{x})$ is the Jacobian matrix associated with the transformation $S(\cdot)$: the (i,j)th component of $J(\mathbf{x})$ is $\partial S_i(\mathbf{x})/\partial x_j$, where $S_i(\mathbf{x})$ is the ith component of $S(\mathbf{x})$. Because the transformation is affine, we have $J(\mathbf{x}) = \mathbf{D}$, which leads to the formula in the lemma. $\square$

As we mentioned earlier, the ellipsoid method can be used to decide whether a given polyhedron

$$P = \big\{\mathbf{x} \in \Re^n \mid \mathbf{A}\mathbf{x} \geq \mathbf{b}\big\}$$

is nonempty. We will first explain intuitively how the algorithm works. The algorithm generates a sequence E_t of ellipsoids with centers $\mathbf{x}_t$, such that P is contained in E_t. If $\mathbf{x}_t \in P$, then P is nonempty and the algorithm terminates. If $\mathbf{x}_t \notin P$, then there exists a constraint which is violated, i.e., $\mathbf{x}_t$ satisfies $\mathbf{a}'\mathbf{x}_t < b$, where $\mathbf{a}'$ is one of the rows of $\mathbf{A}$, and b is the corresponding entry of $\mathbf{b}$. Any element $\mathbf{x}$ of P satisfies $\mathbf{a}'\mathbf{x} \geq b$ and, therefore, $\mathbf{a}'\mathbf{x} \geq \mathbf{a}'\mathbf{x}_t$. Thus, P is contained in the halfspace $\{\mathbf{x} \in \Re^n \mid \mathbf{a}'\mathbf{x} \geq \mathbf{a}'\mathbf{x}_t\}$. In other words, if $\mathbf{x}_t$ is infeasible, P is contained in the intersection of the ellipsoid E_t and a halfspace that passes through the center of the ellipsoid (see Figure 8.1). We call this intersection a half-ellipsoid. A key geometric property of ellipsoids is that we can find a new ellipsoid E_{t+1} that covers the half-ellipsoid and whose volume is only a fraction of the volume of the previous ellipsoid E_t. Repeating this process, we either find a point in P, or we conclude that the volume of P is very small and, therefore, P is empty. The last step is based on the fact, to be proved in Lemma 8.4, that the volume of a nonempty "full-dimensional" polyhedron cannot be smaller than a certain threshold.

In the next theorem, we analytically construct the ellipsoid E_{t+1} and calculate the reduction of its volume explicitly.

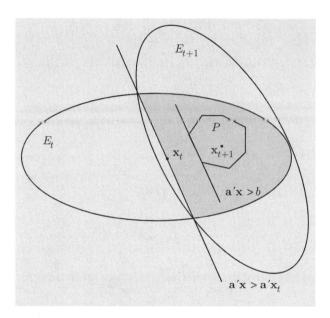

Figure 8.1: An iteration of the algorithm, in which $\mathbf{x}_t \notin P$ but $\mathbf{x}_{t+1} \in P$. The shaded area is the intersection of the ellipsoid E_t with the halfspace $\{\mathbf{x} \mid \mathbf{a}'\mathbf{x} \geq \mathbf{a}'\mathbf{x}_t\}$, and is covered by the new ellipsoid E_{t+1}.

Theorem 8.1 *Let $E = E(\mathbf{z}, \mathbf{D})$ be an ellipsoid in $\Re^n$, and let $\mathbf{a}$ be a nonzero n-vector. Consider the halfspace $H = \{\mathbf{x} \in \Re^n \mid \mathbf{a}'\mathbf{x} \geq \mathbf{a}'\mathbf{z}\}$ and let*

$$\overline{\mathbf{z}} = \mathbf{z} + \frac{1}{n+1}\frac{\mathbf{Da}}{\sqrt{\mathbf{a}'\mathbf{Da}}},$$

$$\overline{\mathbf{D}} = \frac{n^2}{n^2-1}\left(\mathbf{D} - \frac{2}{n+1}\frac{\mathbf{Daa}'\mathbf{D}}{\mathbf{a}'\mathbf{Da}}\right).$$

The matrix $\overline{\mathbf{D}}$ is symmetric and positive definite and thus $E' = E(\overline{\mathbf{z}}, \overline{\mathbf{D}})$ is an ellipsoid. Moreover,

(a) $E \cap H \subset E'$,

(b) $\mathrm{Vol}(E') < e^{-1/(2(n+1))}\,\mathrm{Vol}(E)$.

Proof. (a) We first prove the theorem for the case $\mathbf{z} = \mathbf{0}$, $\mathbf{D} = \mathbf{I}$, and $\mathbf{a} = \mathbf{e}_1 = (1, 0, \ldots, 0)$ (see Figure 8.2). (The more general case will be handled by means of a suitable coordinate transformation.) Here, the ellipsoid E is the unit ball $E_0 = \{\mathbf{x} \in \Re^n \mid \mathbf{x}'\mathbf{x} \leq 1\}$ and the halfspace H becomes $H_0 = \{\mathbf{x} \in \Re^n \mid x_1 \geq 0\}$.

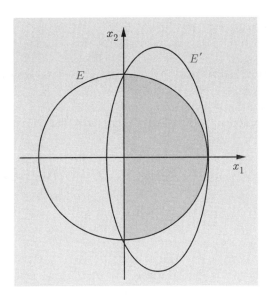

Figure 8.2: Illustration of Theorem 8.1 for the case $E = E(\mathbf{0}, \mathbf{I})$ and $H = \{\mathbf{x} \in \Re^n \mid x_1 \geq 0\}$.

In this case, the ellipsoid E' (written as E'_0 to indicate that the initial ellipsoid is E_0) becomes:

$$E'_0 = E\left(\frac{\mathbf{e}_1}{n+1}, \frac{n^2}{n^2-1}\left(\mathbf{I} - \frac{2}{n+1}\mathbf{e}_1\mathbf{e}'_1\right)\right).$$

The ellipsoid E'_0 can be written as follows:

$$E'_0 = \left\{\mathbf{x} \in \Re^n \;\middle|\; \left(\frac{n+1}{n}\right)^2\left(x_1 - \frac{1}{n+1}\right)^2 + \frac{n^2-1}{n^2}\sum_{i=2}^{n} x_i^2 \leq 1\right\}.$$

We can rewrite the previous expression and obtain

$$
E'_0 = \left\{\mathbf{x} \in \Re^n \;\middle|\; \frac{n^2-1}{n^2}\sum_{i=1}^{n} x_i^2 + \frac{2(n+1)}{n^2}x_1^2 \right.
$$
$$
\left. + \left(\frac{n+1}{n}\right)^2\left(-\frac{2x_1}{n+1} + \frac{1}{(n+1)^2}\right) \leq 1\right\}
$$
$$
= \left\{\mathbf{x} \in \Re^n \;\middle|\; \frac{n^2-1}{n^2}\sum_{i=1}^{n} x_i^2 + \frac{1}{n^2} + \frac{2(n+1)}{n^2}x_1(x_1-1) \leq 1\right\}.
$$

Let $\mathbf{x} \in E_0 \cap H_0$. Then $0 \leq x_1 \leq 1$ and therefore $x_1(x_1 - 1) \leq 0$. Since $\mathbf{x} \in E_0$, we have $\sum_{i=1}^{n} x_i^2 \leq 1$. Therefore,

$$\frac{n^2-1}{n^2}\sum_{i=1}^{n} x_i^2 + \frac{1}{n^2} + \frac{2(n+1)}{n^2}x_1(x_1-1) \leq \frac{n^2-1}{n^2} + \frac{1}{n^2} = 1,$$

i.e., $\mathbf{x} \in E'_0$, proving that $E_0 \cap H_0 \subset E'_0$.

We now consider the general case. We will construct an affine transformation $T(\cdot)$, such that $T(E) = E_0$, $T(H) = H_0$ and $T(E') = E'_0$. Then, the desired result will follow from the elementary observation that affine transformations preserve set inclusion, i.e., if $A \subset B \subset \Re^n$ and $T(\cdot)$ is an affine transformation, then $T(A) \subset T(B)$.

Given the ellipsoid $E = E(\mathbf{z}, \mathbf{D})$, we consider the affine transformation

$$S(\mathbf{x}) = \mathbf{D}^{-1/2}(\mathbf{x} - \mathbf{z}).$$

Here $\mathbf{D}^{1/2}$ is a symmetric matrix such that $(\mathbf{D}^{1/2})(\mathbf{D}^{1/2}) = \mathbf{D}$ and $\mathbf{D}^{-1/2}$ is its inverse. Both $\mathbf{D}^{1/2}$ and $\mathbf{D}^{-1/2}$ are guaranteed to exist and can be taken to be positive definite. It can be shown that $S(E) = E_0$. However, $S(H) \neq H_0$ and $S(E') \neq E'_0$. For this reason, we modify the affine transformation $S(\cdot)$ as follows.

In Exercise 8.1, the reader is asked to show that for every vector $\mathbf{u}$, there exists a matrix $\mathbf{R}$ (called a *rotation matrix*), such that

$$\mathbf{R}'\mathbf{R} = \mathbf{I}, \qquad \mathbf{R}\mathbf{u} = \|\mathbf{u}\|\mathbf{e}_1,$$

where $\|\mathbf{u}\| = (\mathbf{u}'\mathbf{u})^{1/2}$. Note that the matrix $\mathbf{R}$ basically rotates the unit ball so that $\mathbf{u}$ is aligned with the first unit vector $\mathbf{e}_1$. Let $\mathbf{R}$ be the rotation matrix corresponding to the vector $\mathbf{u} = \mathbf{D}^{1/2}\mathbf{a}$, i.e.,

$$\mathbf{R}'\mathbf{R} = \mathbf{I}, \qquad \mathbf{R}\mathbf{D}^{1/2}\mathbf{a} = \|\mathbf{D}^{1/2}\mathbf{a}\|\mathbf{e}_1.$$

We next introduce the affine transformation

$$T(\mathbf{x}) = \mathbf{R}S(\mathbf{x}) = \mathbf{R}\mathbf{D}^{-1/2}(\mathbf{x} - \mathbf{z}).$$

Note that

$$
\begin{aligned}
\mathbf{x} \in E &\Leftrightarrow (\mathbf{x} - \mathbf{z})'\mathbf{D}^{-1}(\mathbf{x} - \mathbf{z}) \leq 1 \\
&\Leftrightarrow (\mathbf{x} - \mathbf{z})'\mathbf{D}^{-1/2}\mathbf{R}'\mathbf{R}\mathbf{D}^{-1/2}(\mathbf{x} - \mathbf{z}) \leq 1 \\
&\Leftrightarrow \mathbf{R}\mathbf{D}^{-1/2}(\mathbf{x} - \mathbf{z}) \in E_0 \\
&\Leftrightarrow T(\mathbf{x}) \in E_0,
\end{aligned}
$$

which implies that

$$T(E) = E_0.$$

Similarly,

$$
\begin{aligned}
\mathbf{x} \in H &\Leftrightarrow \mathbf{a}'(\mathbf{x} - \mathbf{z}) \geq 0 \\
&\Leftrightarrow \mathbf{a}'\mathbf{D}^{1/2}\mathbf{R}'\mathbf{R}\mathbf{D}^{-1/2}(\mathbf{x} - \mathbf{z}) \geq 0 \\
&\Leftrightarrow \|\mathbf{D}^{1/2}\mathbf{a}\|\mathbf{e}_1'T(\mathbf{x}) \geq 0 \\
&\Leftrightarrow \mathbf{e}_1'T(\mathbf{x}) \geq 0 \\
&\Leftrightarrow T(\mathbf{x}) \in H_0,
\end{aligned}
$$

which implies that

$$T(H) = H_0.$$

After some algebraic manipulations that we omit (Exercise 8.2) we can show that

$$T(E') = E_0',$$

and that the matrix $\overline{\mathbf{D}}$ is positive definite. We have shown earlier that $E_0 \cap H_0 \subset E_0'$, i.e., $T(E) \cap T(H) \subset T(E')$. Affine transformations preserve set inclusion. Thus, we obtain that

$$E \cap H \subset E',$$

proving the first part of the theorem.

(b) From Lemma 8.1 (affine transformations multiply volumes by a constant factor), we obtain

$$\frac{\text{Vol}(E')}{\text{Vol}(E)} = \frac{\text{Vol}(T(E'))}{\text{Vol}(T(E))} = \frac{\text{Vol}(E_0')}{\text{Vol}(E_0)}.$$

Recall that

$$E_0' = E\left(\frac{\mathbf{e}_1}{n+1}, \frac{n^2}{n^2-1}\left(\mathbf{I} - \frac{2}{n+1}\mathbf{e}_1\mathbf{e}_1' \right) \right).$$

We introduce the affine transformation

$$F(\mathbf{x}) = \left(\frac{n^2}{n^2-1}\left(\mathbf{I} - \frac{2}{n+1}\mathbf{e}_1\mathbf{e}_1' \right) \right)^{-1/2}\left(\mathbf{x} - \frac{\mathbf{e}_1}{n+1} \right).$$

It is elementary to show that $F(E_0') = E_0$. [This is the same as the argument used earlier to show that $T(E) = E_0$, with $\mathbf{R} = \mathbf{I}$.] Applying Lemma 8.1, we obtain

$$\text{Vol}(E_0) = \left| \det\left(\left(\frac{n^2}{n^2-1}\left(\mathbf{I} - \frac{2}{n+1}\mathbf{e}_1\mathbf{e}_1' \right) \right)^{-1/2} \right) \right| \text{Vol}(E_0').$$

Therefore, using the property $\left| \det(\mathbf{D}^{-1/2}) \right| = 1/\sqrt{|\det(\mathbf{D})|}$,

$$\text{Vol}(E_0') = \sqrt{\det\left(\frac{n^2}{n^2-1}\left(\mathbf{I} - \frac{2}{n+1}\mathbf{e}_1\mathbf{e}_1' \right) \right)} \text{Vol}(E_0),$$

and hence,

$$\frac{\text{Vol}(E_0')}{\text{Vol}(E_0)} = \left(\frac{n^2}{n^2-1} \right)^{n/2}\left(1 - \frac{2}{n+1} \right)^{1/2}$$

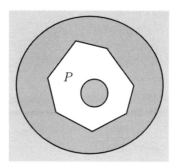

Figure 8.3: A bounded and full-dimensional polyhedron contains a ball and is contained in a ball.

$$
\begin{aligned}
&= \frac{n}{n+1}\left(\frac{n^2}{n^2-1}\right)^{(n-1)/2} \\
&= \left(1-\frac{1}{n+1}\right)\left(1+\frac{1}{n^2-1}\right)^{(n-1)/2} \\
&< e^{-1/(n+1)}\left(e^{1/(n^2-1)}\right)^{(n-1)/2} \\
&= e^{-1/(2(n+1))},
\end{aligned}
$$

where we applied twice the inequality $1+a < e^a$, which is true for all $a \neq 0$. Therefore,

$$
\frac{\mathrm{Vol}(E')}{\mathrm{Vol}(E)} < e^{-1/(2(n+1))}. \qquad\qquad \square
$$

8.3   The ellipsoid method for the feasibility problem

In this section, we describe formally the ellipsoid method for deciding whether a polyhedron

$$
P = \{\mathbf{x} \in \Re^n \mid \mathbf{A}\mathbf{x} \geq \mathbf{b}\}
$$

is empty or not. We will first present the algorithm for full-dimensional polyhedra defined as follows.

Definition 8.7 *A polyhedron P is **full-dimensional** if it has positive volume.*

In order to simplify the presentation and highlight the fundamental geometric ideas we make the following two assumptions, which we relax later.

(a) The polyhedron P is bounded and either empty or full-dimensional (see Figure 8.3). Boundedness implies that there exists a ball $E_0 = E(\mathbf{x}_0, r^2 \mathbf{I})$, with volume V, that contains P. The second part requires that either P is empty, or P has positive volume, i.e., $\mathrm{Vol}(P) > v$ for some $v > 0$ (for other characterizations of full-dimensional polyhedra, see Exercise 8.5). We will assume initially that the ellipsoid E_0, as well as the numbers v, V, are a priori known.

(b) We can make our calculations in infinite precision. In particular, we assume that square roots can be computed exactly in unit time.

The ellipsoid method

Input:

(a) A matrix $\mathbf{A}$ and a vector $\mathbf{b}$ that define the polyhedron $P = \{\mathbf{x} \in \Re^n \mid \mathbf{a}_i' \mathbf{x} \geq b_i, \ i = 1, \ldots, m\}$.

(b) A number v, such that either P is empty or $\mathrm{Vol}(P) > v$.

(c) A ball $E_0 = E(\mathbf{x}_0, r^2 \mathbf{I})$ with volume at most V, such that $P \subset E_0$.

Output:
A feasible point $\mathbf{x}^* \in P$ if P is nonempty, or a statement that P is empty.

Algorithm:

1. (Initialization)
   Let $t^* = \lceil 2(n+1) \log(V/v) \rceil$; $E_0 = E(\mathbf{x}_0, r^2 \mathbf{I})$; $\mathbf{D}_0 = r^2 \mathbf{I}$; $t = 0$.

2. (Main iteration)

   (a) If $t = t^*$ stop; P is empty.

   (b) If $\mathbf{x}_t \in P$ stop; P is nonempty.

   (c) If $\mathbf{x}_t \notin P$ find a violated constraint, that is, find an i such that $\mathbf{a}_i' \mathbf{x}_t < b_i$.

   (d) Let $H_t = \{\mathbf{x} \in \Re^n \mid \mathbf{a}_i' \mathbf{x} \geq \mathbf{a}_i' \mathbf{x}_t\}$. Find an ellipsoid E_{t+1} containing $E_t \cap H_t$ by applying Theorem 8.1, i.e., let $E_{t+1} = E(\mathbf{x}_{t+1}, \mathbf{D}_{t+1})$ with

   $$\mathbf{x}_{t+1} = \mathbf{x}_t + \frac{1}{n+1} \frac{\mathbf{D}_t \mathbf{a}_i}{\sqrt{\mathbf{a}_i' \mathbf{D}_t \mathbf{a}_i}},$$

   $$\mathbf{D}_{t+1} = \frac{n^2}{n^2 - 1} \left(\mathbf{D}_t - \frac{2}{n+1} \frac{\mathbf{D}_t \mathbf{a}_i \mathbf{a}_i' \mathbf{D}_t}{\mathbf{a}_i' \mathbf{D}_t \mathbf{a}_i} \right).$$

   (e) $t := t + 1$.

We next prove the correctness of the algorithm.

Theorem 8.2 *Let P be a bounded polyhedron that is either empty or full-dimensional and for which the prior information $\mathbf{x}_0$, r, v, V is available. Then, the ellipsoid method decides correctly whether P is nonempty or not, i.e., if $\mathbf{x}_{t^*-1} \notin P$, then P is empty.*

Proof. If $\mathbf{x}_t \in P$ for $t < t^*$, then the algorithm correctly decides that P is nonempty. Let us now assume that $\mathbf{x}_0, \ldots, \mathbf{x}_{t^*-1} \notin P$. We will show that P is empty. To achieve this we will prove by induction on k that $P \subset E_k$ for $k = 0, 1, \ldots, t^*$. Note that $P \subset E_0$, by the assumptions of the algorithm, and this starts the induction.

We assume that $P \subset E_k$ for some $k < t^*$. Since $\mathbf{x}_k \notin P$, there exists a violated inequality. Let $\mathbf{a}'_{i(k)}\mathbf{x} \geq \mathbf{b}_{i(k)}$ be a violated inequality, i.e., $\mathbf{a}'_{i(k)}\mathbf{x}_k < \mathbf{b}_{i(k)}$, where $\mathbf{x}_k$ is the center of the ellipsoid E_k. For any $\mathbf{x} \in P$, we have

$$\mathbf{a}'_{i(k)}\mathbf{x} \geq \mathbf{b}_{i(k)} > \mathbf{a}'_{i(k)}\mathbf{x}_k.$$

Hence, $P \subset H_k$ where H_k is the halfspace

$$H_k = \big\{\mathbf{x} \in \Re^n \mid \mathbf{a}'_{i(k)}\mathbf{x} \geq \mathbf{a}'_{i(k)}\mathbf{x}_k\big\}.$$

Therefore, $P \subset E_k \cap H_k$. The new ellipsoid E_{k+1} is constructed by applying Theorem 8.1. From Theorem 8.1(a) we obtain $E_k \cap H_k \subset E_{k+1}$. Therefore, $P \subset E_{k+1}$ and the induction is complete.

From Theorem 8.1(b), we obtain

$$\frac{\text{Vol}(E_{t+1})}{\text{Vol}(E_t)} < e^{-1/(2(n+1))},$$

and

$$\frac{\text{Vol}(E_{t^*})}{\text{Vol}(E_0)} < e^{-t^*/(2(n+1))}.$$

Therefore,

$$\text{Vol}(E_{t^*}) < V e^{-\lceil 2(n+1)\log \frac{V}{v}\rceil/(2(n+1))} \leq V e^{-\log \frac{V}{v}} = v.$$

If the ellipsoid method has not terminated after t^* iterations, then $\text{Vol}(P) \leq \text{Vol}(E_{t^*}) \leq v$. According to the assumptions of the algorithm, this implies that P is empty. $\qquad\square$

Example 8.1 (The ellipsoid method and binary search) In this example, we show that in dimension $n = 1$, the ellipsoid method closely resembles binary search, a technique to decide if several intervals in the real line have a nonempty intersection. In one dimension, ellipsoids are intervals. Consider the polyhedron

$$P = \big\{x \in \Re \mid x \geq 0, x \geq 1, x \leq 2, x \leq 3\big\}.$$

Let E_0 be the interval $[0, 5]$, centered at $x_0 = 2.5$. Since $x_0 \notin P$, the algorithm chooses the violated inequality $x \le 2$ and constructs an ellipsoid E_1 that contains the interval $E_0 \cap \{x \mid x \le 2.5\} = [0, 2.5]$. The ellipsoid E_1 is the interval $[0, 2.5]$ itself. Its center $x_1 = 1.25$ belongs to P. Notice that this is a binary search algorithm, i.e., it always halves the search interval.

The assumptions of boundedness and full-dimensionality revisited

In our development of the ellipsoid method, we have assumed that the polyhedron P is bounded and is either empty or full-dimensional. Moreover, we assumed that numbers v and V were available, such that if P is full-dimensional, then $v < \text{Vol}(P) < V$. We next show how to modify the input to the ellipsoid method if the polyhedron P is unbounded or not full-dimensional. Moreover, we compute bounds on v and V that depend only on the number of variables n and the largest number in $\mathbf{A}$ and $\mathbf{b}$.

We first show that we can restrict our attention to bounded polyhedra.

Lemma 8.2 *Let $\mathbf{A}$ be an $m \times n$ integer matrix and let $\mathbf{b}$ a vector in $\Re^n$. Let U be the largest absolute value of the entries in $\mathbf{A}$ and $\mathbf{b}$.*

(a) *Every extreme point of the polyhedron $P = \{\mathbf{x} \in \Re^n \mid \mathbf{A}\mathbf{x} \ge \mathbf{b}\}$ satisfies*
$$-(nU)^n \le x_j \le (nU)^n, \quad j = 1, \dots, n.$$

(b) *Every extreme point of the standard form polyhedron $P = \{\mathbf{x} \in \Re^n \mid \mathbf{A}\mathbf{x} = \mathbf{b}, \ \mathbf{x} \ge \mathbf{0}\}$ satisfies*
$$-(mU)^m \le x_j \le (mU)^m, \quad j = 1, \dots, n.$$

Proof.   (a) Let $\mathbf{x}$ be an extreme point of P. By choosing n linearly independent active constraints, we see that $\mathbf{x}$ satisfies $\hat{\mathbf{A}}\mathbf{x} = \hat{\mathbf{b}}$, where $\hat{\mathbf{A}}$ is an $n \times n$ invertible submatrix of $\mathbf{A}$, and $\hat{\mathbf{b}}$ is an n-dimensional subvector of $\mathbf{b}$. Solving for $\mathbf{x}$, we obtain

$$\mathbf{x} = \hat{\mathbf{A}}^{-1}\hat{\mathbf{b}}.$$

From Cramer's rule, the jth component of $\mathbf{x} = \hat{\mathbf{A}}^{-1}\hat{\mathbf{b}}$ is

$$x_j = \frac{\det(\hat{\mathbf{A}}^j)}{\det(\hat{\mathbf{A}})},$$

where

$$\hat{\mathbf{A}}^j = \begin{bmatrix} \hat{a}_{11} & \hat{a}_{12} & \cdots & \hat{b}_1 & \cdots & \hat{a}_{1n} \\ \vdots & \vdots & \vdots & \vdots & \vdots & \vdots \\ \hat{a}_{n1} & \hat{a}_{n2} & \cdots & \hat{b}_n & \cdots & \hat{a}_{nn} \end{bmatrix},$$

i.e., the jth column of $\hat{\mathbf{A}}^j$ is the vector $\hat{\mathbf{b}}$. We can expand the determinant $\det(\hat{\mathbf{A}}^j)$ in the form

$$\det(\hat{\mathbf{A}}^j) = \sum_{\sigma} (-1)^{|\sigma|} \prod_{i=1}^{n} \tilde{a}_{i,\sigma(i)},$$

where the summation is over all $n!$ permutations $\sigma = (\sigma(1), \ldots, \sigma(n))$ of $(1, \ldots, n)$, $\tilde{a}_{ij} = \hat{b}_j$, and $\tilde{a}_{ik} = \hat{a}_{ik}$ for $k \neq j$. Note that $|\sigma|$ denotes the number of inversions of the permutation σ [we say that the permutation σ has an inversion if $i < j$ and $\sigma(i) > \sigma(j)$]. Therefore,

$$\left|\det(\hat{\mathbf{A}}^j)\right| \leq \sum_{\sigma} \prod_{i=1}^{n} |\tilde{a}_{i,\sigma(i)}|.$$

Since $|\tilde{a}_{i,\sigma(i)}| \leq U$, we obtain

$$\left|\det(\hat{\mathbf{A}}^j)\right| \leq n! \, U^n \leq (nU)^n, \qquad j = 1, \ldots, n.$$

Furthermore, since $\hat{\mathbf{A}}$ is invertible, $\det(\hat{\mathbf{A}}) \neq 0$. Since all entries in $\mathbf{A}$ are integer, $\left|\det(\hat{\mathbf{A}})\right| \geq 1$. Therefore, the extreme point $\mathbf{x}$ satisfies $|x_j| \leq (nU)^n$, for all j.

(b) Exactly the same argument proves the result for polyhedra in standard form. The only difference is that instead of the $n \times n$ matrix $\hat{\mathbf{A}}$, we use a basis matrix $\mathbf{B}$. The dimensions of $\mathbf{B}$ are $m \times m$ if $\mathbf{A}$ has linearly independent rows; otherwise, we eliminate redundant rows of $\mathbf{A}$, and $\mathbf{B}$ has even smaller dimension. In any case, n can be replaced by m. $\qquad \square$

The previous lemma establishes that all extreme points $\mathbf{x}$ of the polyhedron $P = \{\mathbf{x} \in \Re^n \mid \mathbf{Ax} \geq \mathbf{b}\}$ are contained in the bounded polyhedron P_B defined by

$$P_B = \{\mathbf{x} \in P \mid |x_j| \leq (nU)^n, \ j = 1, \ldots, n\}. \qquad (8.1)$$

Assuming that the rows of $\mathbf{A}$ span $\Re^n$, P is nonempty if and only if it has an extreme point. This is the case if and only if P_B is nonempty, and the algorithm can be applied to P_B instead of P. Notice that P_B is a bounded polyhedron contained in the ball $E(\mathbf{0}, n(nU)^{2n}\mathbf{I})$. Therefore, we can start the ellipsoid method with $E_0 = E(\mathbf{0}, n(nU)^{2n}\mathbf{I})$. Note that the volume of E_0 is less than

$$V = \left(2n(nU)^n\right)^n = (2n)^n (nU)^{n^2}.$$

This number V will be part of the input of the ellipsoid method.

We next discuss the assumption that the polyhedron P, if nonempty, has full dimension, i.e., it has positive volume. Why do we need this assumption? If P is nonempty, but has dimension lower than n, then $\text{Vol}(P) = 0$. Consider for example the polyhedron $P = \{(x_1, x_2) \mid x_1 + x_2 = 1, x_1, x_2 \geq 0\}$. Clearly, its volume is zero, even though the polyhedron is nonempty. Because the polyhedron has zero volume, the algorithm could terminate after t^* steps and decide incorrectly that P is empty.

We next prove that a small perturbation of a nonempty polyhedron produces a polyhedron that has full dimension.

Lemma 8.3 Let $P = \{\mathbf{x} \in \Re^n \mid \mathbf{A}\mathbf{x} \geq \mathbf{b}\}$. We assume that $\mathbf{A}$ and $\mathbf{b}$ have integer entries, which are bounded in absolute value by U. Let

$$\epsilon = \frac{1}{2(n+1)} \big((n+1)U\big)^{-(n+1)}.$$

Let

$$P_\epsilon = \big\{\mathbf{x} \in \Re^n \mid \mathbf{A}\mathbf{x} \geq \mathbf{b} - \epsilon\mathbf{e}\big\},$$

where $\mathbf{e} = (1, 1, \ldots, 1)$.

(a) If P is empty, then P_ϵ is empty.

(b) If P is nonempty, then P_ϵ is full-dimensional.

Proof. (a) Suppose that P is empty. Consider the infeasible linear programming problem

$$\begin{aligned} \text{minimize} \quad & \mathbf{0}'\mathbf{x} \\ \text{subject to} \quad & \mathbf{A}\mathbf{x} \geq \mathbf{b}, \end{aligned}$$

and its dual

$$\begin{aligned} \text{maximize} \quad & \mathbf{p}'\mathbf{b} \\ \text{subject to} \quad & \mathbf{p}'\mathbf{A} = \mathbf{0}' \\ & \mathbf{p} \geq \mathbf{0}. \end{aligned}$$

Since the primal problem is infeasible, the dual problem has value $+\infty$. Therefore, there exists some $\mathbf{p} \geq \mathbf{0}$ with

$$\mathbf{p}'\mathbf{A} = \mathbf{0}', \qquad \mathbf{p}'\mathbf{b} = 1.$$

By Lemma 8.2(b), there exists a basic feasible solution $\hat{\mathbf{p}}$ to the constraints $\mathbf{p}'\mathbf{A} = \mathbf{0}'$, $\mathbf{p}'\mathbf{b} = 1$, $\mathbf{p} \geq \mathbf{0}$, such that

$$\hat{p}_i \leq \big((n+1)U\big)^{n+1}, \qquad \forall\, i.$$

(We have $n + 1$ instead of n, because there are $n + 1$ equality constraints.) Since $\hat{\mathbf{p}}$ is a basic feasible solution, at most $n + 1$ of its components are nonzero and we have

$$\sum_{i=1}^{m} \hat{p}_i \leq (n+1)\big((n+1)U\big)^{n+1}.$$

Therefore,

$$\hat{\mathbf{p}}'(\mathbf{b} - \epsilon\mathbf{e}) = 1 - \epsilon \sum_{i=1}^{m} \hat{p}_i \geq \frac{1}{2} > 0.$$

Hence, when $\mathbf{b}$ is replaced with $\mathbf{b} - \epsilon\mathbf{e}$, the value of the dual problem remains $+\infty$, the primal problem remains infeasible, and P_ϵ is empty.

(b) Let $\mathbf{x}$ be an element of P, so that $\mathbf{A}\mathbf{x} \geq \mathbf{b}$. Let $\mathbf{y}$ be a vector such that $|y_j - x_j| \leq \epsilon/(nU)$ for all j. The ith component of $\mathbf{A}\mathbf{y}$ satisfies

$$\sum_{j=1}^{n} a_{ij} y_j \geq \sum_{j=1}^{n} a_{ij} x_j - \frac{\epsilon}{nU} \sum_{j=1}^{n} |a_{ij}|$$
$$\geq b_i - \frac{\epsilon}{nU} nU$$
$$= b_i - \epsilon.$$

Therefore, any such vector $\mathbf{y}$ belongs to P_ϵ. Furthermore, the set of all such vectors $\mathbf{y}$ is a cube whose volume is positive. ☐

Part of the input of the ellipsoid method, is a number v such that if the polyhedron P is nonempty, then $\text{Vol}(P) > v$. We next establish a bound on v in terms of the problem data.

Lemma 8.4 Let $P = \{\mathbf{x} \in \Re^n \mid \mathbf{A}\mathbf{x} \geq \mathbf{b}\}$ be a full-dimensional bounded polyhedron, where the entries of $\mathbf{A}$ and $\mathbf{b}$ are integer and have absolute value bounded by U. Then,

$$\text{Vol}(P) > n^{-n}(nU)^{-n^2(n+1)}.$$

Proof. If P has full dimension and has at least one extreme point, then P has $n+1$ extreme points $\mathbf{v}^0, \ldots, \mathbf{v}^n$ which are not on a common hyperplane (Exercise 8.5). Let

$$Q = \left\{ \mathbf{x} \in \Re^n \;\middle|\; \mathbf{x} = \sum_{k=0}^{n} \lambda_k \mathbf{v}^k, \; \sum_{k=0}^{n} \lambda_k = 1, \; \lambda_k \geq 0 \right\}.$$

Clearly, Q is contained in P. Therefore, $\text{Vol}(P) \geq \text{Vol}(Q)$. The volume of Q can be calculated (Exercise 8.6) as follows:

$$\text{Vol}(Q) = \frac{1}{n!} \left| \det \begin{bmatrix} 1 & \cdots & 1 \\ \mathbf{v}^0 & \cdots & \mathbf{v}^n \end{bmatrix} \right|.$$

Notice that the ith coordinate of $\mathbf{v}^k$ is a rational number p_i^k/q_i^k with $\left|q_i^k\right| \leq (nU)^n$, using the argument in the proof of Lemma 8.2. Expanding the above determinant, we obtain

$$\text{Vol}(Q) \geq \frac{1}{n!} \left| \frac{a}{\prod_{i=1}^n \prod_{k=0}^n q_i^k} \right|,$$

where a is a nonzero integer, i.e., $|a| \geq 1$. Therefore,

$$\text{Vol}(Q) > \frac{1}{n^n} \frac{1}{\prod_{i=1}^n \prod_{k=0}^n (nU)^n} = n^{-n}(nU)^{-n^2(n+1)},$$

and hence $\text{Vol}(P) > n^{-n}(nU)^{-n^2(n+1)}$. $\qquad\qquad\qquad\qquad \Box$

The complexity of the ellipsoid method

Consider now a polyhedron $P = \{\mathbf{x} \in \Re^n \mid \mathbf{A}\mathbf{x} \geq \mathbf{b}\}$, where $\mathbf{A}$, $\mathbf{b}$ have integer entries with magnitude bounded by some U, and assume that the rows of $\mathbf{A}$ span $\Re^n$. If the polyhedron P is bounded and either empty or full-dimensional, we have shown in Theorem 8.2 that the ellipsoid method correctly decides whether P is empty or not in $O\big(n \log(V/v)\big)$ iterations. We have shown that we can choose v and V in terms of n and U as follows:

$$v = n^{-n}(nU)^{-n^2(n+1)}, \qquad V = (2n)^n(nU)^{n^2}.$$

These estimates lead to an upper bound on the number of iterations of the ellipsoid method, which is

$$O\big(n^4 \log(nU)\big).$$

If the polyhedron P is arbitrary, we first form the bounded polyhedron P_B [cf. Eq. (8.1)], and then perturb P_B as in Lemma 8.3, to form a new polyhedron $P_{B,\epsilon}$. As already noted, P is nonempty if and only if it has an extreme point, in which case P_B is nonempty. By Lemma 8.3, P_B is nonempty if and only if $P_{B,\epsilon}$ is nonempty. We can therefore apply the ellipsoid algorithm to $P_{B,\epsilon}$, and decide whether P is empty or not. It is not hard to check that the number of iterations is

$$O\big(n^6 \log(nU)\big).$$

In order to argue that the ellipsoid method correctly decides whether P is nonempty in polynomial time, we also need to ensure that the number of arithmetic operations per iteration is polynomially bounded in n and $\log U$. There are two difficulties, however. First, the computation of the new ellipsoid involves taking a square root. Although this might seem easy, taking square roots in a computer cannot be done exactly (the square root of an integer can be an irrational number). Therefore, we need to show that if we only perform calculations in finite precision, the error we make at each step of the computation will not lead to large inaccuracies in later stages of the computation. Second, we need to show that the numbers we generate at each step of the computation have polynomial size. A potential difficulty is that as numbers get multiplied, we might create numbers as large as 2^U. The number of bits needed to represent such a number would be $O(U)$, which is exponential in $\log U$.

We can overcome the difficulties mentioned in the preceding paragraph. It has been shown that if we only use $O(n^3 \log U)$ binary digits of precision, the numbers computed during the algorithm have polynomially bounded size and the algorithm still correctly decides whether P is empty in $O(n^6 \log(nU))$ iterations. We do not cover these results as they are very technical and do not offer much insight.

This discussion leads to the following theorem.

Theorem 8.3 *The linear programming feasibility problem with integer data can be solved in polynomial time.*

8.4   The ellipsoid method for optimization

So far we have described the ellipsoid method for deciding whether a polyhedron P is empty or not. We next consider the following optimization problem and its dual:

$$\begin{array}{ll} \text{minimize} & \mathbf{c'x} \\ \text{subject to} & \mathbf{Ax} \geq \mathbf{b}, \end{array} \qquad \begin{array}{ll} \text{maximize} & \mathbf{b'p} \\ \text{subject to} & \mathbf{A'p} = \mathbf{c} \\ & \mathbf{p} \geq \mathbf{0}. \end{array}$$

By strong duality, both the primal and dual optimization problems have optimal solutions if and only if the following system of linear inequalities is feasible:

$$\mathbf{b'p} = \mathbf{c'x}, \qquad \mathbf{Ax} \geq \mathbf{b}, \qquad \mathbf{A'p} = \mathbf{c}, \qquad \mathbf{p} \geq \mathbf{0}.$$

Let Q be the feasible set of this system of inequalities. We can apply the ellipsoid method to decide whether Q is nonempty. If it is indeed nonempty and a feasible solution $(\mathbf{x}, \mathbf{p})$ is obtained, then $\mathbf{x}$ is an optimal solution to the original optimization problem and $\mathbf{p}$ is an optimal solution to its dual. If the polyhedron Q is not full-dimensional and is first perturbed to Q_ϵ, as in Lemma 8.3, the ellipsoid method may terminate with some $(\mathbf{x}_\epsilon, \mathbf{p}_\epsilon) \in Q_\epsilon$, which does not necessarily belong to Q. However, provided that ϵ is sufficiently small, an element of Q can be obtained using a suitable rounding procedure. This fact together with Theorem 8.3, leads to the following result.

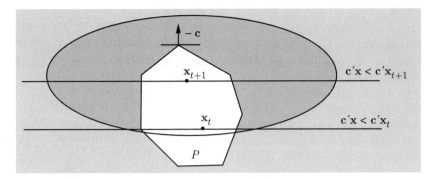

Figure 8.4: The ellipsoid method initially found a feasible solution $\mathbf{x}_t$ of P. It is then applied to $P' = P \cap \{\mathbf{x} \in \Re^n \mid \mathbf{c}'\mathbf{x} < \mathbf{c}'\mathbf{x}_t\}$, and generates the ellipsoid indicated in the figure. Its center $\mathbf{x}_{t+1}$ belongs in P'. The method is then applied to $P \cap \{\mathbf{x} \in \Re^n \mid \mathbf{c}'\mathbf{x} < \mathbf{c}'\mathbf{x}_{t+1}\}$.

Theorem 8.4 *The linear programming problem with integer data can be solved in polynomial time.*

An alternative but more direct method of solving the linear programming problem is to use the so-called *sliding objective ellipsoid method*, which we describe next.

Sliding objective ellipsoid method

We first run the ellipsoid method to find a feasible solution $\mathbf{x}_0 \in P = \{\mathbf{x} \in \Re^n \mid \mathbf{A}\mathbf{x} \geq \mathbf{b}\}$. It can be shown that the same ellipsoid method can be applied to linear programming problems involving some strict inequality constraints. We apply the ellipsoid method to decide whether the set

$$P \cap \{\mathbf{x} \in \Re^n \mid \mathbf{c}'\mathbf{x} < \mathbf{c}'\mathbf{x}_0\}$$

is empty. If it is empty, then $\mathbf{x}_0$ is optimal. If it is nonempty, we find a new solution $\mathbf{x}_1$ in P with objective function value strictly smaller than $\mathbf{c}'\mathbf{x}_0$. More generally, every time a better feasible solution $\mathbf{x}_t$ is found, we take $P \cap \{\mathbf{x} \in \Re^n \mid \mathbf{c}'\mathbf{x} < \mathbf{c}'\mathbf{x}_t\}$ as the new set of inequalities and reapply the ellipsoid method.

Note that in every iteration we add a constraint in the direction of vector $\mathbf{c}$. All the constraints $\mathbf{c}'\mathbf{x} < \mathbf{c}'\mathbf{x}_t$ we add in the course of the algorithm are parallel to each other. This explains the name of the algorithm. Figure 8.4 illustrates a typical iteration.

Performance of the ellipsoid method in practice

The ellipsoid method solves linear programming problems in $O\big(n^6 \log(nU)\big)$ iterations. Since the number of arithmetic operations per iteration is a polynomial function of n and $\log U$, this results in a polynomial number of arithmetic operations. This running time compares favorably with the worst-case running time of the simplex method, which is exponential. However, the ellipsoid method has not been practically successful, because it needs a very large number of iterations even on moderate size linear programming problems. In contrast, the theoretically inefficient simplex method needs a small number of iterations on most practical linear programming problems.

This behavior of the ellipsoid method emphasizes the pitfalls in identifying polynomial time algorithms with efficient algorithms. The difficulty arises because we insist on *a universal polynomial bound for all instances* of the problem. The ellipsoid method achieves a polynomial bound for all instances. However, it *typically* exhibits slow convergence. There have been several proposed improvements to accelerate the convergence of the ellipsoid method, such as the idea of *deep cuts* (see Exercise 8.3). However, it does not seem that these modifications can fundamentally affect the speed of convergence.

Rather than revolutionizing linear programming, the ellipsoid method has shown that linear programming is efficiently solvable from a theoretical point of view. In this sense, the ellipsoid method can be seen as a tool for classifying the complexity of linear programming problems. This is important, because a theoretically efficient algorithm is usually followed by the development of practical methods. This has been the case with interior point methods, which are the subject of the next chapter.

8.5 Problems with exponentially many constraints*

In this section, we explain how the ellipsoid method can be applied to problems with exponentially many constraints, in order to solve them in polynomial time. We first describe the main ideas, and then discuss at some length, two particular examples.

Consider the linear programming problem of minimizing $\mathbf{c}'\mathbf{x}$ subject to constraints of the form $\mathbf{Ax} \geq \mathbf{b}$. We assume that $\mathbf{A}$ is an $m \times n$ matrix and that the entries of $\mathbf{A}$ and $\mathbf{b}$ are integer. Recall that the number of iterations in the ellipsoid method is polynomial in n and $\log U$, where n is the dimension of $\mathbf{x}$, and U is a bound on the magnitude of the entries of $\mathbf{A}$ and $\mathbf{b}$. What is remarkable about this result is that the number of iterations is independent of the number m of constraints. This suggests that we may be able to solve, in time polynomial in n and $\log U$, problems in which the number m of constraints is very large, e.g., exponential in n.

This turns out to be possible in several situations, but there are a couple of obstacles to be overcome, which we discuss next.

The first obstacle is the following. If m is, for example, equal to 2^n, we need $\Omega(2^n)$ time just to input problem data, such as the matrix $\mathbf{A}$. An algorithm which is polynomial in n would then appear to be impossible. The way around this obstacle is to assume that the input $\mathbf{A}$ and $\mathbf{b}$ is not given as an explicit listing of all entries. Instead, we will assume that $\mathbf{A}$ and $\mathbf{b}$ are given in some concise form, maybe in terms of formulas involving a relatively small number of parameters. For a concrete example, consider the set of constraints

$$\sum_{i \in S} a_i x_i \geq |S|, \qquad \text{for all subsets } S \text{ of } \{1, \ldots, n\}.$$

(More natural examples will be provided in Examples 8.2 and 8.3.) We have here a total of 2^n constraints, but they are described concisely in terms of the n scalar parameters $a_1, \ldots, a_n$.

We are interested in the problem of minimizing a linear cost function over a polyhedron P, where P is assumed to belong to a particular family of polyhedra. The polyhedra in this family can have arbitrary dimension, but they must have a special structure, in the following sense. A typical polyhedron is described by specifying the dimension n and an integer vector $\mathbf{h}$ of *primary data*, of dimension $O(n^k)$, where $k \geq 1$ is some constant. [In our example, $\mathbf{h} = (a_1, \ldots, a_n)$ and $k = 1$.] Let U_0 be the largest magnitude of the entries of $\mathbf{h}$. We then have some mapping which, given n and $\mathbf{h}$, defines an integer matrix $\mathbf{A}$, with n columns, and an integer vector $\mathbf{b}$. No restriction is placed on the number of rows of $\mathbf{A}$. Let U be the largest magnitude of the entries of $\mathbf{A}$ and $\mathbf{b}$. The only assumption that we make is that there exist constants C and ℓ such that

$$\log U \leq C n^\ell \log^\ell U_0, \tag{8.2}$$

no matter what n and $\mathbf{h}$ is. Note that the size of a typical instance of this problem, as described by n and $\mathbf{h}$, is $O(n^k \log U_0)$.

If we apply the ellipsoid method to a problem with the above structure, the number of iterations is

$$O(n^6 \log(nU)) = O(n^6 \log n + n^{6+\ell} \log^\ell U_0),$$

which is polynomial in the size of the primary problem data. Does this mean that we have an algorithm which is polynomial in n and U_0? Not necessarily, because we also need to account for the computational complexity of a typical iteration.

In reference to our description of the ellipsoid method, there are some algebraic manipulations, such as in Step 2(d). These can be carried out in polynomial time, up to the necessary precision, as discussed at the end of Section 8.4. The critical steps, however, are 2(b) and 2(c). In these steps, we need to check whether the current vector $\mathbf{x}$ is feasible and, if not, we have to display a violated constraint. In general, this is accomplished by examining each one of the m constraints. But if m is exponential in n, this would result in an exponential time algorithm. Hence, the key to a polynomial time algorithm, when m is large, hinges on our ability to carry out Steps 2(b)-(c), in polynomial time. These steps are important enough to have a name of their own.

Definition 8.8 *Given a polyhedron $P \subset \Re^n$ and a vector $\mathbf{x} \in \Re^n$, the* **separation problem** *is to:*

(a) *Either decide that $\mathbf{x} \in P$, or*

(b) *Find a vector $\mathbf{d}$ such that $\mathbf{d}'\mathbf{x} < \mathbf{d}'\mathbf{y}$ for all $\mathbf{y} \in P$.*

In the terminology of Chapter 4, if $\mathbf{x} \notin P$, then the separation problem is nothing but the problem of finding a separating hyperplane. It is also the same as the problem encountered in each iteration of the cutting plane method of Section 6.3.

Let us note a small difference between the above definition and Steps 2(b)-(c) of the ellipsoid method. The ellipsoid method, in the form that we gave it, asks for a separating hyperplane which corresponds to one of the constraints in the description of P. In the separation problem, however, any separating hyperplane is acceptable. It turns out that this difference is of no significance. It can be easily verified that all the properties of the ellipsoid method remain valid if we allow for general separating hyperplanes.

Let us now assume that we can somehow solve the separation problem (for the polyhedra within the family of interest) without having to examine all the constraints, and that this can be accomplished in time polynomial in n and $\log U$. As will be seen in Examples 8.2 and 8.3, this is sometimes possible. Then, the computational requirements of each iteration are polynomial in n and $\log U$, and the overall running time of the ellipsoid method is also polynomial in n and $\log U$ (as well as polynomial in n and $\log U_0$). We summarize our discussion in the following theorem.

Theorem 8.5 *If we can solve the separation problem (for a family of polyhedra) in time polynomial in n and $\log U$, then we can also solve linear optimization problems in time polynomial in n and $\log U$. If condition (8.2) holds, the running time is also polynomial in n and $\log U_0$.*

In fact, under some technical conditions the converse is also true, i.e., we can solve the separation problem for a family of polyhedra in time polynomial in n and $\log U$, if and only if we can solve the optimization problem over the polyhedra in that family in time polynomial in n and $\log U$. We illustrate these ideas with the following two examples. (See also Exercise 8.10 for an application of the converse to Theorem 8.5.)

Example 8.2 (A bound for the traveling salesman problem) Perhaps the most famous problem in discrete optimization, the traveling salesman problem, is defined as follows. Given an undirected graph $G = (\mathcal{N}, \mathcal{E})$ with n nodes, and costs c_e for every edge $e \in \mathcal{E}$, the goal is to find a *tour* (a cycle that visits all nodes) of minimum cost. In order to model the problem, we define for every edge $e \in \mathcal{E}$ a variable x_e, which is 1 if edge e is included in the tour, and 0 otherwise. To facilitate the formulation we define for every nonempty $S \subset \mathcal{N}$,

$$\delta(S) = \{e \mid e = \{i,j\},\ i \in S,\ j \notin S\}.$$

In particular, $\delta(\{i\})$ is the set of edges incident to i. Since in every tour, each node is incident to two edges, we have

$$\sum_{e \in \delta(\{i\})} x_e = 2, \qquad i \in \mathcal{N}.$$

In addition, if we partition the nodes into two nonempty sets S and $\mathcal{N} \setminus S$, then in every tour there are at least two edges connecting S and $\mathcal{N} \setminus S$. Therefore,

$$\sum_{e \in \delta(S)} x_e \geq 2, \qquad S \subset \mathcal{N},\ S \neq \emptyset, \mathcal{N}.$$

The following linear programming problem provides a lower bound (see also Section 10.2) to the optimal cost of the traveling salesman problem:

$$
\begin{aligned}
\text{minimize} \quad & \sum_{e \in \mathcal{E}} c_e x_e \\
\text{subject to} \quad & \sum_{e \in \delta(\{i\})} x_e = 2, && i \in \mathcal{N}, \\
& \sum_{e \in \delta(S)} x_e \geq 2, && S \subset \mathcal{N},\ S \neq \emptyset, \mathcal{N}, \\
& x_e \leq 1, \\
& x_e \geq 0.
\end{aligned}
$$

This problem has an exponential number of constraints, because $\mathcal{N}$ has $2^n - 2$ nonempty proper subsets S. From the previous discussion, in order to solve this problem in polynomial time, it suffices to be able to solve the separation problem in polynomial time.

We next show how to solve the separation problem in polynomial time. Given a vector $\mathbf{x}^*$, we need to check whether it satisfies the above constraints and if not, to exhibit a violated inequality. We first check whether

$$\sum_{e \in \delta(\{i\})} x_e^* = 2,$$

for all $i \in \mathcal{N}$ (there are only n of these constraints). The constraints $0 \leq x_e^* \leq 1$ are also easily checked. In order to check whether one of the remaining constraints is violated, we consider the graph G and assign a capacity x_e^* to every edge $e \in \mathcal{E}$. We then calculate a minimum cut, where the minimum is also taken over all choices of the source and sink nodes. Let S_0 be a minimum cut. If the capacity of this cut is larger than or equal to 2, then the point $\mathbf{x}^*$ is feasible, since for all S,

$$\sum_{e \in \delta(S)} x_e^* \geq \sum_{e \in \delta(S_0)} x_e^* \geq 2.$$

If not, then the inequality corresponding to the set S_0 is violated, i.e.,

$$\sum_{e \in \delta(S_0)} x_e^* < 2.$$

Finding a minimum cut in a directed graph is equivalent to solving a maximum flow problem (see Section 7.5), and this can be done in polynomial time. By replacing each undirected edge e by two directed arcs, it follows that we can also solve the minimum cut in an undirected graph in time polynomial in n. Thus, we can solve the separation problem in polynomial time and therefore, by Theorem 8.5, this particular bound to the cost of an optimal traveling salesman tour can be computed in polynomial time.

Example 8.3 (A probability consistency problem) We are given n events $A_1, \ldots, A_n$ in a probability space. Let $N = \{1, \ldots, n\}$. Based on some information we have obtained, we believe that

$$\mathrm{P}(A_i) \leq p_i, \qquad i \in N,$$

where the notation $\mathrm{P}(A)$ denotes the probability of event A. Moreover, we have made a judgement on a lower bound for the joint probability of these events. In particular, we believe that

$$\mathrm{P}(A_i \cap A_j) \geq p_{ij}, \qquad i, j \in N, \ i < j.$$

Given the numbers p_i and p_{ij}, which are between 0 and 1, we would like to know whether these beliefs are consistent with the laws of probability.

In order to completely specify a probability space we should assign numerical values to the probabilities

$$x(S) = \mathrm{P}\left(\left(\cap_{i \in S} A_i \right) \cap \left(\cap_{i \notin S} \overline{A}_i \right) \right),$$

for all 2^n subsets S of $N = \{1, \ldots, n\}$. Here, $\overline{A}_i$ are the complements of the events A_i. Note that $x(S)$ represents the probability that events A_i, $i \in S$, occur and none of the events A_i, $i \notin S$, does. We treat the probabilities $x(S)$ as variables. Since $P(A_i) \leq p_i$, we have

$$\sum_{\{S | i \in S\}} x(S) \leq p_i.$$

Moreover, since $P(A_i \cap A_j) \geq p_{ij}$,

$$\sum_{\{S | i, j \in S\}} x(S) \geq p_{ij}.$$

Finally,

$$\sum_S x(S) = 1,$$

and $x(S) \geq 0$ for all sets S. Therefore, the beliefs regarding the probability distribution are consistent if and only if the following system of linear inequalities is feasible:

$$\sum_{\{S|i\in S\}} x(S) \leq p_i, \qquad i \in N,$$

$$\sum_{\{S|i,j\in S\}} x(S) \geq p_{ij}, \qquad i, j \in N, \ i < j,$$

$$\sum_S x(S) = 1,$$

$$x(S) \geq 0, \qquad \forall \ S.$$

Note that this system has an exponential number of variables, namely 2^n.

Consider the problem of maximizing $\sum_S 0x(S)$ subject to the above constraints. Using duality, this linear programming problem is feasible if and only if there does not exist a vector $(\mathbf{u}, \mathbf{y}, z)$ such that

$$\sum_{i,j\in S, i<j} y_{ij} + \sum_{i\in S} u_i + z \geq 0, \qquad \forall \ S,$$

$$\sum_{i,j\in N, i<j} p_{ij}y_{ij} + \sum_{i\in N} p_i u_i + z \leq -1,$$

$$y_{ij} \leq 0, \ u_i \geq 0, \qquad i, j \in N, \ i < j.$$

We have therefore reduced the probability consistency problem to checking whether the above system of (exponentially many) inequalities is infeasible. We will show that the corresponding separation problem is solvable in polynomial time.

The separation problem is as follows: given a vector $(\mathbf{u}^*, \mathbf{y}^*, z^*)$ we would like to check whether it satisfies all of the constraints and if not, find a violated inequality. We first check whether the inequalities

$$\sum_{i,j\in N, i<j} p_{ij}y_{ij}^* + \sum_{i\in N} p_i u_i^* + z^* \leq -1,$$

$$y_{ij}^* \leq 0, \ u_i \geq 0,$$

are satisfied. If not, we have identified a violated inequality. Otherwise, it remains to check whether the inequality

$$\sum_{i,j\in S, i<j} y_{ij}^* + \sum_{i\in S} u_i^* + z^* \geq 0$$

holds for all S.

Since there are exponentially many sets S we cannot check them individually in polynomial time. We will instead look for a set S that minimizes $f(S)$, where

$$f(S) = \sum_{i,j\in S, i<j} y_{ij}^* + \sum_{i\in S} u_i^*.$$

Let S_0 be a set that achieves the minimum. If $f(S_0) \geq -z^*$, the vector $(\mathbf{u}^*, \mathbf{y}^*, z^*)$ is feasible. If not, we have

$$\sum_{i,j \in S_0, i < j} y^*_{ij} + \sum_{i \in S_0} u^*_i + z^* < 0,$$

and the inequality associated with S_0 is violated.

We next reduce the problem of minimizing $f(S)$ to a minimum cut problem. We construct a network $G = (V_1 \cup V_2 \cup \{s, t\}, \mathcal{A})$, where $V_1 = \{(i, j) \mid i, j \in N, \ i < j, \ y^*_{ij} < 0\}$, $V_2 = \{i \mid i \in N, \ u^*_i > 0\}$, and

$$\mathcal{A} = \Big\{ \big(s, (i,j)\big) \mid (i,j) \in V_1 \Big\}$$

$$\cup \Big\{ (i,t) \mid i \in V_2 \Big\}$$

$$\cup \Big\{ \big((i,j), i\big) \mid (i,j) \in V_1, \ i \in V_2 \Big\}$$

$$\cup \Big\{ \big((i,j), j\big) \mid (i,j) \in V_1, \ j \in V_2 \Big\}.$$

Arcs of the form $\big(s, (i,j)\big)$, have capacity $-y^*_{ij}$. Arcs of the form (i, t) have capacity u^*_i. Arcs of the form $\big((i,j), i\big)$, and arcs of the form $\big((i,j), j\big)$ have infinite capacity. For an example, see Figure 8.5.

In Exercise 8.7, the reader is asked to verify that every minimal capacity s-t cut in the network G is of the form $\{s\} \cup W \cup S$, where S is some subset of $\{1, 2, \ldots, n\}$, and $W = \{(i, j) \mid i \in S, \ j \in S\}$. In particular, the cut can be completely characterized by the set S, and we use $c(S)$ to denote its capacity. Furthermore, $c(S)$ is given by

$$c(S) = f(S) - \sum_{i,j \in N, i < j} y^*_{ij}.$$

Therefore, the problem of minimizing $f(S)$ reduces to the problem of finding a minimum cut in G. Since we can find a minimum cut in a network in polynomial time, we can solve the separation problem in polynomial time. Therefore, by Theorem 8.5, we can solve the original probability consistency problem in polynomial time.

In the exercises, we will use the equivalence of separation and optimization to show that we can compute bounds for the optimal cost of difficult integer programming problems in polynomial time. These bounds are obtained by solving linear programming problems with an exponential number of constraints.

As a final note, we remark that an efficient algorithm for the separation problem leads not only to a polynomial algorithm for the optimization problem, but also to a potentially practical cutting plane method (see also Section 12.5). As discussed in Section 6.3, the cutting plane method relies on the ability to identify a violated constraint, whenever we have an infeasible solution. This is the same as solving a separation problem.

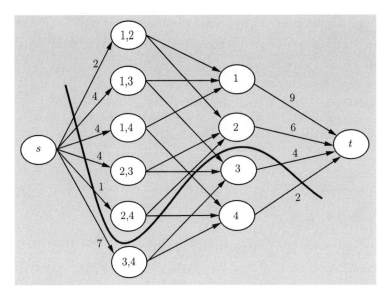

Figure 8.5: Suppose we want to check whether the solution $y_{12}^* = -2$, $y_{13}^* = -4$, $y_{14}^* = -4$, $y_{23}^* = -4$, $y_{24}^* = -1$, $y_{34}^* = -7$, $u_1^* = 9$, $u_2^* = 6$, $u_3^* = 4$, $u_4^* = 2$, and $z^* = 2$ satisfies the family of constraints $\sum_{i,j \in S} y_{ij}^* + \sum_{i \in S} u_i^* + z^* \geq 0$ for all $S \subset N$. We construct the network G shown in the figure and compute the minimum cut. (The numbers next to each arc are the arc capacities.) The minimum cut indicated corresponds to the set $S_0 = \{3, 4\}$. The value of the cut is $c(S_0) = 21$. Then,

$$f(S_0) = \sum_{i,j \in S_0, i < j} y_{ij}^* + \sum_{i \in S_0} u_i^* = -7 + 4 + 2 = -1,$$

$$f(S) + z^* \geq f(S_0) + z^* = -1 + 2 = 1 > 0, \qquad \forall\ S,$$

and the given solution $(\mathbf{y}^*, \mathbf{u}^*, z^*)$ is feasible.

8.6   Summary

In this chapter, we presented the notion of an efficient algorithm, defined as one that solves all instances of a problem in time polynomial in the size of the instance. We recalled that the simplex method is not an efficient algorithm in this sense, as there are examples where it needs an exponential number of iterations to find an optimal solution. We then showed that the ellipsoid method is a polynomial time algorithm.

In addition, we introduced the separation problem for a family of polyhedra and showed that the ellipsoid method can solve linear programming problems with an exponential number of constraints in polynomial time, provided that the separation problem is solvable in polynomial time. In this respect, the ellipsoid method can be seen as a tool for classifying the complexity of large scale linear programming problems.

The fact that the linear programming problem belongs to the class of polynomially solvable problems is a fundamental and deep property. However, given that the ellipsoid method is not a practical algorithm, one might have legitimate concerns about the relevance of the concept of polynomial time solvability. In the next chapter, we resolve this question by introducing algorithms for linear programming that are polynomial as well as practical.

8.7 Exercises

Exercise 8.1 Let $e_1 = (1, 0, \ldots, 0)$ and $\mathbf{u} \in \Re^n$. We introduce the following matrix:

$$\mathbf{R} = 2 \frac{\left(\mathbf{u} + \|\mathbf{u}\| e_1\right)\left(\mathbf{u} + \|\mathbf{u}\| e_1\right)'}{\left\|\mathbf{u} + \|\mathbf{u}\| e_1\right\|^2} - \mathbf{I}.$$

Show that

$$\mathbf{R}'\mathbf{R} = \mathbf{I}, \qquad \mathbf{R}\mathbf{u} = \|\mathbf{u}\| e_1.$$

Exercise 8.2 Let $\mathbf{D}$ be a symmetric positive definite matrix and $\mathbf{z} \in \Re^n$. Given a vector $\mathbf{a}$, let $\mathbf{R}$ be a rotation matrix such that $\mathbf{R}\mathbf{D}^{1/2}\mathbf{a} = \|\mathbf{D}^{1/2}\mathbf{a}\| e_1$ (cf. Exercise 8.1). Let $T(\mathbf{x})$ be the affine transformation defined by

$$T(\mathbf{x}) = \mathbf{R}\mathbf{D}^{-1/2}(\mathbf{x} - \mathbf{z}).$$

Let $E' = E(\overline{\mathbf{z}}, \overline{\mathbf{D}})$ be the ellipsoid determined by

$$\overline{\mathbf{z}} = \mathbf{z} + \frac{1}{n+1} \frac{\mathbf{D}\mathbf{a}}{\sqrt{\mathbf{a}'\mathbf{D}\mathbf{a}}},$$

$$\overline{\mathbf{D}} = \frac{n^2}{n^2 - 1}\left(\mathbf{D} - \frac{2}{n+1}\frac{\mathbf{D}\mathbf{a}\mathbf{a}'\mathbf{D}}{\mathbf{a}'\mathbf{D}\mathbf{a}}\right).$$

Let

$$E'_0 = E\left(\frac{e_1}{n+1}, \frac{n^2}{n^2-1}\left(\mathbf{I} - \frac{2}{n+1}e_1 e_1'\right)\right).$$

Prove that

$$T(E') = E'_0.$$

Exercise 8.3 * **(Deep cuts)** In this exercise, we show how to construct cuts that are deeper than the ones we have used in this chapter. Let $P = \{\mathbf{x} \in \Re^n \mid \mathbf{A}\mathbf{x} \geq \mathbf{b}\}$. Let $E = E(\mathbf{z}, \mathbf{D})$ be an ellipsoid in $\Re^n$ such that $P \subset E$. Assume that $\mathbf{a}'\mathbf{x} \geq b$ is a violated inequality and hence $\mathbf{a}'\mathbf{z} < b$. In Theorem 8.1, we constructed a new ellipsoid E' that contains $E \cap \{x \mid a'x \geq a'z\}$. However, the polyhedron P is also contained in the smaller set $E \cap \{x \mid a'x \geq b\}$. Let

$$\alpha = \frac{b - a'z}{\sqrt{a'Da}},$$

$$\tau = \frac{n\alpha + 1}{n + 1},$$

$$\delta = (1 - \alpha^2)\frac{n^2}{n^2 - 1},$$

$$\sigma = \frac{2(n\alpha + 1)}{(1 + \alpha)(n + 1)}.$$

Let also

$$\hat{z} = z + \tau\frac{Da}{\sqrt{a'Da}},$$

$$\hat{D} = \delta\left(D - \sigma\frac{Daa'D}{a'Da}\right).$$

The matrix $\hat{D}$ can be shown to be positive definite and thus $E'' = E(\hat{z}, \hat{D})$ is an ellipsoid. Show that:

(a) $E \cap \{x \mid a'x \geq b\} \subset E''$.

(b) $\text{Vol}(E'') = \left(\frac{n^2(1 - \alpha^2)}{n^2 - 1}\right)^{(n-1)/2}\frac{n(1 - \alpha)}{n + 1}\text{Vol}(E)$.

Exercise 8.4 * (The sliding objective ellipsoid method) Let $P = \{x \in \Re^n \mid Ax \geq b\}$ be a bounded full-dimensional polyhedron with at least one extreme point. Consider the linear programming problem

$$\text{minimize} \quad c'x$$
$$\text{subject to} \quad Ax \geq b,$$

and let z be the optimal cost. We assume that the entries of A, b, and c are integer, and have absolute value bounded by U. Fix some $\epsilon > 0$. Prove that the sliding objective ellipsoid method finds a solution x_t with cost

$$c'x_t \leq z + \epsilon,$$

after a number of iterations polynomial in n, $\log U$, and $\log(1/\epsilon)$.

Exercise 8.5 (Characterization of full-dimensional polyhedra) We have defined a polyhedron

$$P = \{x \in \Re^n \mid Ax \geq b\}$$

to be full-dimensional if it has positive volume. Assume that P is bounded and all rows of A are nonzero. Show that the following are equivalent.

(a) The polyhedron P has full dimension.

(b) There exists a point x in P such that $Ax > b$.

(c) There are $n+1$ extreme points of P that do not lie on a common hyperplane.

Exercise 8.6 Let $\mathbf{v}^k$, $k = 0, \ldots, n$, be $n+1$ given vectors in $\Re^n$. Let

$$Q = \left\{ \mathbf{x} \in \Re^n \mid \mathbf{x} = \sum_{k=0}^{n} \lambda_k \mathbf{v}^k, \; \sum_{k=0}^{n} \lambda_k = 1, \; \lambda_k \geq 0 \right\}.$$

Prove that

$$\text{Vol}(Q) = \frac{1}{n!} \left| \det \left(\begin{bmatrix} 1 & \cdots & 1 \\ \mathbf{v}^0 & \cdots & \mathbf{v}^n \end{bmatrix} \right) \right|.$$

Exercise 8.7 Consider the network G in Example 8.3.

(a) Show that every minimal capacity s-t cut in the network G is of the form $\{s\} \cup W \cup S$, where S is some subset of $\{1, 2, \ldots, n\}$, and $W = \{(i, j) \mid i \in S, \; j \in S\}$.

(b) Show that the capacity of such a cut is equal to

$$f(S) - \sum_{i,j \in N, i<j} y_{ij}^*.$$

Exercise 8.8 (The min-cut problem, revisited) Given an undirected graph $G = (\mathcal{N}, \mathcal{E})$, two special nodes $s, t \in \mathcal{N}$ and weights c_e for all $e \in \mathcal{E}$, we would like to find a minimum weight set of edges that intersects every path from s to t. Let $\mathcal{K}$ be the set of all such paths. One way of formulating this problem is as follows:

$$
\begin{aligned}
\text{minimize} \quad & \sum_{e \in \mathcal{E}} c_e x_e \\
\text{subject to} \quad & \sum_{e \in K} x_e \geq 1, \qquad \forall \, K \in \mathcal{K}, \\
& 0 \leq x_e \leq 1, \qquad \forall \, e \in \mathcal{E}.
\end{aligned}
$$

It turns out that the extreme points of the feasible set are vectors with $0-1$ coordinates, and that an optimal basic feasible solution corresponds to a minimum cut. Prove that the associated separation problem can be solved in polynomial time.

Exercise 8.9 Given a complete undirected graph $G = (\mathcal{N}, \mathcal{E})$ (all possible edges are present) and a function $f(S)$ defined for all $S \subset \mathcal{N}$, consider the problem

$$
\begin{aligned}
\text{minimize} \quad & \sum_{e \in \mathcal{E}} c_e x_e \\
\text{subject to} \quad & \sum_{e \in \delta(S)} x_e \geq f(S), \quad S \subset \mathcal{N}, \; S \neq \emptyset, \mathcal{N}, \\
& 0 \leq x_e \leq 1, \qquad \forall \, e \in \mathcal{E}.
\end{aligned}
$$

The above linear programming problem provides a lower bound for the optimal cost of the corresponding integer programming problem, in which each x_e must take values 0 or 1. Solve the separation problem for the linear programming problems corresponding to the following cases.

(a) Let

$$f(S) = \max_{e \in \delta(S)} r_e,$$

where $r_e \geq 0$, for all $e \in \mathcal{E}$. The corresponding integer programming problem is called the *survivable network design* problem.

(b) Given a set $T \subset N$, let

$$f(S) = \begin{cases} 1, & \text{if } S \cap T \neq \emptyset, T, \\ 0, & \text{otherwise.} \end{cases}$$

The corresponding integer programming problem is called the *Steiner tree* problem.

Exercise 8.10 * (Submodular function minimization) We are given a finite set $N = \{1, \ldots, n\}$, and a function $f(S)$ defined for all subsets S of N. We assume that $f(S)$ is *submodular*, that is

$$f(S) + f(T) \geq f(S \cap T) + f(S \cup T), \qquad \forall\, S, T \subset N.$$

In this exercise, we show how to use the equivalence of separation and optimization to solve the problem of minimizing $f(S)$ over all $S \subset N$.

(a) Suppose first that $f(S)$ is submodular and *nondecreasing*, i.e.,

$$f(S) \leq f(T), \qquad \text{if } S \subset T,$$

and $f(\emptyset) = 0$. Consider the polyhedron

$$P(f) = \left\{ \mathbf{x} \geq \mathbf{0} \,\middle|\, \sum_{j \in S} x_j \leq f(S),\ \forall\, S \subset N \right\},$$

and the following linear programming problem:

$$\begin{aligned}
\text{maximize} \quad & \sum_{j=1}^{n} c_j x_j \\
\text{subject to} \quad & \sum_{j \in S} x_j \leq f(S), \quad S \subset N, \\
& x_j \geq 0, \qquad\qquad j \in N.
\end{aligned}$$

Suppose that $c_1 \geq c_2 \geq \cdots \geq c_k > 0 \geq c_{k+1} \geq \cdots \geq c_n$. Let $S^j = \{1, \ldots, j\}$ for $j \in N$, and $S^0 = \emptyset$. By considering the dual problem, prove that the following solution is optimal

$$x_j = \begin{cases} f(S^j) - f(S^{j-1}), & \text{for } 1 \leq j \leq k, \\ 0, & \text{for } j > k. \end{cases}$$

(b) Consider a submodular, but not necessarily nondecreasing, set function $f(S)$. Let

$$f_{\mathrm{mon}}(S) = \min\left\{ f(T) \mid S \subset T \subset N \right\} - \min\left\{ f(T) \mid T \subset N \right\}.$$

Prove that $f_{\mathrm{mon}}(S)$ is submodular and nondecreasing, and that

$$P(f) = P(f_{\mathrm{mon}}).$$

(c) Assume that for all S, $f(S)$ is integer and $|f(S)| \leq U$, for some U. Using
the equivalence of separation and optimization show that the problem of
minimizing a submodular function can be solved in a number of iterations
polynomial in n and $\log U$, where each iteration involves evaluating the
given submodular set function $f(S)$ for a particular set S. Assume that any
technical conditions needed for the converse of Theorem 8.5 are satisfied.

8.8   Notes and sources

8.1 The idea to measure the running time of an algorithm as a function
of the size of its input is quite old. The polynomial time criterion
is mentioned implicitly by von Neumann (1953) and explicitly by
Cobham (1965) and Edmonds (1965a). Edmonds (1965b) introduced
the term "good" for polynomial time algorithms. The relationship
between the arithmetic and the bit model is discussed in Schrijver
(1986). This reference provides a careful analysis of the fact that the
Gaussian elimination algorithm only produces numbers whose size is
bounded by a polynomial in n and in the size of the entries of the
matrix to be inverted.

8.3 The ellipsoid method was developed by Shor (1970), and Yudin and
Nemirovskii (1977). It has its origin in the method of centers of
gravity due to Levin (1965), in which simplices rather than ellipsoids
were used. The polynomial time complexity of the method was shown
by Khachian (1979). A full proof of the polynomiality of the ellipsoid
method can be found in the books by Papadimitriou and Steiglitz
(1982), and Grötschel, Lovász, and Schrijver (1988).

8.4 The book by Grötschel et al. (1988) contains an extended treatment of the ellipsoid method (including the sliding objective ellipsoid
method).

8.5 The observation that the ellipsoid method can be used to solve linear
programming problems with an exponential number of constraints
was made independently by Padberg and Rao (1980), Grötschel et al.
(1981), and Karp and Papadimitriou (1982). The book by Grötschel
et al. (1988) establishes the equivalence of separation and optimization and contains several further applications of the ellipsoid method.

8.7 The ellipsoid method with deep cuts (Exercise 8.3) is described in
the survey paper by Bland, Goldfard, and Todd (1981). The problem
of minimizing a submodular set function (Exercise 8.10), is a central problem in discrete optimization. For a thorough discussion, see
Grötschel et al. (1988).

Chapter 9

Interior point methods

Contents

The simplex method solves linear programming problems by visiting extreme points, on the boundary of the feasible set, each time improving the cost. In the mid 1980s new algorithms for linear programming were devised that find an optimal solution while moving in the interior of the feasible set; for this reason, they are generally called interior point methods. In practice, these methods are competitive with the simplex method and, especially for large, sparse problems, they often outperform the simplex method.

Interior point methods represent a significant development in the theory and practice of linear programming. They combine the advantages of the simplex method and of the ellipsoid algorithm. From a theoretical point of view, they lead to efficient (polynomial time) algorithms and use interesting geometric ideas; from a practical point of view, they allow the solution to large scale problems that arise in many applications.

In order to understand the key aspects of interior point methods, we will present their three major types and discuss their geometry.

(a) **The affine scaling algorithm.** This is perhaps the simplest interior point algorithm. It combines simplicity with very good practical performance. In some ways, this algorithm is the closest to the simplex method. It has been observed empirically that if we start the algorithm near an extreme point, it moves (approximately) along the edges of the feasible set. The algorithm illustrates well one of the central geometric ideas in interior point methods: approximating a polyhedron by an ellipsoid. We have already seen this idea in the context of the ellipsoid method. The difference is that in interior point methods, the approximating ellipsoid is contained in the polyhedron, while in the ellipsoid method the approximating ellipsoid contains the polyhedron.

(b) **The potential reduction algorithm.** This algorithm introduces the second idea in interior point methods. Rather than measuring progress towards optimality by the reduction in the objective function value (as both the simplex and affine scaling algorithms do), we measure progress by the reduction in a certain nonlinear potential function. This potential function attempts to balance two conflicting objectives:

   (i) decreasing the objective function value, and,

   (ii) staying away from the boundary of the feasible set.

We will construct an algorithm of this type, which has polynomial time complexity.

(c) **Path following algorithms.** This class of algorithms combines excellent behavior in theory and practice. It is based on three ideas:

   (i) transform the constrained linear programming problem to an unconstrained one, by incorporating the constraints in a logarithmic barrier function that imposes a growing penalty as we approach the boundary (this barrier function is similar to the potential function in the potential reduction algorithm);

(ii) solve the unconstrained logarithmic barrier problem approximately by applying Newton's method, which is a technique for solving nonlinear equations or unconstrained optimization problems;

(iii) as the strength of the barrier function is decreased, the optimum of the unconstrained problem follows a certain path (hence the term "path following") that ends at an optimal solution to the original problem.

We present both a primal version that matches the time complexity of the potential reduction algorithm and a primal-dual version that has excellent practical performance and is the method of choice in large scale implementations.

9.1 The affine scaling algorithm

In this section, we present one of the most efficient and yet simple interior point algorithms for solving the linear programming problem

$$\begin{aligned}\text{minimize} \quad & \mathbf{c}'\mathbf{x} \\ \text{subject to} \quad & \mathbf{Ax} = \mathbf{b} \\ & \mathbf{x} \geq \mathbf{0},\end{aligned}$$

and its dual

$$\begin{aligned}\text{maximize} \quad & \mathbf{p}'\mathbf{b} \\ \text{subject to} \quad & \mathbf{p}'\mathbf{A} \leq \mathbf{c}',\end{aligned}$$

where $\mathbf{A}$ is an $m \times n$ matrix.

The main geometric idea in this algorithm is the following. Let $P = \{\mathbf{x} \mid \mathbf{Ax} = \mathbf{b}, \ \mathbf{x} \geq \mathbf{0}\}$ be the feasible set. We will call $\{\mathbf{x} \in P \mid \mathbf{x} > \mathbf{0}\}$ the *interior* of P and its elements *interior points*. While it may be difficult to minimize $\mathbf{c}'\mathbf{x}$ over the polyhedron P in closed form, it is rather easy to optimize the same cost function over an ellipsoid, and the solution can be obtained in closed form. So, instead of minimizing directly over P, we solve a series of optimization problems over ellipsoids. Starting with a feasible solution $\mathbf{x}^0 > \mathbf{0}$, in the interior of P, we form an ellipsoid S_0 centered at $\mathbf{x}^0$, which is contained in the interior of P. We then optimize the linear objective $\mathbf{c}'\mathbf{x}$ over all $\mathbf{x} \in S_0$, and find a new interior point $\mathbf{x}^1$. We draw another ellipsoid S_1 centered at $\mathbf{x}^1$ and proceed in a similar way. See Figure 9.1 for an illustration.

We now recast these geometric ideas in algebraic terms. The first step is to create an ellipsoid centered at a given vector $\mathbf{y}$ such that all elements of the ellipsoid are positive.

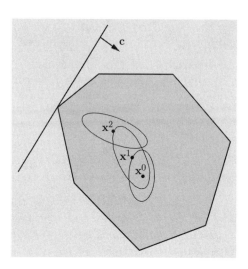

Figure 9.1: Illustration of the affine scaling algorithm. The vector $\mathbf{x}^1$ minimizes $\mathbf{c}'\mathbf{x}$ over all $\mathbf{x}$ in the ellipsoid centered at $\mathbf{x}^0$. The vector $\mathbf{x}^2$ minimizes $\mathbf{c}'\mathbf{x}$ over all $\mathbf{x}$ in the ellipsoid centered at $\mathbf{x}^1$.

Lemma 9.1 *Let $\beta \in (0,1)$ be a scalar, let $\mathbf{y} \in \Re^n$ satisfy $\mathbf{y} > \mathbf{0}$, and let*

$$S = \left\{ \mathbf{x} \in \Re^n \ \Big| \ \sum_{i=1}^n \frac{(x_i - y_i)^2}{y_i^2} \le \beta^2 \right\}.$$

Then, $\mathbf{x} > \mathbf{0}$ for every $\mathbf{x} \in S$.

Proof. Let $\mathbf{x} \in S$. Then, for each i, we have $(x_i - y_i)^2 \le \beta^2 y_i^2 < y_i^2$. Therefore, $|x_i - y_i| < y_i$. In particular, $-x_i + y_i < y_i$ and it follows that $x_i > 0$. $\square$

Fix some $\mathbf{y} \in \Re^n$ satisfying $\mathbf{y} > \mathbf{0}$ and $\mathbf{A}\mathbf{y} = \mathbf{b}$. Let $\mathbf{Y} = \mathrm{diag}(y_1, \ldots, y_n)$ denote the $n \times n$ diagonal matrix whose diagonal entries are $y_1, \ldots, y_n$. (Note that $\mathbf{Y}$ is invertible, since its diagonal entries are positive.) Then, the relation $\mathbf{x} \in S$ can be written as

$$\left\| \mathbf{Y}^{-1}(\mathbf{x} - \mathbf{y}) \right\| \le \beta,$$

where $\|\cdot\|$ stands for the Euclidean norm. The set S is an ellipsoid centered at $\mathbf{y}$. The set $S_0 = S \cap \{\mathbf{x} \mid \mathbf{A}\mathbf{x} = \mathbf{b}\}$ is a section of the ellipsoid S, and is itself an ellipsoid contained in the feasible set; see Figure 9.2. We next replace the original linear programming problem with the problem of

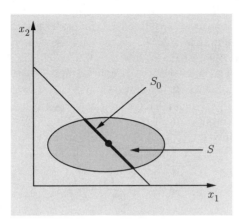

Figure 9.2: The sets S and S_0 for the case where $n = 2$ and there is a single equality constraint $x_1 + x_2 = 1$.

minimizing over the ellipsoid S_0:

$$\begin{array}{ll} \text{minimize} & \mathbf{c}'\mathbf{x} \\ \text{subject to} & \mathbf{A}\mathbf{x} = \mathbf{b} \\ & \left\| \mathbf{Y}^{-1}(\mathbf{x} - \mathbf{y}) \right\| \leq \beta. \end{array} \tag{9.1}$$

We introduce a new variable $\mathbf{d} = \mathbf{x} - \mathbf{y}$. Since $\mathbf{y}$ is feasible, we have $\mathbf{A}\mathbf{y} = \mathbf{b}$. Furthermore, for every $\mathbf{x} \in S_0$, we have $\mathbf{A}\mathbf{x} = \mathbf{b}$. It follows that $\mathbf{A}\mathbf{d} = \mathbf{0}$. If we optimize over $\mathbf{d}$, instead of $\mathbf{x}$, the problem (9.1) becomes

$$\begin{array}{ll} \text{minimize} & \mathbf{c}'\mathbf{d} \\ \text{subject to} & \mathbf{A}\mathbf{d} = \mathbf{0} \\ & \left\| \mathbf{Y}^{-1}\mathbf{d} \right\| \leq \beta. \end{array} \tag{9.2}$$

We now derive a closed form solution to the problem (9.2).

Lemma 9.2 *Assume that the rows of* $\mathbf{A}$ *are linearly independent and that* $\mathbf{c}$ *is not a linear combination of the rows of* $\mathbf{A}$. *Let* $\mathbf{y}$ *be a positive vector. Then, an optimal solution* $\mathbf{d}^*$ *to problem (9.2) is given by*

$$\mathbf{d}^* = -\beta \frac{\mathbf{Y}^2(\mathbf{c} - \mathbf{A}'\mathbf{p})}{\left\| \mathbf{Y}(\mathbf{c} - \mathbf{A}'\mathbf{p}) \right\|},$$

where

$$\mathbf{p} = (\mathbf{A}\mathbf{Y}^2\mathbf{A}')^{-1}\mathbf{A}\mathbf{Y}^2\mathbf{c}.$$

Furthermore, the vector $\mathbf{x} = \mathbf{y} + \mathbf{d}^*$ *belongs to* P *and*

$$\mathbf{c}'\mathbf{x} = \mathbf{c}'\mathbf{y} - \beta \left\| \mathbf{Y}(\mathbf{c} - \mathbf{A}'\mathbf{p}) \right\| < \mathbf{c}'\mathbf{y}.$$

Proof. Let $\mathbf{d}^*$ and $\mathbf{p}$ be as defined in the statement of the lemma. We first argue that the matrix $\mathbf{AY}^2\mathbf{A}'$ is invertible so that $\mathbf{p}$ is well defined. If it is not invertible, there exists some $\mathbf{z} \neq \mathbf{0}$ such that $\mathbf{z}'\mathbf{AY}^2\mathbf{A}'\mathbf{z} = 0$. Let $\mathbf{w} = \mathbf{YA}'\mathbf{z}$. We then have $\mathbf{w}'\mathbf{w} = 0$ which implies that $\mathbf{w} = \mathbf{0}$. Since $\mathbf{Y}$ has positive diagonal entries, it follows that $\mathbf{A}'\mathbf{z} = \mathbf{0}$, which means that the rows of $\mathbf{A}$ are linearly dependent, contradicting our assumption. Also, since $\mathbf{c}$ is not a linear combination of the rows of $\mathbf{A}$, it follows that $\mathbf{c} - \mathbf{A}'\mathbf{p} \neq \mathbf{0}$ and $\mathbf{d}^*$ is well defined.

We now show that $\mathbf{d}^*$ is a feasible solution to problem (9.2). We have

$$\mathbf{Y}^{-1}\mathbf{d}^* = -\beta\frac{\mathbf{Y}(\mathbf{c} - \mathbf{A}'\mathbf{p})}{\|\mathbf{Y}(\mathbf{c} - \mathbf{A}'\mathbf{p})\|},$$

which shows that $\|\mathbf{Y}^{-1}\mathbf{d}^*\| = \beta$. In order to show that $\mathbf{Ad}^* = \mathbf{0}$, it suffices to show that $\mathbf{AY}^2(\mathbf{c} - \mathbf{A}'\mathbf{p}) = \mathbf{0}$, and this follows from the definition of $\mathbf{p}$.

We next show the optimality of $\mathbf{d}^*$. For any feasible solution $\mathbf{d}$ to problem (9.2), we have $\mathbf{Ad} = \mathbf{0}$ and $\|\mathbf{Y}^{-1}\mathbf{d}\| \leq \beta$. Using these facts and the Schwartz inequality (see Section 1.5), we obtain

$$\begin{aligned}
\mathbf{c}'\mathbf{d} &= (\mathbf{c}' - \mathbf{p}'\mathbf{A})\mathbf{d} \\
&= (\mathbf{c}' - \mathbf{p}'\mathbf{A})\mathbf{YY}^{-1}\mathbf{d} \\
&\geq -\|\mathbf{Y}(\mathbf{c} - \mathbf{A}'\mathbf{p})\| \cdot \|\mathbf{Y}^{-1}\mathbf{d}\| \\
&\geq -\beta\|\mathbf{Y}(\mathbf{c} - \mathbf{A}'\mathbf{p})\|.
\end{aligned}$$

On the other hand,

$$\begin{aligned}
\mathbf{c}'\mathbf{d}^* &= (\mathbf{c}' - \mathbf{p}'\mathbf{A})\mathbf{d}^* \\
&= -(\mathbf{c}' - \mathbf{p}'\mathbf{A})\beta\frac{\mathbf{Y}^2(\mathbf{c} - \mathbf{A}'\mathbf{p})}{\|\mathbf{Y}(\mathbf{c} - \mathbf{A}'\mathbf{p})\|} \\
&= -\beta\frac{(\mathbf{Y}(\mathbf{c} - \mathbf{A}'\mathbf{p}))'(\mathbf{Y}(\mathbf{c} - \mathbf{A}'\mathbf{p}))}{\|\mathbf{Y}(\mathbf{c} - \mathbf{A}'\mathbf{p})\|} \\
&= -\beta\|\mathbf{Y}(\mathbf{c} - \mathbf{A}'\mathbf{p})\|.
\end{aligned}$$

It follows that $\mathbf{d}^*$ is optimal. In addition, $\mathbf{c}'\mathbf{x} = \mathbf{c}'\mathbf{y} + \mathbf{c}'\mathbf{d}^* = \mathbf{c}'\mathbf{y} - \beta\|\mathbf{Y}(\mathbf{c} - \mathbf{A}'\mathbf{p})\|$, which is strictly smaller that $\mathbf{c}'\mathbf{y}$ because $\mathbf{c} - \mathbf{A}'\mathbf{p} \neq \mathbf{0}$. Finally, $\mathbf{x} \in P$, because the feasible set S_0 of the problem (9.1) is contained in P. ☐

Note that if $\mathbf{d}^* \geq \mathbf{0}$, the feasible set of the original linear programming problem is unbounded, since $\mathbf{x}+\alpha\mathbf{d}^* > \mathbf{0}$ for all $\alpha > 0$, and $\mathbf{Ad}^* = \mathbf{0}$. Given that $\mathbf{c}'\mathbf{d}^* < 0$ (Lemma 9.2), it follows that the optimal cost in the original problem is $-\infty$.

We next provide an interpretation of the formula for $\mathbf{p}$. Although in Lemma 9.2 we use some $\mathbf{y} > \mathbf{0}$, let us examine what happens if we let $\mathbf{y}$ be a nondegenerate basic feasible solution and apply the same formula to define a vector $\mathbf{p}$. Let $\mathbf{B}$ be the corresponding basis. We assume without loss of generality that the first m variables are basic, so that $\mathbf{A} = [\mathbf{B} \ \mathbf{N}]$ for some matrix $\mathbf{N}$ of dimensions $m \times (n-m)$. If $\mathbf{Y} = \mathrm{diag}(y_1, \ldots, y_m, 0, \ldots, 0)$ and $\mathbf{Y}_0 = \mathrm{diag}(y_1, \ldots, y_m)$, then $\mathbf{A}\mathbf{Y} = [\mathbf{B}\mathbf{Y}_0 \ \ \mathbf{0}]$ and

$$
\begin{aligned}
\mathbf{p} &= (\mathbf{A}\mathbf{Y}^2\mathbf{A}')^{-1}\mathbf{A}\mathbf{Y}^2\mathbf{c} \\
&= (\mathbf{B}')^{-1}\mathbf{Y}_0^{-2}\mathbf{B}^{-1}\mathbf{B}\mathbf{Y}_0^2\mathbf{c}_B \\
&= (\mathbf{B}')^{-1}\mathbf{c}_B,
\end{aligned}
$$

which is the corresponding dual basic solution (see Chapter 4). Hence, we call the vectors $\mathbf{p}$, corresponding to the primal solutions $\mathbf{y}$, the *dual estimates* even if $\mathbf{y}$ is not a basic feasible solution. Moreover, the vector $\mathbf{r} = \mathbf{c} - \mathbf{A}'\mathbf{p}$ becomes

$$
\mathbf{r} = \mathbf{c} - \mathbf{A}'(\mathbf{B}')^{-1}\mathbf{c}_B,
$$

which is the reduced cost vector in the simplex method. Notice that if $\mathbf{y}$ is degenerate, then the matrix $\mathbf{A}\mathbf{Y}^2\mathbf{A}'$ is not invertible, and this interpretation breaks down. We will assume that all primal basic feasible solutions are nondegenerate.

Suppose that $\mathbf{r} = \mathbf{c} - \mathbf{A}'\mathbf{p}$ is nonnegative. In this case, the vector $\mathbf{p}$ is a dual feasible solution. Note, in addition, that

$$
\mathbf{r}'\mathbf{y} = (\mathbf{c} - \mathbf{A}'\mathbf{p})'\mathbf{y} = \mathbf{c}'\mathbf{y} - \mathbf{p}'\mathbf{A}\mathbf{y} = \mathbf{c}'\mathbf{y} - \mathbf{p}'\mathbf{b},
$$

i.e., the difference in objective values between the primal solution $\mathbf{y}$ and the dual solution $\mathbf{p}$ is simply $\mathbf{r}'\mathbf{y}$. We call this difference the *duality gap*. By weak duality, the duality gap $\mathbf{r}'\mathbf{y}$ is always nonnegative. If $\mathbf{r}'\mathbf{y} = 0$, then the complementary slackness conditions hold and the vectors $\mathbf{y}$ and $\mathbf{p}$ are primal and dual optimal solutions, respectively.

We next show that if the duality gap satisfies $\mathbf{r}'\mathbf{y} < \epsilon$, where $\epsilon > 0$ is small, then the primal and the dual solutions are near-optimal.

Lemma 9.3 *Let $\mathbf{y}$ and $\mathbf{p}$ be a primal and a dual feasible solution, respectively, such that*

$$
\mathbf{c}'\mathbf{y} - \mathbf{b}'\mathbf{p} < \epsilon.
$$

Let $\mathbf{y}^*$ and $\mathbf{p}^*$ be optimal primal and dual solutions, respectively. Then,

$$
\mathbf{c}'\mathbf{y}^* \leq \mathbf{c}'\mathbf{y} < \mathbf{c}'\mathbf{y}^* + \epsilon,
$$
$$
\mathbf{b}'\mathbf{p}^* - \epsilon < \mathbf{b}'\mathbf{p} \leq \mathbf{b}'\mathbf{p}^*.
$$

Proof. Since $\mathbf{y}$ is a primal feasible solution and $\mathbf{y}^*$ is an optimal primal solution, $\mathbf{c}'\mathbf{y}^* \leq \mathbf{c}'\mathbf{y}$. By weak duality, $\mathbf{b}'\mathbf{p} \leq \mathbf{c}'\mathbf{y}^*$. Since $\mathbf{c}'\mathbf{y} - \mathbf{b}'\mathbf{p} < \epsilon$, we have

$$
\mathbf{c}'\mathbf{y} < \mathbf{b}'\mathbf{p} + \epsilon \leq \mathbf{c}'\mathbf{y}^* + \epsilon.
$$

Similarly, we obtain

$$\mathbf{b}'\mathbf{p}^* = \mathbf{c}'\mathbf{y}^* \leq \mathbf{c}'\mathbf{y} < \mathbf{b}'\mathbf{p} + \epsilon. \qquad\qquad \square$$

The previous lemma suggests a termination criterion. The algorithm terminates when $\mathbf{r} \geq \mathbf{0}$ (dual feasibility) and the duality gap $\mathbf{r}'\mathbf{y} = \mathbf{y}'\mathbf{r} = \mathbf{e}'\mathbf{Y}\mathbf{r}$ is small, where $\mathbf{e} = (1, 1, \dots, 1)$. Then, the primal and dual solutions $\mathbf{y}$ and $\mathbf{p}$ are "near-optimal" in the sense that their cost is within ϵ from optimality (ϵ-optimal).

We can now provide a complete description of the algorithm. Here, k is an integer variable used to index successive iterations and ϵ is a nonnegative constant used to measure the closeness to optimality in the sense of Lemma 9.3. Furthermore, the vector $\mathbf{x}^k$ and the matrix $\mathbf{X}_k$ play the role of $\mathbf{y}$ and $\mathbf{Y}$, respectively.

The affine scaling algorithm algorithm uses the following inputs:

(a) the data of the problem $(\mathbf{A}, \mathbf{b}, \mathbf{c})$;

(b) an initial primal feasible solution $\mathbf{x}^0 > \mathbf{0}$;

(c) the optimality tolerance $\epsilon > 0$;

(d) the parameter $\beta \in (0, 1)$.

The affine scaling algorithm

1. (Initialization) Start with some feasible $\mathbf{x}^0 > \mathbf{0}$; let $k = 0$.

2. (Computation of dual estimates and reduced costs) Given some feasible $\mathbf{x}^k > \mathbf{0}$, let

$$\begin{aligned}
\mathbf{X}_k &= \operatorname{diag}(x_1^k, \dots, x_n^k), \\
\mathbf{p}^k &= (\mathbf{A}\mathbf{X}_k^2\mathbf{A}')^{-1}\mathbf{A}\mathbf{X}_k^2\mathbf{c}, \\
\mathbf{r}^k &= \mathbf{c} - \mathbf{A}'\mathbf{p}^k.
\end{aligned}$$

3. (Optimality check) Let $\mathbf{e} = (1, 1, \dots, 1)$. If $\mathbf{r}^k \geq \mathbf{0}$ and $\mathbf{e}'\mathbf{X}_k\mathbf{r}^k < \epsilon$, then stop; the current solution $\mathbf{x}^k$ is primal ϵ-optimal and $\mathbf{p}^k$ is dual ϵ-optimal.

4. (Unboundedness check) If $-\mathbf{X}_k^2\mathbf{r}^k \geq \mathbf{0}$ then stop; the optimal cost is $-\infty$.

5. (Update of primal solution) Let

$$\mathbf{x}^{k+1} = \mathbf{x}^k - \beta\frac{\mathbf{X}_k^2\mathbf{r}^k}{\|\mathbf{X}_k\mathbf{r}^k\|}. \qquad\qquad (9.3)$$

There are other variants of the affine scaling algorithm, which differ in the choice of stepsize. Given a vector $\mathbf{u}$, we introduce the notation:

$$\|\mathbf{u}\|_\infty = \max_i |u_i|,$$
$$\gamma(\mathbf{u}) = \max\{u_i \mid u_i > 0\}.$$

It is easy to check that

$$\gamma(\mathbf{u}) \le \|\mathbf{u}\|_\infty \le \|\mathbf{u}\|.$$

The version of affine scaling we presented is called the *short-step* method. In contrast, in *long-step* variants, we update in the same direction $-\mathbf{X}_k^2 \mathbf{r}^k$ but take a larger step. More specifically, Eq. (9.3) is replaced by

$$\mathbf{x}^{k+1} = \mathbf{x}^k - \beta \frac{\mathbf{X}_k^2 \mathbf{r}^k}{\|\mathbf{X}_k \mathbf{r}^k\|_\infty}, \tag{9.4}$$

or

$$\mathbf{x}^{k+1} = \mathbf{x}^k - \beta \frac{\mathbf{X}_k^2 \mathbf{r}^k}{\gamma(\mathbf{X}_k \mathbf{r}^k)}. \tag{9.5}$$

Note that the new vector $\mathbf{x}^{k+1}$, as determined by both long-step versions, is also feasible and positive. This is because Eq. (9.4) yields

$$\left\|\mathbf{X}_k^{-1}(\mathbf{x}^{k+1} - \mathbf{x}^k)\right\|_\infty = \beta \frac{\|\mathbf{X}_k \mathbf{r}^k\|_\infty}{\|\mathbf{X}_k \mathbf{r}^k\|_\infty} = \beta < 1.$$

In particular, we have for all i, $|x_i^{k+1} - x_i^k|/x_i^k \le \beta < 1$, which implies that $x_i^{k+1} > 0$. [The argument under the stepsize in Eq. (9.5) is similar]. In addition, since long-step methods make a larger step along a direction of cost decrease, the resulting reduction in the objective function is largest for the stepsize in Eq. (9.5) and smallest for the stepsize in Eq. (9.3). As a result, the stepsize in Eq. (9.5) is more popular in practice.

At this point, several questions arise naturally and will be addressed shortly.

(a) Does the affine scaling algorithm terminate?

(b) How do we start the algorithm?

(c) How does the algorithm perform in practice?

Convergence

The convergence of the affine scaling algorithm has attracted a lot of research activity. Nevertheless, its convergence has been understood only recently. We state some assumptions and summarize the main convergence results that are available. A related convergence result will be proved in the next section.

We will first impose the following set of assumptions, without loss of generality.

Assumption 9.1

(a) *The rows of the matrix **A** are linearly independent.*

(b) *The vector **c** is not a linear combination of the rows of **A**.*

(c) *There exists an optimal solution.*

(d) *There exists a positive feasible solution.*

Note that if Assumption 9.1(b) fails to hold, then there exists some vector $\mathbf{p}$ such $\mathbf{c}' = \mathbf{p}'\mathbf{A}$. In that case, the cost of every feasible vector $\mathbf{x}$ is the same, namely $\mathbf{c}'\mathbf{x} = \mathbf{p}'\mathbf{A}\mathbf{x} = \mathbf{p}'\mathbf{b}$, and every feasible solution is optimal. Regarding Assumption 9.1(d), we will show later that any problem can be modified so that it has a positive feasible solution.

We will also invoke the following nondegeneracy assumption for the primal and the dual problems.

Assumption 9.2

(a) *Every basic feasible solution to the primal problem is nondegenerate.*

(b) *At every basic feasible solution to the primal problem, the reduced cost of every nonbasic variable is nonzero.*

Assumption 9.2(b) implies that for every basic feasible solution to the primal, the corresponding dual basic solution is nondegenerate. Moreover, Assumptions 9.2(a)-(b) and 9.1(c) imply that both the primal and the dual problems have a unique optimal solution.

Next, we present the principal convergence results for the long-step affine scaling variants. The results for the short-step algorithm are similar and we will discuss them in detail in the next section.

Theorem 9.1 *If we apply the long-step affine scaling algorithm with $\epsilon = 0$, the following hold:*

(a) *For the stepsize in Eqs. (9.4) or (9.5), under Assumptions 9.1 and 9.2, and if $0 < \beta < 1$, the sequences $\mathbf{x}^k$ and $\mathbf{p}^k$ converge to the optimal primal and dual solutions, respectively.*

(b) *For the stepsize in Eq. (9.5), under Assumption 9.1, and if $0 < \beta < 2/3$, the sequences $\mathbf{x}^k$ and $\mathbf{p}^k$ converge to some primal and dual optimal solutions, respectively.*

Note that in part (b) of the theorem, degeneracy is allowed. The proof for this case is rather involved, and is not well understood geometrically. Moreover, there exists an example (see Exercise 9.4) that satisfies Assumption 9.1, but not Assumption 9.2, such that if $\beta > 2/3$, the sequence $\mathbf{p}^k$ does not converge. However, no example has been constructed so far, in which the primal iterates also fail to converge. Thus, although we know that the value $\beta = 2/3$ is the right threshold below which dual convergence is guaranteed, the corresponding threshold for primal convergence is not known.

Initialization

In order to start the affine scaling algorithm, we need an interior feasible solution. Such a feasible solution can be constructed as follows. Let $\mathbf{e} \in \Re^n$ be the vector with all components equal to 1. We introduce a new variable x_{n+1}. We create a new column $\mathbf{A}_{n+1} = \mathbf{b} - \mathbf{A}\mathbf{e}$ and consider the problem

$$
\begin{aligned}
\text{minimize} \quad & \mathbf{c}'\mathbf{x} + \quad\quad Mx_{n+1} \\
\text{subject to} \quad & \mathbf{A}\mathbf{x} + (\mathbf{b} - \mathbf{A}\mathbf{e})x_{n+1} = \mathbf{b} \\
& (\mathbf{x}, x_{n+1}) \geq \mathbf{0},
\end{aligned}
$$

where M is a large positive scalar. Notice that $(\mathbf{x}, x_{n+1}) = (\mathbf{e}, 1)$ is a positive feasible solution to the augmented problem and the affine scaling algorithm can be applied. If M is very large, and as long as the original problem has an optimal solution, it can be shown that an optimal solution to the augmented problem will have $x_{n+1} = 0$, and will therefore provide an optimal solution to the original problem. (See also Theorem 9.6 in Section 9.3 for some related results.)

Computational performance

The main advantages of the affine scaling algorithm are its simplicity and its excellent performance in practice. At each iteration, the computational bottleneck is the calculation of the dual estimates $\mathbf{p}^k$. This involves computing the matrix $\mathbf{A}\mathbf{X}_k^2\mathbf{A}'$, which takes $O(m^2n)$ arithmetic operations. We then solve a system of linear equations involving the matrix $\mathbf{A}\mathbf{X}_k^2\mathbf{A}'$, which takes $O(m^3)$ arithmetic operations. In total, each step of the algorithm needs $O(m^2n + m^3)$ arithmetic operations. Since $m \leq n$, the total number of arithmetic operations per iteration is $O(n^3)$.

It has been observed that if we start the algorithm very close to an extreme point, it tends to travel along the edges of the feasible set (approximately). As a result, it is widely believed, but not formally proven, that the running time of the affine scaling algorithm is exponential in the worst case. Moreover, if the current point is near the boundary of the feasible set, the approximating ellipsoids can be very small and the algorithm takes small steps. On the other hand, if the current point lies "deep" inside the feasible set, the approximating ellipsoids are large and the algorithm makes rapid progress. Indeed, it has been observed that the objective function

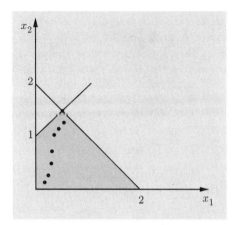

Figure 9.3: The trajectory of the the short-step affine scaling algorithm in Example 9.1.

value decreases very fast in early iterations, but the rate of decrease slows down considerably in the vicinity of an optimal solution.

Example 9.1 In order to illustrate how the algorithm works, we consider the following example:

$$
\begin{aligned}
\text{maximize} \quad & x_1 + 2x_2 \\
\text{subject to} \quad & x_1 + x_2 \le 2 \\
& -x_1 + x_2 \le 1 \\
& x_1, x_2 \ge 0.
\end{aligned}
$$

By introducing slack variables we transform the problem to:

$$
\begin{aligned}
\text{minimize} \quad & -x_1 - 2x_2 \\
\text{subject to} \quad & x_1 + x_2 + x_3 \qquad\quad = 2 \\
& -x_1 + x_2 \qquad\ + x_4 = 1 \\
& x_1, x_2, x_3, x_4 \ge 0.
\end{aligned}
$$

Starting with the vector $(x_1, x_2, x_3, x_4) = (0.1, 0.1, 1.8, 1)$ and using $\beta = 0.995$, we obtain the sequence of iterates for the short-step affine scaling algorithm shown in Table 9.1. The trajectory of the algorithm is depicted in Figure 9.3.

9.2   Convergence of affine scaling*

In this section, we prove the convergence of the short-step affine scaling algorithm, in the absence of degeneracy, for every $\beta \in (0, 1)$. Under the same assumptions, the proof for the long-step version with the stepsize in Eq. (9.4) is similar and will be left as an exercise.

In preparation for the proof, we introduce some terminology. Consider a sequence $\mathbf{x}^k$, $k = 1, 2, \ldots$, and let k_j, $j = 1, 2, \ldots$ be an increasing

x_1	0.100	0.144	0.198	0.262	0.364	0.530	0.546	0.499
x_2	0.100	0.188	0.359	0.667	1.068	1.339	1.439	1.491

Table 9.1: The results of consecutive iterations of the short-step affine scaling algorithm with $\beta = 0.995$. Note that the optimal solution is $x_1^* = 1/2$ and $x_2^* = 3/2$.

sequence of positive integers. Then, the sequence $\mathbf{x}^{k_1}, \mathbf{x}^{k_2}, \ldots$, is said to be a *subsequence* of the original sequence. The limit of a subsequence, if it exists, is said to be a *limit point* of the original sequence. We will use the following basic fact from real analysis, which we state without proof.

Theorem 9.2 *Every bounded sequence of elements of $\Re^n$ has a convergent subsequence.*

We will also use some consequences of our nondegeneracy assumptions, which are summarized in the following result. Roughly speaking, it states that for the nondegenerate case, any feasible solution has at least m positive components and if it has exactly m positive elements, then it must be a basic feasible solution.

Lemma 9.4 *Consider the standard form polyhedron $P = \{\mathbf{x} \in \Re^n \mid \mathbf{Ax} = \mathbf{b}, \ \mathbf{x} \geq \mathbf{0}\}$. Suppose that $\mathbf{A}$ has m rows and that they are linearly independent. Assume also that every basic feasible solution is nondegenerate. Let $\overline{\mathbf{x}}$ be an element of P and let $N = \{i \mid \overline{x}_i > 0\}$. Then:*

(a) *There exist indices $B(1), \ldots, B(m) \in N$ such that the vectors $\mathbf{A}_{B(1)}, \ldots, \mathbf{A}_{B(m)}$ are linearly independent and the corresponding basic solution is feasible. In particular, $|N| \geq m$.*

(b) *If $|N| = m$, then $\overline{\mathbf{x}}$ is a basic feasible solution.*

Proof.

(a) Consider some $\overline{\mathbf{x}} \in P$ and let $N = \{i \mid \overline{x}_i > 0\}$. If the columns $\mathbf{A}_i$, $i \in N$, are linearly dependent, there exist coefficients λ_i, $i \in N$, not all of them zero, such that

$$\sum_{i \in N} \lambda_i \mathbf{A}_i = \mathbf{0}.$$

Note that we have

$$\sum_{i \in N} \mathbf{A}_i(\bar{x}_i + \theta\lambda_i) = \mathbf{b}, \qquad \forall\, \theta.$$

Let us choose θ so that $\bar{x}_i + \theta\lambda_i \geq 0$ for all $i \in N$, and $\bar{x}_k + \theta\lambda_k = 0$ for some $k \in N$. (Such a k exists because a standard form polyhedron contains no lines, and, therefore, there exists a value θ for which one of the constraints is about to be violated.) We then obtain an element $\hat{\mathbf{x}}$ of P such that $\{i \mid \hat{x}_i > 0\}$ is a proper subset of N. By repeating this procedure as many times as needed, we arrive at some $\tilde{\mathbf{x}} \in P$, such that $I = \{i \mid \tilde{x}_i > 0\}$ is a proper subset of N, and the columns $\mathbf{A}_i$, $i \in I$, are linearly independent. If $|I| < m$, we can augment the columns $\mathbf{A}_i$, $i \in I$, to obtain m linearly independent columns (a basis). The corresponding basic feasible solution is $\tilde{\mathbf{x}}$, which is degenerate, and we have arrived at a contradiction. Hence $|I| = m$. This implies that $|N| \geq m$. Furthermore, since $I \subset N$, the columns $\mathbf{A}_i$, $i \in I$, are m linearly independent columns associated with positive components of $\bar{\mathbf{x}}$.

(b) Using the result of part (a), the m vectors $\mathbf{A}_i$, $i \in N$, are linearly independent and, therefore, $\bar{\mathbf{x}}$ is a basic feasible solution. $\qquad\square$

Theorem 9.3 *Consider the short-step affine scaling algorithm, with $\epsilon = 0$. If Assumptions 9.1 and 9.2 hold, and if $0 < \beta < 1$, then $\mathbf{x}^k$ and $\mathbf{p}^k$ converge to the optimal solutions of the primal and the dual, respectively.*

Proof. Let $\mathbf{x}^*$ be an optimal basic feasible solution to the primal problem. By Assumption 9.2, the reduced costs of all nonbasic variables are positive. This implies that $\mathbf{x}^*$ is the unique optimal solution to the primal problem.

Using the optimality of $\mathbf{x}^*$, and Lemma 9.2 with $\mathbf{y} = \mathbf{x}^k, \mathbf{x} = \mathbf{x}^{k+1}$, we have

$$\mathbf{c}'\mathbf{x}^* \leq \mathbf{c}'\mathbf{x}^{k+1} = \mathbf{c}'\mathbf{x}^k - \beta\|\mathbf{X}_k(\mathbf{c} - \mathbf{A}'\mathbf{p}^k)\| < \mathbf{c}'\mathbf{x}^k.$$

Thus, the sequence $\mathbf{c}'\mathbf{x}^k$ is monotonically decreasing and bounded below, which implies that it converges. In particular, $\mathbf{c}'\mathbf{x}^{k+1} - \mathbf{c}'\mathbf{x}^k$ converges to zero, and we conclude that $\mathbf{X}_k(\mathbf{c} - \mathbf{A}'\mathbf{p}^k)$ converges to zero. Using the definition of $\mathbf{X}_k$, we obtain

$$\lim_{k \to \infty} x_i^k(c_i - \mathbf{A}_i'\mathbf{p}^k) = 0, \qquad i = 1, \ldots, n, \tag{9.6}$$

which shows that complementary slackness holds in the limit.

We will now show that the sequence $\mathbf{x}^k$ is bounded. Consider the problem

$$\text{maximize} \quad \sum_{i=1}^{n} x_i$$
$$\text{subject to} \quad \mathbf{Ax} = \mathbf{b}$$
$$\mathbf{c'x} \leq \mathbf{c'x}^*$$
$$\mathbf{x} \geq \mathbf{0}.$$

The above problem has finite optimal cost, because $\mathbf{x}^*$ is the only feasible solution. Therefore, using Theorem 4.14, the same is true for the problem

$$\text{maximize} \quad \sum_{i=1}^{n} x_i$$
$$\text{subject to} \quad \mathbf{Ax} = \mathbf{b}$$
$$\mathbf{c'x} \leq \mathbf{c'x}^0$$
$$\mathbf{x} \geq \mathbf{0}.$$

It follows that the set $\{\mathbf{x} \mid \mathbf{Ax} = \mathbf{b}, \ \mathbf{x} \geq \mathbf{0}, \ \mathbf{c'x} \leq \mathbf{c'x}^0\}$ is bounded. Since $\mathbf{c'x}^k \leq \mathbf{c'x}^0$, the sequence $\mathbf{x}^k$ is bounded.

Recall that Eq. (9.6) establishes complementary slackness, in the limit. Given Assumptions 9.1 and 9.2, it can be shown that if a pair $(\mathbf{x}, \mathbf{p})$, with $\mathbf{x}$ primal feasible, satisfies complementary slackness, then $\mathbf{x}$ is a basic feasible solution (Exercise 9.3). Using similar arguments, we will show next that complementary slackness, in the limit, implies that $\mathbf{x}^k$ approaches the set of basic feasible solutions.

Having shown that the sequence $\mathbf{x}^k$ is bounded, we use Theorem 9.2 to conclude that there exists a sequence k_j of positive integers such that $\mathbf{x}^{k_j}$ converges to some $\overline{\mathbf{x}}$. It is easily seen that $\overline{\mathbf{x}}$ is a feasible solution. Let $N = \{i \mid \overline{x}_i > 0\}$. Using Lemma 9.4(a), the set N has at least m elements and there exist $B(1), \ldots, B(m) \in N$ such that the columns $\mathbf{A}_{B(1)}, \ldots, \mathbf{A}_{B(m)}$ are linearly independent, and such that the corresponding basic solution $\hat{\mathbf{x}}$ is feasible. Let $\mathbf{B}$ be the corresponding basis matrix and let $\mathbf{c}_B = (c_{B(1)}, \ldots, c_{B(m)})$. Using Eq. (9.6), $x_i^{k_j}(c_i - \mathbf{A}_i'\mathbf{p}^{k_j})$ converges to zero as $j \to \infty$, for all i. For $i = 1, \ldots, m$, we have $B(1), \ldots, B(m) \in N$ and $x_{B(i)}^{k_j}$ converges to $\overline{x}_{B(i)}$, which is positive because $B(i) \in N$. It follows that $c_{B(i)} - \mathbf{A}_{B(i)}'\mathbf{p}^{k_j}$ converges to zero. In matrix notation, we have that $\mathbf{c}_B - \mathbf{B}'\mathbf{p}^{k_j}$ converges to zero. Hence, $\mathbf{p}^{k_j}$ converges to $(\mathbf{B}')^{-1}\mathbf{c}_B$. Consequently, for every i, $c_i - \mathbf{A}_i'\mathbf{p}^{k_j}$ converges to $c_i - \mathbf{A}_i'(\mathbf{B}')^{-1}\mathbf{c}_B$, which is the reduced cost of the ith variable, at the basic feasible solution $\hat{\mathbf{x}}$. By Assumption 9.2(b), we have $c_i - \mathbf{A}_i'(\mathbf{B}')^{-1}\mathbf{c}_B \neq 0$ for $i \neq B(1), \ldots, B(m)$. Thus, for $i \neq B(1), \ldots, B(m)$, $c_i - \mathbf{A}_i'\mathbf{p}^{k_j}$ converges to a nonzero value. We use Eq. (9.6) once more to conclude that $\overline{x}_i = 0$ for $i \neq B(1), \ldots, B(m)$. In particular, $N = \{B(1), \ldots, B(m)\}$ and $\overline{\mathbf{x}}$ is the basic feasible solution associated with the basis matrix $\mathbf{B}$.

We have proved so far that the sequence $\mathbf{x}^k$ has at least one limit point and that every limit point must be a basic feasible solution. We now argue that there can only be a single limit point. Let $\delta > 0$ be such that every basic variable at every basic feasible solution is larger than δ. Because of the nondegeneracy assumption, basic variables are always positive and, therefore, such a δ exists. Let $\epsilon = \delta/3$. Since every possible limit point of the sequence $\mathbf{x}^k$ is a basic feasible solution, it follows that there exists some K such that for all k larger than K, $\mathbf{x}^k$ is within ϵ of some basic feasible solution. (If this were not the case, we could construct a subsequence $\mathbf{x}^{\ell_i}$ such that each $\mathbf{x}^{\ell_i}$ is more than ϵ away from the closest basic feasible solution. This subsequence must have a limit point but no basic feasible solution could be one of its limit points, a contradiction.)

Suppose that there exists some $k \geq K$ and two different basic feasible solutions $\overline{\mathbf{x}}$, $\hat{\mathbf{x}}$ such that $\|\mathbf{x}^k - \overline{\mathbf{x}}\| \leq \epsilon$, $\|\mathbf{x}^{k+1} - \hat{\mathbf{x}}\| \leq \epsilon$. We assume that the ith variable is nonbasic at $\overline{\mathbf{x}}$ (in particular, $\overline{x}_i = 0$) and basic at $\hat{\mathbf{x}}$ (in particular, $\hat{x}_i \geq \delta$). It then follows that $x_i^k \leq \epsilon$ and $x_i^{k+1} \geq \delta - \epsilon = 2\epsilon$. On the other hand, Eq. (9.3) yields

$$x_i^{k+1} = x_i^k \left(1 - \beta \frac{x_i^k r_i^k}{\|\mathbf{X}_k \mathbf{r}^k\|}\right) \leq x_i^k(1 + \beta) < 2x_i^k \leq 2\epsilon \leq x_i^{k+1}.$$

This is a contradiction. It establishes that if $k \geq K$ and if $\mathbf{x}^k$ is within ϵ of $\overline{\mathbf{x}}$, then the same must be true for $\mathbf{x}^{k+1}$. We conclude that no basic feasible solution other than $\overline{\mathbf{x}}$ can be a limit point and therefore the sequence $\mathbf{x}^k$ converges to $\overline{\mathbf{x}}$. As shown earlier, $\mathbf{p}^k$ also converges to the associated dual basic solution.

It remains to show that the limit $\overline{\mathbf{x}}$ must be optimal. If $\overline{\mathbf{x}}$ is not optimal, then there exists some nonbasic variable x_i whose reduced cost is negative. As shown earlier, $r_i^k = c_i - \mathbf{A}_i' \mathbf{p}^k$ converges to the reduced cost of x_i and, therefore, r_i^k eventually becomes and stays negative. It follows from Eq. (9.3) that eventually x_i^k becomes a strictly increasing sequence. On the other hand, x_i^k converges to $\overline{x}_i$, which is zero because x_i is a nonbasic variable, and we obtain a contradiction. $\qquad\square$

Despite its intricacy, the proof we have given provides us with a fair amount of understanding of the convergence mechanism. In particular, the proof indicates that there are three different regimes:

(a) If $\mathbf{x}^k$ is sufficiently far from every basic feasible solution, $\mathbf{X}_k \mathbf{r}_k$ is sufficiently different than zero and this results in a substantial cost improvement. Since an infinite number of substantial cost improvements would drive the cost to $-\infty$, the algorithm must eventually come close to a basic feasible solution.

(b) A nonoptimal basic feasible solution is "repelling." In particular, in the vicinity of a nonoptimal basic feasible solution, every nonbasic variable with negative reduced costs must increase, thus driving $\mathbf{x}^k$ away from that basic feasible solution.

(c) Finally, once the algorithm reaches the vicinity of the optimal basic
    feasible solution, it is attracted to it. This fact is amplified by a
    result (developed in Exercise 9.1) which shows that if $\mathbf{x}^k$ is near the
    optimal basic feasible solution, the cost $\mathbf{c}'\mathbf{x}^k$ decreases at the rate of
    a geometric progression.

9.3   The potential reduction algorithm

In this section, we develop an interior point algorithm for linear programming that only requires a polynomial number of iterations. The algorithm
solves the linear programming problem

$$\begin{array}{ll} \text{minimize} & \mathbf{c}'\mathbf{x} \\ \text{subject to} & \mathbf{A}\mathbf{x} = \mathbf{b} \\ & \mathbf{x} \geq \mathbf{0}, \end{array}$$

and its dual

$$\begin{array}{ll} \text{maximize} & \mathbf{p}'\mathbf{b} \\ \text{subject to} & \mathbf{p}'\mathbf{A} + \mathbf{s}' = \mathbf{c}' \\ & \mathbf{s} \geq \mathbf{0}, \end{array}$$

under the following assumption.

Assumption 9.3   *The matrix* $\mathbf{A}$ *has linearly independent rows and
there exist* $\mathbf{x} > \mathbf{0}$ *and* $(\mathbf{p}, \mathbf{s})$ *with* $\mathbf{s} > \mathbf{0}$, *which are feasible for the
primal and the dual problem, respectively.*

    In Section 9.1, we have seen that the affine scaling algorithm decreases
the objective function value at each step (cf. Lemma 9.2). As a result, the
sequence of iterates approaches the boundary of the feasible set quickly
and then the algorithm is forced to take very small steps as the approximating ellipsoids become smaller and smaller. A possible way to address
this difficulty is to "repel" the current point away from the boundary of
the feasible set, so that the algorithm can make significant progress in future steps. Speaking intuitively, we would like an interior point algorithm
to make progress towards optimality by decreasing the objective function
value while staying away from the boundary of the feasible set.
    In order to capture these two conflicting objectives, we introduce the
potential function $G(\mathbf{x}, \mathbf{s})$ defined by

$$G(\mathbf{x}, \mathbf{s}) = q \log \mathbf{s}'\mathbf{x} - \sum_{j=1}^n \log x_j - \sum_{j=1}^n \log s_j,$$

where q is a constant larger than n. If $\mathbf{x}$ and $(\mathbf{p}, \mathbf{s})$ are primal and dual
feasible solutions, respectively, the observation

$$\mathbf{c}'\mathbf{x} - \mathbf{b}'\mathbf{p} = (\mathbf{s}' + \mathbf{p}'\mathbf{A})\mathbf{x} - \mathbf{x}'\mathbf{A}'\mathbf{p} = \mathbf{s}'\mathbf{x},$$

implies that the first term is a measure of the duality gap. The second and third terms penalize proximity to the boundary of the feasible sets for the primal and the dual, respectively. In the next theorem, we show that if we can decrease the potential function $G(\mathbf{x}, \mathbf{s})$ at each step by a certain amount, we can get an ϵ-optimal solution to the linear programming problem after a small number of iterations.

Theorem 9.4 *Let $\mathbf{x}^0 > \mathbf{0}$ and $(\mathbf{p}^0, \mathbf{s}^0)$ with $\mathbf{s}^0 > \mathbf{0}$, be feasible solutions to the primal and dual problem, respectively. Let $\epsilon > 0$ be the optimality tolerance. Any algorithm that maintains primal and dual feasibility and reduces $G(\mathbf{x}, \mathbf{s})$ by an amount greater than or equal to $\delta > 0$ at each iteration, finds a solution to the primal and dual problems with duality gap*

$$(\mathbf{s}^K)'\mathbf{x}^K \le \epsilon,$$

after

$$K = \left\lceil \frac{G(\mathbf{x}^0, \mathbf{s}^0) + (q - n)\log(1/\epsilon) - n \log n}{\delta} \right\rceil$$

iterations.

Proof. Note that

$$G(\mathbf{x}, \mathbf{s}) = q \log \mathbf{s}'\mathbf{x} - \sum_{j=1}^{n} \log x_j - \sum_{j=1}^{n} \log s_j$$

$$= n \log \mathbf{s}'\mathbf{x} - \sum_{j=1}^{n} \log x_j - \sum_{j=1}^{n} \log s_j + (q - n)\log \mathbf{s}'\mathbf{x}$$

$$\ge n \log n + (q - n)\log \mathbf{s}'\mathbf{x}.$$

The inequality follows, because the expression $n \log \mathbf{s}'\mathbf{x} - \sum_{j=1}^{n} \log x_j - \sum_{j=1}^{n} \log s_j$ attains its minimum when $x_j s_j = \mathbf{s}'\mathbf{x}/n$. This can be verified by setting the derivative to zero and then checking that the second derivative is nonnegative. Hence,

$$n \log \mathbf{s}'\mathbf{x} - \sum_{j=1}^{n} \log x_j - \sum_{j=1}^{n} \log s_j \ge n \log n. \tag{9.7}$$

Fix some $\delta > 0$ and suppose we have an algorithm with the property

$$G(\mathbf{x}^{k+1}, \mathbf{s}^{k+1}) - G(\mathbf{x}^k, \mathbf{s}^k) \le -\delta, \quad \forall\, k.$$

After K steps we have

$$G(\mathbf{x}^K, \mathbf{s}^K) - G(\mathbf{x}^0, \mathbf{s}^0) \le -K\delta.$$

For the value of K stated in the theorem, we obtain

$$G(\mathbf{x}^K, \mathbf{s}^K) \leq -(q - n) \log \frac{1}{\epsilon} + n \log n.$$

Using the definition of $G(\mathbf{x}, \mathbf{s})$ and Eq. (9.7), we obtain

$$G(\mathbf{x}^K, \mathbf{s}^K) \geq n \log n + (q - n) \log (\mathbf{s}^K)' \mathbf{x}^K.$$

Therefore,

$$(\mathbf{s}^K)' \mathbf{x}^K \leq \epsilon,$$

i.e., we can bring the duality gap below the desired tolerance ϵ with K iterations.   □

The previous theorem motivates us to devise an algorithm that decreases the potential function $G(\mathbf{x}, \mathbf{s})$ by a constant amount at each step. For this reason, the algorithm is called the *potential reduction algorithm*.

Intuitively, the main idea is as follows: starting with a primal feasible solution $\mathbf{x} > \mathbf{0}$ and a dual feasible solution with $\mathbf{s} > \mathbf{0}$, we try to find a direction $\mathbf{d}$, such that $G(\mathbf{x} + \mathbf{d}, \mathbf{s}) < G(\mathbf{x}, \mathbf{s})$. The direction $\mathbf{d}$ should satisfy

$$\mathbf{A}\mathbf{d} = \mathbf{0}, \qquad \|\mathbf{X}^{-1}\mathbf{d}\| \leq \beta < 1,$$

so that the new point $\mathbf{x} + \mathbf{d}$ is feasible, as we have shown in Lemma 9.1. The problem of minimizing $G(\mathbf{x} + \mathbf{d}, \mathbf{s})$ subject to the above constraints is a difficult nonlinear optimization problem. For this reason, we approximate the nonlinear potential function $G(\mathbf{x} + \mathbf{d}, \mathbf{s})$ by its first order Taylor series expansion in $\mathbf{d}$, and solve the following problem:

$$
\begin{aligned}
\text{minimize} \quad & \nabla_{\mathbf{x}} G(\mathbf{x}, \mathbf{s})' \mathbf{d} \\
\text{subject to} \quad & \mathbf{A}\mathbf{d} = \mathbf{0} \\
& \|\mathbf{X}^{-1}\mathbf{d}\| \leq \beta,
\end{aligned}
$$

for some $\beta < 1$. Note that the above problem is the same as the one encountered in affine scaling [cf. Eq. (9.2)], except that the objective function vector is $\hat{\mathbf{c}} = \nabla_{\mathbf{x}} G(\mathbf{x}, \mathbf{s})$ instead of $\mathbf{c}$. In particular, the ith component of the cost vector is

$$\hat{c}_i = \frac{\partial G(\mathbf{x}, \mathbf{s})}{\partial x_i} = \frac{q s_i}{\mathbf{s}' \mathbf{x}} - \frac{1}{x_i}.$$

Applying Lemma 9.2 with $\mathbf{Y} = \mathbf{X}$ and $\mathbf{c} = \hat{\mathbf{c}}$, we obtain that the optimal direction is

$$\mathbf{d}^* = -\beta \mathbf{X} \frac{\mathbf{u}}{\|\mathbf{u}\|}, \tag{9.8}$$

where

$$\mathbf{u} = \mathbf{X}\left(\hat{\mathbf{c}} - \mathbf{A}'(\mathbf{A}\mathbf{X}^2\mathbf{A}')^{-1}\mathbf{A}\mathbf{X}^2\hat{\mathbf{c}}\right).$$

Since
$$\mathbf{X}\hat{\mathbf{c}} = \frac{q}{\mathbf{s'x}}\mathbf{Xs} - \mathbf{e},$$
we obtain
$$\mathbf{u} = \left(\mathbf{I} - \mathbf{XA'}(\mathbf{AX^2A'})^{-1}\mathbf{AX}\right)\left(\frac{q}{\mathbf{s'x}}\mathbf{Xs} - \mathbf{e}\right).$$

Moreover, $G(\mathbf{x}, \mathbf{s})$ decreases by $\beta\|\mathbf{u}\| + O(\beta^2)$, where the first term comes from Lemma 9.2 and the second term is due to the omitted higher order terms in the Taylor series expansion of $G(\mathbf{x}, \mathbf{s})$.

By bounding the higher order terms carefully, we can show (cf. Theorem 9.5) that if $\|\mathbf{u}\|$ is larger than a certain threshold γ, then the potential function decreases by at least a constant amount. Notice that in this step of the algorithm, the dual variables $\mathbf{s}$ and $\mathbf{p}$ remain unchanged. If, however, $\|\mathbf{u}\| < \gamma$, we cannot decrease the potential function sufficiently, so we update the dual variables to achieve the required decrease of the potential function.

The potential reduction algorithm uses the following inputs:

(a)   the data of the problem $(\mathbf{A},\ \mathbf{b},\ \mathbf{c})$; the matrix $\mathbf{A}$ is assumed to have full row rank;

(b)   the initial primal and dual feasible solutions $\mathbf{x}^0 > \mathbf{0}$, $\mathbf{s}^0 > \mathbf{0}$, $\mathbf{p}^0$;

(c)   the optimality tolerance $\epsilon > 0$;

(d)   the parameters β, γ, q.

The potential reduction algorithm

1.   (Initialization) Start with some feasible solution $\mathbf{x}^0 > \mathbf{0}$, $\mathbf{s}^0 > \mathbf{0}$, $\mathbf{p}^0$, and set $k = 0$.

2.   (Optimality test) If $(\mathbf{s}^k)'\mathbf{x}^k < \epsilon$ stop; else go to Step 3.

3.   (Computation of update direction) Let

$$\mathbf{X}_k = \operatorname{diag}(x_1^k, \ldots, x_n^k),$$
$$\overline{\mathbf{A}}^k = (\mathbf{AX}_k)'(\mathbf{AX}_k^2\mathbf{A'})^{-1}\mathbf{AX}_k,$$
$$\mathbf{u}^k = (\mathbf{I} - \overline{\mathbf{A}}^k)\left(\frac{q}{(\mathbf{s}^k)'\mathbf{x}^k}\mathbf{X}_k\mathbf{s}^k - \mathbf{e}\right),$$
$$\mathbf{d}^k = -\beta\mathbf{X}_k\mathbf{u}^k/\|\mathbf{u}^k\|.$$

4.   (Primal step) If $\|\mathbf{u}^k\| \geq \gamma$, then let

$$\mathbf{x}^{k+1} = \mathbf{x}^k + \mathbf{d}^k,$$
$$\mathbf{s}^{k+1} = \mathbf{s}^k,$$
$$\mathbf{p}^{k+1} = \mathbf{p}^k.$$

---

5. (Dual step) If $\|\mathbf{u}^k\| < \gamma$, then let

$$\mathbf{x}^{k+1} = \mathbf{x}^k,$$

$$\mathbf{s}^{k+1} = \frac{(\mathbf{s}^k)'\mathbf{x}^k}{q}(\mathbf{X}_k)^{-1}(\mathbf{u}^k + \mathbf{e}),$$

$$\mathbf{p}^{k+1} = \mathbf{p}^k + (\mathbf{A}\mathbf{X}_k^2\mathbf{A}')^{-1}\mathbf{A}\mathbf{X}_k\left(\mathbf{X}_k\,\mathbf{s}^k - \frac{(\mathbf{s}^k)'\mathbf{x}^k}{q}\mathbf{e}\right).$$

6. Let $k := k + 1$ and go to Step 2.

It is easily shown that for every k, the vectors $\mathbf{x}^k$ and $(\mathbf{p}^k, \mathbf{s}^k)$ are primal and dual feasible solutions, respectively. If $\|\mathbf{u}^k\| \geq \gamma$ we say that the algorithm performs a *primal step*, while if $\|\mathbf{u}^k\| < \gamma$, we say that the algorithm performs a *dual step*. We have given an interpretation of the primal step. Unfortunately, an equally intuitive motivation of the dual update formulas is not available. We next analyze the behavior of the algorithm.

Theorem 9.5 *The potential reduction algorithm with $\beta < 1$ and $\gamma < 1$, has the following properties.*

(a) *If $\|\mathbf{u}^k\| \geq \gamma$ (primal step), then*

$$G(\mathbf{x}^{k+1}, \mathbf{s}^{k+1}) - G(\mathbf{x}^k, \mathbf{s}^k) \leq -\beta\gamma + \frac{\beta^2}{2(1-\beta)}.$$

(b) *If $\|\mathbf{u}^k\| < \gamma$ (dual step), then*

$$G(\mathbf{x}^{k+1}, \mathbf{s}^{k+1}) - G(\mathbf{x}^k, \mathbf{s}^k) \leq -(q - n) + n\log\frac{q}{n} + \frac{\gamma^2}{2(1-\gamma)}.$$

(c) *If $q = n + \sqrt{n}$, $\beta \approx 0.285$ and $\gamma \approx 0.479$, then the potential reduction algorithm reduces $G(\mathbf{x}, \mathbf{s})$ by at least $\delta = 0.079$ at each iteration.*

Proof. As explained in the motivation of the algorithm, if we perform a primal step, the potential function decreases by

$$G(\mathbf{x}^{k+1}, \mathbf{s}^{k+1}) - G(\mathbf{x}^k, \mathbf{s}^k) = -\beta\|\mathbf{u}^k\| + O(\beta^2).$$

We now develop a more detailed estimate of the cost decrease.

Let $\mathbf{x}$ and $(\mathbf{p}, \mathbf{s})$ be the current solutions to the primal and dual problems respectively. If the potential reduction algorithm takes a primal step, the new point is $(\mathbf{x} + \mathbf{d}, \mathbf{s})$, where $\mathbf{d} = -\beta \mathbf{X} \mathbf{u} / \|\mathbf{u}\|$. Then,

$$G(\mathbf{x} + \mathbf{d}, \mathbf{s}) - G(\mathbf{x}, \mathbf{s}) = q \log\left(1 + \frac{\mathbf{s}'\mathbf{d}}{\mathbf{s}'\mathbf{x}}\right) - \sum_{j=1}^{n} \log\left(1 + \frac{d_j}{x_j}\right). \qquad (9.9)$$

Since $1 + y \le e^y$ for all y, we obtain

$$\log(1 + y) \le y, \qquad \forall\, y > -1. \qquad (9.10)$$

Moreover, from the Taylor series expansion of $\log(1 + y)$, we obtain for $|y| \le \beta < 1$,

$$
\begin{aligned}
\log(1 + y) &= y - \frac{y^2}{2} + \frac{y^3}{3} - \cdots \\
&\ge y - \frac{|y|^2}{2} - \frac{|y|^3}{3} - \cdots \\
&\ge y - \frac{|y|^2}{2}\left(1 + |y| + |y|^2 + \cdots\right) \\
&= y - \frac{|y|^2}{2(1 - |y|)} \\
&\ge y - \frac{|y|^2}{2(1 - \beta)}. \qquad (9.11)
\end{aligned}
$$

Since $|d_j / x_j| = |\beta u_j| / \|\mathbf{u}\| \le \beta < 1$, we apply inequalities (9.10) and (9.11) to Eq. (9.9), and obtain

$$
\begin{aligned}
G(\mathbf{x} + \mathbf{d}, \mathbf{s}) - G(\mathbf{x}, \mathbf{s}) &\le q\frac{\mathbf{s}'\mathbf{d}}{\mathbf{s}'\mathbf{x}} - \sum_{j=1}^{n}\left(\frac{d_j}{x_j} - \frac{d_j^2}{2(1 - \beta)x_j^2}\right) \\
&= \left(q\frac{\mathbf{s}}{\mathbf{s}'\mathbf{x}} - \mathbf{X}^{-1}\mathbf{e}\right)'\mathbf{d} + \frac{\|\mathbf{X}^{-1}\mathbf{d}\|^2}{2(1 - \beta)} \\
&= \left(q\frac{\mathbf{s}}{\mathbf{s}'\mathbf{x}} - \mathbf{X}^{-1}\mathbf{e}\right)'\mathbf{d} + \frac{\beta^2}{2(1 - \beta)} \\
&= \hat{\mathbf{c}}'\mathbf{d} + \frac{\beta^2}{2(1 - \beta)} \\
&= -\beta\|\mathbf{u}\| + \frac{\beta^2}{2(1 - \beta)},
\end{aligned}
$$

where the last equality follows from our discussion of the motivation of the algorithm and its connection with affine scaling (cf. Lemma 9.2). Therefore, if $\|\mathbf{u}\| \ge \gamma$,

$$G(\mathbf{x} + \mathbf{d}, \mathbf{s}) - G(\mathbf{x}, \mathbf{s}) \le -\beta\gamma + \frac{\beta^2}{2(1 - \beta)}.$$

We next address the case $\|\mathbf{u}\| < \gamma$ (dual step). Since

$$\mathbf{u} = (\mathbf{I} - \overline{\mathbf{A}})\left(\frac{q}{\mathbf{s}'\mathbf{x}}\mathbf{X}\mathbf{s} - \mathbf{e}\right),$$

we obtain by rearranging,

$$\overline{\mathbf{A}}\left(\frac{q}{\mathbf{s}'\mathbf{x}}\mathbf{X}\mathbf{s} - \mathbf{e}\right) + \mathbf{u} + \mathbf{e} - \frac{q}{\mathbf{s}'\mathbf{x}}\mathbf{X}\mathbf{s} = \mathbf{0}.$$

This leads to

$$\mathbf{A}'(\mathbf{A}\mathbf{X}^2\mathbf{A}')^{-1}\mathbf{A}\mathbf{X}\left(\mathbf{X}\mathbf{s} - \frac{\mathbf{s}'\mathbf{x}}{q}\mathbf{e}\right) + \frac{\mathbf{s}'\mathbf{x}}{q}\mathbf{X}^{-1}(\mathbf{u} + \mathbf{e}) - \mathbf{s} = \mathbf{0}.$$

If we select

$$\overline{\mathbf{s}} = \frac{\mathbf{s}'\mathbf{x}}{q}\mathbf{X}^{-1}(\mathbf{u} + \mathbf{e})$$

$$\overline{\mathbf{p}} = \mathbf{p} + (\mathbf{A}\mathbf{X}^2\mathbf{A}')^{-1}\mathbf{A}\mathbf{X}\left(\mathbf{X}\mathbf{s} - \frac{\mathbf{s}'\mathbf{x}}{q}\mathbf{e}\right),$$

we obtain

$$\mathbf{A}'(\overline{\mathbf{p}} - \mathbf{p}) + \overline{\mathbf{s}} - \mathbf{s} = \mathbf{0},$$

and thus,

$$\mathbf{A}'\overline{\mathbf{p}} + \overline{\mathbf{s}} = \mathbf{A}'\mathbf{p} + \mathbf{s} = \mathbf{c}.$$

Notice that since $\|\mathbf{u}\| < \gamma < 1$, we have $\mathbf{u} + \mathbf{e} > \mathbf{0}$, and therefore, $\overline{\mathbf{s}} > \mathbf{0}$. Hence, the solution $(\overline{\mathbf{p}}, \overline{\mathbf{s}})$ is dual feasible.

The difference in the potential function after a dual step becomes

$$G(\mathbf{x}, \overline{\mathbf{s}}) - G(\mathbf{x}, \mathbf{s}) = q\log\left(\frac{\overline{\mathbf{s}}'\mathbf{x}}{\mathbf{s}'\mathbf{x}}\right) - \sum_{j=1}^{n}\log\overline{s}_j + \sum_{j=1}^{n}\log s_j. \tag{9.12}$$

We next bound the various terms appearing in (9.12). Note that $\mathbf{x}'\mathbf{X}^{-1} = \mathbf{e}'$ and therefore,

$$\overline{\mathbf{s}}'\mathbf{x} = \mathbf{x}'\overline{\mathbf{s}} = \frac{\mathbf{s}'\mathbf{x}}{q}\mathbf{x}'\mathbf{X}^{-1}(\mathbf{u} + \mathbf{e}) = \frac{\mathbf{s}'\mathbf{x}}{q}(\mathbf{e}'\mathbf{u} + n). \tag{9.13}$$

Moreover,

$$\sum_{j=1}^{n}\log\overline{s}_j = \sum_{j=1}^{n}\log\left(\frac{(\mathbf{s}'\mathbf{x})(1 + u_j)}{qx_j}\right)$$

$$= n\log\frac{\mathbf{s}'\mathbf{x}}{q} + \sum_{j=1}^{n}\log(1 + u_j) - \sum_{j=1}^{n}\log x_j$$

$$\geq n\log\frac{\mathbf{s}'\mathbf{x}}{q} + \sum_{j=1}^{n}\left(u_j - \frac{u_j^2}{2(1 - \gamma)}\right) - \sum_{j=1}^{n}\log x_j$$

$$\geq n\log\frac{\mathbf{x}'\mathbf{s}}{q} + \mathbf{e}'\mathbf{u} - \sum_{j=1}^{n}\log x_j - \frac{\gamma^2}{2(1 - \gamma)}, \tag{9.14}$$

where we have used Eq. (9.11) and the fact that $|u_j| \leq \|\mathbf{u}\| \leq \gamma$. Substituting Eqs. (9.13) and (9.14) into Eq. (9.12), we obtain

$$
G(\mathbf{x}, \bar{\mathbf{s}}) - G(\mathbf{x}, \mathbf{s}) \leq q \log \frac{\mathbf{e}'\mathbf{u} + n}{q} + n \log q - \mathbf{e}'\mathbf{u} + \frac{\gamma^2}{2(1 - \gamma)}
$$
$$
- \left(n \log(\mathbf{s}'\mathbf{x}) - \sum_{j=1}^{n} \log x_j - \sum_{j=1}^{n} \log s_j \right).
$$

Using Eq. (9.7) to bound the last part of the above expression, we obtain

$$
G(\mathbf{x}, \bar{\mathbf{s}}) - G(\mathbf{x}, \mathbf{s}) \leq q \log \left(1 - \frac{q - n - \mathbf{e}'\mathbf{u}}{q} \right) + n \log \frac{q}{n} - \mathbf{e}'\mathbf{u} + \frac{\gamma^2}{2(1 - \gamma)}
$$
$$
\leq q \left(-\frac{q - n - \mathbf{e}'\mathbf{u}}{q} \right) + n \log \frac{q}{n} - \mathbf{e}'\mathbf{u} + \frac{\gamma^2}{2(1 - \gamma)}
$$
$$
= -(q - n) + n \log \frac{q}{n} + \frac{\gamma^2}{2(1 - \gamma)}.
$$

For $q = n + \sqrt{n}$, the potential change after a dual step is less than or equal to

$$
-\sqrt{n} + n \log \left(1 + \frac{1}{\sqrt{n}} \right) + \frac{\gamma^2}{2(1 - \gamma)} \leq -0.3 + \frac{\gamma^2}{2(1 - \gamma)}.
$$

Using $\beta = 0.28537$ and $\gamma = 0.479056$, and substituting in the bounds we have obtained, we find that both the primal and the dual step reduce $G(\mathbf{x}, \mathbf{s})$ by at least $\delta = 0.079$ at each iteration. $\qquad \square$

Initialization

In this subsection, we show how to select an initial solution that can be used to start the algorithm. Consider the following pair of artificial primal and dual problems:

$$
\begin{array}{lll}
\text{minimize} & \mathbf{c}'\mathbf{x} + & M_1 x_{n+1} \\
\text{subject to} & \mathbf{A}\mathbf{x} + (\mathbf{b} - \mathbf{A}\mathbf{e})x_{n+1} & = \mathbf{b} \\
& (\mathbf{e} - \mathbf{c})'\mathbf{x} & + x_{n+2} = M_2 \\
& x_1, \ldots, x_{n+2} \geq 0,
\end{array}
$$

$$
\begin{array}{lll}
\text{maximize} & \mathbf{p}'\mathbf{b} & + p_{m+1} M_2 \\
\text{subject to} & \mathbf{p}'\mathbf{A} & + p_{m+1}(\mathbf{e} - \mathbf{c})' + \mathbf{s}' & = \mathbf{c}' \\
& \mathbf{p}'(\mathbf{b} - \mathbf{A}\mathbf{e}) & + s_{n+1} = M_1 \\
& p_{m+1} & + s_{n+2} = 0 \\
& s_1, \ldots, s_{n+2} \geq 0.
\end{array}
$$

Here, x_{n+1}, x_{n+2} are artificial primal variables, $p_{m+1}, s_{n+1}, s_{n+2}$ are artificial dual variables, and M_1, M_2 are large positive numbers to be specified later. The coefficient M_2 must satisfy $M_2 > (\mathbf{e} - \mathbf{c})'\mathbf{e}$. The vectors

$$(\mathbf{x}^0, x_{n+1}^0, x_{n+2}^0) = (\mathbf{e}, 1, M_2 - (\mathbf{e} - \mathbf{c})'\mathbf{e}),$$
$$(\mathbf{p}^0, p_{m+1}^0, \mathbf{s}^0, s_{n+1}^0, s_{n+2}^0) = (\mathbf{0}, -1, \mathbf{e}, M_1, 1),$$

are feasible solutions to the artificial primal and dual problems, respectively, and can be used to start the potential reduction algorithm. The relation between the artificial and the original problems is described next.

Theorem 9.6 *Let* $\mathbf{x}^*$ *and* $(\mathbf{p}^*, \mathbf{s}^*)$ *be optimal solutions to the original primal and dual problems, respectively, whose existence is assumed. If*

$$M_1 \geq \max\{(\mathbf{b} - \mathbf{Ae})'\mathbf{p}^*, 0\} + 1,$$

and

$$M_2 \geq \max\{(\mathbf{e} - \mathbf{c})'\mathbf{x}^*, (\mathbf{e} - \mathbf{c})'\mathbf{e}, 0\} + 1,$$

then the following hold:

(a) *A feasible solution* $(\overline{\mathbf{x}}, \overline{x}_{n+1}, \overline{x}_{n+2})$ *to the artificial primal problem is optimal if and only if* $\overline{\mathbf{x}}$ *is an optimal solution to the original primal problem and* $\overline{x}_{n+1} = 0$.

(b) *A feasible solution* $(\overline{\mathbf{p}}, \overline{p}_{m+1}, \overline{\mathbf{s}}, \overline{s}_{n+1}, \overline{s}_{n+2})$ *to the artificial dual problem is optimal if and only if* $(\overline{\mathbf{p}}, \overline{\mathbf{s}})$ *is an optimal solution to the original dual problem and* $\overline{p}_{m+1} = 0$.

Proof.   (a) Let $(\overline{\mathbf{x}}, \overline{x}_{n+1}, \overline{x}_{n+2})$ be an optimal solution to the artificial primal problem. We will first show that $\overline{x}_{n+1} = 0$. Assume that $\overline{x}_{n+1} > 0$.

Since $\mathbf{x}^*$ is feasible for the original problem, we can define $x_{n+1}^* = 0$ and $x_{n+2}^* = M_2 - (\mathbf{e} - \mathbf{c})'\mathbf{x}^*$, so that the solution $(\mathbf{x}^*, x_{n+1}^*, x_{n+2}^*)$ is feasible for the artificial primal problem. Then,

$$\mathbf{c}'\mathbf{x}^* + M_1 x_{n+1}^* = (\mathbf{p}^*)'\mathbf{b} = (\mathbf{p}^*)'\big(\mathbf{A}\overline{\mathbf{x}} + (\mathbf{b} - \mathbf{Ae})\overline{x}_{n+1}\big).$$

Since $(\mathbf{p}^*)'\mathbf{A} + (\mathbf{s}^*)' = \mathbf{c}'$, $\overline{x}_{n+1} > 0$, and $M_1 > (\mathbf{b} - \mathbf{Ae})'\mathbf{p}^*$, we obtain

$$\mathbf{c}'\mathbf{x}^* + M_1 x_{n+1}^* < (\mathbf{c} - \mathbf{s}^*)'\overline{\mathbf{x}} + M_1 \overline{x}_{n+1} \leq \mathbf{c}'\overline{\mathbf{x}} + M_1 \overline{x}_{n+1},$$

because $(\mathbf{s}^*)'\overline{\mathbf{x}} \geq 0$. This contradicts the optimality of $(\overline{\mathbf{x}}, \overline{x}_{n+1}, \overline{x}_{n+2})$. Therefore, $\overline{x}_{n+1} = 0$. In addition, the previous inequality shows that the solution $(\mathbf{x}^*, x_{n+1}^*, x_{n+2}^*)$ is optimal for the artificial primal problem and the optimal cost of the artificial primal problem is $\mathbf{c}'\overline{\mathbf{x}} = \mathbf{c}'\mathbf{x}^*$. Since $\overline{\mathbf{x}}$ satisfies all the constraints of the original primal problem, it must be an optimal solution.

Conversely, let $\mathbf{x}^*$ be an optimal solution to the original primal problem. Then $(\overline{\mathbf{x}}, \overline{x}_{n+1}, \overline{x}_{n+2})$ with $\overline{\mathbf{x}} = \mathbf{x}^*$, $\overline{x}_{n+1} = 0$, $\overline{x}_{n+2} = M_2 - (\mathbf{e} - \mathbf{c})'\mathbf{x}^*$, is feasible for the artificial primal problem. The objective value $\mathbf{c}'\overline{\mathbf{x}} + M_1 \overline{x}_{n+1}$ coincides with the optimal cost $\mathbf{c}'\mathbf{x}^* + M_1 x_{n+1}^*$, and therefore we have an optimal solution to the artificial primal problem.

(b) The proof of this part is similar and is left as an exercise.   □

On the complexity of the algorithm

Suppose that $\mathbf{A}$, $\mathbf{b}$, and $\mathbf{c}$ have integer entries whose magnitude is bounded by U. If $\mathbf{x}^*$ and $(\mathbf{p}^*, \mathbf{s}^*)$ are optimal basic feasible solutions to the primal and dual problem, respectively, the components of $\mathbf{x}^*$ and $\mathbf{p}^*$ are bounded by $(nU)^n$ [see Lemma 8.2(b) in Section 8.3]. From Theorem 9.6, it follows that we can select some M_1, M_2 of the order of $(nU)^{n+2}$, solve the artificial problems, and obtain an optimal solution to the original problems. Furthermore, it is easily checked that the initial potential function satisfies

$$G(\mathbf{x}^0, \mathbf{s}^0) = O\big(qn \log(nU)\big).$$

Applying Theorems 9.4 and 9.5 with $q = n + \sqrt{n}$ and $G(\mathbf{x}^0, \mathbf{s}^0)$ given above, we conclude that the potential reduction algorithm finds solutions $\mathbf{x}^K, \mathbf{s}^K$, with duality gap

$$(\mathbf{s}^K)'\mathbf{x}^K \le \epsilon,$$

after

$$K = O\left(\sqrt{n} \log \frac{1}{\epsilon} + n^2 \log(nU)\right)$$

iterations. Moreover, the dependence of this bound on ϵ is tight, since there exist examples that require at least

$$\Omega\left(\sqrt{n} \log \frac{1}{\epsilon}\right)$$

iterations (see Exercise 9.6).

The work per iteration involves the matrix inversion $(\mathbf{A}\mathbf{X}_k^2\mathbf{A}')^{-1}$ and two matrix multiplications to calculate $\overline{\mathbf{A}}^k$. Therefore, each iteration requires $O(nm^2 + m^3)$ arithmetic operations. Since $m \le n$, each iteration requires at most $O(n^3)$ arithmetic operations. As a result, the potential reduction algorithm finds an ϵ-optimal solution using

$$O\left(n^{3.5} \log \frac{1}{\epsilon} + n^5 \log(nU)\right)$$

arithmetic operations. Notice that this bound grows only polynomially in n, $\log U$, and $\log(1/\epsilon)$. If ϵ is taken to be sufficiently small, an exact solution can be found by rounding. This results in a polynomial time (in n and $\log U$) algorithm. In contrast, the simplex method (cf. Section 3.7) can take an exponential (in n) number of iterations in the worst case.

Computational performance

The computational performance of the potential reduction algorithm can be greatly enhanced by allowing line searches in the potential function as follows. In our presentation of the algorithm, we have found a direction $\mathbf{d}$ such that $G(\mathbf{x} + \mathbf{d}, \mathbf{s}) < G(\mathbf{x}, \mathbf{s})$. Having found the direction $\mathbf{d}$, we can produce a larger decrease in the potential function by solving the one-dimensional optimization problem

$$
\begin{aligned}
\text{minimize} \quad & G(\mathbf{x} + \beta\mathbf{d}, \mathbf{s}) \\
\text{subject to} \quad & \beta \geq 0.
\end{aligned}
$$

In this way, we obtain the largest possible decrease in the potential function at each primal update. The potential reduction algorithm with line searches is a very effective algorithm. However, it can be shown that the worst-case complexity of the algorithm does not improve, even if we use line searches (see Exercise 9.7).

9.4   The primal path following algorithm

In this and the next section, we present a class of interior point algorithms that matches the best known time complexity, offers interesting geometric insights and, from a practical perspective, has been incorporated in large scale implementations. In this section, we present the primal version of the path following algorithm, and prove that is has polynomial time complexity. The algorithm solves the linear programming problem

$$
\begin{aligned}
\text{minimize} \quad & \mathbf{c}'\mathbf{x} \\
\text{subject to} \quad & \mathbf{A}\mathbf{x} = \mathbf{b} \\
& \mathbf{x} \geq \mathbf{0},
\end{aligned}
$$

and its dual

$$
\begin{aligned}
\text{maximize} \quad & \mathbf{p}'\mathbf{b} \\
\text{subject to} \quad & \mathbf{p}'\mathbf{A} + \mathbf{s}' = \mathbf{c}' \\
& \mathbf{s} \geq \mathbf{0}.
\end{aligned}
$$

The first idea in the path following algorithm is motivated from the observation that the core difficulty in linear programming is the presence of the inequality constraints $\mathbf{x} \geq \mathbf{0}$. For this reason, we convert the linear programming problem to a problem with only equality constraints, using a barrier function that prevents any variable from reaching the boundary ($x_j = 0$). We achieve this by adding terms $-\log x_j$ to the objective function. These terms will cause the objective to increase without bound as x_j approaches 0. Let $\mu > 0$. We introduce the following *barrier function*:

$$
B_\mu(\mathbf{x}) = \mathbf{c}'\mathbf{x} - \mu \sum_{j=1}^{n} \log x_j.
$$

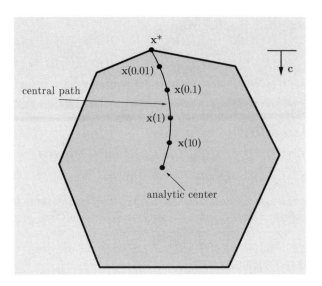

Figure 9.4: The central path and the analytic center.

The barrier function is defined to be infinity, if $x_j \leq 0$ for some j. We next consider the following family of nonlinear programming problems (called *barrier problems*), parameterized by $\mu > 0$:

$$\begin{aligned} \text{minimize} \quad & B_\mu(\mathbf{x}) \\ \text{subject to} \quad & \mathbf{Ax} = \mathbf{b}. \end{aligned} \tag{9.15}$$

Assume that for all $\mu > 0$, the barrier problem has an optimal solution denoted by $\mathbf{x}(\mu)$. [It is not hard to show that it cannot have multiple solutions because the barrier function is "strictly convex."] As μ varies, the minimizers $\mathbf{x}(\mu)$ form the *central path*, which is illustrated in Figure 9.4. In particular, it can be shown that $\lim_{\mu \to 0} \mathbf{x}(\mu)$ exists and is an optimal solution $\mathbf{x}^*$ to the initial linear programming problem (see Example 9.3). The intuitive reason is that when μ is very small, the logarithmic term is negligible almost everywhere, except that it still prevents us from landing on the boundary.

A barrier problem originating from the dual problem is

$$\begin{aligned} \text{maximize} \quad & \mathbf{p}'\mathbf{b} + \mu \sum_{j=1}^{n} \log s_j \\ \text{subject to} \quad & \mathbf{p}'\mathbf{A} + \mathbf{s}' = \mathbf{c}'. \end{aligned} \tag{9.16}$$

Let $\mathbf{p}(\mu)$, $\mathbf{s}(\mu)$ be the optimal solution to the problem (9.16) for $\mu > 0$. Problems (9.15) and (9.16) are convex optimization problems, i.e., we are optimizing a convex function subject to constraints that define a convex feasible set (in this case linear equalities). Similar to the complementary slackness for a linear optimization problem, we show in Lemma 9.5 that the following set of conditions (called the Karush-Kuhn-Tucker optimality conditions) are sufficient (they are also necessary) for an optimal solution to problems (9.15) and (9.16):

$$
\begin{aligned}
\mathbf{A}\mathbf{x}(\mu) &= \mathbf{b} \\
\mathbf{x}(\mu) &\geq \mathbf{0} \\
\mathbf{A}'\mathbf{p}(\mu) + \mathbf{s}(\mu) &= \mathbf{c} \\
\mathbf{s}(\mu) &\geq \mathbf{0} \\
\mathbf{X}(\mu)\mathbf{S}(\mu)\mathbf{e} &= \mathbf{e}\mu,
\end{aligned}
\tag{9.17}
$$

where $\mathbf{X}(\mu) = \mathrm{diag}\big(x_1(\mu),\ldots,x_n(\mu)\big)$ and $\mathbf{S}(\mu) = \mathrm{diag}\big(s_1(\mu),\ldots,s_n(\mu)\big)$. Note that for $\mu = 0$, Eq. (9.17) corresponds to the complementary slackness conditions for linear programming.

Lemma 9.5 *If* $\mathbf{x}^*$, $\mathbf{p}^*$, *and* $\mathbf{s}^*$ *satisfy conditions (9.17), then they are optimal solutions to problems (9.15) and (9.16), i.e.,*

$$
\mathbf{x}^* = \mathbf{x}(\mu), \qquad \mathbf{p}^* = \mathbf{p}(\mu), \qquad \mathbf{s}^* = \mathbf{s}(\mu).
$$

Proof. Let $\mathbf{x}^*$, $\mathbf{p}^*$, and $\mathbf{s}^*$ be as in the statement of the lemma, and let $\mathbf{x}$ be an arbitrary vector that satisfies $\mathbf{x} \geq \mathbf{0}$, and $\mathbf{A}\mathbf{x} = \mathbf{b}$. We then have

$$
\begin{aligned}
B_\mu(\mathbf{x}) &= \mathbf{c}'\mathbf{x} - \mu \sum_{j=1}^{n} \log x_j \\
&= \mathbf{c}'\mathbf{x} - (\mathbf{p}^*)'(\mathbf{A}\mathbf{x} - \mathbf{b}) - \mu \sum_{j=1}^{n} \log x_j \\
&= (\mathbf{s}^*)'\mathbf{x} + (\mathbf{p}^*)'\mathbf{b} - \mu \sum_{j=1}^{n} \log x_j \\
&\geq \mu n + (\mathbf{p}^*)'\mathbf{b} - \mu \sum_{j=1}^{n} \log \left(\frac{\mu}{s_j^*} \right).
\end{aligned}
$$

The last inequality was obtained because the expression $s_j^* x_j - \mu \log x_j$ is minimized when $x_j = \mu/s_j^*$, as can be verified by setting its derivative to zero. The inequality holds with equality if and only if $x_j = \mu/s_j^* = x_j^*$ for all $j = 1,\ldots,n$, which proves that $B_\mu(\mathbf{x}^*) \leq B_\mu(\mathbf{x})$ for all feasible $\mathbf{x}$. In particular, $\mathbf{x}^*$ is the unique optimal solution to the primal barrier problem and $\mathbf{x}^* = \mathbf{x}(\mu)$.

The proof that $\mathbf{p}^* = \mathbf{p}(\mu)$ and $\mathbf{s}^* = \mathbf{s}(\mu)$ is entirely symmetrical and is omitted. $\qquad\square$

The minimizer corresponding to $\mu = \infty$ is the solution to the optimization problem

$$\text{minimize} \quad -\sum_{j=1}^{n} \log x_j$$
$$\text{subject to} \quad \mathbf{Ax} = \mathbf{b}.$$

The optimal solution to this problem is called the *analytic center* of the feasible set[1] (see Figure 9.4).

Example 9.2 (A simple barrier problem) Consider the problem

$$\text{minimize} \quad x$$
$$\text{subject to} \quad x \geq 0.$$

The barrier function in this case is

$$B_\mu(x) = x - \mu \log x.$$

Using calculus, we find that the minimizer $x(\mu)$ is equal to μ. Notice that as μ decreases to zero, the optimal solution approaches $x^* = 0$.

Example 9.3 (Computation of the central path) Consider the problem

$$\text{minimize} \quad x_2$$
$$\text{subject to} \quad x_1 + x_2 + x_3 = 1$$
$$x_1, x_2, x_3 \geq 0.$$

Let P be the feasible set. In order to compute the central path we need to solve the optimization problem

$$\text{minimize} \quad x_2 - \mu \log x_1 - \mu \log x_2 - \mu \log x_3$$
$$\text{subject to} \quad x_1 + x_2 + x_3 = 1.$$

Substituting $x_3 = 1 - x_1 - x_2$, we need to solve the following unconstrained nonlinear optimization problem:

$$\text{minimize} \quad x_2 - \mu \log x_1 - \mu \log x_2 - \mu \log(1 - x_1 - x_2).$$

By taking derivatives, and setting them equal to zero we find that the central path is given by

$$x_1(\mu) = \frac{1 - x_2(\mu)}{2}$$
$$x_2(\mu) = \frac{1 + 3\mu - \sqrt{1 + 9\mu^2 + 2\mu}}{2}$$
$$x_3(\mu) = \frac{1 - x_2(\mu)}{2}.$$

---

[1] We can also define the analytic center of a general polyhedron $P = \{(\mathbf{x}, \mathbf{s}) \mid \mathbf{a}_i'\mathbf{x} \leq b_i, \ i = 1, \ldots, m\}$ as the minimizer of the barrier function $-\sum_{j=1}^{m} \log(b_i - \mathbf{a}_i'\mathbf{x})$. Unlike the standard form case, the analytic center is not a geometric, i.e., representation independent, property. It depends on the linear system of inequalities used to represent the polyhedron: if we add a redundant constraint, the analytic center changes.

The analytic center can be found by letting $\mu \to \infty$. It is the point $(1/3, 1/3, 1/3)$.

Let Q be the set of optimal solutions to the original linear programming problem, which is given by

$$Q = \big\{ \mathbf{x} \mid \mathbf{x} = (x_1, 0, x_3),\ x_1 + x_3 = 1,\ \mathbf{x} \geq \mathbf{0} \big\}.$$

The analytic center of the polyhedron Q is the point $(1/2, 0, 1/2)$. Note that this is the point we obtain if we let $\mu = 0$, showing that the central path for $\mu = 0$ finds an optimal solution that is the analytic center of the set of optimal solutions. See Figure 9.5.

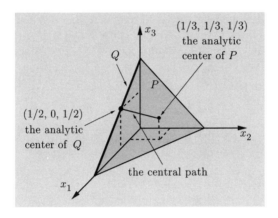

Figure 9.5: The central path and the analytic center in Example 9.3.

We next describe an algorithm based on the barrier function. The barrier problem is still difficult to solve, because the objective function is neither linear nor quadratic. For this reason, we approximate the function $B_\mu(\mathbf{x})$ around some given $\mathbf{x}$ by the first three terms of its Taylor series expansion, thus obtaining a quadratic function. We first calculate the derivatives of the barrier function $B_\mu(\mathbf{x})$, which are:

$$\frac{\partial B_\mu(\mathbf{x})}{\partial x_i} = c_i - \frac{\mu}{x_i},$$

$$\frac{\partial^2 B_\mu(\mathbf{x})}{\partial x_i^2} = \frac{\mu}{x_i^2},$$

$$\frac{\partial^2 B_\mu(\mathbf{x})}{\partial x_i \partial x_j} = 0, \quad i \neq j.$$

Given a vector $\mathbf{x} > \mathbf{0}$, the Taylor series expansion of the barrier function is as follows:

$$B_\mu(\mathbf{x} + \mathbf{d}) \approx B_\mu(\mathbf{x}) + \sum_{i=1}^{n} \frac{\partial B_\mu(\mathbf{x})}{\partial x_i} d_i + \frac{1}{2} \sum_{i,j=1}^{n} \frac{\partial^2 B_\mu(\mathbf{x})}{\partial x_i \partial x_j} d_i d_j$$

$$= B_\mu(\mathbf{x}) + (\mathbf{c}' - \mu\mathbf{e}'\mathbf{X}^{-1})\mathbf{d} + \frac{1}{2}\mu\mathbf{d}'\mathbf{X}^{-2}\mathbf{d},$$

where $\mathbf{X} = \text{diag}(x_1, \ldots, x_n)$. Instead of minimizing the barrier function, we will find a direction $\mathbf{d}$ that minimizes the Taylor series expansion of $B_\mu(\mathbf{x} + \mathbf{d})$. Then, the approximating problem becomes:

$$\text{minimize} \quad (\mathbf{c}' - \mu\mathbf{e}'\mathbf{X}^{-1})\mathbf{d} + \frac{1}{2}\mu\mathbf{d}'\mathbf{X}^{-2}\mathbf{d}$$
$$\text{subject to} \quad \mathbf{Ad} = \mathbf{0}.$$

This problem can be solved in closed form using the method of Lagrange multipliers as follows. We associate a vector $\mathbf{p}$ of Lagrange multipliers to the constraints $\mathbf{Ad} = \mathbf{0}$ and form the Lagrangean function

$$L(\mathbf{d}, \mathbf{p}) = (\mathbf{c}' - \mu\mathbf{e}'\mathbf{X}^{-1})\mathbf{d} + \frac{1}{2}\mu\mathbf{d}'\mathbf{X}^{-2}\mathbf{d} - \mathbf{p}'\mathbf{Ad}.$$

We require that

$$\frac{\partial L(\mathbf{d}, \mathbf{p})}{\partial d_j} = 0, \qquad \frac{\partial L(\mathbf{d}, \mathbf{p})}{\partial p_i} = 0,$$

which leads to:

$$\begin{aligned} \mathbf{c} - \mu\mathbf{X}^{-1}\mathbf{e} + \mu\mathbf{X}^{-2}\mathbf{d} - \mathbf{A}'\mathbf{p} &= \mathbf{0}, \\ \mathbf{Ad} &= \mathbf{0}. \end{aligned} \tag{9.18}$$

Notice that this is a system of $m+n$ linear equations, with $m+n$ unknowns (d_j, $j = 1, \ldots, n$, and p_i, $i = 1, \ldots, m$). The solution to the system is given by

$$\begin{aligned} \mathbf{d}(\mu) &= \left(\mathbf{I} - \mathbf{X}^2\mathbf{A}'(\mathbf{A}\mathbf{X}^2\mathbf{A}')^{-1}\mathbf{A}\right)\left(\mathbf{X}\mathbf{e} - \frac{1}{\mu}\mathbf{X}^2\mathbf{c}\right), \\ \mathbf{p}(\mu) &= (\mathbf{A}\mathbf{X}^2\mathbf{A}')^{-1}\mathbf{A}(\mathbf{X}^2\mathbf{c} - \mu\mathbf{X}\mathbf{e}). \end{aligned} \tag{9.19}$$

The vector $\mathbf{d}(\mu)$ is called the *Newton direction* and the process of calculating this direction is called a *Newton step*. Starting with the given solution $\mathbf{x}$, the new primal solution is $\mathbf{x} + \mathbf{d}(\mu)$. The corresponding dual solution becomes $(\mathbf{p}, \mathbf{s}) = (\mathbf{p}(\mu), \mathbf{c} - \mathbf{A}'\mathbf{p}(\mu))$. We then decrease μ to $\overline{\mu} = \alpha\mu$, and continue similarly. Here, α is a parameter that satisfies $0 < \alpha < 1$ and which is kept fixed throughout the algorithm.

We next give a geometric interpretation of the algorithm (see Figure 9.6). If we were to fix μ and carry out several Newton steps, then it can be shown that $\mathbf{x}$ would converge to $\mathbf{x}(\mu)$. By carrying out a single Newton step, we can guarantee that $\mathbf{x}$ is close to $\mathbf{x}(\mu)$. We then reduce μ to $\overline{\mu} = \alpha\mu$. When α is sufficiently close to 1, then $\overline{\mu}$ is close to μ, and $\mathbf{x}(\overline{\mu})$ is also close to $\mathbf{x}(\mu)$. Thus, $\mathbf{x}$ is also relatively close to $\mathbf{x}(\overline{\mu})$. By carrying out a Newton step, with μ set to $\overline{\mu}$, $\mathbf{x}$ moves even closer to $\mathbf{x}(\overline{\mu})$. Thus, while our "target" $\mathbf{x}(\mu)$ keeps changing with μ, our feasible solution $\mathbf{x}$ always

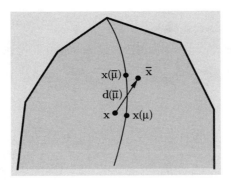

Figure 9.6: Approximating the central path with Newton steps. The vector $\mathbf{x}$ is close to $\mathbf{x}(\mu)$. We change μ to $\bar{\mu}$, and we have a new target $\mathbf{x}(\bar{\mu})$. A Newton step brings us to $\bar{\mathbf{x}}$, which is close to $\mathbf{x}(\bar{\mu})$.

stays close to $\mathbf{x}(\mu)$ and approximately follows the central path, hence the name *path following*. We will show later that throughout the algorithm, the solutions $\mathbf{x}$ and $\mathbf{s}$ satisfy for some $0 < \beta < 1$:

$$\left\| \frac{1}{\mu} \mathbf{XSe} - \mathbf{e} \right\| \leq \beta, \tag{9.20}$$

where $\mathbf{X} = \mathrm{diag}(\mathbf{x}_1, \dots, \mathbf{x}_n)$ and $\mathbf{S} = \mathrm{diag}(\mathbf{s}_1, \dots, \mathbf{s}_n)$. Equation (9.20) can be viewed as an approximate version of the optimality condition $\mathbf{XSe}/\mu - \mathbf{e} = \mathbf{0}$ [cf. Eq. (9.17)].

As μ decreases to zero, $\mathbf{XSe}$ should tend to zero in order for (9.20) to hold. Therefore, the complementarity slackness condition for linear programming will be satisfied in the limit.

We can now provide a complete description of the algorithm. The primal path following algorithm uses the following inputs:

(a) the data of the problem $(\mathbf{A}, \mathbf{b}, \mathbf{c})$; the matrix $\mathbf{A}$ has full row rank;

(b) initial primal and dual feasible solutions $\mathbf{x}^0 > \mathbf{0}$, $\mathbf{s}^0 > \mathbf{0}$, $\mathbf{p}^0$;

(c) the optimality tolerance $\epsilon > 0$;

(d) the initial value of the barrier parameter μ^0, and the parameter α, where $0 < \alpha < 1$.

The primal path following algorithm

1. (Initialization) Start with some primal and dual feasible $\mathbf{x}^0 > \mathbf{0}$, $\mathbf{s}^0 > \mathbf{0}$, $\mathbf{p}^0$, and set $k = 0$.

2. (Optimality test) If $(\mathbf{s}^k)'\mathbf{x}^k < \epsilon$ stop; else go to Step 3.

3. Let

$$\mathbf{X}_k = \text{diag}(x_1^k, \ldots, x_n^k),$$
$$\mu^{k+1} = \alpha\mu^k.$$

4. (Computation of directions) Solve the linear system

$$\mu^{k+1}\mathbf{X}_k^{-2}\mathbf{d} - \mathbf{A}'\mathbf{p} = \mu^{k+1}\mathbf{X}_k^{-1}\mathbf{e} - \mathbf{c},$$
$$\mathbf{A}\mathbf{d} = \mathbf{0}, \tag{9.21}$$

for $\mathbf{p}$ and $\mathbf{d}$.

5. (Update of solutions) Let

$$\mathbf{x}^{k+1} = \mathbf{x}^k + \mathbf{d},$$
$$\mathbf{p}^{k+1} = \mathbf{p},$$
$$\mathbf{s}^{k+1} = \mathbf{c} - \mathbf{A}'\mathbf{p}.$$

6. Let $k := k + 1$ and go to Step 2.

In the next theorem, we prove that the primal path following algorithm produces feasible, near-optimal, primal and dual solutions, and we analyze its complexity.

Theorem 9.7 *Assume that the primal path following algorithm uses*

$$\alpha = 1 - \frac{\sqrt{\beta} - \beta}{\sqrt{\beta} + \sqrt{n}},$$

where $\beta < 1$, and starts with an initial primal and dual feasible solution $(\mathbf{x}^0, \mathbf{s}^0, \mathbf{p}^0)$, with $\mathbf{x}^0 > \mathbf{0}$, $\mathbf{s}^0 > \mathbf{0}$, that satisfies

$$\left\| \frac{1}{\mu^0}\mathbf{X}_0\mathbf{S}_0\mathbf{e} - \mathbf{e} \right\| \leq \beta.$$

Then, after

$$K = \left\lceil \frac{\sqrt{\beta} + \sqrt{n}}{\sqrt{\beta} - \beta} \log \frac{(\mathbf{s}^0)'\mathbf{x}^0(1 + \beta)}{\epsilon(1 - \beta)} \right\rceil$$

iterations, it finds a primal and dual feasible solution $(\mathbf{x}^K, \mathbf{s}^K, \mathbf{p}^K)$ with duality gap

$$(\mathbf{s}^K)'\mathbf{x}^K \leq \epsilon.$$

Proof. We will first prove by induction on k that $\mathbf{x}^k$, $\mathbf{s}^k$ are primal and dual feasible solutions with $\mathbf{x}^k > \mathbf{0}$, $\mathbf{s}^k > \mathbf{0}$ that satisfy

$$\left\|\frac{1}{\mu^k}\mathbf{X}_k\mathbf{S}_k\mathbf{e} - \mathbf{e}\right\| \leq \beta.$$

For $k = 0$ we have assumed that the induction hypothesis is satisfied. We assume that it holds for k and then show it for $k + 1$. We first show that

$$\left\|\frac{1}{\mu^{k+1}}\mathbf{X}_k\mathbf{S}_k\mathbf{e} - \mathbf{e}\right\| \leq \sqrt{\beta}.$$

Indeed, we have

$$\left\|\frac{1}{\mu^{k+1}}\mathbf{X}_k\mathbf{S}_k\mathbf{e} - \mathbf{e}\right\| = \left\|\frac{1}{\alpha\mu^k}\mathbf{X}_k\mathbf{S}_k\mathbf{e} - \mathbf{e}\right\|$$

$$= \left\|\frac{1}{\alpha}\left(\frac{1}{\mu^k}\mathbf{X}_k\mathbf{S}_k\mathbf{e} - \mathbf{e}\right) + \frac{1-\alpha}{\alpha}\mathbf{e}\right\|$$

$$\leq \frac{1}{\alpha}\left\|\frac{1}{\mu^k}\mathbf{X}_k\mathbf{S}_k\mathbf{e} - \mathbf{e}\right\| + \frac{1-\alpha}{\alpha}\|\mathbf{e}\|$$

$$\leq \frac{\beta}{\alpha} + \frac{1-\alpha}{\alpha}\sqrt{n}$$

$$= \sqrt{\beta}.$$

We next show that $\|\mathbf{X}_k^{-1}\mathbf{d}\| \leq \sqrt{\beta} < 1$, where $\mathbf{d} = \mathbf{x}^{k+1} - \mathbf{x}^k$. Recall that the direction $\mathbf{d}$ solves the linear system [cf. Eq. (9.21)]

$$\mu^{k+1}\mathbf{X}_k^{-2}\mathbf{d} - \mathbf{A}'\mathbf{p} = \mu^{k+1}\mathbf{X}_k^{-1}\mathbf{e} - \mathbf{c},$$

$$\mathbf{A}\mathbf{d} = \mathbf{0}.$$

By left-multiplying the first equation by $\mathbf{d}'$, and using the second equation, we obtain

$$\mu^{k+1}\mathbf{d}'\mathbf{X}_k^{-2}\mathbf{d} = \mathbf{d}'\left(\mu^{k+1}\mathbf{X}_k^{-1}\mathbf{e} - \mathbf{c}\right).$$

Therefore,

$$\|\mathbf{X}_k^{-1}\mathbf{d}\|^2 = \mathbf{d}'\mathbf{X}_k^{-2}\mathbf{d}$$

$$= \left(\mathbf{X}_k^{-1}\mathbf{e} - \frac{1}{\mu^{k+1}}\mathbf{c}\right)'\mathbf{d}$$

$$= \left(\mathbf{X}_k^{-1}\mathbf{e} - \frac{1}{\mu^{k+1}}(\mathbf{s}^k + \mathbf{A}'\mathbf{p}^k)\right)'\mathbf{d}$$

$$= \left(\mathbf{X}_k^{-1}\mathbf{e} - \frac{1}{\mu^{k+1}}\mathbf{s}^k \right)' \mathbf{d}$$

$$= -\left(\frac{1}{\mu^{k+1}}\mathbf{X}_k\mathbf{S}_k\mathbf{e} - \mathbf{e} \right)' \mathbf{X}_k^{-1}\mathbf{d}$$

$$\leq \left\| \frac{1}{\mu^{k+1}}\mathbf{X}_k\mathbf{S}_k\mathbf{e} - \mathbf{e} \right\| \|\mathbf{X}_k^{-1}\mathbf{d}\|$$

$$\leq \sqrt{\beta}\|\mathbf{X}_k^{-1}\mathbf{d}\|$$

and therefore, $\|\mathbf{X}_k^{-1}\mathbf{d}\| \leq \sqrt{\beta} < 1$.

We next show that $\mathbf{x}^{k+1}$ and $(\mathbf{p}^{k+1}, \mathbf{s}^{k+1})$ are primal and dual feasible, assuming that this is true for $\mathbf{x}^k$ and $(\mathbf{p}^k, \mathbf{s}^k)$. Since $\mathbf{Ad} = 0$, we have

$$\mathbf{Ax}^{k+1} = \mathbf{b}.$$

In addition,

$$\mathbf{x}^{k+1} = \mathbf{x}^k + \mathbf{d} = \mathbf{X}_k(\mathbf{e} + \mathbf{X}_k^{-1}\mathbf{d}) > 0,$$

because $\|\mathbf{X}_k^{-1}\mathbf{d}\| < 1$. Hence, $\mathbf{x}^{k+1}$ is a primal feasible solution. Moreover,

$$\mathbf{A}'\mathbf{p}^{k+1} + \mathbf{s}^{k+1} = \mathbf{c},$$

by construction. Also, using Eq. (9.21),

$$\mathbf{s}^{k+1} = \mathbf{c} - \mathbf{A}'\mathbf{p}^{k+1} = \mu^{k+1}\mathbf{X}_k^{-1}(\mathbf{e} - \mathbf{X}_k^{-1}\mathbf{d}) > 0,$$

where again the last inequality follows because $\|\mathbf{X}_k^{-1}\mathbf{d}\| < 1$. Hence, the solution $(\mathbf{p}^{k+1}, \mathbf{s}^{k+1})$ is dual feasible.

Note that

$$x_j^{k+1} = x_j^k \left(1 + \frac{d_j}{x_j^k} \right),$$

$$s_j^{k+1} = \frac{\mu^{k+1}}{x_j^k} \left(1 - \frac{d_j}{x_j^k} \right).$$

Therefore,

$$\frac{1}{\mu^{k+1}}x_j^{k+1}s_j^{k+1} - 1 = \frac{1}{\mu^{k+1}}x_j^k \left(1 + \frac{d_j}{x_j^k} \right)\frac{\mu^{k+1}}{x_j^k}\left(1 - \frac{d_j}{x_j^k} \right) - 1$$

$$= -\left(\frac{d_j}{x_j^k} \right)^2. \tag{9.22}$$

We define $\mathbf{D} = \mathrm{diag}(d_1, \ldots, d_n)$ and we let $\| \cdot \|_1$ denote the norm defined by $\|\mathbf{u}\|_1 = \sum_i |u_i|$. Note that $\|\mathbf{u}\| \leq \|\mathbf{u}\|_1$. Then, using Eq. (9.22) to obtain the first equality below,

$$\left\| \frac{1}{\mu^{k+1}} \mathbf{X}_{k+1} \mathbf{S}_{k+1} \mathbf{e} - \mathbf{e} \right\| = \left\| \mathbf{X}_k^{-2} \mathbf{D}^2 \mathbf{e} \right\|$$
$$\leq \left\| \mathbf{X}_k^{-2} \mathbf{D}^2 \mathbf{e} \right\|_1$$
$$= \mathbf{e}' \mathbf{X}_k^{-2} \mathbf{D}^2 \mathbf{e}$$
$$= \mathbf{e}' \mathbf{D} \mathbf{X}_k^{-2} \mathbf{D} \mathbf{e}$$
$$= \mathbf{d}' \mathbf{X}_k^{-2} \mathbf{d}$$
$$= \left\| \mathbf{X}_k^{-1} \mathbf{d} \right\|^2$$
$$\leq (\sqrt{\beta})^2$$
$$= \beta,$$

and hence the induction is complete.

Since at every iteration

$$\left\| \frac{1}{\mu^k} \mathbf{X}_k \mathbf{S}_k \mathbf{e} - \mathbf{e} \right\| \leq \beta,$$

we obtain

$$-\beta \leq \frac{1}{\mu^k} x_j^k s_j^k - 1 \leq \beta.$$

This implies that

$$n\mu^k (1 - \beta) \leq (\mathbf{s}^k)' \mathbf{x}^k \leq n\mu^k (1 + \beta). \tag{9.23}$$

Moreover,

$$\mu^k = \alpha^k \mu^0 = \left(1 - \frac{\sqrt{\beta} - \beta}{\sqrt{\beta} + \sqrt{n}} \right)^k \mu^0 \leq e^{-k \frac{\sqrt{\beta} - \beta}{\sqrt{\beta} + \sqrt{n}}} \mu^0.$$

After

$$\left\lceil \frac{\sqrt{\beta} + \sqrt{n}}{\sqrt{\beta} - \beta} \log \frac{\mu^0 n (1 + \beta)}{\epsilon} \right\rceil \leq \left\lceil \frac{\sqrt{\beta} + \sqrt{n}}{\sqrt{\beta} - \beta} \log \frac{(\mathbf{s}^0)' \mathbf{x}^0 (1 + \beta)}{\epsilon (1 - \beta)} \right\rceil = K$$

iterations, the primal path following algorithm finds primal and dual solutions $\mathbf{x}^K$, $(\mathbf{p}^K, \mathbf{s}^K)$, that have duality gap $(\mathbf{s}^K)' \mathbf{x}^K$ less than or equal to ϵ. $\qquad \square$

Initialization

We now discuss how to start the primal path following algorithm for an arbitrary linear programming problem,

$$\begin{aligned} \text{minimize} \quad & \mathbf{c}' \mathbf{x} \\ \text{subject to} \quad & \mathbf{A}\mathbf{x} = \mathbf{b} \\ & \mathbf{x} \geq \mathbf{0}, \end{aligned}$$

and its dual

$$\text{maximize} \quad \mathbf{p'b}$$
$$\text{subject to} \quad \mathbf{p'A} \leq \mathbf{c'},$$

so that we can guarantee that the initial solution $(\mathbf{x}^0, \mathbf{s}^0, \mathbf{p}^0)$ is primal and dual feasible with $\mathbf{x}^0 > \mathbf{0}$, $\mathbf{s}^0 > \mathbf{0}$, and $\|\frac{1}{\mu^0}\mathbf{X}_0\mathbf{S}_0\mathbf{e} - \mathbf{e}\| \leq \beta$, with $\beta = 1/4$.

We assume that all entries of $\mathbf{A}$, $\mathbf{b}$, and $\mathbf{c}$ are integer with absolute values bounded by U. Using Lemma 8.2(b) in Section 8.3 we obtain that all basic feasible solutions to the primal problem satisfy $\mathbf{e'x} \leq n(mU)^m$. This implies that an optimal solution to the linear programming

$$\text{minimize} \quad \mathbf{c'x}$$
$$\text{subject to} \quad \mathbf{Ax} = \mathbf{b}$$
$$\mathbf{e'x} \leq n(mU)^m$$
$$\mathbf{x} \geq \mathbf{0},$$

is also optimal for the original problem. By setting $\overline{\mathbf{b}} = (n+2)\mathbf{b}/(n(mU)^m)$, we obtain that the latter problem is equivalent to

$$\text{minimize} \quad \mathbf{c'x}$$
$$\text{subject to} \quad \mathbf{Ax} = \overline{\mathbf{b}}$$
$$\mathbf{e'x} \leq n+2$$
$$\mathbf{x} \geq \mathbf{0}.$$

Next, we consider the artificial primal and dual problems

$$\begin{array}{llll}
\text{minimize} & \mathbf{c'x} & + & Mx_{n+1} \\
\text{subject to} & \mathbf{Ax} & + (\overline{\mathbf{b}} - \mathbf{Ae})x_{n+1} & = \overline{\mathbf{b}} \\
& \mathbf{e'x} & + \quad x_{n+1} + x_{n+2} & = n+2 \\
& x_1, \ldots, x_{n+2} \geq 0, &
\end{array}$$

$$\begin{array}{lllll}
\text{maximize} & \mathbf{p'\overline{b}} & + \; p_{m+1}(n+2) \\
\text{subject to} & \mathbf{p'A} & + \; p_{m+1}\mathbf{e'} & + \; \mathbf{s'} & = \mathbf{c'} \\
& \mathbf{p'(\overline{b} - Ae)} & + \; p_{m+1} & + \; s_{n+1} & = M \\
& & p_{m+1} & + \; s_{n+2} & = 0 \\
& s_1, \ldots, s_{n+2} \geq 0, &
\end{array}$$

where x_{n+1}, x_{n+2} are artificial primal variables, p_{m+1}, s_{n+1}, s_{n+2} are artificial dual variables, and M is a large positive number.

Let $\mu^0 = 4\sqrt{\|\mathbf{c}\|^2 + M^2}$. Notice that the vectors

$$(\mathbf{x}^0, x_{n+1}^0, x_{n+2}^0) = (\mathbf{e}, 1, 1),$$
$$(\mathbf{p}^0, p_{m+1}^0, \mathbf{s}^0, s_{n+1}^0, s_{n+2}^0) = (\mathbf{0}, -\mu^0, \mathbf{c} + \mu^0\mathbf{e}, M + \mu^0, \mu^0),$$

are feasible solutions with all primal and dual slack variables positive. By selecting M large, it can be shown that an optimal solution satisfies $x_{n+1} =$

0 and we, therefore, have an optimal solution to the original problem. It is easy to check that

$$\left\| \frac{1}{\mu^0} \mathbf{X}_0 \mathbf{S}_0 \mathbf{e} - \mathbf{e} \right\| = \frac{1}{4}.$$

This allows us to apply the algorithm to the artificial problems with $\beta = \frac{1}{4}$, and use the result in Theorem 9.7 to establish convergence.

On the complexity of the algorithm

The work per iteration involves solving a linear system with $m+n$ equations in $m + n$ unknowns. Given that $m \le n$, the work per iteration is $O(n^3)$. Let $\epsilon_0 = (\mathbf{s}^0)'\mathbf{x}^0$ be the initial duality gap. By starting the algorithm as indicated in the previous subsection, we obtain that the primal path following algorithm needs

$$O\left(\sqrt{n} \log \frac{\epsilon_0}{\epsilon}\right)$$

iterations to reduce the duality gap from ϵ_0 to ϵ, with $O(n^3)$ arithmetic operations per iteration. It can be verified that for the particular initialization given in the previous subsection, $\log \epsilon_0$ is polynomial in n and $\log U$. Therefore, the number of iterations needed to find an ϵ-optimal solution is polynomial in n, $\log U$, and $\log(1/\epsilon)$.

9.5   The primal-dual path following algorithm

In this section, we describe the primal-dual version of the path following algorithm we introduced in the previous section. It uses the idea of approximating the central path by taking Newton steps, but finds Newton directions both in the primal and the dual space. This algorithm has excellent performance in large scale applications and it is the method of choice in commercial implementations of interior point methods.

The point of departure for our development are the barrier optimization problems

$$\begin{array}{ll} \text{minimize} & \mathbf{c}'\mathbf{x} - \mu \sum_{j=1}^{n} \log x_j \\ \text{subject to} & \mathbf{Ax} = \mathbf{b}, \end{array} \tag{9.24}$$

and

$$\begin{array}{ll} \text{maximize} & \mathbf{p}'\mathbf{b} + \mu \sum_{j=1}^{n} \log s_j \\ \text{subject to} & \mathbf{p}'\mathbf{A} + \mathbf{s}' = \mathbf{c}'. \end{array} \tag{9.25}$$

We have mentioned in the previous section that the necessary and sufficient conditions for the point $\mathbf{x}(\mu)$ to be the optimal solution to problem (9.24), and for $\big(\mathbf{p}(\mu), \mathbf{s}(\mu)\big)$ to be the optimal solution to problem (9.25) are the following equations:

$$\begin{aligned}
\mathbf{A}\mathbf{x}(\mu) &= \mathbf{b} \\
\mathbf{x}(\mu) &\geq \mathbf{0} \\
\mathbf{A}'\mathbf{p}(\mu) + \mathbf{s}(\mu) &= \mathbf{c} \\
\mathbf{s}(\mu) &\geq \mathbf{0} \\
\mathbf{X}(\mu)\mathbf{S}(\mu)\mathbf{e} &= \mathbf{e}\mu,
\end{aligned} \qquad (9.26)$$

where $\mathbf{X}(\mu) = \mathrm{diag}\big(x_1(\mu), \ldots, x_n(\mu)\big)$ and $\mathbf{S}(\mu) = \mathrm{diag}\big(s_1(\mu), \ldots, s_n(\mu)\big)$.

The above system of equations is unfortunately nonlinear, because of the equations $\mathbf{X}(\mu)\mathbf{S}(\mu)\mathbf{e} = \mathbf{e}\mu$, and therefore difficult to solve directly. Instead we will solve this system of nonlinear equations iteratively using Newton's method for finding roots of nonlinear equations, which we describe next.

Newton's method for finding roots of nonlinear equations

Let $\mathbf{F}$ be a mapping from $\Re^r$ into $\Re^r$. We are interested in finding a $\mathbf{z}^*$ such that

$$\mathbf{F}(\mathbf{z}^*) = \mathbf{0}.$$

Assume that we have a vector $\mathbf{z}^k$, which is our current approximation for $\mathbf{z}^*$. We develop a method for improving our approximation. We use a first order multivariable Taylor series expansion of the function $\mathbf{F}(\mathbf{z})$ around $\mathbf{z} = \mathbf{z}^k$:

$$\mathbf{F}(\mathbf{z}^k + \mathbf{d}) \approx \mathbf{F}(\mathbf{z}^k) + \mathbf{J}(\mathbf{z}^k)\mathbf{d}.$$

Here $\mathbf{J}(\mathbf{z}^k)$ is the $r \times r$ Jacobian matrix whose (i, j)th element is given by

$$\left. \frac{\partial F_i(\mathbf{z})}{\partial z_j} \right|_{\mathbf{z}=\mathbf{z}^k}.$$

In an effort to find $\mathbf{d}$ such that $\mathbf{F}(\mathbf{z}^k + \mathbf{d}) = \mathbf{0}$, we set its approximation equal to zero and look for some $\mathbf{d}$ that satisfies

$$\mathbf{F}(\mathbf{z}^k) + \mathbf{J}(\mathbf{z}^k)\mathbf{d} = \mathbf{0}. \qquad (9.27)$$

We then set $\mathbf{z}^{k+1} = \mathbf{z}^k + \mathbf{d}$. The direction $\mathbf{d}$ is called a *Newton direction*[2]. When the matrix $\mathbf{J}(\mathbf{z}^*)$ is nonsingular and the starting point $\mathbf{z}^0$ is "close

---

[2]If we are interested in minimizing a function $f : \Re^n \mapsto \Re$, we want to set the gradient of f to zero. Newton's method, then involves the Jacobian of ∇f, which is the matrix of second derivatives of f. The resulting iteration is equivalent to forming and minimizing a second order Taylor series approximation of $f(\mathbf{x} + \mathbf{d})$, with respect to $\mathbf{d}$. Thus, the Newton method considered in the preceding section is a special case of the one we discuss here.

to" $\mathbf{z}^*$, the method converges quickly to $\mathbf{z}^*$. However, if $\mathbf{z}^0$ is not close to $\mathbf{z}^*$, the method can diverge.

Application of Newton's method to linear programming

Recall that the primal path following method used Newton's method to solve the barrier problem (9.24). In contrast, the primal-dual method uses Newton's method to solve the system of nonlinear equations (9.26). In this case $\mathbf{z} = (\mathbf{x}, \mathbf{p}, \mathbf{s})$, $r = 2n + m$, and the function $\mathbf{F}(\mathbf{z})$ is given by

$$\mathbf{F}(\mathbf{z}) = \begin{bmatrix} \mathbf{Ax} - \mathbf{b} \\ \mathbf{A'p} + \mathbf{s} - \mathbf{c} \\ \mathbf{XSe} - \mu\mathbf{e} \end{bmatrix}.$$

[We ignore the nonnegativity constraints in Eq. (9.26), since the algorithm we construct will always satisfy them.] Let $(\mathbf{x}^k, \mathbf{p}^k, \mathbf{s}^k)$ be the current primal and dual feasible solution, with $\mathbf{x}^k > \mathbf{0}$, $\mathbf{s}^k > \mathbf{0}$, and let μ^k be the current value of μ. By applying Eq. (9.27), the Newton direction $\mathbf{d} = (\mathbf{d}_x^k, \mathbf{d}_p^k, \mathbf{d}_s^k)$ is determined by the following system of equations:

$$\begin{bmatrix} \mathbf{A} & \mathbf{0} & \mathbf{0} \\ \mathbf{0} & \mathbf{A'} & \mathbf{I} \\ \mathbf{S}_k & \mathbf{0} & \mathbf{X}_k \end{bmatrix} \begin{bmatrix} \mathbf{d}_x^k \\ \mathbf{d}_p^k \\ \mathbf{d}_s^k \end{bmatrix} = - \begin{bmatrix} \mathbf{Ax}^k - \mathbf{b} \\ \mathbf{A'p}^k + \mathbf{s}^k - \mathbf{c} \\ \mathbf{X}_k\mathbf{S}_k\mathbf{e} - \mu^k\mathbf{e} \end{bmatrix}.$$

Since $\mathbf{Ax}^k = \mathbf{b}$ and $\mathbf{A'p}^k + \mathbf{s}^k = \mathbf{c}$, this is equivalent to the following system of equations:

$$\mathbf{Ad}_x^k = \mathbf{0}, \tag{9.28}$$
$$\mathbf{A'd}_p^k + \mathbf{d}_s^k = \mathbf{0}, \tag{9.29}$$
$$\mathbf{S}_k\mathbf{d}_x^k + \mathbf{X}_k\mathbf{d}_s^k = \mu^k\mathbf{e} - \mathbf{X}_k\mathbf{S}_k\mathbf{e}. \tag{9.30}$$

It can be verified that the solution to this linear system is given by

$$\mathbf{d}_x^k = \overline{\mathbf{D}}_k(\mathbf{I} - \mathbf{P}_k)\mathbf{v}^k(\mu^k),$$
$$\mathbf{d}_p^k = -(\mathbf{A}\overline{\mathbf{D}}_k^2\mathbf{A'})^{-1}\mathbf{A}\overline{\mathbf{D}}_k\mathbf{v}^k(\mu^k),$$
$$\mathbf{d}_s^k = \overline{\mathbf{D}}_k^{-1}\mathbf{P}_k\mathbf{v}^k(\mu^k),$$

where

$$\overline{\mathbf{D}}_k^2 = \mathbf{X}_k\mathbf{S}_k^{-1},$$
$$\mathbf{P}_k = \overline{\mathbf{D}}_k\mathbf{A'}(\mathbf{A}\overline{\mathbf{D}}_k^2\mathbf{A'})^{-1}\mathbf{A}\overline{\mathbf{D}}_k,$$
$$\mathbf{v}^k(\mu^k) = \mathbf{X}_k^{-1}\overline{\mathbf{D}}_k(\mu^k\mathbf{e} - \mathbf{X}_k\mathbf{S}_k\mathbf{e}).$$

Step lengths

After obtaining a Newton direction at the kth iteration, the new solution is:

$$\mathbf{x}^{k+1} = \mathbf{x}^k + \beta_P^k \mathbf{d}_x^k,$$
$$\mathbf{p}^{k+1} = \mathbf{p}^k + \beta_D^k \mathbf{d}_p^k,$$
$$\mathbf{s}^{k+1} = \mathbf{s}^k + \beta_D^k \mathbf{d}_s^k,$$

where β_P^k and β_D^k are step lengths for the primal and dual variables, respectively. The nonnegativity requirements for $\mathbf{x}^{k+1}$ and $\mathbf{s}^{k+1}$ dictate the choice of β_P^k and β_D^k. One possibility for preserving nonnegativity is to take

$$\beta_P^k = \min\left\{1, \alpha \min_{\{i|(d_x^k)_i<0\}} \left(-\frac{x_i^k}{(d_x^k)_i}\right)\right\},$$

$$\beta_D^k = \min\left\{1, \alpha \min_{\{i|(d_s^k)_i<0\}} \left(-\frac{s_i^k}{(d_s^k)_i}\right)\right\},$$

where $0 < \alpha < 1$. Here $(d_x^k)_i$ and $(d_s^k)_i$ is the ith component of $\mathbf{d}_x^k$ and $\mathbf{d}_s^k$, respectively. The reason we want α to be less than 1 is to avoid approaching the boundary of the primal and dual feasible set, respectively. We finally note that the equality constraints of the primal and the dual problems are also satisfied, because of Eqs. (9.28)-(9.29). Thus, the new solution is feasible.

Updating the barrier parameter μ

Note that the Newton direction depends on the parameter μ^k. In order to approach the point $\left(\mathbf{x}(\mu^k), \mathbf{p}(\mu^k), \mathbf{s}(\mu^k)\right)$ in the central path corresponding to the current value of μ^k, several Newton steps need to be taken with μ^k kept fixed. However, since we are not interested in the optimal solution for this value of μ^k, only one Newton step is taken with the current μ^k. In the next iteration, we lower the value of μ^k. One way to update μ^k that has had excellent computational performance is to use

$$\mu^k = \frac{(\mathbf{x}^k)'\mathbf{s}^k}{n},$$

i.e., the value of μ^k is proportional to the duality gap.

We now summarize the algorithm. The primal-dual path following algorithm uses the following inputs:

(a) the data of the problem $(\mathbf{A}, \mathbf{b}, \mathbf{c})$; the matrix $\mathbf{A}$ is assumed to have full row rank;

(b) the initial primal and dual feasible solutions $\mathbf{x}^0 > \mathbf{0}$, $\mathbf{s}^0 > \mathbf{0}$, $\mathbf{p}^0$;

(c) the optimality tolerance $\epsilon > 0$;

(d) the parameter α, with $0 < \alpha < 1$.

The primal-dual path following algorithm

1. (Initialization) Start with some feasible $\mathbf{x}^0 > 0$, $\mathbf{s}^0 > 0$, $\mathbf{p}^0$, and set $k = 0$.

2. (Optimality test) If $(\mathbf{s}^k)'\mathbf{x}^k < \epsilon$ stop; else go to Step 3.

3. (Computation of Newton directions) Let

$$\mu^k = \frac{(\mathbf{s}^k)'\mathbf{x}^k}{n},$$

$$\mathbf{X}_k = \mathrm{diag}(x_1^k, \ldots, x_n^k),$$

$$\mathbf{S}_k = \mathrm{diag}(s_1^k, \ldots, s_n^k).$$

Solve the linear system (9.28)-(9.30) for $\mathbf{d}_x^k$, $\mathbf{d}_p^k$, and $\mathbf{d}_s^k$.

4. (Find step lengths) Let

$$\beta_P^k = \min\left\{ 1, \alpha \min_{\{i|(d_x^k)_i < 0\}} \left(-\frac{x_i^k}{(d_x^k)_i} \right) \right\},$$

$$\beta_D^k = \min\left\{ 1, \alpha \min_{\{i|(d_s^k)_i < 0\}} \left(-\frac{s_i^k}{(d_s^k)_i} \right) \right\}.$$

5. (Solution update) Update the solution vectors according to

$$\mathbf{x}^{k+1} = \mathbf{x}^k + \beta_P^k \mathbf{d}_x^k,$$

$$\mathbf{p}^{k+1} = \mathbf{p}^k + \beta_D^k \mathbf{d}_p^k,$$

$$\mathbf{s}^{k+1} = \mathbf{s}^k + \beta_D^k \mathbf{d}_s^k.$$

6. Let $k := k + 1$ and go to Step 2.

Worst-case complexity

With a slightly different choice of μ^k and the step length, it has been shown that the algorithm takes $O(\sqrt{n}\log(\epsilon_0/\epsilon))$ iterations to reduce the duality gap from ϵ_0 to ϵ.

Infeasible primal-dual path following methods

In practice, a variation of the primal-dual path following method has also proved to be very successful. This method starts from an initial point $\mathbf{x}^0 > 0$, $\mathbf{s}^0 > 0$, $\mathbf{p}^0$, which is not necessarily feasible for either the primal or the dual problem, i.e., $\mathbf{A}\mathbf{x}^0 \neq \mathbf{b}$ and/or $\mathbf{A}'\mathbf{p}^0 + \mathbf{s}^0 \neq \mathbf{c}$. The algorithm is the same as the standard primal-dual path following algorithm, except that iterates are not necessarily feasible at each iteration. The Newton direction $\mathbf{d} = (\mathbf{d}_x^k, \mathbf{d}_p^k, \mathbf{d}_s^k)$ is derived in exactly the same manner and requires us to solve the following system of equations:

$$
\begin{bmatrix}
\mathbf{A} & \mathbf{0} & \mathbf{0} \\
\mathbf{0} & \mathbf{A}' & \mathbf{I} \\
\mathbf{S}_k & \mathbf{0} & \mathbf{X}_k
\end{bmatrix}
\begin{bmatrix}
\mathbf{d}_x^k \\
\mathbf{d}_p^k \\
\mathbf{d}_s^k
\end{bmatrix}
= -
\begin{bmatrix}
\mathbf{A}\mathbf{x}^k - \mathbf{b} \\
\mathbf{A}'\mathbf{p}^k + \mathbf{s}^k - \mathbf{c} \\
\mathbf{X}_k\mathbf{S}_k\mathbf{e} - \mu^k\mathbf{e}
\end{bmatrix}.
$$

The method is known to converge to an optimal solution, and has been implemented with excellent results.

Self-dual methods

In this subsection, we present an alternative method for initializing the primal-dual path following algorithm that finds an ϵ-optimal solution after a polynomial number of iterations without using large numbers ("big M" constants).

We consider the linear programming problem

$$
\begin{array}{ll}
\text{minimize} & \mathbf{c}'\mathbf{x} \\
\text{subject to} & \mathbf{A}\mathbf{x} = \mathbf{b} \\
& \mathbf{x} \geq \mathbf{0},
\end{array}
\tag{9.31}
$$

and its dual

$$
\begin{array}{ll}
\text{maximize} & \mathbf{p}'\mathbf{b} \\
\text{subject to} & \mathbf{p}'\mathbf{A} + \mathbf{s}' = \mathbf{c}' \\
& \mathbf{s} \geq \mathbf{0}.
\end{array}
\tag{9.32}
$$

Given an initial possibly infeasible point $(\mathbf{x}^0, \mathbf{p}^0, \mathbf{s}^0)$ with $\mathbf{x}^0 > \mathbf{0}$ and $\mathbf{s}^0 > \mathbf{0}$, we consider the problem

$$
\begin{array}{ll}
\text{minimize} & \big((\mathbf{x}^0)'\mathbf{s}^0 + 1\big)\theta \\
\text{subject to} & \mathbf{A}\mathbf{x} - \mathbf{b}\tau + \bar{\mathbf{b}}\theta = 0 \\
& -\mathbf{A}'\mathbf{p} + \mathbf{c}\tau - \bar{\mathbf{c}}\theta - \mathbf{s} = 0 \\
& \mathbf{b}'\mathbf{p} - \mathbf{c}'\mathbf{x} + \bar{z}\theta - \kappa = 0 \\
& -\bar{\mathbf{b}}'\mathbf{p} + \bar{\mathbf{c}}'\mathbf{x} - \bar{z}\tau = -\big((\mathbf{x}^0)'\mathbf{s}^0 + 1\big) \\
& \mathbf{x} \geq \mathbf{0}, \ \tau \geq 0, \ \mathbf{s} \geq \mathbf{0}, \ \kappa \geq 0,
\end{array}
\tag{9.33}
$$

where

$$
\bar{\mathbf{b}} = \mathbf{b} - \mathbf{A}\mathbf{x}^0, \qquad \bar{\mathbf{c}} = \mathbf{c} - \mathbf{A}'\mathbf{p}^0 - \mathbf{s}^0, \qquad \bar{z} = \mathbf{c}'\mathbf{x}^0 + 1 - \mathbf{b}'\mathbf{p}^0.
$$

It is easy to check that the above linear programming problem is *self-dual*, i.e., its dual is equivalent with itself. Note that

$$
(\mathbf{x}, \mathbf{p}, \mathbf{s}, \tau, \theta, \kappa) = (\mathbf{x}^0, \mathbf{p}^0, \mathbf{s}^0, 1, 1, 1),
$$

is a feasible interior solution to problem (9.33). Since both the primal and the dual problems are feasible, they have optimal solutions. Since the dual is equivalent to the primal, the optimal value of (9.33) is zero.

It has been established that the primal-dual path following method finds an optimal solution $(\mathbf{x}^*, \mathbf{p}^*, \mathbf{s}^*, \tau^*, \theta^*, \kappa^*)$ that satisfies

$$\theta^* = 0, \qquad \mathbf{x}^* + \mathbf{s}^* > \mathbf{0}, \qquad \tau^* + \kappa^* > 0,$$
$$(\mathbf{s}^*)'\mathbf{x}^* = 0, \qquad \tau^* \kappa^* = 0. \tag{9.34}$$

(Such a solution satisfies a condition known as strict complementarity, which is the subject of Exercise 4.19). In addition, the following result is known to hold.

Theorem 9.8 Let $(\mathbf{x}^*, \mathbf{p}^*, \mathbf{s}^*, \tau^*, \theta^*, \kappa^*)$ be an optimal solution to problem (9.33) that satisfies the conditions (9.34).

(a) Problem (9.31) has an optimal solution if and only if $\tau^* > 0$. In this case, $\mathbf{x}^*/\tau^*$ is an optimal solution to problem (9.31) and $(\mathbf{p}^*/\tau^*, \mathbf{s}^*/\tau^*)$ is an optimal solution to problem (9.32).

(b) Problem (9.31) does not have an optimal solution if and only if $\kappa^* > 0$. In this case, if $\mathbf{c}'\mathbf{x}^* < 0$, then the primal problem (9.31) is unbounded and the dual problem (9.32) is infeasible; if $-\mathbf{b}'\mathbf{p}^* < 0$, then the dual problem (9.32) is unbounded and the primal problem (9.31) is infeasible; if both $\mathbf{c}'\mathbf{x}^* < 0$ and $-\mathbf{b}'\mathbf{p}^* < 0$, then both problems (9.31) and (9.32) are infeasible.

Using Theorem 9.8, it follows that the primal-dual path following algorithm applied to problem (9.33), initialized with the interior solution $(\mathbf{x}^0, \mathbf{p}^0, \mathbf{s}^0, 1, 1, 1)$, correctly solves the original linear programming problems (9.31) and (9.32). This solution approach has several advantages:

(a) It solves linear programming problems without any assumptions concerning the existence of feasible, interior feasible, or optimal solutions.

(b) It can start at any solution, feasible or not.

(c) Its computational requirements per iteration are comparable to those for other path following methods.

(d) It finds an ϵ-optimal solution in polynomial time without using any "big M" constants.

Computational performance

The primal-dual path following algorithm (especially the infeasible variant) has been used in several large scale implementations. While the worst-case behavior of path following algorithms is

$$O\big(\sqrt{n}\log(\epsilon_0/\epsilon)\big)$$

iterations to reduce the duality gap from ϵ_0 to ϵ, the observed ("average") behavior is

$$O\left(\log n \log(\epsilon_0/\epsilon)\right)$$

iterations. There has been some theoretical analysis of this behavior, but no satisfactory explanation has been achieved yet.

9.6   An overview

In this section, we provide some more geometric intuition into the interior point algorithms that we covered in this chapter.

Let $\mathbf{x} > \mathbf{0}$ be a feasible solution to the linear programming problem

$$\begin{array}{ll}
\text{minimize} & \mathbf{c}'\mathbf{x} \\
\text{subject to} & \mathbf{A}\mathbf{x} = \mathbf{b} \\
& \mathbf{x} \geq \mathbf{0}.
\end{array}$$

Let $\mathbf{X} = \operatorname{diag}(x_1, \ldots, x_n)$. Recall (cf. Lemma 9.2) that the affine scaling algorithm takes a step that is proportional to the direction

$$\mathbf{d}_{\text{affine}} = -\mathbf{X}^2\left(\mathbf{I} - \mathbf{A}'(\mathbf{A}\mathbf{X}^2\mathbf{A}')^{-1}\mathbf{A}\mathbf{X}^2\right)\mathbf{c}.$$

Note that the objective function decreases along this direction.

In contrast, the primal path following algorithm takes a step that is proportional to the direction [cf. Eq. (9.19)]

$$\mathbf{d}_{\text{path-following}} = \left(\mathbf{I} - \mathbf{X}^2\mathbf{A}'(\mathbf{A}\mathbf{X}^2\mathbf{A}')^{-1}\mathbf{A}\right)\left(\mathbf{X}\mathbf{e} - \frac{1}{\mu}\mathbf{X}^2\mathbf{c}\right).$$

The direction corresponding to $\mu = \infty$ [recall that in this case $\mathbf{x}(\mu)$ is the analytic center of the feasible set] is called the centering direction and is given by

$$\mathbf{d}_{\text{centering}} = \left(\mathbf{I} - \mathbf{X}^2\mathbf{A}'(\mathbf{A}\mathbf{X}^2\mathbf{A}')^{-1}\mathbf{A}\right)\mathbf{X}\mathbf{e}.$$

This direction corresponds to a move towards the analytic center of $\mathbf{A}\mathbf{x} = \mathbf{b}$, $\mathbf{x} \geq \mathbf{0}$. Note that

$$\mathbf{d}_{\text{path-following}} = \mathbf{d}_{\text{centering}} + \frac{1}{\mu}\mathbf{d}_{\text{affine}},$$

i.e., the direction along which the path following algorithm moves is a linear combination of the affine scaling direction and the centering direction. This equation gives insight into the behavior of the primal path following algorithm. When μ is large, then the centering direction dominates, i.e., in the beginning, the path following algorithm takes steps towards the analytic center. When μ is small, then the affine scaling direction dominates, i.e., towards the end, the path following algorithm behaves like the affine scaling algorithm.

We now turn our attention to the potential reduction algorithm. From Eq. (9.8), the direction in the primal step of the algorithm is proportional to

$$
\begin{aligned}
\mathbf{d}_{\text{potential}} &= -\mathbf{X}\Big(\mathbf{I} - \mathbf{X}\mathbf{A}'(\mathbf{A}\mathbf{X}^2\mathbf{A}')^{-1}\mathbf{A}\mathbf{X}\Big)\Big(\frac{q}{\mathbf{s}'\mathbf{x}}\mathbf{X}\mathbf{s} - \mathbf{e}\Big) \\
&= -\mathbf{X}\Big(\mathbf{I} - \mathbf{X}\mathbf{A}'(\mathbf{A}\mathbf{X}^2\mathbf{A}')^{-1}\mathbf{A}\mathbf{X}\Big)\Big(\frac{q}{\mathbf{s}'\mathbf{x}}\mathbf{X}(\mathbf{c} - \mathbf{A}'\mathbf{p}) - \mathbf{e}\Big) \\
&= -\mathbf{X}\Big(\mathbf{I} - \mathbf{X}\mathbf{A}'(\mathbf{A}\mathbf{X}^2\mathbf{A}')^{-1}\mathbf{A}\mathbf{X}\Big)\Big(\frac{q}{\mathbf{s}'\mathbf{x}}\mathbf{X}\mathbf{c} - \mathbf{e}\Big) \\
&= \Big(\mathbf{I} - \mathbf{X}^2\mathbf{A}'(\mathbf{A}\mathbf{X}^2\mathbf{A}')^{-1}\mathbf{A}\Big)\mathbf{X}\mathbf{e} \\
&\quad - \frac{q}{\mathbf{s}'\mathbf{x}}\mathbf{X}^2\Big(\mathbf{I} - \mathbf{A}'(\mathbf{A}\mathbf{X}^2\mathbf{A}')^{-1}\mathbf{A}\mathbf{X}^2\Big)\mathbf{c} \\
&= \mathbf{d}_{\text{centering}} + \frac{q}{\mathbf{s}'\mathbf{x}}\mathbf{d}_{\text{affine}}.
\end{aligned}
$$

As before, the direction of the potential reduction algorithm is a linear combination of the affine scaling and the centering directions. When the duality gap is large (presumably in the beginning of the algorithm), and the algorithm takes a primal step, then the centering direction dominates. When the duality gap is small (presumably at the end of the algorithm) and the algorithm takes a primal step, then the affine scaling direction dominates.

Recall that both the primal path following and the potential reduction algorithms take a polynomial number of iterations to find a near-optimal solution, while there is no polynomial bound for the number of iterations of the affine scaling algorithm. This suggests that the presence of the centering direction is responsible for the polynomiality of the path following and potential reduction algorithms.

Computational aspects of interior point methods

Interior point methods represent a significant advance in the computational practice of linear programming. Although the determination of whether the simplex or an interior point method performs better depends on the problem as well as on the instance, we provide next some qualitative guidelines:

(a) The simplex method tends to perform poorly on large, massively degenerate problems, whereas interior point methods are much less affected. So, one can expect an interior point algorithm to outperform the simplex method to the extent that the underlying problem has massive degeneracy. This is the case in certain large scheduling problems, for instance.

(b) The most computationally intensive step of an interior point method is the solution of a linear system of equations of the form

$$\left(\mathbf{A}\mathbf{X}_k^2\mathbf{A}'\right)\mathbf{d} = \mathbf{f}.$$

In implementations of interior point methods, the matrix $\mathbf{A}\mathbf{X}_k^2\mathbf{A}'$ is usually written as

$$\mathbf{A}\mathbf{X}_k^2\mathbf{A}' = \mathbf{L}\mathbf{L}',$$

where $\mathbf{L}$ is a square lower triangular matrix called the *Cholesky factor* of the matrix $\mathbf{A}\mathbf{X}_k^2\mathbf{A}'$. Then, the system of equations $\left(\mathbf{A}\mathbf{X}_k^2\mathbf{A}'\right)\mathbf{d} = \mathbf{f}$ can be solved by first solving for $\mathbf{y}$ the triangular system $\mathbf{L}\mathbf{y} = \mathbf{f}$, and then solving for $\mathbf{d}$ the triangular system $\mathbf{L}'\mathbf{d} = \mathbf{y}$. These triangular systems can be solved easily in $O(n^2)$ arithmetic operations. The construction of the Cholesky factor $\mathbf{L}$ requires $O(n^3)$ arithmetic operations, but the actual computational effort is highly dependent on the sparsity (number of nonzero entries) of $\mathbf{L}$. For this reason, large scale implementations employ heuristics that aim at improving the sparsity of $\mathbf{L}$. These heuristics involve a reordering of the rows and columns of $\mathbf{A}$. To the extent that the matrix $\mathbf{A}$ is conducive to producing relatively sparse Cholesky factors of the matrix $\mathbf{A}\mathbf{X}_k^2\mathbf{A}'$, interior point methods can be expected to outperform the simplex method. Such is the case in large staircase multiperiod linear programming problems for example.

For further discussion of computational issues regarding interior point algorithms in the context of large scale applications, see Sections 12.2 and 12.3.

9.7 Exercises

Exercise 9.1 Consider the short-step affine scaling algorithm, under Assumptions 9.1 and 9.2. Let $\mathbf{x}^*$ be the optimal solution and assume that $x_1, \ldots, x_m$ are the basic variables at $\mathbf{x}^*$. Suppose that $|x_i^k - x_i^*|/x_i^k \le \gamma$ for $i = 1, \ldots, m$, where γ is a positive constant.

(a) Show that

$$\mathbf{c}'\mathbf{x}^k - \mathbf{c}'\mathbf{x}^* \le \frac{1}{\beta}(\mathbf{c}'\mathbf{x}^k - \mathbf{c}'\mathbf{x}^{k+1})(n - m + m\gamma^2)^{1/2}.$$

(b) Show that

$$\mathbf{c}'\mathbf{x}^{k+1} - \mathbf{c}'\mathbf{x}^* \le \left(1 - \frac{\beta}{(n - m + m\gamma^2)^{1/2}}\right)(\mathbf{c}'\mathbf{x}^k - \mathbf{c}'\mathbf{x}^*).$$

Exercise 9.2 Indicate where and how the proof of Theorem 9.3 should be modified to prove the same result for the affine scaling method with stepsize given in Eq. (9.4).

Exercise 9.3 We consider the linear programming problem,

$$\begin{aligned} \text{minimize} \quad & \mathbf{c}'\mathbf{x} \\ \text{subject to} \quad & \mathbf{A}\mathbf{x} = \mathbf{b} \\ & \mathbf{x} \geq \mathbf{0}. \end{aligned}$$

We assume that the rows of $\mathbf{A}$ are linearly independent and that Assumption 9.2 holds. Let $\mathbf{x}$ be some feasible solution and suppose that we have a vector $\mathbf{p}$ such that

$$x_i(c_i - \mathbf{A}_i'\mathbf{p}) = 0, \qquad \forall \ i.$$

Show that $\mathbf{x}$ is a basic feasible solution.

Exercise 9.4 * (Nonconvergence of the affine scaling algorithm for large step lengths) We have shown that in the absence of degeneracy in the primal and in the dual problem, the affine scaling algorithm converges for all step lengths β such that $0 < \beta < 1$. In this exercise, we show that in the presence of degeneracy, the sequence of dual solutions generated by the affine scaling algorithm with stepsize given in Eq. (9.5) can fail to converge for $\beta > 2/3$. This bound is sharp because the algorithm converges for $\beta \leq 2/3$, when the problem is degenerate.

Consider the degenerate linear programming problem

$$\begin{aligned} \text{minimize} \quad & x_1 + x_2 + x_3 \\ \text{subject to} \quad & x_1 + x_2 - x_3 - x_4 = 0 \\ & x_1, x_2, x_3, x_4 \geq 0, \end{aligned}$$

and its dual

$$\begin{aligned} \text{maximize} \quad & 0p \\ \text{subject to} \quad & 0 \leq p \leq 1. \end{aligned}$$

(a) Calculate, for the affine scaling algorithm with stepsize given in Eq. (9.5), the scalar p^k and the vectors $\mathbf{r}^k$, $\mathbf{x}^{k+1}$, as a function of $\mathbf{x}^k$.

(b) Show that the sequence of dual solutions p^k does not converge for $\beta > 2/3$.

Exercise 9.5 (Behavior of affine scaling near extreme points) Consider the following linear program

$$\begin{aligned} \text{maximize} \quad & x_n \\ \text{subject to} \quad & \epsilon \leq x_1 \leq 1 \\ & \epsilon x_{j-1} \leq x_j \leq 1 - \epsilon x_{j-1}, \quad j = 2, \ldots, n, \end{aligned}$$

where $0 < \epsilon < 1/2$. In Section 3.7, we have seen that the simplex method could take $2^n - 1$ pivots to find an optimal solution. Implement the affine scaling algorithm with stepsize given in Eq. (9.5) and test it on the above problem, for $n = 3$ and $n = 4$. Initialize the algorithm at the following points and report the behavior of the algorithm.

(a) In the interior of the feasible set but close to the extreme point $(\epsilon, \epsilon^2, \ldots, \epsilon^n)$. Vary the degree of closeness and report the algorithm's behavior. Does it resemble the path of the simplex method ?

(b) At the point $\dfrac{1}{2}\mathbf{e}$.

(c) In the interior of the feasible set but close to the extreme point $(\epsilon, 1 - \epsilon^2, \ldots, \epsilon^{n-2}(1-\epsilon^2))$. Vary the degree of closeness and report the algorithm's behavior. Does it resemble the path of the simplex method ?

Exercise 9.6 * **(Worst-case complexity of potential reduction algorithms)** Let n be an even positive integer. Consider the linear programming problem

$$\text{minimize} \quad \sum_{i=1}^{n/2} x_i + 2^n \sum_{i=1}^{n} x_i$$

$$\text{subject to} \quad \sum_{i=1}^{n} x_i = 1$$

$$x_1, \ldots, x_n \geq 0,$$

and its dual

$$\text{maximize} \quad y$$

$$\text{subject to} \quad y + s_i = 2^n + 1, \qquad i = 1, \ldots, \frac{n}{2},$$

$$y + s_i = 2^n, \qquad i = \frac{n}{2} + 1, \ldots, n,$$

$$s_1, \ldots, s_n \geq 0.$$

We choose as initial solution:

$$\mathbf{x}^0 = \frac{1}{n}\mathbf{e}, \qquad \mathbf{s}^0 = \frac{1}{2}\mathbf{e} + (\mathbf{e}_{n/2}, \mathbf{0}), \qquad y^0 = -\frac{1}{2} + 2^n,$$

where $\mathbf{e}_{n/2}$ is an $n/2$-dimensional vector with all entries equal to 1.

(a) Prove that at the kth iteration of the potential reduction algorithm, we have

$$
\begin{array}{llll}
u_i^k = u_j^k, & x_i^k = x_j^k, & s_i^k = s_j^k, & i, j \leq n/2, \\
u_i^k = u_j^k, & x_i^k = x_j^k, & s_i^k = s_j^k, & i, j > n/2.
\end{array}
$$

(b) Prove that the primal objective values before and after iteration k of the potential reduction algorithm satisfy:

$$\frac{\mathbf{c}'(\mathbf{x}^{k+1} - \mathbf{x}^*)}{\mathbf{c}'(\mathbf{x}^k - \mathbf{x}^*)} \geq 1 - \frac{\sqrt{2}\beta}{\sqrt{n}},$$

where $\mathbf{x}^*$ is an optimal solution to the problem.

(c) Show that the potential reduction algorithm for $n \geq 32\beta^2/9$ needs at least

$$\frac{\sqrt{n}}{2\sqrt{2}\beta} \log \frac{1}{2\epsilon}$$

iterations to find a primal and dual solution with duality gap at most ϵ.
Hint: Use $\log(1 - x) > -2x$, for $0 \leq x \leq 3/4$.

Exercise 9.7 * (Potential reduction with line searches) In this exercise, we show that we cannot improve the worst-case complexity of potential reduction algorithms, even if we use line searches at each iteration. We consider the linear programming problem

$$\text{minimize} \quad \sum_{i=1}^{2n} x_i$$
$$\text{subject to} \quad x_i = x_{i+1}, \qquad i \neq n, \ i \neq 2n,$$
$$x_1, \ldots, x_{2n} \geq 0,$$

and its dual

$$\text{maximize} \quad \mathbf{0}'\mathbf{y} + \mathbf{0}'\mathbf{s}$$
$$\text{subject to} \quad y_i + s_i = 1, \qquad i \in \{1, n+1\},$$
$$-y_i + s_i = 1, \qquad i \in \{n, 2n\},$$
$$y_i - y_{i-1} + s_i = 1, \qquad i \notin \{1, n, n+1, 2n\},$$
$$s_1, \ldots, s_{2n} \geq 0.$$

Obviously the primal iterates in the potential reduction algorithm have $x_i^k = r^k$ for $i \leq n$, and $x_i^k = t^k$ for $i \geq n+1$, where r^k and t^k are some positive scalars. Moreover, the duality gap is $(\mathbf{x}^k)'\mathbf{s}^k = n(r^k + t^k)$.

(a) Let $q = 2n + \nu\sqrt{n}$, in the potential reduction algorithm, where ν is a positive constant. Prove that $\overline{\mathbf{A}}^k$ is independent of k and that

$$\overline{\mathbf{A}}^k = \begin{bmatrix} \mathbf{I}_n - \dfrac{1}{n}\mathbf{e}_n\mathbf{e}_n' & \mathbf{0} \\[2mm] \mathbf{0} & \mathbf{I}_n - \dfrac{1}{n}\mathbf{e}_n\mathbf{e}_n' \end{bmatrix}.$$

Here, $\mathbf{I}_n$ is the $n \times n$ identity matrix and $\mathbf{e}_n$ is an n-dimensional vector with all entries equal to one.

(b) For every iteration, prove that $u_i^k = u_{i+1}^k$, for all $i \notin \{n, 2n\}$, and that

$$u_i^k = \begin{cases} \dfrac{(2 + \frac{\nu}{\sqrt{n}})r^k}{r^k + t^k} - 1, & i \leq n, \\[4mm] \dfrac{(2 + \frac{\nu}{\sqrt{n}})t^k}{r^k + t^k} - 1, & i \geq n+1. \end{cases}$$

(c) Suppose that at every primal step, a stepsize β is chosen that minimizes $G(\mathbf{x}^k + \beta\mathbf{d}^k)$ over all $\beta \geq 0$. Show that the optimal step size only depends on the ratio r^k/t^k, i.e., prove that there exists a function $g : \Re \mapsto \Re$, such that $\beta = g(r^k/t^k)$. Furthermore, show that

$$g\left(\frac{r^k}{t^k}\right) = g\left(\frac{t^k}{r^k}\right).$$

(d) Let $\bar{\nu} = \nu/\sqrt{n}$, and

$$\beta^* = \frac{2 + \bar{\nu}}{(1 + \bar{\nu})^2}.$$

Let $x_1^0 = r^0 = 1 + (\bar{\nu}/\sqrt{n})$, $x_{n+1}^0 = t^0 = 1$, $s^0 = e$, and $y^0 = 0$ be the initial interior solutions to the problem. Show that

$$\frac{t^1}{r^1} = \frac{r^0}{t^0},$$

$$\beta^* = \arg \min_{\beta \geq 0} G(x^0 - \beta X^0 u^0, s^0).$$

(e) Show that for all primal steps, $\beta^k = \beta^*$. Moreover, show that

$$\frac{r^k}{t^k} = \frac{t^{k+1}}{r^{k+1}}, \qquad \forall\ k.$$

(f) Show that the potential reduction algorithm with exact line searches needs

$$\Omega\left(\frac{\sqrt{n}}{\nu} \log \frac{1}{\epsilon}\right)$$

primal steps to find an ϵ-optimal solution, when started from the solution x^0, s^0, y^0.

Exercise 9.8 (Implementation of the potential reduction algorithm)
Implement the potential reduction algorithm and test it on Example 9.1 and on the class of instances in Exercise 9.5. Compare the behavior of the algorithm to the behavior of the affine scaling algorithm with stepsize given in Eq. (9.5).

Exercise 9.9 (Implementation of the primal path following algorithm)
Implement the primal path following algorithm and test it on Example 9.1 and on the class of instances in Exercise 9.5. Compare the behavior of the algorithm to the behavior of the affine scaling algorithm with stepsize given in Eq. (9.5).

Exercise 9.10 (Implementation of the primal-dual path following algorithm) Implement the primal-dual path following algorithm and test it on Example 9.1 and on the class of instances in Exercise 9.5. Compare the behavior of the algorithm to the behavior of the affine scaling algorithm with stepsize given in Eq. (9.5).

Exercise 9.11 (Computation of the central path) Consider the problem

$$
\begin{aligned}
\text{minimize} \quad & x_1 + x_2 \\
\text{subject to} \quad & x_1 + x_2 + x_3 = 1 \\
& x_1, x_2, x_3 \geq 0.
\end{aligned}
$$

(a) Show that the central path is given as follows:

$$x_1(\mu) = \frac{1 + 3\mu - \sqrt{1 + 9\mu^2 - 2\mu}}{4},$$

$$x_2(\mu) = x_1(\mu),$$

$$x_3(\mu) = 1 - 2x_1(\mu).$$

(b) Show that as μ decreases to zero, $(x_1(\mu), x_2(\mu), x_3(\mu))$ converges to the unique optimal solution.

Exercise 9.12 * (**The dual step in the potential reduction algorithm**)

(a) Suppose that we wish to compute $\mathbf{x}^k$, $\mathbf{s}^k$, recursively, according to the potential reduction algorithm. What are the computational requirements during a typical dual step?

(b) Suppose that the parameter q in the potential reduction algorithm satisfies $q \geq n + \sqrt{n}$. Show that the direction $\mathbf{u}^k$ that the algorithm calculates at the kth step satisfies $(\mathbf{u}^k)'\mathbf{e} \geq 0$. If the kth step in the algorithm is a dual step, show that

$$\|\mathbf{u}^{k+1}\| \geq \|\mathbf{u}^k\|.$$

Exercise 9.13 Prove Theorem 9.6(b).

Exercise 9.14 * Prove Theorem 9.8.

Exercise 9.15 (**Primal-dual path following algorithm for convex quadratic programming**) Consider the optimization problem

$$\begin{aligned}
\text{minimize} \quad & \mathbf{c}'\mathbf{x} + \frac{1}{2}\mathbf{x}'\mathbf{Q}\mathbf{x} \\
\text{subject to} \quad & \mathbf{A}\mathbf{x} = \mathbf{b} \\
& \mathbf{x} \geq \mathbf{0},
\end{aligned}$$

where $\mathbf{Q}$ is an $n \times n$ positive semidefinite matrix (that is, $\mathbf{x}'\mathbf{Q}\mathbf{x} \geq 0$ for all $\mathbf{x}$). We introduce the logarithmic barrier problem:

$$\begin{aligned}
\text{minimize} \quad & \mathbf{c}'\mathbf{x} + \frac{1}{2}\mathbf{x}'\mathbf{Q}\mathbf{x} - \mu \sum_{j=1}^{n} \log x_j \\
\text{subject to} \quad & \mathbf{A}\mathbf{x} = \mathbf{b}.
\end{aligned}$$

The associated Karush-Kuhn-Tucker optimality conditions are:

$$\begin{aligned}
\mathbf{A}\mathbf{x}(\mu) &= \mathbf{b}, \\
-\mathbf{Q}\mathbf{x}(\mu) + \mathbf{A}'\mathbf{p}(\mu) + \mathbf{s}(\mu) &= \mathbf{c}, \\
\mathbf{X}(\mu)\mathbf{S}(\mu)\mathbf{e} &= \mathbf{e}\mu,
\end{aligned}$$

where $\mathbf{X}(\mu) = \text{diag}\big(x_1(\mu), \ldots, x_n(\mu)\big)$ and $\mathbf{S}(\mu) = \text{diag}\big(s_1(\mu), \ldots, s_n(\mu)\big)$.

(a) By applying the ideas of Section 9.5, show that a Newton direction can be found by solving the following system of equations.

$$\begin{aligned}
\mathbf{A}\mathbf{d}_x^k &= \mathbf{0}, \\
-\mathbf{Q}\mathbf{d}_x^k + \mathbf{A}'\mathbf{d}_p^k + \mathbf{d}_s^k &= \mathbf{0}, \\
\mathbf{S}_k\mathbf{d}_x^k + \mathbf{X}_k\mathbf{d}_s^k &= \mu^k\mathbf{e} - \mathbf{X}_k\mathbf{S}_k\mathbf{e}.
\end{aligned}$$

(b) Show that the solution to the system of equations in part (a) is given by

$$\begin{aligned}
\mathbf{d}_p^k &= -\big(\mathbf{A}(\mathbf{S}_k + \mathbf{X}_k\mathbf{Q})^{-1}\mathbf{X}_k\mathbf{A}'\big)^{-1}\mathbf{A}(\mathbf{S}_k + \mathbf{X}_k\mathbf{Q})^{-1}\mathbf{v}^k(\mu^k), \\
\mathbf{d}_x^k &= (\mathbf{S}_k + \mathbf{X}_k\mathbf{Q})^{-1}\big(\mathbf{X}_k\mathbf{A}'\mathbf{d}_p^k + \mathbf{v}^k(\mu^k)\big), \\
\mathbf{d}_s^k &= \mathbf{X}_k^{-1}\big(\mathbf{v}^k(\mu^k) - \mathbf{S}_k\mathbf{d}_x^k\big).
\end{aligned}$$

with $\mathbf{v}^k(\mu^k) = \mu^k \mathbf{e} - \mathbf{X}_k \mathbf{S}_k \mathbf{e}$.

(c) Based on part (b) develop a primal-dual path following interior point algorithm. You do not need to prove convergence.

Exercise 9.16 (The von Neumann algorithm for linear programming)
The goal of this exercise is to develop an early "interior" point algorithm for linear programming. Consider the problem of finding a feasible solution to the following set of constraints, which includes a convexity constraint:

$$\sum_{j=1}^{n} \mathbf{A}_j y_j = \mathbf{b},$$

$$\sum_{j=1}^{n} y_j = 1, \qquad (9.35)$$

$$y_1, \ldots, y_n \geq 0,$$

where $\mathbf{A}_j$, $j = 1, \ldots, n$, and $\mathbf{b}$ are vectors in $\Re^m$. Let

$$\mathbf{P}_j = \frac{\mathbf{A}_j - \mathbf{b}}{\|\mathbf{A}_j - \mathbf{b}\|}.$$

Note that $\|\mathbf{P}_j\| = 1$. The constraints (9.35) are feasible if and only if the same is true for the following constraints:

$$\sum_{j=1}^{n} \mathbf{P}_j x_j = \mathbf{0},$$

$$\sum_{j=1}^{n} x_j = 1, \qquad (9.36)$$

$$x_1, \ldots, x_n \geq 0.$$

To see this we argue as follows. If $\mathbf{x}$ is a feasible solution to (9.36), then it is easy to check that $\mathbf{y}$ is a feasible solution to (9.35), where

$$y_j = \left(\frac{x_j}{\|\mathbf{A}_j - \mathbf{b}\|} \right) \Big/ \left(\sum_{k=1}^{n} \frac{x_k}{\|\mathbf{A}_k - \mathbf{b}\|} \right).$$

Conversely, if $\mathbf{y}$ satisfies the system (9.35), then it is easy to check that $\mathbf{x}$ satisfies the system (9.36), where

$$x_j = \left(y_j \|\mathbf{A}_j - \mathbf{b}\| \right) \Big/ \left(\sum_{k=1}^{n} y_k \|\mathbf{A}_k - \mathbf{b}\| \right).$$

Geometrically, the columns $\mathbf{P}_j$ can be viewed as points in $\Re^m$ lying on a hypersphere with radius 1 and center at the origin (see Figure 9.7). Problem (9.36) then becomes one of assigning nonnegative weights x_j to the points $\mathbf{P}_j$, so that their center of gravity is the origin $\mathbf{0}$. We next propose an algorithm for problem (9.36):

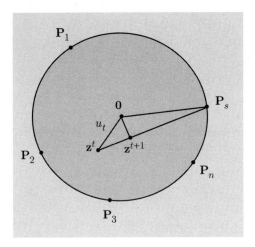

Figure 9.7: Illustration of the von Neumann algorithm.

1. (Initialization) Let $\mathbf{x}^1 = \mathbf{e}_1$, $\mathbf{z}^1 = \mathbf{P}_1$, $u_1 = \|\mathbf{z}^1\|$, $t = 1$. Here, $\mathbf{e}_1$ is the first unit vector.

2. (Computation of direction) At the start of iteration t, one is given an approximate solution $\mathbf{x} = \mathbf{x}^t$, such that $\mathbf{e}'\mathbf{x}^t = 1$. Let

$$\mathbf{z}^t = \sum_{j=1}^t \mathbf{P}_j x_j^t, \qquad u_t = \|\mathbf{z}^t\|.$$

   Among all vectors $\mathbf{P}_j$, $j = 1, \ldots, n$, find a vector $\mathbf{P}_s$, such that

$$\mathbf{P}_s'\mathbf{z}^t \le \mathbf{P}_j'\mathbf{z}^t, \qquad \forall\, j.$$

3. (Check for infeasibility) Let $v_t = \mathbf{P}_s'\mathbf{z}^t$. If $v_t > 0$, stop; the problem (9.36) is infeasible.

4. Choose as the next approximation $\mathbf{z}^{t+1}$ the closest point to the origin on the line segment joining $\mathbf{z}^t$ and $\mathbf{P}_s$ (see Figure 9.7). This can be accomplished by letting

$$\lambda = \frac{1 - v_t}{u_t^2 - 2v_t + 1},$$
$$\mathbf{z}^{t+1} = \lambda \mathbf{z}^t + (1 - \lambda)\mathbf{P}_s,$$
$$x_j^{t+1} = \begin{cases} \lambda x_j^t, & j \ne s, \\ \lambda x_s^t + (1 - \lambda), & j = s. \end{cases}$$

   Let $t := t + 1$ and go to Step 2.

(a) Show that if $v_t > 0$, then Problem (9.36) is infeasible.

(b) Verify the formulas in Step 4 of the algorithm.

(c) Show that

$$u_{t+1}^2 = \frac{u_t^2 - v_t^2}{u_t^2 - 2v_t + 1}.$$

(d) Show that

$$\frac{1}{u_t^2} + 1 \leq \frac{1}{u_{t+1}^2}.$$

(e) Suppose that the problem is feasible. Show that after $O(1/\epsilon^2)$ iterations, the algorithm finds a solution such that

$$u_t = \left\| \sum_{j=1}^{n} \mathbf{P}_j x_j \right\| \leq \epsilon.$$

Note the remarkable property that the number of iterations to find an approximately feasible solution is independent of the dimensions of the problem.

9.8   Notes and sources

9.1 The field of interior point methods has its origins in the work of Karmarkar (1984), who introduced the first interior point algorithm with polynomial time complexity. His algorithm is of the potential reduction type. He introduced the potential function idea (although he used a slightly different potential function) as a way of measuring progress towards optimality. In addition, his algorithm uses certain projective transformations. In contrast, the affine scaling algorithm uses affine transformations. The affine scaling algorithm was introduced much earlier by Dikin (1967), but remained mostly unnoticed. After the appearance of Karmarkar's paper, the affine scaling algorithm was rediscovered by Barnes (1986), and Vanderbei, Meketon, and Freedman (1986). Megiddo and Shub (1989) indicated that the trajectory leading to the optimal solution by the affine scaling algorithm depends strongly upon the starting solution.

9.2 Dikin (1974) analyzed the convergence of short-step affine scaling under a primal nondegeneracy assumption [see Vanderbei and Lagarias (1990) for a discussion of Dikin's proof]. Convergence results for different variants of affine scaling, without any nondegeneracy assumptions, have been developed by Tsuchiya (1991), Tseng and Luo (1992), and Tsuchiya and Muramatsu (1995). The latter paper contains a proof of Theorem 9.1(b). The proof of convergence of the affine scaling algorithm that we give here is adapted from Barnes (1986).

9.3 The potential reduction method is due to Ye (1991) [see also Gonzaga (1990)]. The algorithm we presented is due to Freund (1991), and is a simplification of Ye's method.

9.4-5 Path following algorithms are widely considered the most effective interior point methods; see e.g. McShane, Monma, and Shanno (1991). The idea of using a logarithmic barrier function for convex programming problems can be traced back to Frisch (1956). Its properties in the context of nonlinear programming have been carefully studied by Fiacco and McCormick (1968). Megiddo (1989) introduced them in linear programming through the study of the central path, and proposed a primal-dual framework. Using this framework Kojima, Mizuno, and Yoshise (1989) presented an $O(n \log(\epsilon_0/\epsilon))$ iterations path following algorithm for linear programming problems. Renegar (1988) presented the first $O(\sqrt{n} \log(\epsilon_0/\epsilon))$ iterations path following algorithm for linear programming, using Newton's method. Monteiro and Adler refined the primal-dual algorithm to converge in $O(\sqrt{n} \log(\epsilon_0/\epsilon))$ iterations for linear programming (1989a) and for convex quadratic problems (1989b). The particular primal path following algorithm we present is from Gonzaga (1989). The complexity analysis is from Tseng (1989). The local rate of convergence of path following algorithms is discussed by Zhang and Tapia (1993). For a comprehensive summary of infeasible path following methods see Mizuno (1996). Self-dual interior point methods were developed in Ye, Todd, and Mizuno (1994). Theorem 9.8 is from that reference. For a textbook presentation of Newton and barrier methods in nonlinear optimization, see Bertsekas (1995b).

9.6 The state of the art of interior point computation is discussed in Lustig, Marsten, and Shanno (1994), and Andersen et al. (1996).

9.7 Exercise 9.1 on the asymptotic rate of convergence of affine scaling is from Barnes (1986). Exercise 9.4 on the nonconvergence of the affine scaling algorithm with stepsize given in Eq. (9.5) is from Hall and Vanderbei (1993). Exercises 9.6 and 9.7 on the tightness of the bound $O(\sqrt{n} \log(1/\epsilon))$ are from Bertsimas and Luo (1997). Exercise 9.15 touches upon the topic of convex optimization using interior point methods. A comprehensive reference on this topic is the monograph by Nesterov and Nemirovskii (1994). Exercise 9.16 describes an early (unpublished) interior point algorithm due to von Neumann [see Dantzig (1992)].

Chapter 10

Integer programming formulations

451

In discrete optimization problems, we seek to find a solution $\mathbf{x}^*$ in a discrete set F that optimizes (minimizes or maximizes) an objective function $c(\mathbf{x})$ defined for all $\mathbf{x} \in F$. Discrete optimization problems arise in a great variety of contexts in science and engineering. A natural and systematic way to study a broad class of discrete optimization problems is to express them as integer programming problems.

The (linear) integer programming problem is the same as the linear programming problem except that some of the variables are restricted to take integer values. In general, given matrices $\mathbf{A}$, $\mathbf{B}$, and vectors $\mathbf{b}$, $\mathbf{c}$, $\mathbf{d}$, the problem

$$\begin{aligned} \text{minimize} \quad & \mathbf{c}'\mathbf{x} + \mathbf{d}'\mathbf{y} \\ \text{subject to} \quad & \mathbf{A}\mathbf{x} + \mathbf{B}\mathbf{y} = \mathbf{b} \\ & \mathbf{x}, \mathbf{y} \geq \mathbf{0} \\ & \mathbf{x} \text{ integer}, \end{aligned}$$

is the *mixed integer programming* problem. Notice that even if there are inequality constraints, we can still write the problem in the above form by adding slack or surplus variables. If there are no continuous variables $\mathbf{y}$, the problem is called the *integer programming* problem. If furthermore, there are no continuous variables and the components of the vector $\mathbf{x}$ are restricted to be either 0 or 1, the problem is called the *zero-one* (or *binary*) *integer programming* problem (ZOIP). Finally, it is customary to assume that the entries of $\mathbf{A}$, $\mathbf{B}$, $\mathbf{b}$, $\mathbf{c}$, $\mathbf{d}$ are integers.

Integer programming is a rather powerful modeling framework that provides great flexibility for expressing discrete optimization problems. On the other hand, the price for this flexibility is that integer programming seems to be a much more difficult problem than linear programming. In this chapter, we introduce general guidelines for obtaining "strong" integer programming formulations for discrete optimization problems. We introduce modeling techniques, discuss what constitutes a strong formulation, and compare alternative formulations of the same problem.

10.1 Modeling techniques

In this section, we outline some modeling techniques that facilitate the formulation of discrete optimization problems as integer programming problems. In comparison to linear programming, integer programming is significantly richer in modeling power. Unfortunately, there is no systematic way to formulate discrete optimization problems, and devising a good model is often an art, which we plan to explore through examples.

Binary choice

An important use of a binary variable x is to encode a choice between two alternatives: we may set x to zero or one, depending on the chosen alternative.

Example 10.1 (The zero-one knapsack problem) The knapsack problem was introduced in Chapter 6. We discuss here another variant of the problem, in which the decision variables are constrained to be binary. We are given n items. The jth item has weight w_j and its value is c_j. Given a bound K on the weight that can be carried in a knapsack, we would like to select items to maximize the total value. In order to model this problem, we define a binary variable x_j which is 1 if item j is chosen, and 0 otherwise. The problem can then be formulated as follows:

$$\text{maximize} \quad \sum_{j=1}^{n} c_j x_j$$

$$\text{subject to} \quad \sum_{j=1}^{n} w_j x_j \leq K$$

$$x_j \in \{0, 1\}, \qquad j = 1, \ldots n.$$

Forcing constraints

A very common feature in discrete optimization problems is that certain decisions are dependent. In particular, suppose decision A can be made only if decision B has also been made. In order to model such a situation, we can introduce binary variables x (respectively, y) equal to 1 if decision A (respectively, B) is chosen, and 0 otherwise. The dependence of the two decisions can be modeled using the constraint

$$x \leq y,$$

i.e., if $y = 0$ (decision B is not made), then $x = 0$ (decision A cannot be made). Next, we present an example where forcing constraints are used.

Example 10.2 (Facility location problems) Suppose we are given n potential facility locations and a list of m clients who need to be serviced from these locations. There is a fixed cost c_j of opening a facility at location j, while there is a cost d_{ij} of serving client i from facility j. The goal is to select a set of facility locations and assign each client to one facility, while minimizing the total cost.

In order to model this problem, we define a binary decision variable y_j for each location j, which is equal to 1 if facility j is selected, and 0 otherwise. In addition, we define a binary variable x_{ij}, which is equal to 1 if client i is served by facility j, and 0 otherwise. The facility location problem is then formulated as follows:

$$\text{minimize} \quad \sum_{j=1}^{n} c_j y_j + \sum_{i=1}^{m} \sum_{j=1}^{n} d_{ij} x_{ij}$$

$$\text{subject to} \quad \sum_{j=1}^{n} x_{ij} = 1, \qquad\qquad \forall\, i, \qquad\qquad (10.1)$$

$$x_{ij} \leq y_j, \qquad\qquad \forall\, i, j,$$

$$x_{ij}, y_j \in \{0, 1\}, \qquad\qquad \forall\, i, j.$$

Here, the forcing constraint $x_{ij} \le y_j$ captures the fact that if there is no facility at location j ($y_j = 0$), then client i cannot be served there, and we must have $x_{ij} = 0$.

Relations between variables

A constraint of the form

$$\sum_{j=1}^{n} x_j \le 1,$$

where all variables are binary, implies that at most one of the variables x_j can be one. Similarly, if the constraint is of the form $\sum_{j=1}^{n} x_j = 1$, then exactly one of the variables x_j should be one.

Disjunctive constraints

Let $\mathbf{x}$ be a nonnegative decision vector. Suppose that we are given two constraints $\mathbf{a}'\mathbf{x} \ge b$ and $\mathbf{c}'\mathbf{x} \ge d$, in which all of the components of $\mathbf{a}$ and $\mathbf{c}$ are nonnegative. We would like to model a requirement that at least one of the two constraints is satisfied. In order to achieve this, we define a binary variable y and impose the constraints:

$$\mathbf{a}'\mathbf{x} \ge yb,$$
$$\mathbf{c}'\mathbf{x} \ge (1-y)d,$$
$$y \in \{0,1\}.$$

More generally, suppose we are given m constraints $\mathbf{a}_i'\mathbf{x} \ge b_i$, $i = 1,\dots,m$, where $\mathbf{a}_i \ge \mathbf{0}$ for each i, and require that at least k of them are satisfied. We can achieve this by introducing m binary variables y_i, $i = 1,\dots,m$, and the constraints:

$$\mathbf{a}_i'\mathbf{x} \ge b_i y_i, \qquad i = 1,\dots,m,$$
$$\sum_{i=1}^{m} y_i \ge k,$$
$$y_i \in \{0,1\}, \quad i = 1,\dots,m.$$

Restricted range of values

Suppose we want to restrict a variable x to take values in a set $\{a_1,\dots,a_m\}$. We can achieve this by introducing m binary variables y_j, $j = 1,\dots,m$, and the constraints

$$x = \sum_{j=1}^{m} a_j y_j,$$
$$\sum_{j=1}^{m} y_j = 1,$$
$$y_j \in \{0,1\}.$$

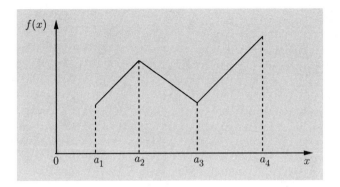

Figure 10.1: A continuous piecewise linear cost function.

Arbitrary piecewise linear cost functions

We have seen in Chapter 1 that a minimization problem involving a piecewise linear convex cost function can be modeled as a linear programming problem. Let us now model the more general case of an arbitrary piecewise linear cost function using binary variables. Suppose that $a_1 < a_2 < \cdots < a_k$, and that we have a continuous piecewise linear function $f(x)$ specified by the points $(a_i, f(a_i))$ for $i = 1, \ldots, k$, defined on the interval $[a_1, a_k]$ (see Figure 10.1). Then, any $x \in [a_1, a_k]$ can be expressed in the form

$$x = \sum_{i=1}^{k} \lambda_i a_i,$$

where $\lambda_1, \ldots, \lambda_k$ are nonnegative scalars that sum to one.

The critical observation is that the choice of coefficients $\lambda_1, \ldots, \lambda_k$ used to represent a particular x is not unique. However, it becomes unique if we require that at most two consecutive coefficients λ_i can be nonzero. In this case, any $x \in [a_i, a_{i+1}]$, is represented uniquely as $x = \lambda_i a_i + \lambda_{i+1} a_{i+1}$, with $\lambda_i + \lambda_{i+1} = 1$, and

$$f(x) = \sum_{i=1}^{k} \lambda_i f(a_i).$$

We also need to model the additional constraint that at most two consecutive coefficients λ_i are nonzero. To this effect, we define the binary variable y_i, $i = 1, \ldots, k - 1$, which is equal to 1 if $a_i \leq x < a_{i+1}$, and 0 otherwise. The problem is then formulated as the following mixed integer programming problem:

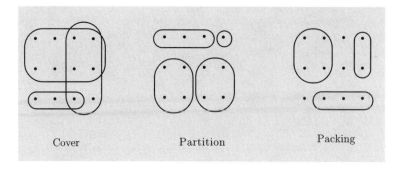

Figure 10.2: A cover, a partition, and a packing.

$$\text{minimize} \quad \sum_{i=1}^{k} \lambda_i f(a_i)$$

$$\text{subject to} \quad \sum_{i=1}^{k} \lambda_i = 1,$$

$$\lambda_1 \leq y_1,$$

$$\lambda_i \leq y_{i-1} + y_i, \qquad i = 2, \ldots, k-1,$$

$$\lambda_k \leq y_{k-1},$$

$$\sum_{i=1}^{k-1} y_i = 1,$$

$$\lambda_i \geq 0,$$

$$y_i \in \{0, 1\}.$$

Notice that if $y_j = 1$, then $\lambda_i = 0$ for i different than j or $j+1$.

The previous collection of examples is by no means an exhaustive list of possible modeling devices. They only serve to illustrate the power of modeling with binary variables. In order to acquire more confidence, we introduce some more examples.

Example 10.3 (The set covering, set packing, and set partitioning problems) Let $M = \{1, \ldots, m\}$ and $N = \{1, \ldots, n\}$. Let $M_1, M_2, \ldots, M_n$ be a given collection of subsets of M. For example, the collection might consist of all subsets of size at least k. We are also given a weight c_j for each set M_j in the collection. We say that a subset F of N is a *cover* of M if $\cup_{j \in F} M_j = M$. We say that F is a *packing* of M if $M_j \cap M_k$ is empty for all $j, k \in F$, $j \neq k$. We say that F is a *partition* of M if it is both a cover and a packing of M (see Figure 10.2). The *weight* of a subset F of N is defined as $\sum_{j \in F} c_j$.

In the *set covering* problem we would like to find a cover F of *minimum weight*, in the *set packing* problem we would like to find a packing F of *maximum weight*, while in the *set partitioning* problem both minimization and maximization versions are possible. In order to formulate these problems as integer programming problems, we introduce the $m \times n$ *incidence matrix* $\mathbf{A}$ of the family $\{M_j \mid j \in N\}$, whose entries are given by

$$a_{ij} = \begin{cases} 1, & \text{if } i \in M_j, \\ 0, & \text{otherwise.} \end{cases}$$

We also define a decision variable x_j, $j = 1, \ldots, n$, which is equal to 1 if $j \in F$, and 0 otherwise. Let $\mathbf{x} = (x_1, \ldots, x_n)$. Then F is a cover, packing, partition if and only if

$$\mathbf{Ax} \geq \mathbf{e}, \qquad \mathbf{Ax} \leq \mathbf{e}, \qquad \mathbf{Ax} = \mathbf{e},$$

respectively, where $\mathbf{e}$ is an m-dimensional vector with all components equal to 1.

The previous formulation types encompass a variety of important problems such as the assignment problem, crew scheduling problems, vehicle routing problems, etc.

A sequencing problem with setup times

A flexible machine can perform m operations, indexed from 1 to m. Each operation j requires a unique tool j. The machine can simultaneously hold B tools in its tool magazine, where $B < m$. Loading or unloading tool j into the machine magazine requires s_j units of setup time. Only one tool at a time can be loaded or unloaded. At the start of the day, n jobs are waiting to be processed by the machine. Each job i requires multiple operations. Let J_i denote the set of operations required by job i, and assume for simplicity that for all i, $|J_i|$ is no larger than the magazine capacity B of the machine. Before the machine can start processing job i, all the required tools belonging to the set J_i must be setup on the machine. If a tool $j \in J_i$, is already loaded on the machine, we avoid the setup time for tool j. If tool $j \in J_i$ is not already loaded, we must set it up, possibly (if the tool magazine is currently full) after unloading an existing tool that job i does not require. Once the tools are setup, all $|J_i|$ operations of job i are processed. Notice that, because of commonality in tool requirements for different jobs and the limited magazine capacity, the setup time required prior to each job is sequence dependent. We want to formulate an integer programming problem to determine the optimal job sequence that minimizes the total setup time to complete all the jobs. We assume that at the start of the day, the tool magazine is completely empty. We define decision variables that capture the job sequence:

$$x_{ir} = \begin{cases} 1, & \text{if job } i \text{ is the } r\text{th job processed,} \\ 0, & \text{otherwise.} \end{cases}$$

In addition, we define decision variables that describe the magazine setups:

$$y_{jr} = \begin{cases} 1, & \text{if tool } j \text{ is on the magazine, while the } r\text{th job is processed,} \\ 0, & \text{otherwise.} \end{cases}$$

We also let $y_{j0} = 0$ for all j, which represents the fact that we are starting with an empty magazine. Since every job needs to be processed,

$$\sum_{r=1}^{n} x_{ir} = 1, \qquad \forall\, i.$$

Since exactly one job will be processed at a time,

$$\sum_{i=1}^{n} x_{ir} = 1, \qquad \forall\, r.$$

In order to process job i, all tools in the set J_i need to be in the magazine. Therefore, we have

$$x_{ir} \le y_{jr}, \qquad \forall\, j \in J_i,\ \forall\, r, i.$$

Since the total capacity of the magazine is B, we have

$$\sum_{j=1}^{m} y_{jr} \le B, \qquad \forall\, r.$$

We incur a setup delay only if we load or unload a tool, which is the case if $y_{jr} \ne y_{j,r-1}$ for some j. Therefore, the objective function is

$$\text{minimize} \quad \sum_{j=1}^{m} \sum_{r=1}^{n} s_j |y_{jr} - y_{j,r-1}|.$$

We obtain an integer programming problem by defining a new decision variable z_{jr}, writing the objective function as

$$\text{minimize} \quad \sum_{j=1}^{m} \sum_{r=1}^{n} s_j z_{jr},$$

and by introducing the constraints

$$z_{jr} \ge y_{jr} - y_{j,r-1}, \qquad \forall\, j, r,$$
$$z_{jr} \ge y_{j,r-1} - y_{jr}, \qquad \forall\, j, r.$$

The overall formulation becomes

$$\text{minimize} \quad \sum_{j=1}^{m} \sum_{r=1}^{n} s_j z_{jr}$$

$$\begin{aligned}
\text{subject to} \quad & z_{jr} \geq y_{jr} - y_{j,r-1}, & & \forall\, j, r, \\
& z_{jr} \geq y_{j,r-1} - y_{jr}, & & \forall\, j, r, \\
& \sum_{r=1}^{n} x_{ir} = 1, & & \forall\, i, \\
& \sum_{i=1}^{n} x_{ir} = 1, & & \forall\, r, \\
& x_{ir} \leq y_{jr}, & & \forall\, j \in J_i,\ \forall\, r, i, \\
& \sum_{j=1}^{m} y_{jr} \leq B, & & \forall\, r, \\
& x_{ir}, y_{jr}, z_{jr} \in \{0, 1\}.
\end{aligned}$$

Allocation of NSF fellowships

Some of the most prestigious fellowships for graduate students are the ones awarded by the National Science Foundation (NSF) every year. Applicants from throughout the US in 19 disciplines apply for these fellowships. Each applicant is given a rank reflecting academic merit and professional potential, as determined by screening panels and test scores. Rank 1 then corresponds to the strongest applicant. In addition to rank, the following information is taken into account for each applicant: the state of high school graduation, the applicant's gender, the applicant's discipline, and the grade level (undergraduate, first year graduate student, or second year graduate student).

As a govermentally funded organization, NSF needs to distribute funds "fairly" amongst states. For this purpose, NSF assigns a fixed percentage of the available fellowships to the applicants with the best rank, irrespective of other considerations. We refer to these recipients as group 1 (G1). The next K applicants in the ranked list form group 2 (G2), where K depends on the funds available. The problem is to allocate fellowships among applicants in group 2 "fairly." The following are some possible definitions of fairness:

(a) Calculate a target number, $T(s)$, for each state $s \in \{1, 2, \ldots, 50\}$, based on the percentage of total US high school graduates from that state. In 1994, there were about 250,000 high school graduates from California, which represents 9.3% of the total number. If there are 1,000 fellowships available, $T(\text{CA}) = 93$. It is desirable that these targets be met, as long as there are enough applicants from each state.

(b) Looking at the entire applicant pool, determine percentages for each gender, discipline, and grade level. Use these percentages to calculate target numbers $T(g)$ for gender $g \in \{M, F\}$, $T(d)$ for discipline $d \in \{1, \ldots, 19\}$, and $T(l)$ for grade level $l \in \{u, g1, g2\}$. We assume that there are enough applicants from each gender, discipline, and grade level. For example, in 1994, 61% of the applicants were male. So if there are 1,000 fellowships available, $T(m) = 610$.

What should the objective function be? Here are some possibilities:

(a) Minimize the sum of the rank numbers of the award recipients in group 2 (all applicants in group 1 receive a fellowship).

(b) Just find a solution that satisfies all of the "fairness" considerations, ignoring the rank of all group 2 applicants.

(c) Minimize the largest (worst) rank amongst those awarded a fellowship, while all group 1 applicants receive a fellowship.

We formulate the fellowship allocation problem using the third objective function.

Data:

$$
\begin{aligned}
r_i &= \text{rank of applicant } i \\
N &= \text{total number of available awards} \\
n_s &= \text{number of applicants from state } s \in \{1, \ldots, 50\} \\
T(s) &= \text{target for state } s \in \{1, \ldots, 50\} \\
F_s &= \text{set of applicants from state } s \\
T(g) &= \text{target for gender } g \in \{M, F\} \\
F_g &= \text{set of applicants of gender } g \\
T(d) &= \text{target for discipline } d \in \{1, \ldots, 19\} \\
F_d &= \text{set of applicants from discipline } d \\
T(l) &= \text{target for grade level } l \in \{u, g1, g2\} \\
F_l &= \text{set of applicants of grade level } l
\end{aligned}
$$

Decision variables:

$$
x_i = \begin{cases} 1, & \text{if applicant } i \text{ receives an award,} \\ 0, & \text{otherwise.} \end{cases}
$$

Since all group 1 applicants receive a fellowship, we require that $x_i = 1$ for $i \in G1$.

The objective function:

The third objective function is:

$$\text{minimize} \ \max_{i \in G2} (r_i x_i),$$

which can be written as

$$\begin{aligned}
\text{minimize} \quad & z \\
\text{subject to} \quad & z \geq r_i x_i, \qquad \forall \, i \in G2.
\end{aligned}$$

The formulation then becomes

$$\begin{aligned}
\text{minimize} \quad & z \\
\text{subject to} \quad & z \geq r_i x_i, & \forall \, i \in G2, \\
& x_i = 1, & \forall \, i \in G1, \\
& \sum_i x_i = N, \\
& \sum_{i \in F_g} x_i \geq T(g), & \forall \, g \in \{M, F\}, \\
& \sum_{i \in F_d} x_i \geq T(d), & \forall \, d \in \{1, \ldots, 19\}, \\
& \sum_{i \in F_l} x_i \geq T(l), & \forall \, l \in \{u, g1, g2\}, \\
& \sum_{i \in F_s} x_i \geq \min \left(T(s), n_s \right), & \forall \, s \in \{1, \ldots, 50\}, \\
& x_i \in \{0, 1\}.
\end{aligned}$$

10.2   Guidelines for strong formulations

In linear programming, a good formulation is one that has a small number n, m of variables and constraints, respectively, because the computational complexity of the problem grows polynomially in n and m. In addition, given the availability of several efficient algorithms for linear programming, the choice of a formulation, although important, does not critically affect our ability to solve the problem. The situation in integer programming is drastically different. Extensive computational experience suggests that the choice of a formulation is crucial. In this section, we provide guidelines for arriving at strong integer programming formulations. The key concept we introduce is that of a linear programming relaxation.

> **Definition 10.1** *Given a mixed integer programming problem*
>
> $$\begin{aligned}
> \text{minimize} \quad & \mathbf{c}'\mathbf{x} + \mathbf{d}'\mathbf{y} \\
> \text{subject to} \quad & \mathbf{Ax} + \mathbf{By} = \mathbf{b} \\
> & \mathbf{x}, \mathbf{y} \geq \mathbf{0} \\
> & \mathbf{x} \text{ integer,}
> \end{aligned}$$
>
> *its* **linear programming relaxation** *is defined as*
>
> $$\begin{aligned}
> \text{minimize} \quad & \mathbf{c}'\mathbf{x} + \mathbf{d}'\mathbf{y} \\
> \text{subject to} \quad & \mathbf{Ax} + \mathbf{By} = \mathbf{b} \\
> & \mathbf{x}, \mathbf{y} \geq \mathbf{0},
> \end{aligned}$$
>
> *where the requirement that* $\mathbf{x}$ *is a vector of integers was relaxed. If the integer variables* x_j *are further restricted to be either 0 or 1, then in the linear programming relaxation,* x_j *takes values between 0 and 1.*

Note that if an optimal solution to the relaxation is feasible for the mixed integer programming problem, it is also an optimal solution to the latter.

Example 10.4 (The facility location problem revisited) In Example 10.2, we presented an integer programming formulation of the facility location problem. Let us consider the following alternative formulation [*aggregate facility location formulation (AFL)*] :

$$\begin{aligned}
\text{minimize} \quad & \sum_{j=1}^{n} c_j y_j + \sum_{i=1}^{m} \sum_{j=1}^{n} d_{ij} x_{ij} \\
\text{subject to} \quad & \sum_{j=1}^{n} x_{ij} = 1, && \forall\ i, \\
& \sum_{i=1}^{m} x_{ij} \leq m y_j, && \forall\ j, \\
& x_{ij}, y_j \in \{0,1\}.
\end{aligned} \qquad (10.2)$$

Notice that the constraint $\sum_{i=1}^{m} x_{ij} \leq m y_j$ forces x_{ij} to be 0 whenever $y_j = 0$, but allows x_{ij} to be 1 if $y_j = 1$. Therefore, this constraint is equivalent to the constraints $x_{ij} \leq y_j$, $i = 1, \ldots, m$, in the original formulation. For this reason, the set of feasible solutions and the optimal cost is the same for both formulations. Notice, however, that the aggregate formulation (10.2) has $m + n$ constraints, while the original formulation (10.1) had $m + mn$ constraints.

In order to compare the two formulations, let us consider their corresponding linear programming relaxations, in which we replace the integrality restrictions $x_{ij}, y_j \in \{0,1\}$ by $0 \leq x_{ij} \leq 1$, $0 \leq y_j \leq 1$. We then define the following

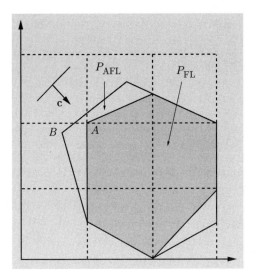

Figure 10.3: The two polyhedra P_{FL} and P_{AFL} contain exactly the same set of integer solutions.

two polyhedra, which are the feasible sets of the two relaxations:

$$P_{\mathrm{FL}} = \left\{ (\mathbf{x}, \mathbf{y}) \;\middle|\; \sum_{j=1}^{n} x_{ij} = 1, \ \forall \, i, \right.$$
$$x_{ij} \leq y_j, \ \forall \, i, j,$$
$$\left. 0 \leq x_{ij} \leq 1, \ 0 \leq y_j \leq 1 \right\},$$

$$P_{\mathrm{AFL}} = \left\{ (\mathbf{x}, \mathbf{y}) \;\middle|\; \sum_{j=1}^{n} x_{ij} = 1, \ \forall \, i, \right.$$
$$\sum_{i=1}^{m} x_{ij} \leq m y_j, \ \forall \, j,$$
$$\left. 0 \leq x_{ij} \leq 1, \ 0 \leq y_j \leq 1 \right\}.$$

Clearly, $P_{\mathrm{FL}} \subset P_{\mathrm{AFL}}$ and the inclusion can be strict (Exercise 10.11). In other words, the feasible set of the linear programming relaxation of formulation (10.1) is closer to the set of integer solutions than the linear programming relaxation of formulation (10.2) (see Figure 10.3).

Let Z_{IP} be the optimal cost of the integer programming problem, and let Z_{FL} and Z_{AFL} be the optimal costs of the two linear programming relaxations we have introduced. Since $P_{\mathrm{FL}} \subset P_{\mathrm{AFL}}$, it follows that $Z_{\mathrm{AFL}} \leq Z_{\mathrm{FL}}$. Moreover, $Z_{\mathrm{FL}} \leq Z_{\mathrm{IP}}$, since an optimal solution to the integer programming problem belongs to P_{FL}. To summarize,

$$Z_{\mathrm{AFL}} \leq Z_{\mathrm{FL}} \leq Z_{\mathrm{IP}}.$$

We next discuss the implications of this ordering. Many methods for solving
integer programming minimization problems depend on the availability of lower
bounds such as Z_{FL}. The sharper the bound, i.e., the closer it is to Z_{IP}, the
better these methods behave.

Consider, for example, an objective function such as the one depicted in
Figure 10.3. For this objective function, the optimal solution over the polyhedron
P_{FL} corresponds to point A in the figure, and is integer. By the previous inequalities, solution A is indeed the optimal solution to the facility location problem.
So, in this case, we have solved the integer programming problem optimally by
just solving a linear programming problem. On the other hand, for the same
objective function, the optimal solution over the polyhedron P_{AFL} is point B,
which is fractional.

Thus, formulation (10.1) is preferable than formulation (10.2), despite the
fact that (10.2) has a significantly smaller number of constraints.

What is then an ideal formulation of an integer programming prob-
lem? Let $T = \{\mathbf{x}^1, \dots, \mathbf{x}^k\}$ be the set of feasible integer solutions to a
particular integer programming problem. We assume that the feasible set
is bounded and, therefore, T is finite. We consider the convex hull of T:

$$\mathrm{CH}(T) = \left\{ \sum_{i=1}^{k} \lambda_i \mathbf{x}^i \;\middle|\; \sum_{i=1}^{k} \lambda_i = 1, \; \lambda_i \geq 0, \; \mathbf{x}^i \in T \right\}.$$

The set $\mathrm{CH}(T)$ is a polyhedron (see Corollary 2.6 in Section 2.8 or Theorem
4.16 in Section 4.9) that has integer extreme points. Furthermore, the
feasible set P of any linear programming relaxation satisfies $\mathrm{CH}(T) \subset P$.
If we knew $\mathrm{CH}(T)$ explicitly, i.e., if we could represent $\mathrm{CH}(T)$ in the form
$\mathrm{CH}(T) = \{\mathbf{x} \mid \mathbf{Dx} \leq \mathbf{d}\}$, we could solve the integer programming problem

$$\begin{aligned} \text{minimize} \quad & \mathbf{c'x} \\ \text{subject to} \quad & \mathbf{x} \in T, \end{aligned}$$

by finding an extreme point solution to the linear programming problem

$$\begin{aligned} \text{minimize} \quad & \mathbf{c'x} \\ \text{subject to} \quad & \mathbf{x} \in \mathrm{CH}(T). \end{aligned}$$

Given our ability to solve linear programming problems efficiently, it
is then desirable to have a formulation whose linear programming relaxation
is indeed the convex hull $\mathrm{CH}(T)$ of the integer feasible solutions (see Figure
10.4). Unfortunately, this is often difficult. In light of this, it is reasonable
to strive for a compromise whereby one tries to come up with a polyhedron
that closely approximates $\mathrm{CH}(T)$. This leads to the central message of this
chapter.

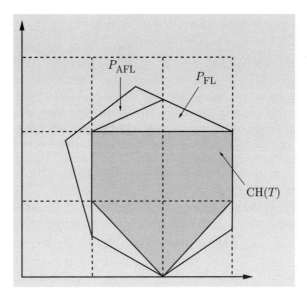

Figure 10.4: The convex hull of the integer feasible solutions to the facility location problem.

The **quality of a formulation** of an integer programming problem with feasible solution set T, can be judged by the closeness of the feasible set of its linear programming relaxation to the convex hull of T. In particular, consider two formulations A and B of the same integer programming problem. If we denote by P_A and P_B the feasible sets of the corresponding linear programming relaxations, we consider formulation A to be at least as **strong** as formulation B if

$$P_A \subset P_B.$$

10.3   Modeling with exponentially many constraints

In this section, we demonstrate through examples that strong formulations and, in particular, the convex hull of integer feasible solutions, may involve an exponential number of linear inequality constraints. However, this does not necessarily prevent the efficient solution of the linear programming relaxation of such problems by cutting plane or other methods (see, e.g., Section 8.5).

The minimum spanning tree problem

Let $G = (\mathcal{N}, \mathcal{E})$ be an undirected graph with node set $\mathcal{N}$ ($|\mathcal{N}| = n$) and edge set $\mathcal{E}$ ($|\mathcal{E}| = m$). Every edge $e \in \mathcal{E}$ has an associated cost c_e. The cost of a tree is simply the sum of the costs of the edges in the tree. In Section 7.10, the minimum spanning tree problem was defined as the problem of finding a spanning tree of minimum cost. Tree optimization problems arise in the design of transportation, communication, and computer networks, since at the very least such networks should be connected. Our goal in this example is to illustrate the effectiveness of alternative formulations and to learn new principles for deriving strong formulations.

In order to formulate the problem, we define for each $e \in \mathcal{E}$, a variable x_e which is equal to one if edge e is included in the tree, and zero otherwise. Since a spanning tree should have $n - 1$ edges, we introduce the constraint

$$\sum_{e \in \mathcal{E}} x_e = n - 1.$$

Moreover, the chosen edges should not contain a cycle. It can be shown (Exercise 10.12) that this is guaranteed if for any nonempty set $S \subset \mathcal{N}$, the number of edges with both endpoints in S is less than equal to $|S| - 1$. For any $S \subset \mathcal{N}$, we define

$$E(S) = \{\{i, j\} \in \mathcal{E} \mid i, j \in S\},$$

and we can express this set of constraints as

$$\sum_{e \in E(S)} x_e \leq |S| - 1, \qquad S \subset \mathcal{N}, \ S \neq \emptyset, \mathcal{N}.$$

This leads to an integer programming formulation of the minimum spanning tree problem:

$$
\begin{aligned}
\text{minimize} \quad & \sum_{e \in \mathcal{E}} c_e x_e \\
\text{subject to} \quad & \sum_{e \in \mathcal{E}} x_e = n - 1, \\
& \sum_{e \in E(S)} x_e \leq |S| - 1, \qquad S \subset \mathcal{N}, \ S \neq \emptyset, \mathcal{N}, \\
& x_e \in \{0, 1\}.
\end{aligned}
$$

This formulation is called the *subtour elimination formulation*, since it contains constraints that eliminate all subtours (cycles). We denote the feasible set of the linear programming relaxation of this formulation by P_{sub}, where we replace the constraint $x_e \in \{0, 1\}$ with $0 \leq x_e \leq 1$. Notice that, besides the integrality constraints, the subtour elimination formulation has an exponential number of constraints, namely $2^n - 1$.

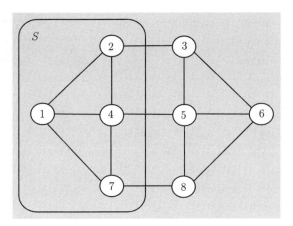

Figure 10.5: Let $S = \{1, 2, 4, 7\}$. Then, $\delta(S) = \big\{\{2, 3\}, \{4, 5\},$ $\{7, 8\}\big\}$, and $E(S) = \big\{\{1, 2\}, \{1, 4\}, \{2, 4\}, \{4, 7\}, \{1, 7\}\big\}$.

The subtour elimination formulation uses the definition of a tree as a subgraph containing $n - 1$ edges and no cycles. Using an alternative, but equivalent definition, a tree is a connected graph containing $n - 1$ edges (see Theorem 7.1). Given a subset S of $\mathcal{N}$, we define the *cutset $\delta(S)$* (see also Figure 10.5) by

$$\delta(S) = \big\{\{i, j\} \in \mathcal{E} \mid i \in S, \ j \notin S\big\}.$$

Note that $\delta(\{i\})$ is the set of edges incident to i. We can then express the connectivity requirement in terms of the constraints

$$\sum_{e \in \delta(S)} x_e \geq 1, \qquad S \subset \mathcal{N}, \ S \neq \emptyset, \mathcal{N}.$$

We call the resulting integer programming formulation the *cutset formulation*, and we denote the feasible set of its linear programming relaxation by P_{cut}. Both formulations have an exponential number of constraints. Are these formulations equally strong? We show that the subtour elimination formulation is stronger than the cutset formulation. The proof will demonstrate how we can compare alternative formulations of discrete optimization problems.

Theorem 10.1 *The following properties hold.*

(a) *We have $P_{\text{sub}} \subset P_{\text{cut}}$, and there exist examples for which the inclusion is strict.*

(b) *The polyhedron P_{cut} can have fractional extreme points.*

Proof. (a) For any set S of nodes, we have

$$\mathcal{E} = E(S) \cup \delta(S) \cup E(\mathcal{N} \setminus S).$$

Therefore,

$$\sum_{e \in E(S)} x_e + \sum_{e \in E(\mathcal{N} \setminus S)} x_e + \sum_{e \in \delta(S)} x_e = \sum_{e \in \mathcal{E}} x_e.$$

For $\mathbf{x} \in P_{\text{sub}}$, and for $S \neq \varnothing, \mathcal{N}$, we have

$$\sum_{e \in E(S)} x_e \leq |S| - 1,$$

and

$$\sum_{e \in E(\mathcal{N} \setminus S)} x_e \leq |\mathcal{N} \setminus S| - 1.$$

Since

$$\sum_{e \in \mathcal{E}} x_e = n - 1,$$

we obtain that

$$\sum_{e \in \delta(S)} x_e \geq 1,$$

and therefore $\mathbf{x} \in P_{\text{cut}}$.

Consider the example in Figure 10.6(a). The solution $\mathbf{x}^*$ shown in Figure 10.6(b) belongs to P_{cut}, but it does not belong to P_{sub}, since the edges in $E(S)$ for $S = \{2, 4, 5\}$ have total weight $5/2$, while the constraints defining P_{sub} dictate that the weight should be less than or equal to $3 - 1 = 2$. The example shows that the inclusion may be strict.

(b) In order to show that the polyhedron P_{cut} may have fractional extreme points, we construct an objective function, under which there is a unique optimal solution which is fractional. This establishes that this unique solution is an extreme point. Consider again the example in Figure 10.6. The unique optimal solution to P_{cut} is the fractional solution $\mathbf{x}^*$ shown in the figure, with a cost of $3/2$. This shows that P_{cut} has a fractional extreme point. ☐

In Theorem 10.1, we have shown that the cutset formulation is weaker than the subtour elimination formulation. In addition, it can be shown that $P_{\text{sub}} = \text{CH}(T)$, i.e., the polyhedron P_{sub} is a representation of the convex hull of the set of vectors corresponding to spanning trees.

According to the principle regarding strong formulations, the subtour elimination formulation is a strong one. This seems somewhat counterintuitive, as the formulation involves an exponential number of constraints. Does this prevent us from optimizing over the feasible set P_{sub} of the linear programming relaxation efficiently? It can be shown that the separation problem over P_{sub} reduces to a minimum cut problem (see Example 8.2 for

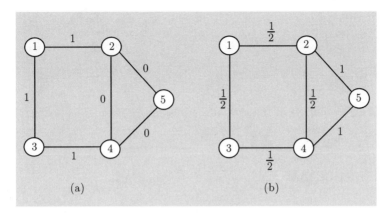

Figure 10.6: An example of a graph, in which a minimum spanning tree has cost 2, while the cost of an optimal solution over P_{cut} is $3/2$. (a) The cost coefficients. (b) An optimal solution $\mathbf{x}^*$ over P_{cut}.

a related problem). Therefore, using the ellipsoid method, we can optimize over P_{sub} in polynomial time. Of course, we would not use the ellipsoid algorithm to solve the minimum spanning tree problem (see Section 7.10 for an efficient algorithm). However, the subtour elimination formulation enables us to classify the complexity of the minimum spanning tree problem using general arguments. Moreover, if there are side constraints, the subtour elimination formulation may form the basis for a cutting plane approach to solving the linear programming relaxation of the problem with side constraints. In Section 12.5, we discuss an application of this technique to scheduling problems.

The traveling salesman problem

In Example 8.2, we have introduced one of the most famous problems in discrete optimization, the traveling salesman problem. We repeat its definition here. Given an undirected graph $G = (\mathcal{N}, \mathcal{E})$ and costs c_e for every edge $e \in \mathcal{E}$, the objective is to find a *tour* (a cycle that visits all nodes) of minimum cost. In order to model the problem, we define for every edge $e \in \mathcal{E}$ a variable x_e equal to one, if edge e is included in the tour, and zero, otherwise. In Example 8.2, we gave the following formulation for the problem. Since each node must participate in two edges of the tour, we have

$$\sum_{e \in \delta(\{i\})} x_e = 2, \qquad i \in \mathcal{N}.$$

Also, if S is a nonempty proper subset of $\mathcal{N}$, there must be at least two edges joining S to $\mathcal{N} \setminus S$, and we have

$$\sum_{e \in \delta(S)} x_e \geq 2, \qquad S \subset \mathcal{N}, \ S \neq \emptyset, \mathcal{N}.$$

A cutset formulation of the traveling salesman problem is as follows:

$$\begin{aligned}
\text{minimize} \quad & \sum_{e \in \mathcal{E}} c_e x_e \\
\text{subject to} \quad & \sum_{e \in \delta(\{i\})} x_e = 2, \qquad i \in \mathcal{N}, \\
& \sum_{e \in \delta(S)} x_e \geq 2, \qquad S \subset \mathcal{N}, \ S \neq \emptyset, \mathcal{N}, \\
& x_e \in \{0, 1\}.
\end{aligned}$$

Using ideas similar to the subtour elimination formulation of the minimum spanning tree problem, we can also formulate the traveling salesman problem in terms of the following constraints:

$$\begin{aligned}
& \sum_{e \in \delta(\{i\})} x_e = 2, \qquad i \in \mathcal{N}, \\
& \sum_{e \in E(S)} x_e \leq |S| - 1, \qquad S \subset \mathcal{N}, \ S \neq \emptyset, \mathcal{N}, \\
& x_e \in \{0, 1\}.
\end{aligned}$$

Let P_{tspcut} and P_{tspsub} be the polyhedra corresponding to the linear programming relaxations of these two formulations. It turns out that the two formulations are equally strong, i.e., $P_{\text{tspcut}} = P_{\text{tspsub}}$ (Exercise 10.14).

Exercise 10.15 deals with a different formulation of the variant of the traveling salesman problem that involves a directed graph. This formulation has a polynomial number of constraints, but it is not as strong as the natural extension of the cutset formulation to directed graphs, which has an exponential number of constraints.

The perfect matching problem

We have an even number n of persons that need to be matched into pairs in order to perform a certain job. If person i is matched with person j, there is a cost of c_{ij}. A matching is a pairing of persons, so that each individual is matched with exactly one other individual. The goal is to find a matching that minimizes the total cost. We represent the set of people by an undirected graph $G = (\mathcal{N}, \mathcal{E})$ where $\mathcal{N}$ is the set of individuals, and the cost of edge $e = \{i, j\}$ is c_e. If $\{i, j\} \notin \mathcal{E}$, this indicates that i and j cannot be matched. We let x_e be one if edge $e = \{i, j\}$ is selected, i.e., persons i

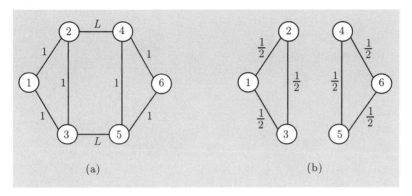

Figure 10.7: An example of a graph, in which an optimal matching has cost $L+2$, while the cost of the optimal solution over P_{degree} has cost 3. (a) The cost coefficients. (b) An optimal solution over P_{degree}.

and j are matched, and zero otherwise. Then the *perfect matching* problem can be formulated as follows:

$$\text{minimize} \quad \sum_{e \in \mathcal{E}} c_e x_e$$

$$\text{subject to} \quad \sum_{e \in \delta(\{i\})} x_e = 1, \qquad i \in \mathcal{N},$$

$$x_e \in \{0,1\}.$$

We denote by P_{degree} the polyhedron corresponding to the linear programming relaxation of the above formulation.

Let M be the set of all vectors $\mathbf{x}$ corresponding to matchings. Figure 10.7 shows that P_{degree} is not equal to the convex hull $\text{CH}(M)$ of the set M.

The example in Figure 10.7 shows that the above formulation of the problem is not particularly strong, as its linear programming relaxation is not equal to the convex hull of vectors corresponding to matchings. A strengthening of the formulation is to consider the class of inequalities

$$\sum_{e \in \delta(S)} x_e \geq 1, \qquad S \subset \mathcal{N}, \; S \neq \mathcal{N}, \; |S| \text{ odd}.$$

Notice that all vectors corresponding to matchings satisfy this inequality, as in every set with an odd number of nodes, there should be at least one edge leaving this set of nodes. Note that the example in Figure 10.7(b) violates this set of inequalities, since for the set $S = \{1, 2, 3\}$ we have $\sum_{e \in \delta(S)} x_e = 0$. We then consider the polyhedron defined by the constraints we have introduced:

$$P_{\text{matching}} = \left\{ \mathbf{x} \;\middle|\; \sum_{e \in \delta(\{i\})} x_e = 1, \quad i \in \mathcal{N}, \right.$$

$$\sum_{e \in \delta(S)} x_e \geq 1, \quad S \subset \mathcal{N}, \; S \neq \mathcal{N}, \; |S| \text{ odd},$$

$$\left. 0 \leq x_e \leq 1, \; e \in \mathcal{E} \right\}.$$

It turns out that $P_{\text{matching}} = \text{CH}(M)$.

Formulations and complexity

As in the case of the minimum spanning tree problem, the description of the convex hull of the set of all matchings is explicitly known. In contrast, the convex hull of the set of integer feasible solutions to the traveling salesman problem is not known. We have already seen (Section 7.10) that the minimum spanning tree problem is efficiently (polynomially) solvable. Moreover, the perfect matching problem is also known to be efficiently (polynomially) solvable. However, there is no known polynomial time algorithm for the traveling salesman problem. This suggests that our ability to find the strongest possible formulations of a discrete optimization problem (the convex hull of all integer feasible solutions) is directly related to our ability to solve it efficiently. In a sense, the complexity of a problem is characterized by our ability to construct an integer programming formulation, with a polynomial number of variables, whose linear programming relaxation is the convex hull of all integer feasible solutions.

10.4   Summary

The main message of this chapter is that unlike linear programming problems, strong formulations are central to being able to solve integer programming problems efficiently. The quality of a formulation is judged by the closeness of its linear programming relaxation to the convex hull of integer feasible solutions. However, strong formulations occasionally require an exponential number of constraints. Finally, formulations give another view of the complexity of a discrete optimization problem, in the sense that for problems that are efficiently solvable, the strongest possible formulations (convex hull of integer feasible solutions) are often known.

10.5   Exercises

Exercise 10.1 (Disjunctive constraints) Suppose that we are given m constraints $\mathbf{a}_i' \mathbf{x} \geq b_i$, $i = 1, \ldots, m$, but without the restriction $\mathbf{a}_i \geq \mathbf{0}$. Model the requirement that at least k of them are satisfied. Assume that there exists a number f such that $\mathbf{a}'_i \mathbf{x} \geq f$ for $i = 1, \ldots, m$, and for all feasible $\mathbf{x}$.

Exercise 10.2 (Selection of the dream team) The coach of the national basketball team is faced with the decision of selecting 12 players for the upcoming international tournament. He has limited his final selection to 20 players, $p_1, \ldots, p_{20}$. For each player, the coach has collected several statistics that can be summarized as follows. His rebounding average r_i, his assists average a_i, his height h_i, his scoring average s_i, and his overall defense ability d_i. The players have been divided into four broad categories: play makers (PM) $(p_1, \ldots, p_5)$, shooting guards (SG) $(p_4, \ldots, p_{11})$, forwards (F) $(p_9, \ldots, p_{16})$, and centers (C) $(p_{16}, \ldots, p_{20})$. Notice that there are players that can be used in multiple roles (for example player p_4 can be used both as a play maker and a shooting guard). Players p_4, p_8, p_{15}, p_{20} play in the NCAA (college level), while all of the rest play in the NBA (professional level). For balance purposes, the team should consist of at least 3 play makers, 4 shooting guards, 4 forwards, and 3 centers, which implies that some players with dual roles should be selected. In addition, at least 2 players from the NCAA should be selected, while the mean rebounding, assists, scoring average, height, and defense ability should be at least r, a, s, h, d, respectively. The problem is further complicated by the fact that there are compatibility problems among some of the players. Player p_5 has declared that if player p_9 is selected, then he does not want to be in the team. Also, players p_2 and p_{19} can only be selected together as they play in the same team for years and feel that they are much more effective together. Finally, at most 3 players from the same team should be selected, so that the coach is not accused of favoritism (players p_1, p_7, p_{12}, p_{16} play for the same team). Faced with these difficulties, the coach has decided that he would like to maximize the scoring average, while satisfying the various constraints. Formulate the problem that the coach is facing as an integer programming problem.

Exercise 10.3 (Playing times for the players in the dream team) This is a continuation of Exercise 10.2. After some careful thought, the coach would also like to decide how much play time to give to each player as some of these players in the initial list of 20, although extremely talented, were returning from long injuries and some were aging. For various reasons (injury, age) each player has an upper bound u_i on the average number of minutes he can play. In international tournaments, the duration of a game is 40 minutes. The coach has decided that there were two team compositions that he will use in the tournament depending on the type of opponent and circumstances in a game: (PM, SG, SG, F, C) or (PM, SG, F, F, C). Looking at the schedule, he predicts that these two schemes will be used equally in the tournament. Therefore, he realizes that the average play time of play makers would be 40 minutes, shooting guards 60 minutes, forwards 60 minutes, and centers 40 minutes. Formulate the combined problem of selection and allocation of average play time in order to maximize the scoring average.

Exercise 10.4 An airline operates a fleet of 15 jet aircraft, all equipped with the JET32 engine. The airline performs its own engine-related repairs and maintenance at its repair facility. The maintenance director is reviewing the spare parts ordering and stocking policy for the next three years. The JET32 engine consists of 4 main modules, A, B, C, and D. When planes come in for repairs, sometimes the entire engine must be replaced because of extensive damage and wear. More often, however, only certain modules need replacement. The following table contains the forecasted requirements for individual engine modules and complete engines for the next 3 years. The airline places orders for complete en-

Year	Module A	Module B	Module C	Module D	Complete Engine
1	5	4	4	2	1
2	2	1	1	7	0
3	3	4	3	0	2

Table 10.1: Forecasted engine/module requirements.

gines and modules at the beginning of the year with JET Inc., the manufacturer of the JET32 engine. The following table shows the projected prices for engines and modules that JET Inc. might charge in the next three years.

Year	Module A	Module B	Module C	Module D	Complete Engine
1	0.5	2.0	5.0	1.0	7.8
2	0.6	2.2	5.5	1.1	7.5
3	0.7	2.5	6.0	1.3	7.0

Table 10.2: Forecasted engine/module prices.

Note that complete engines cost less than the total cost of buying one module of each type. Assume that the cost of "cannibalizing," i.e., breaking a complete engine into four individual modules, is negligible compared to the cost of these modules. The mix of engines and modules that the airline orders from JET Inc. must, therefore, account for the economies in ordering complete engines. Assuming that the airline does not have any inventory of modules or engines in hand, formulate an integer programming problem to determine the order quantities for the next 3 years, while minimizing the total cost of purchases. Assume that there are no inventory carrying costs.

Exercise 10.5 (Plan for a move) Suppose you are planning to move to your new house. You have n items of size a_j, $j = 1, \ldots, n$, that need to be moved. You have rented a truck that has size Q and you have bought m boxes. Box i has size b_i, $i = 1, \ldots, m$. Formulate an integer programming problem in order to decide whether the move is possible.

Exercise 10.6 (A production and distribution problem) A company produces a set of K products at I plants. It then ships these products to J market zones. For $k = 1, \ldots, K$, $i = 1, \ldots, I$, and $j = 1, \ldots, J$, the following data are given:

v_{ik} = variable cost of producing one unit of product k at plant i
c_{ijk} = cost of shipping one unit of product k from plant i to zone j
f_{ik} = fixed cost associated with producing product k at plant i
M_{ik} = maximal quantity of product k produced at plant i
m_{ik} = minimal quantity of product k that can be produced at plant i, if plant i produces a nonzero quantity
q_{ik} = capacity of plant i used to produce one unit of product k
Q_i = capacity of plant i
d_{jk} = demand for product k at market zone j

(a) Formulate the problem of minimizing the total cost of production and transportation that the company is facing, as an integer programming problem. Indicate how your model can incorporate the following additional constraints.

(b) No plant may produce more than K_1 products.

(c) Every product can be produced in at most I_1 plants.

(d) For a particular product k_0, plant 3 must produce it if neither plant 1 nor plant 2 produce it.

(e) Each market zone must be sourced by exactly one plant for all products.

Exercise 10.7 (A dynamic single-item lot sizing problem) We consider the production of a single product over T periods. If we decide to produce at period t, a setup cost c_t is incurred. For $t = 1, \ldots, T$, let d_t be the demand for this product in period t, and let p_t, h_t be the unit production cost and unit storage cost (per period), respectively.

(a) Formulate an integer programming problem in order to minimize the total cost of production, storage, and setup.

(b) Suppose we allow demand to be lost in every period except for period T, at a cost of b_t per unit of lost demand. Show how to modify the model to handle this option.

(c) Suppose that production can occur in at most five periods, but no two such periods can be consecutive. Show how to modify the model to handle this option.

Exercise 10.8 (The vehicle routing problem) An undirected graph $G = (\mathcal{N}, \mathcal{E})$ represents a transportation network. Node $i \in \mathcal{N}$, for $i \neq 1$, represents customers with demand of b_i units. The travel costs are d_e for every arc $e \in \mathcal{E}$. A company has m vehicles, each of capacity Q, that need to visit all customers in order to satisfy demand. Each vehicle is to follow a route that starts at a central depot (node 1), visits some customers, and returns to the depot. Suppose that the demand of each customer can be carried by a single vehicle, i.e., $b_i \leq Q$ for all i. Assuming that the demand of any customer cannot be divided into several vehicles, formulate the problem of constructing routes for the vehicles that minimize the total transportation cost.

Exercise 10.9 (The fixed charge network design problem) We are given a directed graph $G = (\mathcal{N}, \mathcal{A})$ and a demand or supply b_i for each $i \in \mathcal{N}$, such that $\sum_{i \in \mathcal{N}} b_i = 0$. There are two types of costs: transportation costs c_{ij} of shipping one unit from node i to node j, and building costs d_{ij} of establishing a link (i, j) between nodes i and j of capacity u_{ij}. We would like to build such a network in order to minimize the total building and transportation costs, so that all demand is met. Formulate the problem as an integer programming problem

Exercise 10.10 (Job shop scheduling) A factory consists of m machines $M_1, \ldots, M_m$, and needs to process n jobs every day. Job j needs to be processed once by each machine in the order $(M_{j(1)}, \ldots, M_{j(m)})$. Machine M_i takes time p_{ij} to process job j. A machine can only process one job at a time, and once a job is started on any machine, it must be processed to completion. The objective is to minimize the sum of the completion times of all the jobs. Provide an integer programming formulation for this problem.

Exercise 10.11 (Facility location) For the facility location problem, prove that the inclusion $P_{\text{FL}} \subset P_{\text{AFL}}$ can be strict.

Exercise 10.12 Let $G = (\mathcal{N}, \mathcal{E})$ be an undirected graph with n nodes. Show that G is a tree if and only if the total number of edges is $n - 1$, and for any nonempty set $S \subset \mathcal{N}$, the number of edges with both endpoints in S is less than or equal to $|S| - 1$.

Exercise 10.13 (A multicut formulation of the MST problem) Given an undirected graph $G = (\mathcal{N}, \mathcal{E})$, with $|\mathcal{N}| = n$ and $|\mathcal{E}| = m$, consider a partition of $\mathcal{N}$ into disjoint nonempty sets $C_0, C_1, \ldots, C_k$ of nodes whose union is $\mathcal{N}$. Let $\delta(C_0, C_1, \ldots, C_k)$ be the set of edges whose endpoints lie in different sets C_i. Let

$$P_{\text{mcut}} = \left\{ \mathbf{x} \in \Re^m \ \middle| \ 0 \le x_e \le 1, \ \sum_{e \in \mathcal{E}} x_e = n - 1, \right.$$
$$\sum_{e \in \delta(C_0, C_1, \ldots, C_k)} x_e \ge k, \text{ for all } k$$
$$\left. \text{and for all partitions } C_0, C_1, \ldots, C_k \text{ of } \mathcal{N} \right\}.$$

Prove that $P_{\text{mcut}} = P_{\text{sub}}$, where

$$P_{\text{sub}} = \left\{ \mathbf{x} \in \Re^m \ \middle| \ 0 \le x_e \le 1, \ \sum_{e \in \mathcal{E}} x_e = n - 1, \right.$$
$$\left. \sum_{e \in E(S)} x_e \le |S| - 1, \ S \subset \mathcal{N}, S \ne \emptyset, \mathcal{N} \right\}.$$

Exercise 10.14 (The undirected traveling salesman problem) For the undirected traveling salesman problem, prove that

$$P_{\text{tspcut}} = P_{\text{tspsub}}.$$

Exercise 10.15 * (The directed traveling salesman problem) Given a directed graph $G = (\mathcal{N}, \mathcal{A})$, with $|\mathcal{N}| = n$ and $|\mathcal{A}| = m$, a natural extension of the traveling salesman formulation given in Section 10.3, involves the constraints:

$$\sum_{\{i \mid (i,j) \in \mathcal{A}\}} y_{ij} = 1, \qquad j \in \mathcal{N},$$

$$\sum_{\{j \mid (i,j) \in \mathcal{A}\}} y_{ij} = 1, \qquad i \in \mathcal{N},$$

$$\sum_{\{(i,j) \in \mathcal{A} \mid i \in S, \, j \notin S\}} y_{ij} \geq 1, \qquad S \subset \mathcal{N}, \ S \neq \emptyset, \mathcal{N},$$

$$y_{ij} \in \{0, 1\}, \qquad i, j \in \mathcal{N}.$$

Let T be the set of feasible solutions.

(a) Consider now the following set of (polynomially many) constraints:

$$u_i - u_j + n y_{ij} \leq n - 1, \qquad (i,j) \in \mathcal{A}, \ i, j \neq 1,$$

$$\sum_{\{i \mid (i,j) \in \mathcal{A}\}} y_{ij} = 1, \qquad j \in \mathcal{N},$$

$$\sum_{\{j \mid (i,j) \in \mathcal{A}\}} y_{ij} = 1, \qquad i \in \mathcal{N},$$

$$y_{ij} \in \{0, 1\}, \qquad i, j \in \mathcal{N}.$$

Let T' be the set of feasible solutions. Prove that $T = T'$.

(b) Let $P_{\text{tsp-dcut}}$ and $P_{\text{tsp-polynomial}}$ be the polyhedra associated with the linear programming relaxations of the formulations corresponding to T and T', respectively. Prove that

$$P_{\text{tsp-dcut}} \subset P_{\text{tsp-polynomial}},$$

and that the inclusion can be strict, i.e., the first formulation is stronger.

(c) Prove that $P_{\text{tsp-dcut}} \neq \text{CH}(T)$.

10.6   Notes and sources

10.1 The journal *Interfaces* often publishes large scale discrete optimization models. Examples of integer programming modeling techniques can be found in Papadimitriou and Steiglitz (1982), Nemhauser and Wolsey (1988), and Williams (1990). The example regarding NSF fellowships is from Stock (1996).

10.3 Edmonds (1971) has shown that the convex hull of the integer feasible solutions to the minimum spanning tree problem is given by P_{sub}. The survey paper by Magnanti and Wolsey (1995) discusses many different formulations for tree-related problems, and their applications to discrete optimization. Edmonds (1965b) provided a polynomial time algorithm for the matching problem and showed that the convex hull of the integer feasible solutions to the matching problem is given by P_{matching}. For a textbook exposition of matching algorithms see Papadimitriou and Steiglitz (1982), and Nemhauser and Wolsey (1988). Much more information on the traveling salesman problem can be found in Lawler et al. (1985).

Chapter 11

Integer programming methods

Contents

Unlike linear programming problems, integer programming problems are very difficult to solve. In fact, no efficient general algorithm is known for their solution. In this chapter, we review algorithms for integer programming problems, we develop a duality theory that facilitates algorithmic development, and discuss evidence suggesting that that these problems are inherently hard.

There are three main categories of algorithms:

(a) **Exact algorithms** that are guaranteed to find an optimal solution, but may take an exponential number of iterations. They include cutting plane (Section 11.1), branch and bound and branch and cut (Section 11.2), and dynamic programming methods (Section 11.3).

(b) **Approximation algorithms** that provide in polynomial time a sub-optimal solution together with a bound on the degree of suboptimality (Section 11.5).

(c) **Heuristic algorithms** that provide a suboptimal solution, but without a guarantee on its quality. Although the running time is not guaranteed to be polynomial, empirical evidence suggests that some of these algorithms find a good solution fast. As examples we introduce local search methods (Section 11.6), and simulated annealing (Section 11.7).

Duality theory is central to linear programming. Integer programming also has a duality theory, presented in Section 11.4, which provides bounds on the optimal cost. These bounds are very useful in exact algorithms, as they can be used to avoid enumerating too many feasible solutions, and in approximation algorithms, as they provide performance guarantees.

Given our inability to solve integer programming problems efficiently, it is natural to ask whether such problems are inherently hard. Complexity theory, reviewed in Section 11.8, offers some insights on this question. It provides us with a class of problems with the following property: if a polynomial time algorithm exists for any problem in this class, then all integer programming problems can be solved by an efficient algorithm, but this is considered unlikely.

11.1   Cutting plane methods

We consider the integer programming problem

$$
\begin{array}{ll}
\text{minimize} & \mathbf{c'x} \\
\text{subject to} & \mathbf{Ax} = \mathbf{b} \\
& \mathbf{x} \geq \mathbf{0} \\
& \mathbf{x} \text{ integer,}
\end{array}
\tag{11.1}
$$

and its linear programming relaxation

$$\begin{aligned}
\text{minimize} \quad & \mathbf{c'x} \\
\text{subject to} \quad & \mathbf{Ax} = \mathbf{b} \\
& \mathbf{x} \geq \mathbf{0}.
\end{aligned} \tag{11.2}$$

The main idea in cutting plane methods is to solve the integer programming problem (11.1) by solving a sequence of linear programming problems, as follows. We first solve the linear programming relaxation (11.2) and find an optimal solution $\mathbf{x}^*$. If $\mathbf{x}^*$ is integer, then it is an optimal solution to the integer programming problem (11.1). If not, we find an inequality that all integer solutions to (11.1) satisfy, but $\mathbf{x}^*$ does not. We add this inequality to the linear programming problem to obtain a tighter relaxation, and we iterate this step.

A generic cutting plane algorithm

1. Solve the linear programming relaxation (11.2). Let $\mathbf{x}^*$ be an optimal solution.

2. If $\mathbf{x}^*$ is integer stop; $\mathbf{x}^*$ is an optimal solution to (11.1).

3. If not, add a linear inequality constraint to (11.2) that all integer solutions to (11.1) satisfy, but $\mathbf{x}^*$ does not; go to Step 1.

Note that this method is just a variation of the cutting plane algorithm introduced in Section 6.3. As in that section, the main idea is to generate a violated constraint, whenever the relaxed problem gives rise to an infeasible solution. The performance of a cutting plane method depends critically on the choice of the inequality used to "cut" $\mathbf{x}^*$. We review next ways to introduce cuts that give rise to particular cutting plane algorithms.

Example 11.1 (An example of a cut) Let $\mathbf{x}^*$ be an optimal basic feasible solution to (11.2) with at least one fractional basic variable. Let N be the set of indices of the nonbasic variables. Consider any solution to the integer programming problem such that $x_i = 0$ for all $i \in N$. Then, it is a solution to the linear programming problem as well, and it must be the same as the basic feasible solution $\mathbf{x}^*$. Since $\mathbf{x}^*$ is not feasible for the integer programming problem, then all feasible integer solutions satisfy

$$\sum_{j \in N} x_j \geq 1.$$

This is the inequality that we add to the relaxation (11.2). Note that all integer solutions to (11.1) satisfy it, while the optimal solution $\mathbf{x}^*$ to the relaxation violates it.

The Gomory cutting plane algorithm

The first finitely terminating algorithm for integer programming was a cutting plane algorithm proposed by Gomory in 1958, which uses some detailed information from the optimal simplex tableau.

We solve the standard form linear programming problem (11.2) with the simplex method. Let $\mathbf{x}^*$ be an optimal basic feasible solution and let $\mathbf{B}$ be an associated optimal basis. We partition $\mathbf{x}$ into a subvector $\mathbf{x}_B$ of basic variables and a subvector $\mathbf{x}_N$ of nonbasic variables. Recall from Chapter 3 that a tableau provides us with the coefficients of the equation $\mathbf{B}^{-1}\mathbf{A}\mathbf{x} = \mathbf{B}^{-1}\mathbf{b}$. Let N be the set of indices of nonbasic variables. Let $\mathbf{A}_N$ be the submatrix of $\mathbf{A}$ with columns $\mathbf{A}_i$, $i \in N$. From the optimal tableau, we obtain the coefficients of the constraints

$$\mathbf{x}_B + \mathbf{B}^{-1}\mathbf{A}_N\mathbf{x}_N = \mathbf{B}^{-1}\mathbf{b}.$$

Let $\bar{a}_{ij} = \left(\mathbf{B}^{-1}\mathbf{A}_j\right)_i$ and $\bar{a}_{i0} = \left(\mathbf{B}^{-1}\mathbf{b}\right)_i$. We consider one equality from the optimal tableau, in which $\bar{a}_{i0}$ is fractional:

$$x_i + \sum_{j \in N} \bar{a}_{ij} x_j = \bar{a}_{i0}.$$

Since $x_j \geq 0$ for all j, we have

$$x_i + \sum_{j \in N} \lfloor \bar{a}_{ij} \rfloor x_j \leq x_i + \sum_{j \in N} \bar{a}_{ij} x_j = \bar{a}_{i0}.$$

Since x_j should be integer, we obtain

$$x_i + \sum_{j \in N} \lfloor \bar{a}_{ij} \rfloor x_j \leq \lfloor \bar{a}_{i0} \rfloor.$$

This inequality is valid for all integer solutions, but it is not satisfied by $\mathbf{x}^*$. The reason is that $x_i^* = \bar{a}_{i0}$, $x_j^* = 0$ for all nonbasic $j \in N$, and $\lfloor \bar{a}_{i0} \rfloor < \bar{a}_{i0}$ (since $\bar{a}_{i0}$ was assumed fractional).

It has been shown that by systematically adding these cuts, and using the dual simplex method with appropriate anticycling rules, we obtain a finitely terminating algorithm for solving general integer programming problems. See Section 5.1 on how to apply the dual simplex method, when new inequality constraints are added. In practice, however, this method has not been particularly successful.

Example 11.2 (Illustration of the Gomory cutting plane algorithm)
We consider the integer programming problem

$$
\begin{array}{lrcrcl}
\text{minimize} & x_1 & - & 2x_2 & & \\
\text{subject to} & -4x_1 & + & 6x_2 & \leq & 9 \\
& x_1 & + & x_2 & \leq & 4 \\
& \multicolumn{5}{l}{x_1, x_2 \geq 0} \\
& \multicolumn{5}{l}{x_1, x_2 \text{ integer.}}
\end{array}
$$

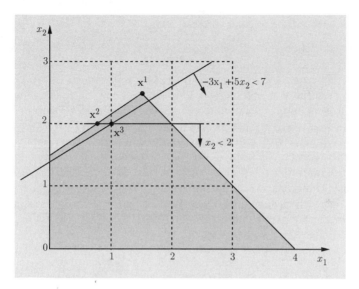

Figure 11.1: The Gomory cutting plane algorithm for Example 11.2. The shaded region is the feasible set of the linear programming relaxation.

We transform the problem in standard form

$$
\begin{aligned}
\text{minimize} \quad & x_1 \;-\; 2x_2 \\
\text{subject to} \quad & -4x_1 \;+\; 6x_2 \;+\; x_3 \;\;\;\;\;\;\;\;\;\;= 9 \\
& x_1 \;+\; x_2 \;\;\;\;\;\;\;\;\;+\; x_4 = 4 \\
& x_1, \ldots, x_4 \geq 0 \\
& x_1, \ldots, x_4 \ \text{integer.}
\end{aligned}
$$

We solve the linear programming relaxation, and the optimal solution (in terms of the original variables) is $\mathbf{x}^1 = (15/10, 25/10)$. One of the equations in the optimal tableau is

$$
x_2 + \frac{1}{10}x_3 + \frac{1}{10}x_4 = \frac{25}{10}.
$$

We apply the Gomory cutting plane algorithm, and we find the cut

$$
x_2 \leq 2.
$$

We augment the linear programming relaxation by adding the constraints $x_2 + x_5 = 2$, $x_5 \geq 0$, and we find that the new optimal solution is $\mathbf{x}^2 = (3/4, 2)$. One of the equations in the optimal tableau is

$$
x_1 - \frac{1}{4}x_3 + \frac{6}{4}x_5 = \frac{3}{4}.
$$

We add a new Gomory cut

$$
x_1 - x_3 + x_5 \leq 0,
$$

which, in terms of the original variables x_1, x_2, is

$$-3x_1 + 5x_2 \leq 7.$$

We add this constraint, together with the previously added constraint $x_2 \leq 2$, and find that the new optimal solution is $\mathbf{x}^3 = (1, 2)$. Since the solution $\mathbf{x}^3$ is integer, it is an optimal solution to the original problem; see Figure 11.1.

A difficulty with general purpose cutting plane algorithms is that the added inequalities cut only a very small piece of the feasible set of the linear programming relaxation. As a result, the practical performance of such algorithms has not been impressive. For this reason, cutting plane algorithms with deeper cuts have been designed. These cuts utilize the structure of the particular integer programming problem. We illustrate such methods with an example.

Example 11.3 (The weighted independent set problem) Given an undirected graph $G = (\mathcal{N}, \mathcal{E})$ and weights w_i for each $i \in \mathcal{N}$, the weighted independent set problem asks for a collection of nodes S of maximum weight, so that no two nodes in S are adjacent. We let $x_i = 1$ if node i is selected in the independent set, and $x_i = 0$, otherwise. The problem can then be formulated as follows:

$$\text{maximize} \quad \sum_{i=1}^{n} w_i x_i$$
$$\text{subject to} \quad x_i + x_j \leq 1, \qquad (i, j) \in \mathcal{E},$$
$$x_i \in \{0, 1\}, \qquad i \in \mathcal{N}.$$

A collection of nodes U such that for any $i, j \in U$, we have $(i, j) \in \mathcal{E}$, is called a *clique*. Clearly the following inequality is valid for all feasible solutions to the independent set problem:

$$\sum_{i \in U} x_i \leq 1, \quad \text{for any clique } U.$$

A set of nodes $U = \{i_1, \ldots, i_k\}$ is called a *cycle* if the only edges joining nodes in U are $\{i_1, i_2\}, \{i_2, i_3\}, \ldots, \{i_k, i_1\}$. For any cycle U of odd cardinality, there can be no more that $(|U| - 1)/2$ nodes in an independent set; otherwise, two of these nodes will be adjacent. Therefore, the inequality

$$\sum_{i \in U} x_i \leq \frac{|U| - 1}{2}, \quad \text{for any cycle } U \text{ such that } |U| \text{ is odd,}$$

must hold.

The inequalities we derived above utilize the particular combinatorial structure of the maximum independent set problem. If we use these inequalities in the generic cutting plane method we described, the performance of the algorithm is greatly enhanced. However, given an $\mathbf{x}^*$, we must search for a violated inequality of either type, which can be difficult.

11.2   Branch and bound

Branch and bound uses a "divide and conquer" approach to explore the set of feasible integer solutions. However, instead of exploring the entire feasible set, it uses bounds on the optimal cost to avoid exploring certain parts of the set of feasible integer solutions.

Let F be the set of feasible solutions to the problem

$$\text{minimize}\quad \mathbf{c}'\mathbf{x}$$
$$\text{subject to}\quad \mathbf{x} \in F.$$

[For example, F could be the set of integer feasible solutions to the problem (11.1).] We partition the set F into a finite collection of subsets $F_1, \ldots, F_k$, and solve separately each one of the subproblems

$$\text{minimize}\quad \mathbf{c}'\mathbf{x}$$
$$\text{subject to}\quad \mathbf{x} \in F_i, \quad i = 1, \ldots, k.$$

We then compare the optimal solutions to the subproblems, and choose the best one. Each subproblem may be almost as difficult as the original problem and this suggests trying to solve each subproblem by means of the same method; that is, by splitting it into further subproblems, etc. This is the branching part of the method and leads to a tree of subproblems; see Figure 11.2.

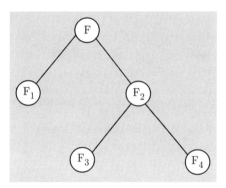

Figure 11.2: A tree of subproblems: the feasible set F is partitioned into F_1 and F_2; also, F_2 is partitioned into F_3 and F_4.

We also assume that there is a fairly efficient algorithm, which for every F_i of interest, computes a *lower bound* $b(F_i)$ to the optimal cost of the corresponding subproblem; that is,

$$b(F_i) \leq \min_{\mathbf{x} \in F_i} \mathbf{c}'\mathbf{x}.$$

The basic idea is that while the optimal cost in a subproblem may be difficult to compute exactly, a lower bound might be a lot easier to obtain.

A popular method to obtain such a bound is to use the optimal cost of the linear programming relaxation.

In the course of the algorithm, we will also occasionally solve certain subproblems to optimality, or simply evaluate the cost of certain feasible solutions. This allows us to maintain an upper bound U on the optimal cost, which could be the cost of the best feasible solution encountered thus far.

The essence of the method lies in the following observation. If the lower bound $b(F_i)$ corresponding to a particular subproblem satisfies $b(F_i) \geq U$, then this subproblem need not be considered further, since the optimal solution to the subproblem is no better than the best feasible solution encountered thus far.

The following is a high-level description of the resulting algorithm. At any point, the algorithm keeps in memory a set of outstanding (active) subproblems and the cost U of the best feasible solution so far. Initially, U is set either to ∞ or to the cost of some feasible solution, if one happens to be available. A typical stage of the algorithm proceeds as follows.

A generic branch and bound algorithm

1. Select an active subproblem F_i.
2. If the subproblem is infeasible, delete it; otherwise, compute $b(F_i)$ for the corresponding subproblem.
3. If $b(F_i) \geq U$, delete the subproblem.
4. If $b(F_i) < U$, either obtain an optimal solution to the subproblem, or break the corresponding subproblem into further subproblems, which are added to the list of active subproblems.

There are several "free parameters" in this algorithm. The best choices are usually dictated by experience.

(a) There are different ways of choosing an active subproblem. Two extreme choices are "breadth-first search" and "depth-first search."

(b) There may be several ways of obtaining a lower bound $b(F_i)$ on the optimal cost of a subproblem. One possibility that we have already mentioned is to consider the linear programming relaxation. We consider other possibilities in Section 11.4.

(c) There are usually several ways of breaking a problem into subproblems.

As an illustration, we use as a lower bound $b(F_i)$ the optimal cost of the linear programming relaxation whereby the integrality constraints are ignored. If an integer optimal solution to the relaxation is obtained, then it is automatically an optimal solution to the corresponding integer programming problem as well, and there is no need for expanding into

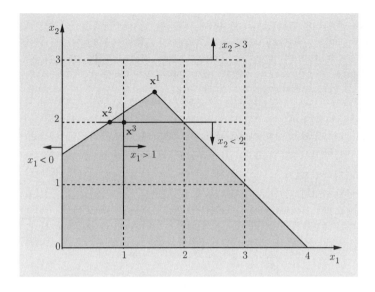

Figure 11.3: Branch and bound in Example 11.4.

further subproblems. We only need to update U (if the cost of this optimal solution is better than the previous value of U), and we can delete the current subproblem. If the optimal solution $\mathbf{x}^*$ to the linear programming relaxation is not integer, we choose a component x_i for which x_i^* is not integer and create two subproblems, by adding either of the constraints

$$x_i \leq \lfloor x_i^* \rfloor, \qquad \text{or} \qquad x_i \geq \lceil x_i^* \rceil.$$

(Note that both constraints are violated by $\mathbf{x}^*$. If $\mathbf{x}^*$ is the unique optimal solution to the linear programming relaxation, then the optimal cost in the relaxation of either of the new subproblems will be strictly larger.) Given that a subproblem differs from its parent only in the fact that a single new constraint has been added, we can solve the linear programming relaxation of a subproblem by means of the dual simplex method, starting from $\mathbf{x}^*$. We may then expect than an optimal solution to the new linear programming problem will be obtained after only a small number of iterations.

Example 11.4 (Illustration of branch and bound) We solve the problem of Example 11.2 by branch and bound; see Figure 11.3. Initially, $U = \infty$. We solve the linear programming relaxation and the optimal solution is $\mathbf{x}^1 = (1.5, 2.5)$. Then, $b(F)$ is the optimal cost of the relaxation, i.e., $b(F) = -3.5$. We create two subproblems, by adding the constraints $x_2 \geq 3$ (subproblem F_1), or $x_2 \leq 2$ (subproblem F_2). The active list of subproblems is $\{F_1, F_2\}$. The linear programming relaxation of subproblem F_1 is infeasible and, therefore, we can delete this subproblem from the active list. The optimal solution to the linear programming relaxation of subproblem F_2 is $\mathbf{x}^2 = (3/4, 2)$, and thus $b(F_2) = -3.25$. We further decompose subproblem F_2 into two subproblems, since either $x_1 \geq 1$ (subproblem F_3), or $x_1 \leq 0$ (subproblem F_4). The active list of subproblems is now $\{F_3, F_4\}$. The optimal solution to the linear programming relaxation of Subproblem F_3 is $\mathbf{x}^3 = (1, 2)$, which is integer and therefore, $U = -3$. We delete subproblem F_3 from the active list. The optimal solution to the linear programming relaxation of subproblem F_4 is $\mathbf{x}^4 = (0, 3/2)$, and thus $b(F_4) = -3$. Since $b(F_4) \geq U$, we do not need to further explore subproblem F_4. Since the active list of subproblems is empty, we terminate. The optimal integer solution is $\mathbf{x}^3 = (1, 2)$.

Example 11.5 (A branch and bound method for the directed traveling salesman problem) Given a directed graph $G = (\mathcal{N}, \mathcal{A})$ with n nodes, and a cost c_{ij} for every arc, we want to solve the traveling salesman problem on G using branch and bound. The objective is to find a tour (a directed cycle that visits all nodes) of minimum cost. We let x_{ij} equal to 1, if i and j are consecutive nodes in a tour, and 0, otherwise. The optimal cost in the problem

$$\text{minimize} \quad \sum_{i=1}^{n} \sum_{j=1}^{n} c_{ij} x_{ij}$$

$$\text{subject to} \quad \sum_{i=1}^{n} x_{ij} = 1, \qquad j = 1, \ldots, n,$$

$$\sum_{j=1}^{n} x_{ij} = 1, \qquad i = 1, \ldots, n,$$

$$x_{ij} \in \{0, 1\},$$

provides a lower bound on the cost of an optimal tour, because every tour must satisfy the above constraints. We recognize this as an assignment problem. However, not every feasible solution to the assignment problem corresponds to a tour, and for this reason the optimal costs for the two problems are not the same. In particular, an optimal solution to the assignment problem may correspond to a collection of "subtours"; see Figure 11.4.

Suppose now that we use the assignment problem to obtain a lower bound on the cost of the traveling salesman problem. If the optimal solution to the assignment problem corresponds to a tour, such a tour is optimal for the traveling salesman problem. If not, we split the problem into subproblems. Each additional subproblem involves a single additional constraint of the form $x_{ij} = 0$. This is equivalent to prohibiting (i, j) from being consecutive nodes in a tour, and can be also accomplished by setting c_{ij} to a prohibitively high value. Note that adding such a constraint to the traveling salesman or to the assignment problem, still leaves us with a traveling salesman or assignment problem, respectively. Therefore, all subproblems constructed in the course of the branch and bound algorithm will also correspond to instances of the traveling salesman problem and lower bounds can be obtained by solving the related assignment problems. The only remaining issue is how to decide which constraints $x_{ij} = 0$ to add. A natural alternative is to choose one or more subtours and let each subproblem

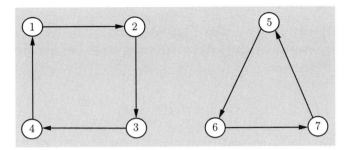

Figure 11.4: Consider a directed traveling salesman problem with seven nodes. The vector **x** corresponding to these two subtours is a feasible solution to the assignment problem.

prohibit one of their arcs. For example, if the optimal solution to the assignment problem is as in Figure 11.4, we can create subproblems by adding one of the constraints $x_{12} = 0$, $x_{23} = 0$, $x_{34} = 0$, $x_{41} = 0$, $x_{56} = 0$, $x_{67} = 0$, $x_{75} = 0$. If the current assignment problem has a unique optimal solution, this solution is made infeasible by the constraints that are added during branching. For this reason, the optimal cost in each subproblem is strictly larger, and improved lower bounds are obtained.

It should be clear that the success of branch and bound methods depends critically on the availability of tight lower bounds. (In Section 11.4 we introduce a duality theory for integer programming that leads to such bounds.) While the branch and bound algorithm may take exponential time in the worst case (see Exercise 11.4), it often produces acceptable solutions in a reasonably short amount of time, especially when tight lower bounds are available.

Branch and cut

Another variant of the method, often called *branch and cut,* utilizes cuts when solving the subproblems. In particular, we augment the formulation of the subproblems with additional cuts, in order to improve the bounds obtained from the linear programming relaxations. We illustrate the method with an example.

Example 11.6 (Illustration of branch and cut) We solve the problem of Example 11.2 by branch and cut. We first solve the linear programming relaxation and find the optimal solution $\mathbf{x}^1 = (1.5, 2.5)$. As before, we create subproblems F_1 (corresponding to $x_2 \geq 3$) and F_2 (corresponding to $x_2 \leq 2$). We delete subproblem F_1, because its linear programming relaxation is infeasible. In order to solve subproblem F_2, we add the constraint $-x_1 + x_2 \leq 1$ which is satisfied by all integer solutions to subproblem F_2. The optimal solution to the linear programming relaxation is now $\mathbf{x} = (1, 2)$, which is integer, and thus we terminate with the optimal solution. Note that by adding the cut $-x_1 + x_2 \le 1$, we avoided further enumeration. This is typical in branch and cut. If we can add "deep" cuts, we can accelerate branch and bound considerably. However, finding such cuts is nontrivial.

11.3 Dynamic programming

In the previous section, we introduced branch and bound, which is an exact, intelligent enumerative technique that attempts to avoid enumerating a large portion of the feasible integer solutions. In this section, we introduce another exact technique, called dynamic programming, that solves integer programming problems sequentially.

We illustrate the method by deriving a dynamic programming algorithm for the traveling salesman problem. We will then discuss general principles on how to develop dynamic programming algorithms for other integer programming problems.

Example 11.7 (A dynamic programming algorithm for the traveling salesman problem) Let $G = (\mathcal{N}, \mathcal{A})$ be a directed graph with n nodes and let c_{ij} be the cost of arc (i, j). We view the choice of a tour as a sequence of choices: we start at node 1; then, at each stage, we choose which node to visit next. After a number of stages, we have visited a subset S of $\mathcal{N}$ and we are at a current node $k \in S$. Let $C(S, k)$ be the minimum cost over all paths that start at node 1, visit all nodes in the set S exactly once, and end up at node k. If we call (S, k) a *state*, this state can be reached from any state of the form $\big(S \setminus \{k\}, m\big)$, with $m \in S \setminus \{k\}$, at a transition cost of c_{mk}. Thus, $C(S, k)$ can be interpreted as the least possible sum of transition costs, over all sequences of transitions that take us from state $\big(\{1\}, 1\big)$ to state (S, k). Therefore, we have the recursion

$$C(S, k) = \min_{m \in S \setminus \{k\}} \Big(C\big(S \setminus \{k\}, m\big) + c_{mk} \Big), \qquad k \in S, \qquad (11.3)$$

and $C\big(\{1\}, 1\big) = 0$. There are 2^n choices for S, $O(n)$ choices for k, and a total of $O(n2^n)$ states (S, k). Each time that $C(S, k)$ is evaluated for some new state according to Eq. (11.3), $O(n)$ arithmetic operations are needed. Therefore, with $O(n^2 2^n)$ operations, we can obtain $C\big(\{1, \ldots, n\}, k\big)$ for all k. The length of an optimal tour is then given by

$$\min_k \Big(C\big(\{1, \ldots, n\}, k\big) + c_{k1} \Big).$$

This algorithm, although exponential, is much better than exhaustive enumeration of all $n!$ tours. Realistically, it can only be used to solve instances of the traveling salesman problem involving up to 20 nodes.

More generally, devising a dynamic programming algorithm for an integer programming problem involves the following steps.

> **Guidelines for constructing dynamic programming algorithms**
>
> 1. View the choice of a feasible solution as a sequence of decisions occurring in stages, and so that the total cost is the sum of the costs of individual decisions.
>
> 2. Define the state as a summary of all relevant past decisions.
>
> 3. Determine which state transitions are possible. Let the cost of each state transition be the cost of the corresponding decision.
>
> 4. Write a recursion on the optimal cost from the origin state to a destination state.

The most crucial step is usually the definition of a suitable state. Let us apply the method to another problem.

A dynamic programming algorithm for the zero-one knapsack problem

Let us consider the version of the zero-one knapsack problem we introduced in Example 10.1:

$$\text{maximize} \quad \sum_{j=1}^{n} c_j x_j$$

$$\text{subject to} \quad \sum_{j=1}^{n} w_j x_j \leq K$$

$$x_j \in \{0, 1\}.$$

We assume that K and all c_j, w_j are positive integers. We derive a dynamic programming algorithm for the zero-one knapsack problem by decomposing it into stages. Instead of picking a vector $(x_1, \ldots, x_n)$ all at once, we visualize the problem as one in which decisions are made for one item at a time. After i decisions, we have decided which ones out of the first i items are to be included in the knapsack, and have therefore determined values for the variables $x_1, \ldots, x_i$. At that point, the value accumulated is $\sum_{j=1}^{i} c_j x_j$ and the weight accumulated is $\sum_{j=1}^{i} w_j x_j$.

Let $W_i(u)$ be the least possible weight that has to be accumulated in order to attain a total value of u using only items in the set $\{1, \ldots, i\}$. Let $W_i(u) = \infty$, if it is impossible to accumulate a total value of u using only the first i items. We use the convention $W_0(0) = 0$, and $W_0(u) = \infty$, if $u \neq 0$, which reflects the fact that the value accumulated using no items is zero. We then have the following recursion:

$$W_{i+1}(u) = \min \left\{ W_i(u), \ W_i(u - c_{i+1}) + w_{i+1} \right\}. \tag{11.4}$$

In words, this recursion means the following. If we wish to accumulate a total value of u, using some of the first $i + 1$ items, while accumulating as little weight as possible, there are two alternatives depending on whether item $i+1$ is used or not. If item $i+1$ is not used, then the best we can do is to accumulate a total value of u, while using only some of the first i items and do that with the least possible accumulated weight, which is $W_i(u)$. Alternatively, if item $i+1$ is used, since it has a value of c_{i+1}, we must have accumulated a total value of $u - c_{i+1}$ using the first i items. Of course, the first i decisions should be made so that the value $u - c_{i+1}$ is accumulated with the least possible weight, which is $W_i(u - c_{i+1})$, and to which we must then add the weight of item $i+1$. We can now interpret recursion (11.4) as stating that $W_{i+1}(u)$ is given by the best of the two alternatives that we have just described.

We continue with a slightly different interpretation of recursion (11.4). Let us say that we are at *state* (i, u) if we have considered the first i items, have picked some of them, and have accumulated a total value of u. We then build a state transition diagram indicating which states can be reached from which other state. Notice that when in state (i, u) we can either decide to pick item $i+1$ and move to state $(i+1, u+c_{i+1})$ or we can decide to skip item $i+1$ and move to state $(i+1, u)$. We represent states as nodes and possible transitions by directed arcs; see Figure 11.5.

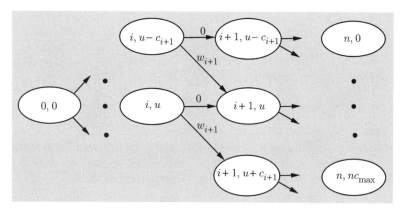

Figure 11.5: The state transition diagram for the dynamic programming approach to the zero-one knapsack problem.

In addition, we associate a weight to each arc (or transition) which is the additional weight added in the course of this transition. Thus, the transition from (i, u) to $(i+1, u)$ carries zero weight, while the transition from (i, u) to $(i+1, u+c_{i+1})$ carries weight w_{i+1}.

Initially, we are at state $(0, 0)$; no item has been considered and no value has been accumulated. A sequence of decisions, involving items $1, \ldots, i$ corresponds to a directed path from node $(0, 0)$ to some node of the form (i, u). Furthermore, the sum of the weights along the path corresponds to the accumulated weight. We conclude that $W_i(u)$ is equal to the least weight of all paths from node $(0, 0)$ to node (i, u), and is equal to infinity if no such path exists. We may then recognize Eq. (11.4) as the Bellman equation associated with this shortest path problem (see Section 7.9).

Let

$$c_{\max} = \max_{i=1,\ldots,n} c_i.$$

If $u > nc_{\max}$, then no state of the form (i, u) is reachable. By restricting to states of the form (i, u) with $u \le nc_{\max}$, we see that the total number of states of interest is of the order of $n^2 c_{\max}$. Using recursion (11.4), the value of $W_i(u)$ for all states of interest, can be computed in time $O(n^2 c_{\max})$. Once this is done, the optimal value u^* is given by

$$u^* = \max \left\{ u \mid W_n(u) \le K \right\},$$

which can be determined with only an additional $O(nc_{\max})$ effort. Optimal values for the variables $x_1, \ldots, x_n$ are then determined by an optimal path from node $(0, 0)$ to node (n, u^*). We have thus proved the following result.

Theorem 11.1 *The zero-one knapsack problem can be solved in time* $O(n^2 c_{\max})$.

An alternative, and somewhat more natural, dynamic programming algorithm for the same problem could be obtained by defining $C_i(w)$ as the maximum value that can be accumulated using some of the first i items subject to the constraint that the total accumulated weight is equal to w. We would then obtain the recursion

$$C_{i+1}(w) = \max \left\{ C_i(w), \; C_i(w - w_{i+1}) + c_{i+1} \right\}.$$

By considering all states of the form (i, w) with $w \le K$, an algorithm with complexity $O(nK)$ would be obtained. However, our previous algorithm is better suited to the purposes of developing an approximation algorithm, which will be done in Section 11.5.

The algorithm of Theorem 11.1 is an exponential time algorithm. This is because the size of an instance of the zero-one knapsack problem is

$$O\left(n\left(\log c_{\max} + \log w_{\max}\right) + \log K\right),$$

where $w_{\max} = \max_i w_i$. However, it becomes polynomial if $c_{\max}$ is bounded by some polynomial in n. More formally, for any integer d, we can define the problem KNAPSACK(d), as the problem consisting of all instances of the zero-one knapsack problem with $c_i \le n^d$ for all i. According to Theorem 11.1, KNAPSACK(d) can be solved in time $O(n^{d+2})$, which is polynomial for every fixed d.

11.4   Integer programming duality

In this section, we develop the duality theory of integer programming. This in turn leads to a method for obtaining tight bounds, that are particularly useful for branch and bound. The methodology is closely related to the subject of Section 4.10, but our discussion here is self-contained.

We consider the integer programming problem

$$
\begin{aligned}
\text{minimize} \quad & \mathbf{c}'\mathbf{x} \\
\text{subject to} \quad & \mathbf{A}\mathbf{x} \geq \mathbf{b} \\
& \mathbf{D}\mathbf{x} \geq \mathbf{d} \\
& \mathbf{x} \text{ integer},
\end{aligned}
\tag{11.5}
$$

and assume that $\mathbf{A}$, $\mathbf{D}$, $\mathbf{b}$, $\mathbf{c}$, $\mathbf{d}$ have integer entries. Let Z_{IP} the optimal cost and let

$$X = \{\mathbf{x} \text{ integer} \mid \mathbf{D}\mathbf{x} \geq \mathbf{d}\}.$$

In order to motivate the method, we assume that optimizing over the set X can be done efficiently; for example X may represent the set of feasible solutions to an assignment problem. However, adding the constraints $\mathbf{A}\mathbf{x} \geq \mathbf{b}$ to the problem, makes the problem difficult to solve. We next consider the idea of introducing a dual variable for every constraint in $\mathbf{A}\mathbf{x} \geq \mathbf{b}$. Let $\mathbf{p} \geq \mathbf{0}$ be a vector of dual variables (also called *Lagrange multipliers*) that has the same dimension as the vector $\mathbf{b}$. For a fixed vector $\mathbf{p}$, we introduce the problem

$$
\begin{aligned}
\text{minimize} \quad & \mathbf{c}'\mathbf{x} + \mathbf{p}'(\mathbf{b} - \mathbf{A}\mathbf{x}) \\
\text{subject to} \quad & \mathbf{x} \in X,
\end{aligned}
\tag{11.6}
$$

and denote its optimal cost by $Z(\mathbf{p})$. We will say that we *relax* or *dualize* the constraints $\mathbf{A}\mathbf{x} \geq \mathbf{b}$. For a fixed $\mathbf{p}$, the above problem can be solved efficiently, as we are optimizing a linear objective over the set X. We next observe that $Z(\mathbf{p})$ provides a bound on Z_{IP}.

Lemma 11.1 *If the problem (11.5) has an optimal solution and if $\mathbf{p} \geq \mathbf{0}$, then $Z(\mathbf{p}) \leq Z_{\mathrm{IP}}$.*

Proof. Let $\mathbf{x}^*$ denote an optimal solution to (11.5). Then, $\mathbf{b} - \mathbf{A}\mathbf{x}^* \leq \mathbf{0}$ and, therefore,

$$\mathbf{c}'\mathbf{x}^* + \mathbf{p}'(\mathbf{b} - \mathbf{A}\mathbf{x}^*) \leq \mathbf{c}'\mathbf{x}^* = Z_{\mathrm{IP}}.$$

Since $\mathbf{x}^* \in X$,

$$Z(\mathbf{p}) \leq \mathbf{c}'\mathbf{x}^* + \mathbf{p}'(\mathbf{b} - \mathbf{A}\mathbf{x}^*),$$

and therefore, $Z(\mathbf{p}) \leq Z_{\mathrm{IP}}$.   □

Since problem (11.6) provides a lower bound to the integer programming problem (11.5) for all $\mathbf{p} \geq \mathbf{0}$, it is natural to consider the tightest such

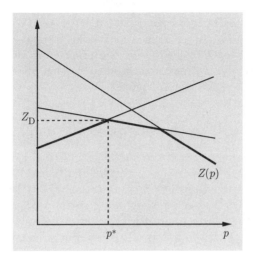

Figure 11.6: The function $Z(\mathbf{p})$ is concave and piecewise linear.

bound. For this reason, we introduce the problem

$$\begin{array}{ll} \text{maximize} & Z(\mathbf{p}) \\ \text{subject to} & \mathbf{p} \geq \mathbf{0}. \end{array} \tag{11.7}$$

We will refer to problem (11.7) as the *Lagrangean dual*. Let

$$Z_{\mathrm{D}} = \max_{\mathbf{p} \geq \mathbf{0}} Z(\mathbf{p}).$$

Suppose for instance, that $X = \{\mathbf{x}^1, \ldots, \mathbf{x}^m\}$. Then $Z(\mathbf{p})$ can be also written as

$$Z(\mathbf{p}) = \min_{i=1,\ldots,m} \left(\mathbf{c}'\mathbf{x}^i + \mathbf{p}'(\mathbf{b} - \mathbf{A}\mathbf{x}^i) \right). \tag{11.8}$$

The function $Z(\mathbf{p})$ is concave and piecewise linear, since it is the minimum of a finite collection of linear functions of $\mathbf{p}$ (see Theorem 1.1 in Section 1.3 and Figure 11.6). As a consequence, the problem of computing Z_{D} [namely, problem (11.7)] can be recast as a linear programming problem, but with a very large number of constraints.

It is clear from Lemma 11.1 that weak duality holds:

Theorem 11.2 *We have* $Z_{\mathrm{D}} \leq Z_{\mathrm{IP}}$.

The previous theorem represents the weak duality theory of integer programming. Unlike linear programming, integer programming does not have a strong duality theory. (Compare with Theorem 4.18 in Section 4.10.)

Indeed in Example 11.8, we show that it is possible to have $Z_D < Z_{IP}$. The procedure of obtaining bounds for integer programming problems by calculating Z_D is called *Lagrangean relaxation*. We next investigate the quality of the bound Z_D, in comparison to the one provided by the linear programming relaxation of problem (11.5).

On the strength of the Lagrangean dual

The characterization (11.8) of the Lagrangean dual objective does not provide particular insight into the quality of the bound. A more revealing characterization is developed in this subsection. Let $CH(X)$ be the convex hull of the set X. We need the following result, whose proof is outlined in Exercise 11.8. Since we already know that the convex hull of a finite set is a polyhedron, this result is of interest when the set $\{x \mid Dx \geq d\}$ is unbounded and the set X is infinite.

Theorem 11.3 *We assume that the system of linear inequalities* $Dx \geq d$ *has a feasible solution, and that the matrix* D *and the vector* d *have integer entries. Let*

$$X = \{x \text{ integer} \mid Dx \geq d\}.$$

Then $CH(X)$ *is a polyhedron.*

The next theorem, which is the central result of this section, characterizes the Lagrangean dual as a linear programming problem.

Theorem 11.4 *The optimal value* Z_D *of the Lagrangean dual is equal to the optimal cost of the following linear programming problem:*

$$\begin{array}{ll} \text{minimize} & c'x \\ \text{subject to} & Ax \geq b \\ & x \in CH(X). \end{array} \qquad (11.9)$$

Proof. By definition,

$$Z(p) = \min_{x \in X} \left(c'x + p'(b - Ax) \right).$$

Since the objective function is linear in x, the optimal cost remains the same if we allow convex combinations of the elements of X. Therefore,

$$Z(p) = \min_{x \in CH(X)} \left(c'x + p'(b - Ax) \right),$$

and hence, we have

$$Z_D = \max_{\mathbf{p} \geq 0} \min_{\mathbf{x} \in \mathrm{CH}(X)} \left(\mathbf{c}'\mathbf{x} + \mathbf{p}'(\mathbf{b} - \mathbf{Ax}) \right).$$

Let $\mathbf{x}^k$, $k \in K$, and $\mathbf{w}^j$, $j \in J$, be the extreme points and a complete set of extreme rays of $\mathrm{CH}(X)$, respectively. Then, for any fixed $\mathbf{p}$, we have

$$Z(\mathbf{p}) = \begin{cases} -\infty, & \text{if } (\mathbf{c}' - \mathbf{p}'\mathbf{A})\mathbf{w}^j < 0, \\ & \text{for some } j \in J, \\ \min_{k \in K} \left(\mathbf{c}'\mathbf{x}^k + \mathbf{p}'(\mathbf{b} - \mathbf{Ax}^k) \right), & \text{otherwise.} \end{cases}$$

Therefore, the Lagrangean dual is equivalent to and has the same optimal value as the problem

$$\begin{aligned} \text{maximize} \quad & \min_{k \in K} \left(\mathbf{c}'\mathbf{x}^k + \mathbf{p}'(\mathbf{b} - \mathbf{Ax}^k) \right) \\ \text{subject to} \quad & (\mathbf{c}' - \mathbf{p}'\mathbf{A})\mathbf{w}^j \geq 0, \qquad j \in J, \\ & \mathbf{p} \geq \mathbf{0}, \end{aligned}$$

or equivalently,

$$\begin{aligned} \text{maximize} \quad & y \\ \text{subject to} \quad & y + \mathbf{p}'(\mathbf{Ax}^k - \mathbf{b}) \leq \mathbf{c}'\mathbf{x}^k, \qquad k \in K, \\ & \mathbf{p}'\mathbf{Aw}^j \leq \mathbf{c}'\mathbf{w}^j, \qquad j \in J, \\ & \mathbf{p} \geq \mathbf{0}. \end{aligned}$$

Taking the linear programming dual of the above problem, and using strong duality, we obtain that Z_D is equal to the optimal cost of the problem

$$\begin{aligned} \text{minimize} \quad & \mathbf{c}' \left(\sum_{k \in K} \alpha_k \mathbf{x}^k + \sum_{j \in J} \beta_j \mathbf{w}^j \right) \\ \text{subject to} \quad & \sum_{k \in K} \alpha_k = 1 \\ & \mathbf{A} \left(\sum_{k \in K} \alpha_k \mathbf{x}^k + \sum_{j \in J} \beta_j \mathbf{w}^j \right) \geq \mathbf{b} \\ & \alpha_k, \beta_j \geq 0, \qquad k \in K, \ j \in J. \end{aligned}$$

Since,

$$\mathrm{CH}(X) = \left\{ \sum_{k \in K} \alpha_k \mathbf{x}^k + \sum_{j \in J} \beta_j \mathbf{w}^j \ \middle| \ \sum_{k \in K} \alpha_k = 1, \ \alpha_k, \beta_j \geq 0, \ k \in K, \ j \in J \right\},$$

the result follows.   □

Example 11.8 (Illustration of Lagrangean relaxation) Consider the problem

$$
\begin{array}{rl}
\text{minimize} & 3x_1 - x_2 \\
\text{subject to} & x_1 - x_2 \geq -1 \\
& -x_1 + 2x_2 \leq 5 \\
& 3x_1 + 2x_2 \geq 3 \\
& 6x_1 + x_2 \leq 15 \\
& x_1, x_2 \geq 0 \\
& x_1, x_2 \text{ integer.}
\end{array}
$$

We relax the first constraint $x_1 - x_2 \geq -1$, and we let X be the set of integer vectors that satisfy the remaining constraints. The set X, shown in Figure 11.7, is then

$$
X = \big\{ (1,0), (2,0), (1,1), (2,1), (0,2), (1,2), (2,2), (1,3), (2,3) \big\}.
$$

For $p \geq 0$, we have

$$
Z(p) = \min_{(x_1, x_2) \in X} \big(3x_1 - x_2 + p(-1 - x_1 + x_2) \big),
$$

which is plotted in Figure 11.8.

Since there are nine points in X, $Z(p)$ is the minimum of nine linear functions. The function $Z(p)$ turns out to be equal to

$$
Z(p) = \left\{
\begin{array}{ll}
-2 + p, & 0 \leq p \leq 5/3, \\
3 - 2p, & 5/3 \leq p \leq 3, \\
6 - 3p, & p \geq 3.
\end{array}
\right.
$$

The Lagrangean dual is maximized for $p = 5/3$, and the optimal value is $Z_D = Z(5/3) = -1/3$. For $p = 5/3$, the corresponding elements of X are $(1,0)$ and $(0,2)$.

In order to illustrate Theorem 11.4, we find first the convex hull $CH(X)$ of X, and intersect it with the constraint $x_1 - x_2 \geq -1$, forming the shaded polyhedron in Figure 11.7. Optimizing the original objective function $3x_1 - x_2$ over this polyhedron, we obtain that the optimal solution is $(1/3, 4/3)$ with value $-1/3$, which is the same as Z_D.

Although we presented the method for the case where the relaxed constraints were inequalities, the method is exactly the same even if we have equality constraints. The only difference is that the corresponding Lagrange multipliers are unrestricted in sign.

Having characterized the optimal value of the Lagrangean dual as the solution to a linear programming problem, it is natural to compare it with the optimal cost Z_{IP} and the optimal cost Z_{LP} of the linear programming relaxation

$$
\begin{array}{rl}
\text{minimize} & \mathbf{c'x} \\
\text{subject to} & \mathbf{Ax} \geq \mathbf{b} \\
& \mathbf{Dx} \geq \mathbf{d}.
\end{array}
$$

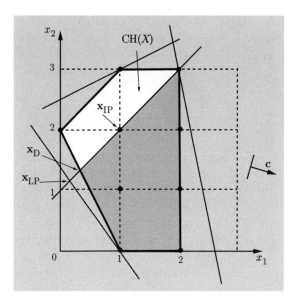

Figure 11.7: The points shown are elements of X. The convex hull of X is the set outlined by the thicker lines. The shaded polyhedron represents the intersection of CH(X) with the set of vectors that satisfy $x_1 - x_2 \geq -1$. The optimal solution to problem (11.9) is $\mathbf{x}_D = \left(1/3, 4/3\right)$, and its cost Z_D is equal to $-1/3$. Note that the optimal solution to the linear programming relaxation is the vector $\mathbf{x}_{LP} = \left(1/5, 6/5\right)$, resulting in a lower bound $Z_{LP} = -9/5$. The optimal solution to the integer programming problem is $\mathbf{x}_{IP} = (1, 2)$, and $Z_{IP} = 1$. Note that $Z_{LP} < Z_D < Z_{IP}$.

In general, the following ordering holds among Z_{LP}, Z_{IP}, and Z_D:

$$Z_{LP} \leq Z_D \leq Z_{IP}.$$

The first inequality follows from Theorem 11.4, because

$$\text{CH}(X) \subset \{\mathbf{x} \mid \mathbf{Dx} \geq \mathbf{d}\},$$

and the second inequality follows from Theorem 11.2. In the next example, we show that, depending on the objective function, these inequalities can be strict.

Example 11.9 We refer again to Example 11.8. It can be verified that we have the following possibilities:

(a) For the original objective function $3x_1 - x_2$, we have $Z_{LP} < Z_D < Z_{IP}$.

(b) If we change the objective function to $-x_1 + x_2$, we have $Z_{LP} < Z_D = Z_{IP}$.

(c) For the objective function $-x_1 - x_2$, we have $Z_{LP} = Z_D = Z_{IP}$.

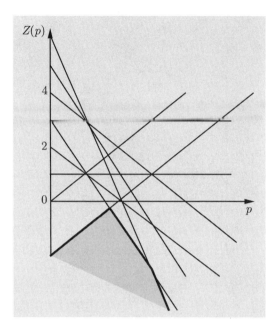

Figure 11.8: The function $Z(p)$. Each line is the plot of the function $3x_1 - x_2 + p(-1 - x_1 + x_2)$, where (x_1, x_2) is set to some particular element of X. The lower envelope of these lines is the function $Z(p)$. The maximum of $Z(p)$ is $-1/3$ and is attained for $p = 5/3$.

One can also construct an example, in which the relation $Z_{\text{LP}} = Z_{\text{D}} < Z_{\text{IP}}$ holds. In this example, however, such an ordering is not possible.

Using Theorem 11.4, we can make the following observations:

Corollary 11.1

(a) We have $Z_{\text{IP}} = Z_{\text{D}}$ for all cost vectors **c**, if and only if

$$\text{CH}\big(X \cap \{\mathbf{x} \mid \mathbf{Ax} \geq \mathbf{b}\}\big) = \text{CH}(X) \cap \{\mathbf{x} \mid \mathbf{Ax} \geq \mathbf{b}\}.$$

(b) We have $Z_{\text{LP}} = Z_{\text{D}}$ for all cost vectors **c**, if

$$\text{CH}(X) = \{\mathbf{x} \mid \mathbf{Dx} \geq \mathbf{d}\}.$$

It is interesting to observe that if the polyhedron $\{\mathbf{x} \mid \mathbf{Dx} \geq \mathbf{d}\}$, has integer extreme points, then $\text{CH}(X) = \{\mathbf{x} \mid \mathbf{Dx} \geq \mathbf{d}\}$, and therefore Z_{D} is equal to the optimal cost of the linear programming relaxation.

Example 11.10 (Improved bounds for the traveling salesman problem) The following set of constraints for the traveling salesman problem on an undirected graph $G = (\mathcal{N}, \mathcal{E})$, was introduced in Section 10.3:

$$\sum_{e \in \delta(\{i\})} x_e = 2, \qquad i \in \mathcal{N},$$

$$\sum_{e \in E(S)} x_e \le |S| - 1, \qquad S \subset \mathcal{N},\ S \ne \emptyset, \mathcal{N},$$

$$x_e \in \{0, 1\}.$$

[Recall that x_e indicates whether edge e participates in the tour. Also, $\delta(\{i\})$ is the set of edges incident to node i, and $E(S)$ is the set of edges with both endpoints in S.] We choose node 1 as a special node, called the root node, and add the redundant equality

$$\sum_{e \in E(\mathcal{N} \setminus \{1\})} x_e = |\mathcal{N}| - 2.$$

The formulation can be then written as follows.

$$\begin{array}{lll}
\text{minimize} & \displaystyle\sum_{e \in \mathcal{E}} c_e x_e & \\[2mm]
\text{subject to} & \displaystyle\sum_{e \in \delta(\{i\})} x_e = 2, & i \in \mathcal{N} \setminus \{1\}, \\[4mm]
& \displaystyle\sum_{e \in \delta(\{1\})} x_e = 2, & \\[4mm]
& \displaystyle\sum_{e \in E(S)} x_e \le |S| - 1, & S \subset \mathcal{N},\ S \ne \emptyset, \mathcal{N}, \\[4mm]
& \displaystyle\sum_{e \in E(\mathcal{N} \setminus \{1\})} x_e = |\mathcal{N}| - 2, & \\[4mm]
& x_e \in \{0, 1\}. &
\end{array}$$

Next, we apply the Lagrangean relaxation methodology to the above formulation, by dualizing the constraints

$$\sum_{e \in \delta(\{i\})} x_e = 2, \qquad i \in \mathcal{N} \setminus \{1\}. \tag{11.10}$$

The binary vectors satisfying all the constraints except for (11.10) constitute the set X. We define an 1-*tree* to be a tree involving all nodes in $\mathcal{N} \setminus \{1\}$, and two additional edges incident to node 1 (see Figure 11.9). It is not hard to show that X is the set of vectors that correspond to 1-trees. As a result, we can optimize over X efficiently, by using the greedy minimum spanning tree algorithm on $\mathcal{N} \setminus \{1\}$, and then adding the two smallest cost edges from node 1. Moreover, it is known that $\text{CH}(X)$ is the polyhedron described by all inequalities except (11.10), and where we replace the integrality constraints with $\mathbf{x} \ge \mathbf{0}$.

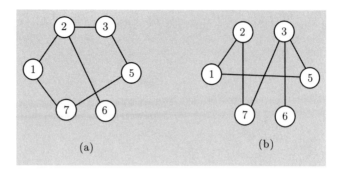

Figure 11.9: Two 1-trees.

We consider the linear programming relaxation of the original formulation, which is

$$\text{minimize} \quad \sum_{e \in \mathcal{E}} c_e x_e$$

$$\text{subject to} \quad \sum_{e \in \delta(\{i\})} x_e = 2, \qquad i \in \mathcal{N},$$

$$\sum_{e \in E(S)} x_e \leq |S| - 1, \quad S \subset \mathcal{N}, \ S \neq \emptyset, \mathcal{N},$$

$$x_e \geq 0.$$

Notice that the constraint $x_e \leq 1$ is implied by the subtour elimination constraints for $S = e = \{i, j\}$, and is therefore omitted.

By Corollary 11.1(b), $Z_D = Z_{LP}$. The optimal value Z_D of the Lagrangean dual is called the *Held-Karp lower bound*. As we mentioned, the calculation of $Z(\mathbf{p})$ for a fixed vector $\mathbf{p}$ can be done efficiently. This leads to an effective algorithm for computing the Held-Karp lower bound.

In general, the combination of branch and bound and Lagrangean relaxation yields some of the most effective methods for many classes of integer programming problems.

Solution of the Lagrangean dual

In this subsection, we outline a method for finding the optimal Lagrange multipliers $\mathbf{p}^*$, that solve the Lagrangean dual problem (11.7). To keep the presentation simple, we assume that X is finite and $X = \{\mathbf{x}^1, \ldots, \mathbf{x}^m\}$. Given a particular value of $\mathbf{p}$, we assume that we can calculate $Z(\mathbf{p})$, which we have defined as follows:

$$Z(\mathbf{p}) = \min_{i=1,\ldots,m} \ \left(\mathbf{c}'\mathbf{x}^i + \mathbf{p}'(\mathbf{b} - \mathbf{A}\mathbf{x}^i) \right).$$

Let $\mathbf{f}_i = \mathbf{b} - \mathbf{A}\mathbf{x}^i$ and $h_i = \mathbf{c}'\mathbf{x}^i$. Then,

$$Z(\mathbf{p}) = \min_{i=1,\ldots,m} \left(h_i + \mathbf{f}_i'\mathbf{p}\right),$$

which is piecewise linear and concave, as discussed earlier.

In order to motivate the following discussion, let us assume for the moment that the function $Z(\mathbf{p})$ is also differentiable. Then, the classical steepest ascent method for maximizing $Z(\mathbf{p})$ is given by the sequence of iterations

$$\mathbf{p}^{t+1} = \mathbf{p}^t + \theta_t \nabla Z(\mathbf{p}^t), \quad t = 1, 2, \ldots$$

In our case, the function $Z(\mathbf{p})$ is not differentiable and thus $\nabla Z(\mathbf{p}^t)$ does not always exist. For this reason, we need to generalize the notion of the gradient to nondifferentiable concave functions. The following alternative characterization of concave functions is helpful in this respect. The proof is based on the supporting hyperplane theorem, which is an extension of the separating hyperplane theorem, and is omitted; see Exercise 11.9.

Lemma 11.2 *A function $f : \Re^n \mapsto \Re$ is concave if and only if for any $\mathbf{x}^* \in \Re^n$, there exists a vector $\mathbf{s} \in \Re^n$ such that*

$$f(\mathbf{x}) \le f(\mathbf{x}^*) + \mathbf{s}'(\mathbf{x} - \mathbf{x}^*),$$

for all $\mathbf{x} \in \Re^n$.

The vectors $\mathbf{s}$ in Lemma 11.2 provide the required generalization.

Definition 11.1 *Let f be a concave function. A vector $\mathbf{s}$ such that*

$$f(\mathbf{x}) \le f(\mathbf{x}^*) + \mathbf{s}'(\mathbf{x} - \mathbf{x}^*),$$

*for all $\mathbf{x} \in \Re^n$, is called a **subgradient** of f at $\mathbf{x}^*$. The set of all subgradients of f at $\mathbf{x}^*$ is denoted by $\partial f(\mathbf{x}^*)$ and is called the **subdifferential** of f at $\mathbf{x}^*$.*

If the function f is differentiable at $\mathbf{x}^*$, then it can be verified that $\partial f(\mathbf{x}^*) = \{\nabla f(\mathbf{x}^*)\}$. If f is not differentiable, then Lemma 11.2 establishes that the subdifferential is nonempty at every point. Figure 11.10 shows an example of a subgradient. Definition 11.1 is the same as Definition 5.1 in Section 5.3, except that the direction of the inequality is reversed; the reason is that here we are dealing with concave as opposed to convex functions.

Note that the inequality $f(\mathbf{x}) \le f(\mathbf{x}^*)$ for all $\mathbf{x} \in \Re^n$, is equivalent to saying that $\mathbf{0}$ is a subgradient of f at $\mathbf{x}^*$. This observation is formally recorded in the following lemma, which establishes a necessary and sufficient condition for the maximum of a concave function.

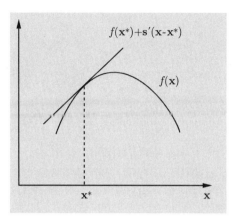

Figure 11.10: A concave function $f(\mathbf{x})$ and a subgradient $\mathbf{s}$ of f at $\mathbf{x}^*$. Note that $f(\mathbf{x}) \leq f(\mathbf{x}^*) + \mathbf{s}'(\mathbf{x} - \mathbf{x}^*)$.

Lemma 11.3 Let $f : \Re^n \mapsto \Re$ be a concave function. A vector $\mathbf{x}^*$ maximizes f over $\Re^n$ if and only if $\mathbf{0} \in \partial f(\mathbf{x}^*)$.

We next characterize exactly the subdifferential of a piecewise linear concave function; see Figure 11.11 for an illustration. The proof is based on Farkas' lemma and is omitted (Exercise 11.10).

Lemma 11.4 Let

$$Z(\mathbf{p}) = \min_{i=1,\ldots,m} \left(h_i + \mathbf{f}_i'\mathbf{p}\right),$$
$$E(\mathbf{p}) = \left\{i \mid Z(\mathbf{p}) = h_i + \mathbf{f}_i'\mathbf{p}\right\}.$$

Then:

(a) For every $i \in E(\mathbf{p}^*)$, $\mathbf{f}_i$ is a subgradient of the function $Z(\cdot)$ at $\mathbf{p}^*$.

(b) $\partial Z(\mathbf{p}^*) = \mathrm{CH}\left(\{\mathbf{f}_i, \ i \in E(\mathbf{p}^*)\}\right)$, i.e., a vector $\mathbf{s}$ is a subgradient of the function $Z(\cdot)$ at $\mathbf{p}^*$ if and only if $Z(\mathbf{p}^*)$ is a convex combination of the vectors $\mathbf{f}_i$, $i \in E(\mathbf{p}^*)$.

The following algorithm generalizes the steepest ascent algorithm and can be used to maximize a nondifferentiable concave function $Z(\cdot)$.

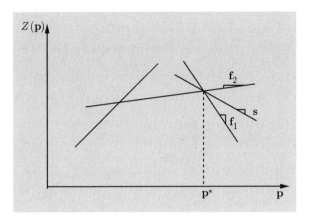

Figure 11.11: The subdifferential of $Z(\mathbf{p})$ at $\mathbf{p}^*$ is the set of all vectors that can be written as convex combinations of $\mathbf{f}_1$ and $\mathbf{f}_2$.

The subgradient optimization algorithm

1. Choose a starting point $\mathbf{p}^1$; let $t = 1$.

2. Given $\mathbf{p}^t$, choose a subgradient $\mathbf{s}^t$ of the function $Z(\cdot)$ at $\mathbf{p}^t$. If $\mathbf{s}^t = \mathbf{0}$, then $\mathbf{p}^t$ is optimal and the algorithm terminates. Else, continue.

3. Let $\mathbf{p}^{t+1} = \mathbf{p}^t + \theta_t \mathbf{s}^t$, where θ_t is a positive stepsize parameter. Increment t and go to Step 2.

We have characterized the subdifferential of a piecewise linear concave function in Lemma 11.4. Typically, however, only the extreme subgradients $\mathbf{f}_i$ are used.

We next specify the stepsize θ_t. It can be proved that $Z(\mathbf{p}^t)$ converges to the unconstrained maximum of $Z(\cdot)$, assuming it is finite, for any stepsize sequence θ_t such that

$$\sum_{t=1}^{\infty} \theta_t = \infty, \qquad \text{and} \qquad \lim_{t \to \infty} \theta_t = 0.$$

An example of such a sequence is $\theta_t = 1/t$. For practical purposes, however, this leads to slow convergence, and other choices for the stepsizes θ_t are often used. An example is

$$\theta_t = \theta_0 \alpha^t, \qquad t = 1, 2, \ldots,$$

where α is a scalar satisfying $0 < \alpha < 1$. A more sophisticated and popular rule is to let

$$\theta_t = \frac{\hat{Z}_D - Z(\mathbf{p}^t)}{\|\mathbf{s}^t\|^2} \alpha^t,$$

t	p^t	s^t	$Z(p^t)$
1	5.00	-3	-9.00
2	2.60	-3	-1.80
3	0.68	1	-1.32
4	1.19	1	-0.81
5	1.60	1	-0.40
6	1.92	-2	-0.84
7	1.40	1	-0.60
8	1.61	1	-0.39
9	1.78	-2	-0.56
10	1.51	1	-0.49

Table 11.1: An example of the subgradient optimization algorithm.

where α satisfies $0 < \alpha < 1$, and $\hat{Z}_D$ is an estimate of the optimal value Z_D. In practice, the stopping criterion $\mathbf{0} \in \partial Z(\mathbf{p}^t)$ is rarely met. Typically, the algorithm is stopped after a fixed number of iterations.

Notice that we are interested in maximizing $Z(\mathbf{p})$ subject to $\mathbf{p} \geq \mathbf{0}$. However, with the algorithm that we have presented, the property $\mathbf{p}^t \geq \mathbf{0}$ is not guaranteed to hold. In order to enforce this condition, we replace Step 3 of the subgradient optimization algorithm by

$$p_j^{t+1} = \max\left\{p_j^t + \theta_t s_j^t, 0\right\}, \qquad \forall j.$$

Example 11.11 We apply subgradient optimization to find Z_D in Example 11.8. In this case,

$$Z(p) = \min\left\{3 - 2p, \ 6 - 3p, \ 2 - p, \ 5 - 2p, \ -2 + p, \ 1, \ 4 - p, \ p, \ 3\right\},$$

corresponding to the points in the set

$$X = \left\{(1,0), (2,0), (1,1), (2,1), (0,2), (1,2), (2,2), (1,3), (2,3)\right\}.$$

We let $\theta_t = 0.8^t$. We start with $p^1 = 5$. Then, the minimum in the formula for $Z(p)$ is obtained for the piece $6 - 3p$ corresponding to $(2,0)$. The new Lagrange multiplier is $p^2 = 5 + 0.8(-3) = 2.6$. The results of the first ten iterations are reported in Table 11.1. The optimal solution is $p^* = 5/3 = 1.66$ and $Z_D = -1/3 = -0.33$. In ten iterations, the best value obtained was in iteration 8, with value -0.39. The example is typical of the behavior of the algorithm. It does not have monotonic convergence, and in order to find a near-optimal solution, several iterations are needed. Another factor at play is that by the tenth iteration, the stepsize has become quite small and the algorithm is losing the ability to make rapid progress.

11.5   Approximation algorithms

In this section, we introduce algorithms that provide a feasible, but suboptimal solution in polynomial time, together with a provable guarantee regarding its degree of suboptimality. We start with a definition.

Definition 11.2 *Algorithm* H *constitutes an* ϵ-**approximation** *algorithm for a minimization problem with optimal cost* Z^*, *if for each instance of the problem, algorithm* H *runs in polynomial time, and returns a feasible solution with cost* Z_{H}, *such that*

$$Z_{\mathrm{H}} \leq (1 + \epsilon)Z^*. \tag{11.11}$$

Symmetrically, for a maximization problem, we require

$$Z_{\mathrm{H}} \geq (1 - \epsilon)Z^*. \tag{11.12}$$

Given an optimization problem, a natural question is whether there exists an ϵ-approximation algorithm for every $\epsilon > 0$. For some problems, this is indeed the case, but there is no general methodology for coming up with such algorithms. An example is provided next.

An ϵ-approximation algorithm for the zero-one knapsack problem

Let us recall the zero-one knapsack problem:

$$\text{maximize} \quad \sum_{j=1}^{n} c_j x_j$$

$$\text{subject to} \quad \sum_{j=1}^{n} w_j x_j \leq K$$

$$x_j \in \{0, 1\}.$$

We have observed in Section 11.3, that the zero-one knapsack problem can be solved in time $O(n^2 c_{\max})$, and becomes polynomially solvable if $c_{\max} \leq n^d$. This motivates an algorithm in which the coefficients c_i are replaced by smaller values and which produces approximately optimal solutions to the original problem. The key idea is the following. Consider a problem in which $c_1 = 105$, $c_2 = 37$, $c_3 = 85$. We expect that the optimal cost does not change much if we consider a new problem with coefficients $\bar{c}_1 = 100$, $\bar{c}_2 = 30$, $\bar{c}_3 = 80$. But the latter problem is equivalent to one with coefficients $\hat{c}_1 = 10$, $\hat{c}_2 = 3$, $\hat{c}_3 = 8$, whose solution is faster by a factor of 10.

More generally, if $c_1, \ldots, c_n$ are the coefficients in the original instance of the problem, let us replace the t least significant digits of each c_i by zeroes. Let $\bar{c}_1, \ldots, \bar{c}_n$ be the resulting numbers. These numbers are integer multiples of 10^t and we can define an equivalent instance (called the *scaled instance*) with coefficients $\hat{c}_1, \ldots, \hat{c}_n$, where $\hat{c}_i = \bar{c}_i/10^t$. We observe that $c_j - 10^t \leq \bar{c}_j \leq c_j$, for all j.

Notice that the weight coefficients $w_1, \ldots, w_n$ have not been changed and the set of feasible solutions is the same for all three instances. Let S (respectively, S') be a set of items chosen by some optimal solution to the problem with coefficients $c_1, \ldots, c_n$ (respectively, $\bar{c}_1, \ldots, \bar{c}_n$). We then have

$$\sum_{j \in S} c_j \geq \sum_{j \in S'} c_j \geq \sum_{j \in S'} \bar{c}_j \geq \sum_{j \in S} \bar{c}_j \geq \sum_{j \in S}(c_j - 10^t) \geq \sum_{j \in S} c_j - n10^t.$$

The first inequality holds because the set S is optimal for the original instance. The second holds because $\bar{c}_j \leq c_j$ for all j. The third holds because the set S' is optimal for the modified instance. The fourth inequality holds because $\bar{c}_j \geq c_j - 10^t$. The last inequality holds because the cardinality of S is at most n.

The difference

$$\sum_{j \in S} c_j - \sum_{j \in S'} c_j$$

is the value $Z^* - Z_H$ lost if an optimal solution is replaced by an optimal solution to the scaled problem. We have shown that the value lost is bounded by $n10^t$. Assuming that $w_j \leq K$ for all j, any single element set is a feasible solution and this implies that $\sum_{j \in S} c_j \geq c_{\max}$. Putting everything together, we have

$$\frac{Z^* - Z_H}{Z^*} = \frac{\sum_{j \in S} c_j - \sum_{j \in S'} c_j}{\sum_{j \in S} c_j} \leq \frac{n10^t}{c_{\max}}. \tag{11.13}$$

The ratio in the left-hand side of Equation (11.13) is the fraction of the optimal value that is lost due to our solving a modified problem. Suppose that we wish this quantity to be bounded by some desired accuracy ϵ. We distinguish two cases:

(a) If $n/c_{\max} > \epsilon$, we solve the problem using the exact algorithm which takes $O(n^2 c_{\max}) = O(n^3/\epsilon)$ time. The approximation error in this case is zero.

(b) If $n/c_{\max} \leq \epsilon$, we find a nonnegative integer t such that

$$\frac{\epsilon}{10} < \frac{n10^t}{c_{\max}} \leq \epsilon,$$

and apply the exact algorithm to the scaled instance. Notice that

$$\hat{c}_{\max} = 10^{-t}\overline{c}_{\max} \leq 10^{-t}c_{\max} < 10n/\epsilon,$$

and the running time is $O(n^2\hat{c}_{\max}) = O(n^3/\epsilon)$. The approximation error is bounded by ϵ, as desired [cf. Eqs. (11.12) and (11.13)].

We summarize this discussion in the following theorem.

Theorem 11.5 *For every $\epsilon > 0$, there exists an ϵ-approximation algorithm for the zero-one knapsack problem that runs in time $O(n^3/\epsilon)$.*

Note that Theorem 11.5 refers to a family of algorithms, one algorithm for each choice of ϵ. For every fixed $\epsilon > 0$, we have a polynomial time algorithm, and we say that we have a *polynomial time approximation scheme*. From a theoretical point of view, given that we do not know of an exact polynomial algorithm for the problem, a polynomial time approximation scheme is rather powerful, as it allows to approximate the problem arbitrarily closely.

Notice, however, an important difference between the running time of some interior point methods for linear programming, and the running time of the approximation scheme for the zero-one knapsack problem. Focusing on the dependence on ϵ, the former require $O\big(\log(1/\epsilon)\big)$ time, while the latter requires $O(1/\epsilon)$ time. (The two are not fully comparable because ϵ in interior point methods is an absolute, not relative, error. Nevertheless the point we are to make is still pertinent.) In order to find an optimal solution to a linear programming problem within an accuracy of k significant digits, the required computation time grows linearly with k. For the knapsack problem, however, the same requirement on the relative accuracy requires computation time that grows exponentially with k.

Unfortunately, it is highly unlikely that all integer programming problems can be approximated arbitrarily closely. We give next an example of a problem that can be approximated within a finite accuracy, but for which an arbitrarily accurate approximation is unlikely to exist.

An approximation algorithm for the traveling salesman problem

We now discuss an example where we have an ϵ-approximation algorithm for $\epsilon = 1$, but for which ϵ-approximation algorithms are not known when ϵ is arbitrarily small.

We consider instances of the undirected traveling salesman problem, in which the costs c_{ij} satisfy the triangle inequality:

$$c_{ij} \leq c_{ik} + c_{kj}, \qquad \forall\, i, k, j.$$

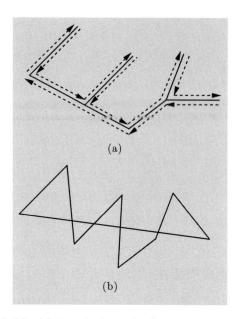

(a)

(b)

Figure 11.12: (a) A walk through all arcs of the spanning tree. (b) The resulting tour if we start with the leftmost node in (a).

Such costs arise, for example, when the c_{ij} correspond to distances between points in the Euclidean plane. We call this problem ΔTSP.

Consider the following algorithm for the ΔTSP. The first step is to find a minimum spanning tree. Let L be its cost. We then construct a walk that starts at some node, visits all nodes, returns to the original node, and never uses an arc outside the minimal spanning tree. It is not hard to see that such a walk can be constructed so as to traverse each arc of the spanning tree exactly twice; see Figure 11.12(a).

The total cost of this walk is $2L$. This walk can be converted into a tour by skipping any intermediate node that has already been visited. Because of the triangle inequality, the cost Z_{H} of this tour is bounded by $2L$. On the other hand, every tour contains a spanning tree (remove one of the arcs in the tour) and therefore, has cost at least L. We then have

$$Z_{\mathrm{H}} \leq 2L \leq 2Z^*,$$

and Eq. (11.11) holds with $\epsilon = 1$. Note that the triangle inequality was instrumental in deriving the inequality $Z_{\mathrm{H}} \leq 2L$.

For the general traveling salesman problem, in which the the distances c_{ij} do not satisfy the triangle inequality, it can be shown that if there exists an ϵ-approximation algorithm (even if ϵ is very large, say, $\epsilon = 1000$), then there exists an exact polynomial algorithm for the problem, a highly unlikely possibility.

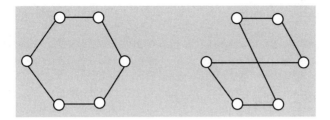

Figure 11.13: Two neighboring tours in 2OPT.

In general, it is not known what properties of integer programming problems allow approximation with an arbitrary ϵ, a fixed ϵ, or no approximation at all. This is an active research area.

11.6   Local search

Local search is a general approach to designing heuristics for an optimization problem

$$\text{minimize}\quad c(\mathbf{x})$$
$$\text{subject to}\quad \mathbf{x} \in F.$$

The main idea is to start at some $\mathbf{x} \in F$, evaluate $c(\mathbf{x})$, and then evaluate $c(\mathbf{y})$ for some $\mathbf{y} \in F$, which is a "neighbor" of $\mathbf{x}$. If a neighbor $\mathbf{y}$ with $c(\mathbf{y}) < c(\mathbf{x})$ is found, select $\mathbf{y}$ and repeat the same procedure. If no such neighbor is found, the process stops: a *local optimum* has been found, that is, a feasible solution which is at least as good as any of its neighbors.

The specifics of local search algorithms are determined once we specify what it means for two feasible solutions to be neighbors, and this is somewhat arbitrary. In the context of linear programming, we can say that two vertices are neighbors if they are connected by an edge of the constraint set (that is, if they are distinct and correspond to bases that differ in exactly one column). Under this definition of neighborhoods, the simplex method can be viewed as a local search method. While the simplex algorithm finds the globally optimal solution, local search methods only guarantee a locally optimal solution, in general.

Example 11.12 (Local Search for the traveling salesman problem) In the context of the undirected traveling salesman problem, let us say that two tours are neighbors if one can be obtained from the other by removing two edges and introducing two new edges. The resulting local search algorithm is known as 2OPT; see Figure 11.13. Note that each tour has $O(n^2)$ neighbors. Alternatively, we could say that two tours are neighbors if one can be obtained from the other by removing three edges and introducing three new edges; see Figure 11.14. The resulting local search algorithm is known as 3OPT. In 3OPT, each tour has $O(n^3)$ neighbors.

It has been found empirically that 3OPT works better than 2OPT. We could also consider the possibility of interchanging four edges at a time, but this has not been found to be advantageous. In terms of practical implementation, once $c(\mathbf{x})$ is computed and when we examine a neighboring tour $\mathbf{y}$, the value of $c(\mathbf{y})$ can be determined using only $O(1)$ arithmetic operations: take the value of $c(\mathbf{x})$, subtract the costs of the removed edges, and add the costs of the new edges.

A generic tradeoff that arises in local search methods is the following. When we consider larger neighborhoods, there are fewer local minima and a better solution is likely to be obtained when the algorithm terminates. On the other hand, the larger the neighborhood the more feasible solutions need to be examined at each iteration, and the algorithm is slowed down. As with the comparison of 2OPT and 3OPT, the proper selection of a neighborhood is often an empirical issue. Finally, when local search methods are used in practice, the algorithm is run repeatedly starting from a number of different initial feasible solutions.

11.7   Simulated annealing

The main drawback of local search algorithms is that they only obtain a local minimum. Simulated annealing is a generic method that attempts to improve upon local search algorithms by allowing occasional moves to feasible solutions with higher costs. We continue with a more detailed description. This discussion assumes basic knowledge of Markov chains.

We have a finite set of F of feasible solutions which we henceforth call *states*, and a cost function $c(\cdot)$ defined on F. Every state $\mathbf{x} \in F$ has a set $N(\mathbf{x}) \subset F$ of neighbors. We assume that the neighborhood relation is symmetric; that is, $\mathbf{y} \in N(\mathbf{x})$ if and only if $\mathbf{x} \in N(\mathbf{y})$. For a concrete example, suppose that each state $\mathbf{x}$ is a tour and $N(\mathbf{x})$ is the set of tours obtained from $\mathbf{x}$ by removing two edges and introducing two new edges.

Once at a certain state $\mathbf{x}$, we select at random a neighbor $\mathbf{y}$ of $\mathbf{x}$. Let $q_{\mathbf{xy}}$ be the probability that $\mathbf{y}$ is selected, given the current state $\mathbf{x}$. Naturally,

$$q_{\mathbf{xy}} \geq 0, \quad \text{and} \quad \sum_{\mathbf{y} \in N(\mathbf{x})} q_{\mathbf{xy}} = 1.$$

Once $\mathbf{y}$ is selected, we compute the difference $c(\mathbf{y}) - c(\mathbf{x})$. If $c(\mathbf{y}) \leq c(\mathbf{x})$, then we move to state $\mathbf{y}$. If $c(\mathbf{y}) > c(\mathbf{x})$, then we move to state $\mathbf{y}$ with probability

$$e^{-(c(\mathbf{y}) - c(\mathbf{x}))/T},$$

and stay in $\mathbf{x}$ otherwise. Here, T is a positive constant commonly called *temperature*, motivated by a certain physical analogy.

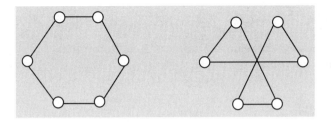

Figure 11.14: Two neighboring tours in 3OPT.

The temperature T controls the likelihood of cost increases: when T is small, cost increases are highly unlikely; when T is large, the value of $c(\mathbf{y}) - c(\mathbf{x})$ has an insignificant effect on the probability of any particular transition.

Let $\mathbf{x}(t)$ be the state of the algorithm after t iterations. Then, $\mathbf{x}(t)$ evolves as a Markov chain on the state space F, according to the following transition probabilities for $\mathbf{y} \in N(\mathbf{x})$:

$$p_{\mathbf{xy}} = \mathrm{P}\big(\mathbf{x}(t{+}1) = \mathbf{y} \mid \mathbf{x}(t) = \mathbf{x}\big) = \begin{cases} q_{\mathbf{xy}} e^{-(c(\mathbf{y})-c(\mathbf{x}))/T}, & \text{if } c(\mathbf{y}) > c(\mathbf{x}), \\ q_{\mathbf{xy}}, & \text{otherwise.} \end{cases}$$

The transition probability $p_{\mathbf{xx}}$ is of course equal to $1 - \sum_{\mathbf{y} \neq \mathbf{x}} p_{\mathbf{xy}}$.

Let

$$A = \sum_{\mathbf{z} \in F} e^{-c(\mathbf{z})/T}$$

and

$$\pi(\mathbf{x}) = \frac{e^{-c(\mathbf{x})/T}}{A}. \tag{11.14}$$

Then $\sum_{\mathbf{x} \in F} \pi(\mathbf{x}) = 1$ and $\pi(\mathbf{x}) \geq 0$ for all $\mathbf{x} \in F$. We next assume that the Markov chain $\mathbf{x}(t)$ is irreducible, i.e., we can move from any state $\mathbf{x}$ to any other state $\mathbf{y}$ after a finite number of transitions with positive probability.

Theorem 11.6 *Suppose that the Markov chain $\mathbf{x}(t)$ is irreducible and that $q_{\mathbf{xy}} = q_{\mathbf{yx}}$ for every $\mathbf{x}$ and every $\mathbf{y}$ in $N(\mathbf{x})$. Then, the vector with components $\pi(\mathbf{x})$, $\mathbf{x} \in F$, is the unique steady-state distribution of the Markov chain $\mathbf{x}(t)$.*

Proof. Consider some pair of neighboring states $\mathbf{x}$ and $\mathbf{y}$. Assume, without loss of generality, that $c(\mathbf{x}) < c(\mathbf{y})$. We then have

$$A\pi(\mathbf{y})p_{\mathbf{yx}} = e^{-c(\mathbf{y})/T} q_{\mathbf{yx}} = e^{-c(\mathbf{x})/T} e^{-(c(\mathbf{y})-c(\mathbf{x}))/T} q_{\mathbf{xy}} = A\pi(\mathbf{x})p_{\mathbf{xy}}.$$

We conclude that $\pi(\mathbf{y})p_{\mathbf{yx}} = \pi(\mathbf{x})p_{\mathbf{xy}}$ for all pairs of neighboring states. This equality is also trivially true if $\mathbf{x} \neq \mathbf{y}$ and $\mathbf{y} \notin N(\mathbf{x})$ (both sides are zero) or if $\mathbf{x} = \mathbf{y}$. We sum over all $\mathbf{x} \in F$ and use the fact $\sum_{\mathbf{x} \in F} p_{\mathbf{yx}} = 1$, to obtain

$$\pi(\mathbf{y}) = \sum_{\mathbf{x} \in F} \pi(\mathbf{x})p_{\mathbf{xy}}.$$

Using the definition of A, we also have

$$\sum_{\mathbf{x} \in F} \pi(\mathbf{x}) = 1.$$

But for an irreducible Markov chain, a vector $\pi(\mathbf{x})$, $\mathbf{x} \in F$, that satisfies the above conditions is the unique steady-state distribution. $\square$

If we let the algorithm run for a sufficiently long time, the probability that the state $\mathbf{x}(t)$ is equal to some particular $\mathbf{x}$ is approximately equal to the steady-state probability $\pi(\mathbf{x})$. Equation (11.14) shows that $\pi(\mathbf{x})$ falls exponentially with $c(\mathbf{x})$. In the limit of very small temperatures ($T \to 0$), almost all of the steady-state probability is concentrated on states at which $c(\mathbf{x})$ is minimized globally. We may therefore set T to some very small constant, and run the algorithm for a long time, until steady-state is reached. At that point, there is high probability that we are at an optimal state. A drawback of this idea is that the lower the value of T, the harder it is to escape from a local minimum and the longer it takes to reach steady-state. A compromise is obtained by letting the temperature vary with time according to a *temperature schedule* $T(t)$. In theoretical studies, schedules of the form

$$T(t) = \frac{C}{\log t}$$

are commonly considered. With such a schedule and if C is sufficiently large, it is known that

$$\lim_{t \to \infty} \mathrm{P}\big(\mathbf{x}(t) \text{ is optimal}\big) = 1,$$

i.e., the method converges to a globally optimal solution.

Despite being a general purpose method, simulated annealing has been found to work reasonably well for several difficult problems. This is more so for unstructured problems for which better alternatives are not apparent. On the other hand, for more structured and well studied problems like the traveling salesman problem, simulated annealing is usually inferior to finely tuned special purpose methods.

11.8   Complexity theory

We have presented in this chapter, a number of algorithms for integer programming. However, no polynomial time algorithm for this problem has been discovered, despite many efforts over the course of several decades. The same is true for many other discrete optimization problems, the traveling salesman problem being a prominent example. As more and more problems of this type emerged, it was realized that many such seemingly intractable problems were closely related. The root cause for their intractability was then sought in complexity theory. This is the theory that studies the resources (e.g., time and memory) needed to solve a computational problem. To a great extent, complexity theory focuses on the relation between different problems and looks at classes of problems that have comparable computational requirements (*complexity classes*). The prime example of an important complexity class is the class $\mathcal{P}$, defined as the set of all problems that can be solved by a polynomial time algorithm. (Throughout this section, all references to computation time assume a bit model of computation.)

In this section, we provide an overview of some complexity-theoretic concepts that are relevant to the subject of this book. We do not intend to be rigorous or comprehensive, but rather to convey some of the main ideas.

Problem reductions and transformations

Reductions are the basic tools used to relate one problem to another, and they permeate all of mathematics: the usual way of approaching a new problem is to try to reduce it to an older problem, that we already know how to solve. The concept of a reduction in complexity theory is similar, except that we need to pay close attention to computation time. In addition, one must be careful in keeping the distinction between problems and instances, that was discussed in Section 8.1.

Definition 11.3 *Suppose there exists an algorithm for some problem Π_1 that consists of a polynomial time computation in addition to a polynomial number of subroutine calls to an algorithm for problem Π_2. We then say that problem Π_1 **reduces** (in polynomial time) to problem Π_2.*

In the above definition, all references to polynomiality are with respect to the size of an instance of problem Π_1.

Our next definition deals with the simplest type of a reduction, where an instance of problem Π_1 is replaced by an "equivalent" instance of problem Π_2. Rather than developing a general definition of "equivalence," it is more convenient to focus on *recognition problems*, that is, problems that have a binary answer (e.g., YES or NO).

Definition 11.4 *Let* Π_1 *and* Π_2 *be two recognition problems. We say that problem* Π_1 **transforms** *to problem* Π_2 *(in polynomial time) if there exists a polynomial time algorithm which given an instance* I_1 *of problem* Π_1, *outputs an instance* I_2 *of* Π_2, *with the property that* I_1 *is a* YES *instance of* Π_1 *if and only if* I_2 *is a* YES *instance of* Π_2.

As already mentioned, the traditional use of reductions in mathematics is to show that a problem is "easy" by reducing it to another "easy" problem. In computational terms, this method is captured by the following result.

Theorem 11.7 *If problem* Π_1 *transforms or reduces to problem* Π_2 *in polynomial time, and if* $\Pi_2 \in \mathcal{P}$, *then* $\Pi_1 \in \mathcal{P}$.

Since we do not have a fully precise model of computation, we are not in a position to provide a rigorous proof. However, the main idea of the proof should be apparent: a polynomial number of subroutine calls, each of which takes polynomial time to execute, can be carried out in polynomial time.

There are two ways of interpreting a reduction of Π_1 to Π_2. The first is to say that Π_1 is "no harder" than Π_2, which is the traditional way reductions have been used in mathematics. The second is to say that Π_2 is "at least as hard" as Π_1, in the sense that if there existed a polynomial time algorithm for Π_2, then the same would be true for Π_1. Thus, if we have some evidence that $\Pi_1 \notin \mathcal{P}$, a reduction of Π_1 to Π_2 would provide equally strong evidence that $\Pi_2 \notin \mathcal{P}$.

Suppose now that problem Π_1 transforms to problem Π_2 and that problem Π_2 transforms to problem Π_3. Consider an instance I_1 of Π_1, of size n_1. The transformation to Π_2 produces an equivalent instance I_2 of Π_2, and requires polynomial time, say $O(n_1^k)$ for some k. Let n_2 be the size of I_2. Since I_2 must be constructed within the $O(n_1^k)$ time available for the transformation, we must have $n_2 = O(n_1^k)$. (We assume that our model of computation is such that an algorithm can output at most one bit at a time; this is the case for any reasonable bit model of computation.) The transformation of Π_2 to Π_3 produces an instance I_3 of Π_3, equivalent to I_3, and requires polynomial time, say $O(n_2^l)$, for some l. Note that this is also polynomial in n_1. We conclude that carrying out the two transformations in sequence results in a transformation of Π_1 to Π_3. This observation will be useful later.

Optimization, evaluation, and recognition problems

Consider a problem whose generic instance consists of a feasible set F and a cost function $c : F \mapsto \Re$. The corresponding *optimization* problem is to find some $\mathbf{x} \in F$ that minimizes $c(\mathbf{x})$ over the set F. We can also define an *evaluation* problem, which is the problem of computing $\min_{\mathbf{x} \in F} c(\mathbf{x})$. Finally, if we are also given a number L (as part of the instance), we can consider the so-called *recognition* problem, in which we need to decide whether $\min_{\mathbf{x} \in F} c(\mathbf{x})$ is less than or equal to L.

These three types of problems are closely related in terms of algorithmic difficulty, as will be discussed shortly. In particular, the difficulty of the recognition problem is usually a very good indicator of the difficulty of the corresponding evaluation and optimization problems. For this reason, we can focus, without much loss of generality, on recognition problems.

We now discuss the relation between the three variants. Let us assume that the cost $c(\mathbf{x})$ of any feasible solution $\mathbf{x} \in F$ can be computed in polynomial time. It is then clear that a polynomial time algorithm for the optimization problem leads to a polynomial time algorithm for the evaluation problem. (Once an optimal solution is found, use it to evaluate – in polynomial time – the optimal cost.) Similarly, a polynomial time for the evaluation problem immediately translates to a polynomial algorithm for the recognition problem. We will now argue that for many interesting problems, the converse is also true: namely, a polynomial time algorithm for the recognition problem often leads to polynomial time algorithms for the evaluation and optimization problems.

Suppose that the optimal cost is known to take one of M values. We can then perform binary search and solve the evaluation problem using $\lceil \log M \rceil$ calls to an algorithm for the recognition problem. If $\log M$ is bounded by a polynomial function of the instance size (which is often the case), and if the recognition algorithm runs in polynomial time, we obtain a polynomial time algorithm for the evaluation problem.

We now show how a polynomial time evaluation algorithm can lead to a polynomial time optimization algorithm. We illustrate this by using the zero-one integer programming problem (ZOIP) as an example. Given an instance I of ZOIP, let us consider a particular component of the vector $\mathbf{x}$ to be optimized, say x_1, and let us form a new instance I' by adding the constraint $x_1 = 0$. We run an evaluation algorithm on the instances I and I'. If the outcome is the same for both instances, we can set x_1 to zero without any loss of optimality. If the outcome is different, we conclude that x_1 should be set to 1. In either case, we have arrived at an instance involving one less variable to be optimized. Continuing the same way, fixing the value of one variable at a time, we obtain an optimization algorithm whose running time is roughly equal to the running time of the evaluation algorithm times the number of variables.

$\mathcal{NP}$-hard and $\mathcal{NP}$-complete problems

We now define a few key concepts in complexity theory. The definitions that we give are somewhat unconventional, but they are equivalent to those in more detailed treatments. Throughout this subsection, we are only concerned with recognition problems. For example, when we refer to ZOIP, we have in mind an instance of zero-one integer programming, together with an integer L, and the problem is to determine whether the optimal cost is less than or equal to L, in which case we say that we have a YES instance.

Our starting point is the fact that ZOIP seems to be a difficult problem, and a polynomial time algorithm is considered unlikely. Hence any problem which is "at least as hard" as ZOIP is also unlikely to be polynomial time solvable. The definition below refers to such problems.

Definition 11.5 *We say that a problem is $\mathcal{NP}$-hard if ZOIP can be transformed to it in polynomial time.*

A polynomial time algorithm for an $\mathcal{NP}$-hard problem would lead to a polynomial time algorithm for ZOIP, which is considered unlikely. For this reason, $\mathcal{NP}$-hardness is viewed as strong evidence that a problem is not polynomially solvable. There are many (literally, thousands) of discrete optimization problems that are known to be $\mathcal{NP}$-hard. Some examples from Chapter 10 are the recognition versions of the knapsack, facility location, set covering, set packing, set partitioning, sequencing with setup times, and traveling salesman problems.

Our next definition refers to problems that are "no harder" than ZOIP.

Definition 11.6 *We say that a problem belongs to $\mathcal{NP}$ if it can be transformed to ZOIP in polynomial time.*

It can be shown that the class $\mathcal{P}$ of polynomially solvable problems is contained in $\mathcal{NP}$. It is not known whether the inclusion is proper, and this is probably the most important open problem in the theory of computation. If it turns out that $\mathcal{P} = \mathcal{NP}$, then ZOIP and all other problems in $\mathcal{NP}$ can be solved in polynomial time. Conversely, if ZOIP belongs to $\mathcal{P}$, then every problem in $\mathcal{NP}$ also belongs to $\mathcal{P}$, since it can be transformed to ZOIP. We therefore have $\mathcal{P} = \mathcal{NP}$ if and only if ZOIP can be solved in polynomial time.

Our last definition refers to problems that are "exactly as hard" as ZOIP.

> **Definition 11.7** *We say that a problem* Π *is* $\mathcal{NP}$**-complete** *if it belongs to* $\mathcal{NP}$ *and is also* $\mathcal{NP}$*-hard; that is, if* Π *can be transformed to ZOIP and ZOIP can be transformed to* Π.

$\mathcal{NP}$-complete problems can be viewed as "the hardest problems in $\mathcal{NP}$." In a sense they are all equivalent: a polynomial time algorithm for any $\mathcal{NP}$-complete problem would translate to a polynomial time algorithm for all of them, and for all of $\mathcal{NP}$. See Figure 11.15 for an illustration of the definitions that we gave.

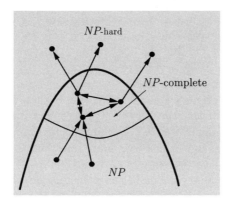

Figure 11.15: Illustration of the relation between $\mathcal{NP}$-hard, $\mathcal{NP}$-complete, and problems in $\mathcal{NP}$. Each dot stands for a different problem. An arc from one problem to another indicates that the first can be reduced to the second in polynomial time.

When does a problem belong to $\mathcal{NP}$?

Given a problem Π, one way of showing that the problem belongs to $\mathcal{NP}$ is to use the definition, that is, reduce the problem to ZOIP. This is the same as coming up with a formulation of our problem as a zero-one integer programming problem. In addition, the size of the formulation (i.e., the size of the instance I' of ZOIP resulting from an instance I of Π) should be bounded by a polynomial in the size of I. In particular, the number of variables and constraints should be bounded by a polynomial in the size of I.

While a ZOIP formulation is sometimes easy to obtain, this is not always the case. However, there is an alternative characterization of $\mathcal{NP}$, which is usually much easier to work with, and which we now discuss. We will not attempt to explain why this new characterization of $\mathcal{NP}$ is equivalent to Definition 11.6. This would require much more background in the theory of computation, and the reader is referred to the literature.

Loosely speaking, a recognition problem belongs to $\mathcal{NP}$ if every YES instance has a "certificate" of being a YES instance, whose validity can be checked in polynomial time. Instead of providing a formal definition of the terms that we have used, we explain them by means of simple examples.

Consider the recognition version of ZOIP whereby we ask whether the optimal cost is less than or equal to some L. Whenever we have a YES instance, any feasible solution $\mathbf{x}$ with cost less than or equal to L can serve as a certificate that we are indeed dealing with a YES instance. Verifying the validity of the certificate is simple: we first check that $\mathbf{x}$ is feasible, by plugging it into each one of the constraints, and we then compute its cost to make sure it is no more than L; all of this can be done in polynomial time. Note that we only require YES instances to have a certificate whose validity is efficiently verifiable. However, such a certificate need not be easy to find. For example, finding the above described certificate for ZOIP is as hard as solving the ZOIP problem.

As a second example, consider the recognition version of the traveling salesman problem where we ask whether the optimal cost is less than or equal to some L. In this case, a certificate of a YES instance is simply a tour whose cost is bounded by L. Checking the validity of such a certificate amounts to checking that it is a legitimate tour, and then adding the costs of its arcs to verify that the sum is no larger than L.

Notice that the argument in the preceding paragraph is much simpler than coming up with a ZOIP formulation of the traveling salesman problem (of polynomially bounded size). In the vast majority of cases, membership of a problem in $\mathcal{NP}$ is established along the lines discussed in this subsection.

Proving $\mathcal{NP}$-hardness

If we wish to prove that a certain problem Π is $\mathcal{NP}$-hard, we can try to use Definition 11.5, and transform ZOIP to Π. However, the task can become much easier by following the route suggested by the result below.

Theorem 11.8 *Suppose that a problem Π_0 is $\mathcal{NP}$-hard and that Π_0 can be transformed (in polynomial time) to another problem Π. Then, Π is $\mathcal{NP}$-hard.*

Theorem 11.8 is proved by transforming ZOIP to Π_0 (using the $\mathcal{NP}$-hardness of Π_0), and then transforming Π_0 to Π. This sequence of transformations amounts to a transformation of ZOIP to Π, and proves that Π is $\mathcal{NP}$-hard.

The usefulness of Theorem 11.8 comes because there is a large list of problems (in the thousands) that are known to be $\mathcal{NP}$-hard. Any one of these problems can play the role of Π_0, and this provides us with a lot of latitude when attempting to prove $\mathcal{NP}$-hardness of a given problem Π. The most common approach is as follows. Given a problem Π whose $\mathcal{NP}$-hardness we wish to establish, we search for a known $\mathcal{NP}$-hard problem Π_0 that appears to be closely related to Π. We then attempt to construct a transformation of Π_0 to Π. Coming up with such transformations is mostly an art, based on ingenuity and experience, and there are very few general guidelines.

We now provide an example where a transformation is relatively easy to construct. Suppose that we wish to establish $\mathcal{NP}$-hardness of the ΔTSP problem, that was discussed in Section 11.5. Here is a formal definition of the corresponding recognition problem.

ΔTSP: An instance consists of a complete undirected graph (all possible edges are present), a nonnegative integer cost $c_{ij} = c_{ji}$ for each edge $\{i, j\}$, and a nonnegative integer L. Furthermore, the edge costs are required to satisfy the triangle inequality

$$c_{ij} \le c_{ik} + c_{kj}, \qquad \forall\ i, j, k.$$

The question is whether there exists a tour (a cycle that visits all nodes) whose cost is no larger than L.

Instead of trying to directly transform ZOIP to this problem (which is difficult), we somehow discover that the following problem is known to be $\mathcal{NP}$-hard.

HAMILTON CIRCUIT: An instance consists of an undirected graph. The question is whether there exists a tour (a cycle that visits every node).

We now transform HAMILTON CIRCUIT to ΔTSP. Since HAMILTON CIRCUIT is $\mathcal{NP}$-hard, this will imply that ΔTSP is also $\mathcal{NP}$-hard. Given an instance $G = (\mathcal{N}, \mathcal{E})$ of HAMILTON CIRCUIT, with n nodes, we construct an instance of ΔTSP, again with n nodes, by defining the costs c_{ij} as follows:

$$c_{ij} = \begin{cases} 1, & \text{if } \{i, j\} \in \mathcal{E}, \\ 2, & \text{otherwise.} \end{cases}$$

We also let $L = n$. It is easily seen that these edge costs satisfy the triangle inequality, and we have a legitimate instance of ΔTSP. Furthermore, this transformation can be carried out in polynomial time [$O(n^2)$ time suffices]. If we have a YES instance of HAMILTON CIRCUIT, there exists a tour that uses the edges in $\mathcal{E}$. Since these edges are assigned unit cost, we obtain a tour of cost n, and we have a YES instance of ΔTSP. This argument can be reversed to show that if we have a YES instance of ΔTSP, then we also have a YES instance of HAMILTON CIRCUIT. This completes the proof. Note that this proof was very simple, but this is not the typical case.

What if a problem is $\mathcal{NP}$-hard?

We now discuss the practical implications of $\mathcal{NP}$-hardness. Suppose that we became interested in a problem arising in some real world application, and that we are unable to devise a polynomial time algorithm. Suppose then that we manage to prove that the problem is $\mathcal{NP}$-hard. What does this truly mean?

$\mathcal{NP}$-hardness is not a definite proof that no polynomial time algorithm exists. For all we know, it is always possible that ZOIP belongs to $\mathcal{P}$, and $\mathcal{P} = \mathcal{NP}$. Nevertheless, $\mathcal{NP}$-hardness suggests that we should stop searching for a polynomial time algorithm, unless we are willing to tackle the $\mathcal{P} = \mathcal{NP}$ question.

$\mathcal{NP}$-hardness can be viewed as a limitation on what can be accomplished with a given problem. However, this is very different from declaring the problem "intractable" and refraining from further work. Many $\mathcal{NP}$-hard problems are routinely solved in practice, using the whole gamut of methods that have been discussed in this chapter. Even when solutions are approximate, without any quality guarantees, the results are often good enough to be useful in a practical setting.

Another point that needs to be appreciated is that not all $\mathcal{NP}$-complete problems are equally hard. It is true that they are equivalent with respect to polynomial time transformations, but, in practical terms, their difficulty can vary a lot. For an example of an "easy" $\mathcal{NP}$-hard problem, let us consider the zero-one knapsack problem. We have seen that it can be solved in time $O(n^2 c_{\max})$. While this is exponential in the size $O\big(n(\log c_{\max} + \log w_{\max}) + \log K\big)$ of the input data, the running time may be acceptable for the range of values of $c_{\max}$ that arise in certain applications.

In the knapsack problem, $\mathcal{NP}$-hardness is only due to the possibility of large numerical input data. Other problems, however, remain $\mathcal{NP}$-hard even if the numerical data are restricted to take small values. Consider, for example, the ΔTSP problem, for the special case where the costs c_{ij} are either 1 or 2. The transformation we described in the preceding subsection shows that this special case is also $\mathcal{NP}$-hard. In a sense, the source of complexity in this problem is the combinatorial structure rather than the numerical data.

Problems can also differ in connection to approximability. Some problems, like the knapsack problem, admit arbitrarily accurate efficient approximation. For other problems, there seems to be a limit on the accuracy achievable by polynomial time algorithms. Finally, for some problems there are no ϵ-approximation algorithms, for any value of ϵ, unless $\mathcal{P} = \mathcal{NP}$. One can build a complexity theory that classifies problems in terms of their approximability properties, and this is an active research area.

11.9   Summary

In this chapter, we outlined several exact and inexact algorithms, as well as bounding methods for integer programming problems. There are many other methods that we did not cover, like genetic algorithms (a special type of local search methods motivated by biological analogies), tabu search, interior point algorithms for integer programming, as well as special purpose methods for particular problems.

Unfortunately, all existing algorithms have a disadvantage: either they take an exponential amount of time in the worst case, or they only give an approximate solution. Complexity theory offers some insight into these limitations by focusing on the class of $\mathcal{NP}$-complete problems. If any $\mathcal{NP}$-complete problem has a polynomial time algorithm, then $\mathcal{P} = \mathcal{NP}$. Deciding whether $\mathcal{P} = \mathcal{NP}$ is probably the most important open problem in the theory of computation.

11.10   Exercises

Exercise 11.1 Consider the integer programming problem:

$$
\begin{array}{rl}
\text{maximize} & x_1 + 2x_2 \\
\text{subject to} & -3x_1 + 4x_2 \leq 4 \\
& 3x_1 + 2x_2 \leq 11 \\
& 2x_1 - x_2 \leq 5 \\
& x_1, x_2 \geq 0 \\
& x_1, x_2 \text{ integer.}
\end{array}
$$

Use a figure to answer the following questions.

(a) What is the optimal cost of the linear programming relaxation? What is the optimal cost of the integer programming problem?

(b) What is the convex hull of the set of all solutions to the integer programming problem?

(c) Illustrate how the Gomory cutting plane algorithm would work. Give the first cut.

(d) Solve the problem by branch and bound. Solve the linear programming relaxations graphically.

(e) Suppose you dualize the constraint $-3x_1 + 4x_2 \leq 4$. What is the optimal value Z_D of the Lagrangean dual?

(f) Suppose you dualize the constraint $2x_1 - x_2 \leq 5$. What is the optimal value Z_D of the Lagrangean dual?

Exercise 11.2 The goal of this exercise is to compare the optimal costs of an integer programming problem and its linear programming relaxation. Consider the integer programming problem

$$
\begin{array}{rl}
\text{minimize} & \mathbf{c'x} \\
\text{subject to} & \mathbf{Ax} \geq \mathbf{b} \\
& \mathbf{x} \geq \mathbf{0} \\
& \mathbf{x} \text{ integer,}
\end{array}
$$

where the entries of $\mathbf{A}$, $\mathbf{b}$, and $\mathbf{c}$ are integer, and its linear programming relaxation

$$\begin{array}{ll} \text{minimize} & \mathbf{c}'\mathbf{x} \\ \text{subject to} & \mathbf{Ax} \geq \mathbf{b} \\ & \mathbf{x} \geq \mathbf{0}. \end{array}$$

(a) Assume that the integer programming problem is feasible. Show that if the linear programming relaxation has optimal cost equal to $-\infty$, then the integer programming problem has optimal cost $-\infty$ as well.

(b) Is it true that there always exists an $a > 0$, such that $Z_{\text{IP}} \leq aZ_{\text{LP}}$?

Exercise 11.3 (Cuts for mixed integer programming problems) Let

$$T = \left\{ (\mathbf{x}, \mathbf{y}) \; \middle| \; \sum_{j \in N} a_j x_j + \sum_{j \in J} d_j y_j \leq b, \; \mathbf{x} \text{ integer}, \; \mathbf{x}, \mathbf{y} \geq \mathbf{0} \right\},$$

where $N = \{1, \ldots, n\}$ and $J = \{1, \ldots, p\}$. Show that the inequality

$$\sum_{j \in N} \lfloor a_j \rfloor x_j + \frac{1}{1 - b + \lfloor b \rfloor} \sum_{j \in J^-} d_j y_j \leq \lfloor b \rfloor,$$

is satisfied by all points of T, where $J^- = \{j \in J \mid d_j < 0\}$. *Hint:* Consider separately the cases

$$\sum_{j \in J} d_j y_j > b - \lfloor b \rfloor - 1, \quad \text{and} \quad \sum_{j \in J} d_j y_j \leq b - \lfloor b \rfloor - 1.$$

Exercise 11.4 (Branch and bound can take exponential time) Consider the integer programming problem

$$\begin{array}{ll} \text{minimize} & x_{n+1} \\ \text{subject to} & 2x_1 + 2x_2 + \cdots + 2x_n + x_{n+1} = n \\ & x_i \in \{0, 1\}. \end{array}$$

Show that any branch and bound algorithm that uses linear programming relaxations to compute lower bounds, and branches by setting a fractional variable to either zero or one, will require the enumeration of an exponential number of subproblems when n is odd.

Exercise 11.5 (A dynamic single-item lot sizing problem) We consider the production process for a single product. For $t = 1, \ldots, T$, let d_t be the demand (assumed integer) for this product in period t, and let c_t, p_t, and h_t be the setup cost (incurred whenever production is nonzero), unit production cost, and unit storage cost per unit period, respectively. Propose a dynamic programming algorithm for the problem of minimizing the total setup, production, and storage cost, while satisfying the demand.

Exercise 11.6 (Typography) The pagination problem faced by a document processing program like TEX can be abstracted as follows. Text consists of a sequence $1, \ldots, n$ of n items (words, formulas, etc.). A page that starts with item i and ends with item j is assigned an attractiveness factor c_{ij}. Assuming that the factors c_{ij} are available, we wish to maximize the total attractiveness of the paginated text. Develop a dynamic programming algorithm for this problem.

Exercise 11.7 (DNA sequencing) Strands of DNA are modeled as a sequence of letters drawn from the alphabet $\{A, C, G, T\}$. Given two sequences of letters S_1 and S_2 of possibly different lengths, molecular biologists are interested in determining the degree of similarity between these sequences. A natural way to measure similarity is to determine the minimum effort required to transform the sequence S_1 to sequence S_2. Such a transformation may consist of the following operations:

(a) Insert an element in S_1, at any place in the sequence, at a cost of c_1 units.

(b) Delete an element in S_1, at any place in the sequence, at a cost of c_2 units.

(c) "Mutate" the jth element a_j of S_1 into the jth element b_j of S_2, at a cost of $c(a_j, b_j)$ units.

Propose a dynamic programming algorithm for the problem of finding a minimum cost transformation.

Exercise 11.8 Let $P = \{x \mid Dx \geq d\}$ be a nonempty unbounded polyhedron with at least one extreme point, and let

$$X = \big\{ x \text{ integer} \mid Dx \geq d \big\}.$$

We assume that D, d have integer entries. Let x^k, $k \in K$, be the extreme points, and w^j, $j \in J$, be a complete set of extreme rays of P.

(a) Show that the extreme rays of P can be chosen to have integer coordinates.

(b) Let

$$Q = \bigg\{ x \text{ integer} \ \bigg| \ x = \sum_{k \in K} \alpha_k x^k + \sum_{j \in J} \beta_j w^j,$$

$$\sum_{k \in K} \alpha_k = 1, \ \alpha_k \geq 0, \ k \in K,$$

$$0 \leq \beta_j \leq 1, \ j \in J \bigg\}.$$

Show that Q is a finite set and $Q \subset X$.

(c) Let q^l, $l \in L$, be the elements of Q. Show that

$$X = \bigg\{ x \ \bigg| \ x = q^l + \sum_{j \in J} \beta_j w^j, \text{ for some } l$$

$$\text{and some nonnegative integers } \beta_j \bigg\}.$$

(d) Show that $\mathrm{CH}(X)$ is a polyhedron and has the same extreme rays as P.

Exercise 11.9 * (Characterization of concave functions) Show that a function $f : \Re^n \mapsto \Re$ is concave if and only if for any $x^* \in \Re^n$ there exists an $s \in \Re^n$ such that

$$f(x) \leq f(x^*) + s'(x - x^*)$$

for all $x \in \Re^n$. *Hint:* Consider the set $S = \big\{ (x, t) \in \Re^{n+1} \mid f(x) \leq t \big\}$. Fix some x^*. Let t_k be a decreasing sequence that converges to $f(x^*)$. Consider a hyperplane that separates (x^*, t_k) from $\big(x^*, f(x^*)\big)$. Then take the limit as $k \to \infty$.

Exercise 11.10 (Characterization of subgradients) Let

$$Z(\mathbf{p}) = \min_{i=1,\dots,m} \left(h_i + \mathbf{f}_i' \mathbf{p} \right),$$
$$E(\mathbf{p}) = \left\{ i \mid Z(\mathbf{p}) = h_i + \mathbf{f}_i' \mathbf{p} \right\}.$$

Show that:

(a) For all $i \in E(\mathbf{p}^*)$, $\mathbf{f}_i$ is a subgradient of $Z(\cdot)$ at $\mathbf{p}^*$.

(b) $\partial Z(\mathbf{p}^*) = \mathrm{CH}\left(\{ \mathbf{f}_i, \ i \in E(\mathbf{p}^*) \} \right)$. *Hint:* Use Farkas' lemma.

Exercise 11.11 (Comparison of relaxations for the traveling salesman problem) Given an undirected graph $G = (\mathcal{N}, \mathcal{E})$, consider the following two formulations of the traveling salesman problem:

$$
\begin{aligned}
\text{minimize} \quad & \sum_{e \in \mathcal{E}} c_e x_e \\
\text{subject to} \quad & \sum_{e \in \delta(\{i\})} x_e = 2, \qquad \forall \, i \in \mathcal{N}, \\
& \sum_{e \in \delta(S)} x_e \geq 2, \qquad \forall \, S \neq \emptyset, \mathcal{N}, \\
& x_e \in \{0, 1\},
\end{aligned}
$$

$$
\begin{aligned}
\text{minimize} \quad & \sum_{e \in \mathcal{E}} c_e x_e \\
\text{subject to} \quad & \sum_{e \in \delta(\{i\})} x_e = 2, \qquad \forall \, i \in \mathcal{N}, \\
& \sum_{e \in E(S)} x_e \leq |S| - 1, \qquad \forall \, S \neq \emptyset, \mathcal{N}, \\
& x_e \in \{0, 1\}.
\end{aligned}
$$

Let Z_{IP} be the common optimal cost of the two formulations. Let Z_1, Z_2 be the optimal cost of the linear programming relaxation of the two formulations, respectively. Let Z_{D1}, Z_{D2} be the values of the Lagrangean duals if we relax the constraints $\sum_{e \in \delta(\{i\})} x_e = 2$ for all $i \neq 1$, in the two formulations. Let Z_{MST} be the cost of a minimum spanning tree with respect to the edge costs c_e. Order the values Z_1, Z_2, Z_{IP}, Z_{D1}, Z_{D2}, Z_{MST}. *Hint:* You can use the result of Exercise 10.14.

Exercise 11.12 (Comparison of relaxations for an assignment problem with a side constraint) We would like to assign n machines to n jobs in order to minimize the total cost of the assignment (it costs c_{ij} to assign machine i to job j). In addition, there is a value d_{ij} if machine i is assigned to job j. We would like the total value from the assignment to be above a threshold b. We formulate the problem as follows:

$$\text{minimize} \quad \sum_{i=1}^{n} \sum_{j=1}^{n} c_{ij} x_{ij}$$

$$\text{subject to} \quad \sum_{i=1}^{n} x_{ij} = 1, \qquad j = 1, \ldots, n,$$

$$\sum_{j=1}^{n} x_{ij} = 1, \qquad i = 1, \ldots, n,$$

$$\sum_{i=1}^{n} \sum_{j=1}^{n} d_{ij} x_{ij} \geq b,$$

$$x_{ij} \in \{0, 1\}.$$

We consider the following alternative relaxations:

(1) We relax the third constraint.

(2) We relax the first and second sets of constraints.

(3) We relax the first set of constraints.

(4) We relax the first set of constraints and the third constraint.

Let $Z_{\text{D}i}$ be the value of the corresponding Lagrangean dual problem, $i = 1, \ldots, 4$. Let Z_{LP} be the optimal cost of the linear programming relaxation. Prove that these relaxations are ordered as follows:

$$Z_{\text{LP}} = Z_{\text{D}1} = Z_{\text{D}4} \leq Z_{\text{D}2} \leq Z_{\text{D}3} \leq Z_{\text{IP}}.$$

Exercise 11.13 (Lagrangean decomposition) More powerful bounds can be obtained by introducing variables $\mathbf{y}$ in problem (11.5) as follows:

$$\text{minimize} \quad \mathbf{c}'\mathbf{x}$$

$$\text{subject to} \quad \mathbf{x} - \mathbf{y} = \mathbf{0}$$

$$\mathbf{A}\mathbf{x} \geq \mathbf{b}$$

$$\mathbf{D}\mathbf{y} \geq \mathbf{d}$$

$$\mathbf{x}, \mathbf{y} \text{ integer.}$$

By associating dual variables $\mathbf{p}$ with the constraints $\mathbf{x} - \mathbf{y} = \mathbf{0}$, we obtain the following problem:

$$\text{minimize} \quad (\mathbf{c} - \mathbf{p})'\mathbf{x} + \mathbf{p}'\mathbf{y}$$

$$\text{subject to} \quad \mathbf{A}\mathbf{x} \geq \mathbf{b}$$

$$\mathbf{D}\mathbf{y} \geq \mathbf{d}$$

$$\mathbf{x} \text{ integer}$$

$$\mathbf{y} \text{ integer.}$$

Let $Z_{\text{LD}}(\mathbf{p})$ be the optimal cost and let

$$Z_{\text{LD}} = \max_{\mathbf{p}} Z_{\text{LD}}(\mathbf{p}).$$

Let $X = \{\mathbf{x} \text{ integer} \mid \mathbf{Ax} \geq \mathbf{b}\}$ and $Y = \{\mathbf{y} \text{ integer} \mid \mathbf{Dy} \geq \mathbf{d}\}$. Show that the value Z_{LD} of the Lagrangean dual produced by the decomposition method is given by the optimal cost of the following linear programming problem:

$$\text{minimize} \quad \mathbf{c}'\mathbf{x}$$
$$\text{subject to} \quad \mathbf{x} \in \mathrm{CH}(X) \cap \mathrm{CH}(Y).$$

Exercise 11.14 (A 1/2-approximation algorithm for the ΔTSP) Consider the traveling salesman problem on the undirected graph $G = (\mathcal{N}, \mathcal{E})$, in which the costs c_{ij} satisfy the triangle inequality. Consider the following approximation algorithm H:

1. Find a minimum spanning tree in G. Let T be the set of edges in the tree.

2. Let S be the set of nodes that have odd degree in T. Find a minimum cost perfect matching of the nodes in S, with respect to the costs c_{ij}. (See Section 10.3 for the definition of the matching problem.) Let M be the set of edges in the matching.

3. Consider the graph $G' = (\mathcal{N}, T \cup M)$. All nodes have even degree in G'. Form a closed walk using all edges in G'. Shortcut the closed walk to form a tour.

Let Z_{H} be the cost of the solution obtained. Show that H is a 1/2-approximation algorithm, i.e.,

$$Z_{\mathrm{H}} \leq \frac{3}{2} Z_{\mathrm{IP}},$$

where Z_{IP} is the cost of an optimal tour.

Exercise 11.15* (The survivable network design problem) Given a complete undirected graph $G = (\mathcal{N}, \mathcal{E})$ (all possible arcs are present), there are costs c_e for every edge $e \in \mathcal{E}$, and requirements r_{ij} for every pair of nodes $i, j \in \mathcal{N}$. The objective is to select a set of edges from $\mathcal{E}$ (an edge can be selected more than once) at minimum cost, so that between every pair of nodes i and j there are at least r_{ij} paths that do not share any edges. The problem arises in the design of communication, utility, and transportation networks. By requiring that there are at least r_{ij} edge disjoint paths, the network has enough connectivity, so that even if some edges in the network become unavailable, nodes i and j could still be connected.

Consider the following formulation of the problem:

$$\text{minimize} \quad \sum_{e \in \mathcal{E}} c_e x_e$$
$$\text{subject to} \quad \sum_{e \in \delta(S)} x_e \geq \max_{\{i,j\} \in \delta(S)} r_{ij}, \qquad \forall\, S \neq \emptyset, \mathcal{N},$$
$$x_e \geq 0, \qquad\qquad\qquad \forall\, e \in \mathcal{E},$$
$$x_e \text{ integer}, \qquad\qquad \forall\, e \in \mathcal{E}.$$

(a) Propose a local search algorithm.

(b) Assume that $r_{ij} = \min(r_i, r_j)$ for all i, j. Let $\{\rho_1, \ldots, \rho_p\}$ be the set of distinct values of all the r_i's. We call the numbers ρ_i the connectivity types. Consider the following approximation algorithm.

In the kth iteration, construct a minimum cost tree spanning all vertices for which $r_i \geq k$. The resulting network is survivable since, at iteration k, we have at least one additional path from i to j if both r_i and r_j are greater than or equal to k. More formally, the tree heuristic can be described as follows:

Tree Heuristic

1.   Prepare a sorted list $L = \{\rho_0 = 0 < \rho_1 < \rho_2 < \cdots < \rho_p\}$ consisting of all distinct connectivity types.

2. $x_e := 0$;
     For $k = 1$ to p, do the following:
     Let $\mathcal{N}_k := \{i \in \mathcal{N} : r_i \geq \rho_k\}$;
     Compute $T_k = (\mathcal{N}_k, \mathcal{E}_k)$, a minimum spanning tree of the graph induced by $\mathcal{N}_k$ with respect to the edge costs c_e;
     Let $x_e := x_e + (\rho_k - \rho_{k-1})$ for all $e \in \mathcal{E}_k$.

Assume that the costs c_e satisfy the triangle inequality. Prove that

$$\frac{Z_{\text{tree}}(\mathbf{r})}{Z_{\text{LP}}} \leq \left(2 - \frac{2}{|\mathcal{N}_1|}\right) \left(\sum_{k=1}^{p} \frac{\rho_k - \rho_{k-1}}{\rho_k}\right),$$

where $Z_{\text{tree}}(\mathbf{r})$ denotes the cost of the solution produced by the tree heuristic, when the connectivity types are given by the vector $\mathbf{r} = (r_1, \ldots, r_n)$, and ρ_i and $\mathcal{N}_1$ are as defined in Steps 1 and 2 of the tree heuristic, and where Z_{LP} is the optimal cost of the linear programming relaxation.

Exercise 11.16 * (An approximation algorithm for maximum satisfiability) This exercise shows the use of randomization in constructing approximation algorithms for the following problem in logic called the maximum satisfiability problem (MAXSAT).

Given a collection $\mathcal{C} = \{C_1, \ldots C_m\}$ of boolean clauses, where each clause is a disjunction of literals (a literal is either a boolean variable x or its negation $\bar{x}$) from a set of variables $\{x_1, \ldots, x_n\}$, and positive weights w_i for each clause C_i, the goal in MAXSAT is to assign truth values to the variables $x_1, \ldots, x_n$ in order to maximize the sum of the weights of the satisfied clauses.

Let us formulate the problem. Let $y_i = 1$ if we set x_i true, and $y_i = 0$, otherwise; let $z_j = 1$ if clause C_j is satisfied. Let I_j^+, I_j^- be the set of literals that are not (respectively, are) negated in clause C_j. Then MAXSAT can be formulated as follows:

$$\text{maximize} \quad \sum_{j=1}^{m} w_j z_j$$

$$\text{subject to} \quad \sum_{i \in I_j^+} y_i + \sum_{i \in I_j^-} (1 - y_i) \geq z_j, \qquad C_j \in \mathcal{C},$$

$$y_i, z_j \in \{0, 1\}.$$

We denote the optimal cost by Z_{IP} and the optimal cost of the linear programming relaxation by Z_{LP}. Consider the following heuristic:

Randomized rounding heuristic

1. Solve the linear programming relaxation and find optimal values y_i^*, z_j^*.

2. Interpret the numbers y_i^* as probabilities. Set y_i to 0 or 1, randomly and independently, with probability

$$\mathrm{P}(y_i = 1) = y_i^*.$$

3. Set the values of z_j to 0 or 1, with preference given to 1, so that the resulting solution is feasible.

The resulting solution is always feasible, but its value is a random variable. Let Z_H be the value of the solution produced by the heuristic and let $E[Z_\mathrm{H}]$ be its expected value. Prove that

$$Z_\mathrm{LP} \geq Z_\mathrm{IP} \geq E[Z_\mathrm{H}] \geq \frac{e-1}{e} Z_\mathrm{LP},$$

where $e = 2.71...$ is the base of the natural logarithms.

Exercise 11.17 Implement the 2OPT algorithm for the traveling salesman problem, as well as the corresponding simulated annealing method. Test the algorithms on instances where each node is a random (uniformly distributed) point in the unit square in $\Re^2$, and c_{ij} is the Euclidean distance between the points associated with i and j. Test and compare the two algorithms for $n = 10$ and $n = 100$.

11.11   Notes and sources

11.1 The first finitely terminating algorithm for integer programming was the cutting plane algorithm by Gomory (1958). For recent work on cutting plane methods see Ceria et al. (1995), and Balas, Ceria, Cornuéjols, and Natraj (1995). There are many other cutting plane algorithms proposed in the literature; see e.g., Schrijver (1986).

11.2 For a comprehensive description of branch and bound, see Nemhauser and Wolsey (1988). A general branch and cut algorithm for mixed ZOIP is proposed in Balas, Ceria, and Cornuéjols (1995).

11.3 The dynamic programming algorithm for the traveling salesman problem is from Held and Karp (1962). For further information about dynamic programming, see Bertsekas (1995a).

11.4 The Lagrangean relaxation method was developed by Held and Karp (1970, 1971) for the traveling salesman problem. There is a large number of applications using this technique [see e.g., Nemhauser and Wolsey (1988)]. A discussion of subgradient methods and their convergence can be found in Poljak (1987) and Bertsekas (1995b).

11.5 The ϵ-approximation algorithm for the knapsack problem is from Ibarra and Kim (1975). For recent developments in the area of approximation algorithms, see the Ph.D. theses of Williamson (1994) and Teo (1996), and the edited volume by Hochbaum (1996).

11.7 The simulated annealing method was used in discrete optimization problems by Kirkpatrick, Gelatt, and Vecchi (1983). Convergence results for simulated annealing have been obtained by Geman and Geman (1984), and have been refined by Hajek (1988). For computational experience with the simulated annealing algorithm, see Johnson et al. (1990, 1992).

11.9 Concepts related to $\mathcal{P}$ and $\mathcal{NP}$ have been discussed by Cobham (1965) and Edmonds (1965a). In particular, Edmonds made the conjecture that the traveling salesman problem does not belong to $\mathcal{P}$. Cook (1971) and Levin (1973) first established that certain problems are $\mathcal{NP}$-complete. Karp (1972) showed that several important discrete optimization problems are $\mathcal{NP}$-complete. For a comprehensive reference on complexity theory, see the books by Garey and Johnson (1979), and by Papadimitriou (1994).

11.10 Exercises 11.6 and 11.7 are adapted from Ahuja, Magnanti and Orlin (1993). Exercise 11.14 is from Christofides (1975). Exercise 11.15 is from Goemans and Bertsimas (1993). Exercise 11.16 is from Goemans and Williamson (1993).

Chapter 12

The art in linear optimization

Contents

In previous chapters, we developed the theory of linear optimization. In this chapter, we turn our attention to the art in linear optimization, i.e., to the process of modeling, exploiting problem structure, and fine tuning of optimization algorithms.

In recent years, the availability of workstations and optimization libraries has advanced optimization capabilities significantly. Large scale linear optimization problems arising in practice involve thousands (sometimes millions) of variables and constraints. Therefore, these constraints must be described efficiently. Towards this goal, special modeling languages have been developed. We briefly discuss modeling languages in Section 12.1. In Section 12.2, we mention some powerful linear optimization libraries, with particular emphasis on the size of the problems they can solve. We also make some general observations on the relative merits of different methods.

Especially for large scale problems, it is important to utilize their special structure in order to solve them efficiently. Although there are some general approaches (cf. Chapter 6), solving large scale problems involves imaginative modeling as well as creative use of optimization libraries. In Section 12.3, we illustrate the art in using optimization algorithms, in the context of the fleet assignment problem, a large scale integer programming problem in air transportation. In Section 12.4, we illustrate the art in modeling linear optimization problems, in the context of controlling air traffic in a network of airports. In Section 12.5, we illustrate the art of combining formulations, optimization algorithms, and heuristics, in the context of job shop scheduling.

12.1 Modeling languages for linear optimization

Most realistic problems involve a large number of variables and constraints. As a result, it would be cumbersome to form a linear optimization problem such as

$$
\begin{aligned}
\text{minimize} \quad & \mathbf{c'x} \\
\text{subject to} \quad & \mathbf{Ax} = \mathbf{b} \\
& \mathbf{x} \geq \mathbf{0} \\
& \mathbf{x} \text{ integer,}
\end{aligned}
$$

by entering the entries of $\mathbf{A}$, $\mathbf{b}$, and $\mathbf{c}$ one at a time. Practical linear optimization problems, however, involve classes of constraints that follow a particular pattern. For example, in the assignment problem, one set of constraints can be described compactly as

$$
\sum_{i=1}^{n} x_{ij} = 1, \qquad j = 1, \ldots, n.
$$

Modeling languages are software packages that recognize compact descriptions of formulations and output the matrix $\mathbf{A}$ and the vectors $\mathbf{b}, \mathbf{c}$.

Although conceptually simple, these programs are very useful as they significantly cut the time from model conception to actual solution. Modeling languages are then connected with particular solvers that on input $\mathbf{A}, \mathbf{b}, \mathbf{c}$, output an optimal solution to the problem. Two particular modeling languages are GAMS and AMPLE.

Example 12.1 If $n = 100$, the previous family of constraints for the assignment problem can be written in GAMS as:
SET

     I /1 ∗ 100/
     J /1 ∗ 100/
VARIABLES
     $X(I, J)$;
EQUATIONS
     Constraint(J);
     Constraint$(J) \ldots SUM(I, X(I, J)) = E = 1$

12.2 Linear optimization libraries and general observations

There are over 200 different commercial linear optimization libraries in the marketplace. These libraries vary by their degree of flexibility, user-friendliness, ability to handle large problems, platforms, support, etc. We mention three of them that have been used to solve large scale linear optimization problems. Our choice of libraries is only for illustration and does not imply that they are better than others.

(a) OSL, which is an optimization subroutine library from IBM; its linear programming code is an implementation of the simplex method. It also includes a branch and bound algorithm for integer programming.

(b) OB1, which is an implementation of interior point methods (variations of the path following methods discussed in Sections 9.4 and 9.5).

(c) CPLEX, which contains implementations of the simplex method, interior point algorithms, and a branch and bound algorithm for integer programming.

These software packages run on a wide variety of computational environments (PCs, workstations, mainframes, supercomputers). In order to give some insight into the size of problems these codes can solve, we report in Table 12.1 examples of the performance of these software packages that have been reported in the literature (all examples are linear programming problems). The reason for presenting these examples, which involve very different problems, is to only offer a rough indication of the size of problems that have been successfully solved in practice. However, the reader should be warned that the running times of the same package on different problems of the same size could be vastly different.

Code	Constraints	Variables	Time	Computer
OSL	105,000	155,000	240 mins	IBM 3090
OSL	750	12,000,000	27 mins	IBM 3090
OB1	10,000	233,000	12 mins	IBM 3090
CPLEX	145	1,000,000	6 mins	Cray Y-MP
CPLEX	41,000	79,000	3 mins	Cray 2

Table 12.1: Sample performance of various linear programming codes.

Some key problem parameters that affect performance are the number of constraints and the sparsity of the constraint matrix $\mathbf{A}$. The running times are also significantly affected by implementation issues like the numerical linear algebra techniques used, the data structures employed, how sparsity is exploited, etc.

We now present some general, mostly empirical, guidelines regarding the performance of various algorithms:

(a) The a priori availability of a basis greatly affects the performance of the simplex method. If we can start with a basis, significantly fewer iterations may be required, particularly if a problem is similar to a previously solved one. Even if the problem is significantly different, using an advanced basis might help. For example, if we are combining several smaller models into a larger one, using an optimal basis from one of the smaller problems can help the solution to the larger problem greatly.

(b) Many linear programming problems solve faster using the dual simplex method rather than primal simplex. In particular, highly degenerate problems with little variability in the right-hand side coefficients, but significant variability in the cost coefficients, solve much faster using the dual simplex method.

(c) If a linear programming problem has some portion with a network structure, the network simplex method can be often used to obtain quickly a good initial basis for the larger problem.

(d) Certain large, sparse problems solve faster using interior point methods. Examples include problems with over 1000 rows or columns, containing a relatively small number of nonzeros per column, and problems with staircase or banded structures in the constraint matrix. In general, the performance of interior point methods is highly dependent on the number of nonzeros in the Cholesky factors, and is also affected by the presence of columns with a relatively high number of nonzero entries.

Simplex and interior point methods have different numerical properties, sensitivities, and behavior. We next discuss some of their major differences:

(a) Solutions provided by the simplex method are always basic, whereas optimal solutions found by an interior point algorithm are not necessarily basic. In the case of multiple optimal solutions, interior point algorithms find a solution in the interior of the set of optimal solutions. Therefore, when an interior point algorithm is used alone, we do not obtain a basis that can be used for reoptimization. In practice, it is rare that one wants to solve only one instance of an optimization problem. Typically, one would like to solve a series of instances of a problem that are small variations of each other. In that case, the simplex method has an advantage compared with an interior point algorithm. Also, since an interior point solution is not basic, there is no information available for sensitivity analysis. A common solution technique for large scale, sparse problems is to use an interior point algorithm to find an optimal solution, convert it to an optimal basic feasible solution, and then use the simplex method for sensitivity analysis and reoptimization.

(b) Interior point algorithms are sensitive to the presence of an unbounded set of optimal solutions, whereas the simplex method is not. On the other hand, the simplex method is sensitive to the presence of degeneracy, whereas interior point algorithms are less so.

(c) Simplex and interior point methods have different memory requirements. Interior point algorithms can require significantly more memory than the simplex method, depending on the sparsity of the Cholesky factors.

We revisit most of these issues in the next sections.

12.3   The fleet assignment problem

In this section, we illustrate the art in using optimization algorithms, in the context of the fleet assignment problem, a large scale integer programming problem in air transportation. Given a flight schedule and a set of aircraft of different types, the fleet assignment problem faced by an airline is to determine which type of aircraft should fly each flight segment on the airline's daily (or weekly) schedule. These strategic decisions have a major impact on revenue. For this reason, many airlines around the world have devoted a lot of resources to solving this problem. We describe some re-

lated research that offers general insights into many of the issues we have
introduced throughout the book.

We use the following notation. There is a set of available fleets, i.e.,
aircraft types, denoted by $\mathcal{F}$. The number of aircraft available in fleet $f \in \mathcal{F}$
is denoted by $S(f)$. There is also a given schedule. The set of cities served
by the schedule is denoted by $\mathcal{C}$. The set of flights in the schedule is denoted
by $\mathcal{L}$, with elements (o, d, t), where $o, d \in \mathcal{C}$ represent the origin and the
destination of the flight, respectively, and t represents time of scheduled
departure. There are costs c_{fodt} for assigning an aircraft from fleet f to the
flight (o, d, t). We pick a particular reference time t_0 (for example 3 a.m.
eastern standard time). Time is partitioned into intervals of equal size.
We have a sequence of times $t_1, \ldots, t_n$, and we assume that arrivals and
departures only happen at these discrete instances. We use t^- to denote
the time preceding t, and t^+, to denote the following time. We let $t(f, o, d)$
be the time fleet f takes to travel from the origin o to the destination d.
We let $O(t_0)$ be the set of all flights $(o, d, t) \in \mathcal{L}$ that are flying during the
interval $[t_0, t_0^+]$, which we assume to be fixed ahead of time. There is also
a set $\mathcal{H}$ of pairs of flights that must be performed by an aircraft of the
same fleet. These flights are called "required through." In the following
discussion, we will ignore issues related to maintenance and crew planning,
so that we can focus on the most important issues.

The objective is to assign an aircraft from some fleet f to each flight
(o, d, t) so as to minimize the total cost. For every $f \in \mathcal{F}$ and $(o, d, t) \in \mathcal{L}$,
we introduce the following decision variables:

$$
x_{fodt} = \begin{cases} 1, & \text{if fleet } f \text{ is used for the flight from } o \text{ to } d \\ & \quad \text{departing at time } t, \\ 0, & \text{otherwise,} \end{cases}
$$

y_{fot} = number of aircraft on the ground from fleet f that stay
    at city o during the interval $[t, t^+]$,

z_{fot} = number of aircraft from fleet f that arrive
    at city o at time t.

The variables z_{fot} and x_{fodt} are related as follows:

$$
z_{fot} = \sum_{\{(d,o,\tau) \in \mathcal{L} \mid \tau + t(f,d,o) = t\}} x_{fdo\tau}.
$$

The model can be formulated as an integer programming problem:

$$
\text{minimize} \quad \sum_{f \in \mathcal{F}} \sum_{(o,d,t) \in \mathcal{L}} c_{fodt} x_{fodt}
$$

subject to the constraints

$$\sum_{f \in \mathcal{F}} x_{fodt} = 1, \qquad \forall \, (o,d,t) \in \mathcal{L},$$

$$z_{fot} + y_{fot^-} - \sum_{d \in \mathcal{C}} x_{fodt} - y_{fot} = 0, \qquad \forall \, f, o, t,$$

$$x_{fodt} - x_{fdd't'} = 0, \qquad \forall \, f \in \mathcal{F},$$
$$\forall \, ((o,d,t),(d,d',t')) \in \mathcal{H},$$

$$\sum_{(o,d,t) \in O(t_0)} x_{fodt} + \sum_{o \in \mathcal{C}} y_{fot_0} \leq S(f), \quad \forall \, f \in \mathcal{F},$$

$$x_{fodt} \in \{0,1\},$$
$$y_{fot} \geq 0,$$
$$y_{fot} \text{ integer.}$$

The first set of constraints requires that each flight should be flown by exactly one fleet. The second set of constraints represents conservation of flow of aircraft. The third set of constraints enforces that an aircraft of the same type flies both legs of "required through" flights. The fourth set of constraints requires that the total number of aircraft in fleet f that are either flying or are on the ground at the reference time t_0 is at most $S(f)$. Because of flow conservation, if this set of constraints is satisfied for one time period, it will be satisfied for all time periods.

We consider three problem instances. The first is a hypothetical smaller instance that is used to test various algorithmic ideas, while the other two are real instances faced by Delta airlines in their daily schedules. We first discuss the solution to the linear programming relaxation. The sizes are reported in Table 12.2.

Inst.	Fleets	Flights	Var.	Rows	Col.	Nonzeros
A	4	1709	6236	13689	17148	42371
B	11	2559	22679	47994	65254	159064
C	11	2589	22746	48109	65164	163472

Table 12.2: Problem sizes for fleet assignment instances. The last column indicates the number of nonzero elements of the constraint matrix **A**.

The effect of preprocessing

Several optimization codes have an algebraic preprocessing option that reduces the size of the problem by eliminating variables whose values are fixed by other variables. For example, a constraint $y = \sum_i a_i x_i$, allows y to be removed from the problem, along with this constraint. Preprocessing can also identify empty rows or columns, and can eliminate redundant rows. The effect of preprocessing in instance A is shown in Table 12.3. The table also reports solution times for the linear programming relaxation of the problem on an IBM RS/6000 Model 320, using OSL Release 2 with primal simplex. It can be seen that preprocessing can dramatically decrease the size of the problem and the computation time, which decreases by a factor of four.

Instance A	Rows	Columns	Iterations	CPU seconds
no prepr.	13689	17148	39429	10094
prepr.	5579	9508	18975	2381

Table 12.3: Preprocessing can dramatically decrease the size and the computation times.

Which simplex algorithm?

As we have seen in earlier chapters, one can use either the primal or the dual simplex algorithm, as well as different pivoting rules to solve linear programming problems. We next illustrate that the use of different simplex variants can have a significant impact on the computation times. In Table 12.4, we report computational results for instances B and C, using three simplex variants, known as:

(a) The primal devex simplex.

(b) The primal steepest edge simplex.

(c) The dual steepest edge simplex.

The computations were performed on an IBM RS/6000 Model 550, using OSL. While the two primal simplex variants are very close, the dual steepest edge simplex algorithm takes approximately half as many iterations and half the time.

Simplex versus interior point methods

The results of Chapter 9 suggest that interior point algorithms take a significantly smaller number of iterations to find an optimal solution. In Table

Simplex variant	Iterations Inst. B	Time Inst. B	Iterations Inst. C	Time Inst. C
Primal Devex	33101	3257.5	29463	2779.9
Primal SE	32097	3194.5	32811	3199.1
Dual SE	15408	1431.8	14954	1461.5

Table 12.4: The effect of different pivoting rules for different simplex variants. The time is in CPU seconds.

12.5, we report computational results for all instances using OSL's interior point code, which is a variant of the path following method covered in Sections 9.4 and 9.5.

The number of iterations of the interior point algorithm is significantly smaller than the number of iterations of any simplex variant. While the computation time is smaller than that of the primal simplex variants, the dual steepest edge simplex is still faster than the interior point method. However, this conclusion might depend on the structure of the particular instances.

Instance	Iterations	Time
A	32	213.3
B	38	2141.8
C	39	2205.2

Table 12.5: The performance of interior point methods.

Avoiding degeneracy through perturbation

The fleet assignment problem is vastly primal and dual degenerate. In order to improve performance, we can randomly perturb the cost vector. This reduces the degree of dual degeneracy and improves the performance of the dual simplex algorithm. The performance of the interior point algorithm is generally not affected.

The crossover problem

Due to dual degeneracy, and when the cost vector was not perturbed, the problem had many optimal solutions. The interior point algorithm did not converge to a basic feasible solution, but rather to an interior point of the set of optimal solutions to the linear programming relaxation. For problems of this type, it has been observed that an optimal basic feasible solution has many variables equal to either zero or one. Thus, if we could extract a basic feasible solution, we would have made progress towards an integer solution. For this reason, it is desirable to extract an optimal basic feasible solution from the optimal interior solution, which is known as the *crossover problem*.

Because OSL allows its simplex algorithm to begin with a nonbasic solution, the code does solve the crossover problem. The interior point algorithm needed 32 iterations and 213.3 CPU seconds to solve instance A. The crossover problem was solved by OSL's primal simplex method in 5873 iterations and 284 seconds. In this example, the time to solve the crossover problem exceeded the time to solve the original problem by an interior point method, but this may not hold in general.

Given that we are interested in an integer solution, the following rounding scheme was used. If a variable is larger than 0.99, it is fixed to 1. If we first fix these variables, then use the preprocessing routines to fix other variables and remove redundant rows, and finally use the crossover routines, the crossover time goes down from 284 seconds to an astonishingly fast 2.2 seconds.

The effect of heuristics in branch and bound

After finding an optimal basic feasible solution to the linear programming relaxation and fixing to 1 the variables that were at least 0.99, we still need to find an integer solution for the remaining variables. For this purpose, the branch and bound routine of OSL was used. One could use the default branching strategies provided by the package or develop specialized branching rules. Table 12.6 compares the default option and two heuristic branching rules. It can be seen that different branching rules that exploit the structure of the problem can significantly affect performance.

Overall performance

The overall algorithms, using the dual steepest edge (respectively, the path following) algorithm, are as follows:

(1) Use optimizer's preprocessing.

(2) Perturb all costs.

(3) Run the dual steepest edge simplex (respectively, the path following) method.

(4) Remove perturbation.

(5) Reoptimize with original cost.

(6) Fix variables with value at least 0.99, to 1.

Rule	Nodes in B&B Inst. B	Time Inst. B	Nodes in B&B Inst. C	Time Inst. C
D	2000+	6743.3	499	809.3
R_1	46	258.9	141	703.2
R_2	96	591.2	60	249.3

Table 12.6: The effect of various branching rules in the branch and bound code. Rule D refers to the default option, while R_1 and R_2 refer to two branching rules that are particular to the fleet assignment problem. The time reported here is the time spent for branch and bound, after obtaining an optimal basic feasible solution to the linear programming relaxation.

(7) Use optimizer's preprocessing to further reduce the size.

(8) Run the dual steepest edge simplex method.

(9) Branch and bound.

Notice that in both cases, we use the simplex method to reoptimize. As a general rule, the simplex method has a clear advantage whenever we start with near optimal solutions.

Tables 12.7 and 12.8 illustrate the performance of the overall algorithm using the dual simplex method and the interior point algorithm, respectively. Notice that the degree of suboptimality, defined as $(Z - Z_{\mathrm{LP}})/Z_{\mathrm{LP}}$, where Z is the cost of the integer solution found, and Z_{LP} is the cost of the linear programming relaxation, is extremely small regardless of the method of solution, and the computational times are quite reasonable. In Tables 12.7 and 12.8, the column % IP-LP represents $100 \times (Z - Z_{\mathrm{LP}})/Z_{\mathrm{LP}}$.

Inst.	Iterations Dual SE	Time Dual SE	Time in B&B	% IP-LP	Total Time
B	15351	1501.8	3360.8	0.020	5027.9
C	14177	1376.0	636.5	0.012	2176.3

Table 12.7: The performance of the overall algorithm, using the dual steepest edge simplex method.

This example offers several insights that seem to have wide applicability. We summarize them next:

Inst.	Time of Interior	Time of Simplex	Time in B&B	% IP-LP	Total Time
B	2141.8	15.33	258.9	0.013	2551.6
C	2205.2	27.11	703.2	0.012	3069.4

Table 12.8: The performance of the overall algorithm based on the interior point algorithm.

(a) Preprocessing can significantly decrease the size of a model and, therefore, drastically improve performance.

(b) Different simplex variants have quite different behavior. Dual steepest edge simplex seems to perform better. In several codes, it is the default option.

(c) Interior point algorithms take few iterations to converge. As the size of the problem increases, they seem to perform better than many, but not all, simplex variants.

(d) As degeneracy can affect performance of the simplex method adversely, perturbation of the cost vector decreases (and often eradicates) dual degeneracy, which improves the performance of the dual simplex method.

(e) Especially for solving integer programming problems, it is important to obtain an optimal basic feasible solution to the linear programming relaxation. Fixing some variables first in an optimal interior solution, using preprocessing again, and then calling the simplex algorithm to find an optimal basic feasible solution seems advantageous.

(f) Fixing some variables in an optimal solution to the linear programming relaxation to zero or one, and using branching rules tailored to the particular problem at hand, leads to significant computational advantages.

12.4 The air traffic flow management problem

While the previous section illustrates the art in developing practical optimization algorithms, this section illustrates the art in developing effective linear optimization models, in the context of the problem of controlling air traffic.

Throughout the United States and Europe, demand for airport use has been increasing rapidly in recent years, while airport capacity has been stagnating. Acute congestion in many major airports has been the unfortunate result. For example, each of the thirty-three major airports in the US was expected to exceed 20,000 hours of annual delays by 1997. The ground and airborne delays caused by congestion create direct costs to the airlines and indirect (opportunity) costs to the passengers. Direct costs from ground delays include crew, maintenance, and depreciation costs, while direct costs from airborne delays include, in addition, fuel and depreciation costs. Although estimates of congestion costs are difficult to measure, there seems to be agreement[1] that they amount to billions of dollars. Given that several European and US airlines have been suffering yearly losses that also amount to billions of dollars[2], congestion is a problem of undeniable practical significance.

Faced with the realities of congestion, the Federal Aviation Administration (FAA) has been using *ground-holding* policies to reduce delay costs. These short-term policies consider airport capacities and flight schedules as fixed for a given time period, and adjust the flow of aircraft on a real-time basis by imposing "ground holds" on certain flights. The FAA uses a computerized procedure based on a first-come, first-served rule, in order to select appropriate ground holds. These selections are further enhanced through the experience of its air traffic controllers. The motivation for ground-holding is as follows. Suppose it has been determined that if an aircraft departs on time, it will encounter congestion, incurring an airborne delay as it awaits landing clearance at its destination airport. However, by delaying its departure, the aircraft could arrive at its destination at a later time when minimal congestion is expected, thus, incurring no airborne delay. As airborne delays are more costly than ground-holding delays, the objective of ground-holding policies is to "translate" anticipated airborne delays to the ground by delaying departures.

In this section, we consider the effect of using a linear optimization approach to control air traffic in a network of airports that could represent either the national US network or the European network. The airspace is divided into sectors. Each flight passes through contiguous sectors while it is en route to its destination. There is a restriction on the number of airplanes that may fly within a sector at any given time. This number is dependent on the number of aircraft that an air traffic controller can manage at any one time, the geographic location, and the weather conditions. We will refer to the restrictions on the number of aircraft in a given sector at a given time as the en route sector capacities. We formulate the problem of minimizing the effects of congestion as a 0-1 integer programming problem.

Consider a set of flights, $\mathcal{F} = \{1, \ldots, F\}$, a set of airports, $\mathcal{K} = \{1, \ldots, K\}$, a set of time periods of unit duration, $\mathcal{T} = \{1, \ldots, T\}$ (note

---

[1]For example, The Stanford Research Institute estimated in 1990 annual costs of $5 billion in Europe due to congestion. The Federal Aviation Administration estimated in 1988 the annual costs of delays in the US at $1.4 billion.

[2]During the years 1991-1994, US airlines sustained losses totaling about $9 billion.

that we have discretized time), a set of sectors $\mathcal{J} = \{1, \ldots, J\}$, and a set of pairs of flights that are continuations of each other, $\mathcal{C} = \{(f', f) \mid f'$ is continued by flight $f\}$. We assume that $\mathcal{K} \subset \mathcal{J}$. In particular, the first and last sector in every flight's path is an airport. Associated with every continued flight f is a turnaround time s_f, which is the minimum time that an airplane needs to stay on the ground in order to be prepared for the next flight. We shall refer to any particular time period t as the "time t." Note that by "flight," we mean a "flight leg" between two airports. Also, flights referred to as "continued" are those flights whose aircraft is scheduled to perform a later flight within some time interval of its scheduled arrival. The problem input data are as follows:

Data:

$$N_f = \text{number of sectors in the path of flight } f$$

$$P(f, i) = \begin{cases} \text{the departure airport,} & \text{if } i = 1, \\ \text{the arrival airport,} & \text{if } i = N_f, \\ \text{the } i\text{th sector in flight } f\text{'s path,} & \text{if } i \neq \{1, N_f\} \end{cases}$$

$$P_f = (P(f, 1), \ldots, P(f, N_f))$$

$D_k(t)$ = departure capacity of airport k at time t

$A_k(t)$ = arrival capacity of airport k at time t

$S_j(t)$ = capacity of sector j at time t

d_f = scheduled departure time of flight f

r_f = scheduled arrival time of flight f

s_f = turnaround time for flight f

c_f^g = cost of holding flight f on the ground for one time period

c_f^a = cost of holding flight f in the air for one time period

l_{fj} = minimum number of time periods that flight f must spend in sector j

T_f^j = set of allowed times for flight f to arrive at sector j

$\underline{T}_f^j$ = first time period in the set T_f^j

$\overline{T}_f^j$ = last time period in the set T_f^j

Objective:
The objective is to decide how long each flight is to be held on the ground and in the air, in order to minimize the total delay cost.

Decision variables:
A very important aspect of the modeling process is the choice of the decision variables. For every flight f, sector j, and time t, we introduce the following

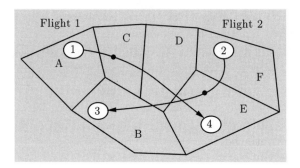

Figure 12.1: Two possible flight routes.

decision variables:

$$w^j_{ft} = \begin{cases} 1, & \text{if flight } f \text{ arrives at sector } j \text{ by time } t, \\ 0, & \text{otherwise.} \end{cases}$$

Recall that the first and last sectors on each flight path are airports. So, if $j = P(f,1)$, then w^j_{ft} equals 1, if flight f takes off from airport $P(f,1)$ by time t, while if $j = P(f,N_f)$, then w^j_{ft} equals 1, if flight f lands at airport $P(f,N_f)$ by time t. The above definition, using *by time t* and not *at time t*, is critical to the understanding of the formulation and the practical success of the model. Also, recall that we have defined for each flight a list P_f including the departure airport, the pertinent sectors, and the arrival airport, so that a variable w^j_{ft} will only be needed for those elements j in the list P_f. Moreover, we have defined T^j_f as the set of feasible times for flight f to arrive at sector j, so that a variable w^j_{ft} will only be needed for those times within T^j_f. Thus, whenever the variable w^j_{ft} is used in the formulation, it is assumed that (f, j, t) is a feasible combination.

Example 12.2 To ensure the clarity of the model, consider two flights traversing a set of sectors; see Figure 12.1. In this example, there are two flights, 1 and 2, each with the following associated data:

$$P_1 = (1, A, C, D, E, 4) \quad \text{and} \quad P_2 = (2, F, E, D, B, 3).$$

If the position of the aircraft at time t is indicated by the dots in the figure, then the variables for these flights at that time will be:

$$w^1_{1,t} = 1, \quad w^A_{1,t} = 1, \quad w^C_{1,t} = 1, \quad w^D_{1,t} = 0, \quad w^E_{1,t} = 0, \quad w^4_{1,t} = 0,$$
$$w^2_{2,t} = 1, \quad w^F_{2,t} = 1, \quad w^E_{2,t} = 1, \quad w^D_{2,t} = 0, \quad w^B_{2,t} = 0, \quad w^3_{2,t} = 0.$$

Having defined the variables w_{ft}^j, we can express several quantities of interest as linear functions of these variables:

(a) The variable u_{ft}^j defined to be 1 if flight f arrives at sector j *at* time t, and 0 otherwise, can be expressed as follows:

$$u_{ft}^j = w_{ft}^j - w_{f,t-1}^j,$$

and vice versa,

$$w_{ft}^j = \sum_{t' \le t} u_{ft'}^j.$$

As discussed earlier, the variables w_{ft}^j are only defined in the time range $T_f^j = [\underline{T}_f^j, \overline{T}_f^j]$, so that $w_{f,\underline{T}_f^j-1}^j = 0$. Furthermore, one variable per flight-sector pair can be eliminated from the formulation by setting $w_{f,\overline{T}_f^j}^j = 1$. Since flight f has to arrive at sector j by the last possible time in its time window, we can simply set it equal to 1 before solving the problem.

(b) Noticing that $P(f,1)$ represents the departure airport for flight f, the total number g_f of time units that flight f is held on the ground is the actual departure time minus the scheduled departure time, i.e.,

$$g_f = \sum_{\{t \in T_f^k \mid k=P(f,1)\}} t u_{ft}^k - d_f$$

$$= \sum_{\{t \in T_f^k \mid k=P(f,1)\}} t(w_{ft}^k - w_{f,t-1}^k) - d_f.$$

(c) Noticing that $P(f,N_f)$ represents the destination airport for flight f, the total number a_f of time units that flight f is held in the air can be expressed as the actual arrival time minus the scheduled arrival time minus the amount of time that the flight has been held on the ground, i.e.,

$$a_f = \sum_{\{t \in T_f^k \mid k=P(f,N_f)\}} t u_{ft}^k - r_f - g_f$$

$$= \sum_{\{t \in T_f^k \mid k=P(f,N_f)\}} t(w_{ft}^k - w_{f,t-1}^k) - r_f - g_f.$$

The objective function:
The objective is to minimize total delay cost. Using the above defined variables g_f and a_f (the ground and air delay, respectively), the objective function can be expressed simply as follows:

$$\text{minimize} \sum_{f \in \mathcal{F}} (c_f^g g_f + c_f^a a_f).$$

A 0-1 integer programming formulation

Substituting the expressions we derived above for the variables g_f and a_f in terms of w_{ft}^j, omitting those terms that do not depend on the decision variables, and rearranging, we obtain the following formulation:

$$\text{minimize} \quad \sum_{f \in \mathcal{F}} \left[(c_f^g - c_f^a) \sum_{\{t \in T_f^k | k = P(f,1)\}} t(w_{ft}^k - w_{f,t-1}^k) \right.$$
$$\left. + c_f^a \sum_{\{t \in T_f^k | k = P(f,N_f)\}} t(w_{ft}^k - w_{f,t-1}^k) \right]$$

subject to the constraints

$$\sum_{\{f | P(f,1)=k\}} (w_{ft}^k - w_{f,t-1}^k) \leq D_k(t), \quad \forall\, k \in \mathcal{K}, \; t \in T,$$

$$\sum_{\{f | P(f,N_f)=k\}} (w_{ft}^k - w_{f,t-1}^k) \leq A_k(t), \quad \forall\, k \in \mathcal{K}, \; t \in T,$$

$$\sum_{\{(f,j') | P(f,i)=j, P(f,i+1)=j', i<N_f\}} (w_{ft}^j - w_{ft}^{j'}) \leq S_j(t), \quad \forall\, j \in \mathcal{J}, \; t \in T$$

$$w_{f,t+l_{fj}}^{j'} - w_{ft}^j \leq 0, \quad \begin{cases} \forall\, f \in \mathcal{F},\; t \in T_f^j,\; j = P(f,i),\; \text{such} \\ \text{that } i < N_f, \text{ and } j' = P(f,i+1), \end{cases}$$

$$w_{ft}^k - w_{f',t-s_{f'}}^k \leq 0, \quad \begin{cases} \forall\, (f', f) \in \mathcal{C},\; t \in T_f^k,\; \text{such that} \\ k = P(f,1) = P(f',N_f), \end{cases}$$

$$w_{f,t}^j - w_{f,t-1}^j \geq 0, \quad \forall\, f \in \mathcal{F},\; j \in P_f,\; t \in T_f^j,$$

$$w_{ft}^j \in \{0,1\}, \quad \forall\, f \in \mathcal{F},\; j \in P_f,\; t \in T_f^j.$$

The first three sets of constraints take into account the capacities of various aspects of the system. The first set of constraints ensures that the number of flights which may take off from airport k at time t, will not exceed the departure capacity of airport k at time t. Likewise, the second set of constraints ensures that the number of flights which may arrive at airport k at time t, will not exceed the arrival capacity of airport k at time t. In each case, the difference $w_{ft}^k - w_{f,t-1}^k$ will be equal to 1, only when the first term is 1 and the second term is 0. Thus, the differences $w_{ft}^k - w_{f,t-1}^k$ capture the time at which a flight uses a given airport. The third set of constraints ensures that the sum of all flights which may be in sector j at time t will not exceed the capacity of sector j at time t. The difference

$$\sum_{f,j'} (w_{ft}^j - w_{ft}^{j'})$$

is the number of flights that are in sector j at time t, since the first term will be 1 if flight f has arrived at sector j by time t, and the second term will be 1 if flight f has arrived at the next sector by time t. So the only flights that will contribute a value of 1 to this sum are the flights that have arrived at j and have not yet departed by time t.

The fourth, fifth, and sixth sets of constraints represent the three types of connectivity in the problem: connectivity between sectors, connectivity within airports, and connectivity in time. The fourth set of constraints represents connectivity between sectors. It stipulates that if a flight arrives at sector j' by time $t + l_{fj}$, then it must have arrived at sector j by time t, where j and j' are consecutive sectors in the path of flight f. In other words, a flight cannot enter the next sector on its path until it has spent at least l_{fj} time units (the minimum possible) traveling through sector j, the current sector in its path.

The fifth set of constraints represents connectivity within airports. It handles the cases in which a flight is continued, i.e., the flight's aircraft is scheduled to perform a later flight within some time interval. We call the first flight f' and the following flight f. This set of constraints states that if flight f departs from airport k by time t, then flight f' must have arrived at airport k by time $t - s_{f'}$, where $s_{f'}$ is the turnaround time.

Finally, the sixth set of constraints represents connectivity in time. Thus, if a flight has arrived at sector j by time t, then $w_{ft'}^j$ has to have a value of 1 for all later time periods, $t' \geq t$.

The major reason we used the variables w_{ft}^j, as opposed to the variables u_{ft}^j, is that the variables w_{ft}^j nicely capture the three types of connectivity in the air traffic control problem: connectivity between sectors, connectivity between airports, and connectivity in time.

Computational results

The preceding formulation has been extensively tested using real data from both the US and the European networks. As an example, two realistic size data sets obtained directly from the Official Airline Guide (OAG) were provided by the FAA. The first one consisted of of 278 flights, 10 airports, and 178 sectors, tested over a 7 hour time frame with 5 minute intervals. The second of these data sets consisted of 1002 flights, 18 airports, and 305 sectors, tested over an 8 hour time frame with 5 minute intervals. The sector crossing times, sector and airport capacities, and required turnaround times were all provided by the FAA. These data sets are comparable to those in the problem being solved daily by the FAA.

For the first problem, consisting of 43226 constraints and 18733 variables, an optimal solution to the linear programming relaxation was found in approximately 30 minutes on a SUN SPARC 20 workstation using CPLEX 3.0 as the optimization solver and GAMS 2.25 as the modeling language. Furthermore, the solution obtained was completely integer. In other words, there is no need to use any integer programming methods. The second and larger data set consisting of 151662 constraints and 69497 variables, was solved to optimality in approximately 2 hours, again achieving completely integer solutions.

Similar results were obtained for the European network. For a data set provided by EUROCONTROL, a problem involving 2293 flights, 25 sectors, and with all costs equal to 1 (i.e., the objective is to minimize the total delay), an optimal completely integer solution was found in approximately one hour on a SUN 10 workstation. The total delay in the optimal solution was 60% lower than the delay under the first-come-first-serve heuristic that is exercised by EUROCONTROL. This illustrates the significant impact that linear optimization can have in practice.

Another observation that is important for achieving short computation times, is that in the absence of capacity constraints, the remaining inequalities define the dual of a network flow problem, for which we know that an integer optimal solution exists and can be found by the network simplex method. As a result, the model is first ran as a network flow problem, ignoring the capacity constraints, and a basis is found. Then, the capacity constraints are introduced and the problem is solved using the dual simplex method.

While the linear programming relaxation does not always have integer optimal solutions, this turned out to be the case for these and other test problems. Compared with other formulations that have been proposed in the literature, the preceding formulation performs significantly better. One naturally wonders why this has been the case. A partial explanation is that the three sets of constraints that express the three types of connectivity in the problem are "facets" of the convex hull of the set of feasible solutions.

We summarize the principal insights from this example, which have wide applicability:

(a) Defining the "right" set of variables for a linear optimization problem can have an important impact on the size and quality of the formulation, as well as on the solution time.

(b) The key to solving large scale integer programming problems is to obtain *strong formulations*, i.e., formulations that closely approximate the convex hull of the set of integer solutions. This can be achieved by introducing constraints that are "facets" of the convex hull of the set of feasible solutions.

(c) Extracting a network subproblem is important in achieving short computational times. The network simplex algorithm, for example, is significantly faster than the general simplex method, and provides a useful initial basis for the solution to the complete problem.

12.5   The job shop scheduling problem

Our objective in this section is to show that strong formulations, even involving an exponential number of constraints, coupled with heuristics

and branch and bound methods, can lead to efficient algorithms for large
scale linear optimization problems. We start with a simple one-machine
scheduling problem, and continue with the job shop scheduling problem, in
which several jobs need to be processed by several machines.

A single machine scheduling problem

A set $\mathcal{N} = \{1, \ldots, n\}$ of jobs needs to be scheduled on a single machine.
The processing time of job $i \in \mathcal{N}$ is some positive number p_i. A schedule
is called *nonpreemptive* if, once the machine begins processing a job, it
must complete processing before starting another job. A schedule is called
nonidling if the machine can only stay idle after all jobs have been processed.
A schedule is called *feasible* if it is nonpreemptive and the machine works
on at most one job at a time.

Let C_i be the completion time of job i, $i \in \mathcal{N}$. The objective is to
find a feasible schedule that minimizes

$$\sum_{i \in \mathcal{N}} w_i C_i,$$

where $w_i \geq 0$, $i \in \mathcal{N}$, are given weights. A natural question is to characterize the set of vectors $(C_1, \ldots, C_n)$ that correspond to feasible schedules.

Clearly, the following conditions need to be satisfied

$$C_j \geq p_j, \qquad j \in \mathcal{N},$$

$$C_j \geq C_k + p_j \quad \text{or} \quad C_k \geq C_j + p_k, \qquad j, k \in \mathcal{N}, \ j \neq k.$$

The last condition states that in every schedule, either job k is processed
before job j, or job j is processed before job k. Figure 12.2 depicts the set
of all feasible completion times vectors for $\mathcal{N} = \{1, 2\}$, and shows that this
set is not convex.

Next, we find constraints on the convex hull of the set of feasible
completion time vectors. Towards this goal, we need the following characterization of the optimal schedule.

Theorem 12.1 *Assume that*

$$\frac{w_1}{p_1} \geq \frac{w_2}{p_2} \geq \cdots \geq \frac{w_n}{p_n}.$$

Then, the sequence of jobs $1, 2, \ldots, n$ is optimal.

Proof. Suppose that there is another optimal schedule. Then, there are
two jobs i, j, such that job j is processed just before job i, $j > i$, and
$w_i/p_i \geq w_j/p_j$. Hence,

$$C_j = C + p_j, \qquad C_i = C + p_i + p_j,$$

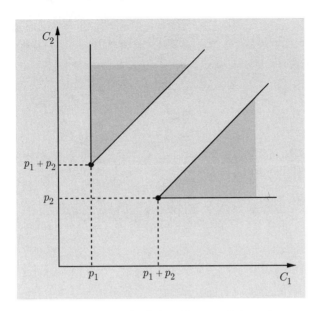

Figure 12.2: The set of all feasible completion times vectors (C_1, C_2) for $\mathcal{N} = \{1, 2\}$. Unfortunately, the feasible set is the union of two disjoint polyhedra. It is not a convex set.

where C is the completion time of the job that precedes job j in the schedule. Let $Z = \sum_{k \in \mathcal{N}} w_k C_k$. Consider now a schedule in which we process job i before job j, and which is otherwise the same. Under the new schedule, all completion times except for those of jobs i and j are the same. The new completion times of jobs i and j become:

$$C_i' = C + p_i, \qquad C_j' = C + p_i + p_j.$$

Let $Z' = \sum_{k \in \mathcal{N}} w_k C_k'$. The difference in cost between the two schedules is

$$
\begin{aligned}
Z' - Z &= w_i C_i' + w_j C_j' - w_i C_i - w_j C_j \\
&= w_i (C + p_i) + w_j (C + p_i + p_j) \\
&\quad - w_j (C + p_j) - w_i (C + p_i + p_j) \\
&= w_j p_i - w_i p_j \\
&= p_i p_j \left(\frac{w_j}{p_j} - \frac{w_i}{p_i} \right) \\
&\leq 0,
\end{aligned}
$$

and therefore, the new schedule is also optimal. Performing more pairwise interchanges, we conclude that the schedule in which jobs are processed in the sequence $1, 2, \ldots, n$ is optimal. $\qquad \square$

Suppose that $w_i = p_i$ for all i. Then, from Theorem 12.1, it follows that all nonidling schedules are optimal. In particular, the schedule in which the ith job processed is job i is optimal. The completion time of job i in this schedule is $C_i^* = \sum_{k=1}^{i} p_k$. Therefore, for all schedules,

$$\sum_{i=1}^{n} p_i C_i \geq \sum_{i=1}^{n} p_i C_i^*$$

$$= \sum_{i=1}^{n} p_i \sum_{k=1}^{i} p_{l_0}$$

$$= \frac{1}{2} \sum_{i=1}^{n} p_i^2 + \frac{1}{2} \left(\sum_{i=1}^{n} p_i \right)^2.$$

Consider a set $S \subset \mathcal{N}$ of jobs. Applying the previous inequality to that set, we obtain

$$\sum_{i \in S} p_i C_i \geq \frac{1}{2} \sum_{i \in S} p_i^2 + \frac{1}{2} \left(\sum_{i \in S} p_i \right)^2, \qquad \forall\, S \subset \mathcal{N}. \tag{12.1}$$

Note that we have exponentially many inequalities.

We have shown that the completion times $(C_1, \ldots, C_n)$ associated with any feasible schedule must satisfy Eq. (12.1). There is also a converse result whose proof we omit: every vector $(C_1, \ldots, C_n)$ that satisfies Eq. (12.1) belongs to the convex hull of feasible completion time vectors.

For $\mathcal{N} = \{1, 2\}$, the convex hull of the set of feasible completion time vectors (see also Figure 12.2) is

$$C_1 \qquad\qquad \geq p_1$$
$$C_2 \geq p_2$$
$$p_1 C_1 + p_2 C_2 \geq p_1^2 + p_2^2 + p_1 p_2.$$

Based on the above discussion, the single machine scheduling problem is equivalent to

$$\text{minimize} \quad \sum_{i=1}^{n} w_i C_i$$

$$\text{subject to} \quad \sum_{i \in S} p_i C_i \geq \frac{1}{2} \sum_{i \in S} p_i^2 + \frac{1}{2} \left(\sum_{i \in S} p_i \right)^2, \qquad \forall\, S \subset \mathcal{N}. \tag{12.2}$$

The function

$$p(S) = \frac{1}{2} \sum_{i \in S} p_i^2 + \frac{1}{2} \left(\sum_{i \in S} p_i \right)^2$$

turns out to be *supermodular*, i.e., for all $S, T \subset \mathcal{N}$,

$$p(S) + p(T) \leq p(S \cap T) + p(S \cup T).$$

Note that a function is supermodular if $-p(S)$ is submodular[3].

As discussed in Chapters 6 and 11, when solving problems with a large number of constraints, it is important to be able to check whether a given vector is feasible, and if not, to be able to generate a violated inequality. (This has been referred to as the *separation* problem; see also Section 8.5.) Since we can efficiently solve the optimization problem (Theorem 12.1), it should not be surprising that the separation problem can also be efficiently solved. This is accomplished by our next result, which exploits the special structure of the function $p(S)$.

Theorem 12.2 *Given a vector* $(C_1, \ldots, C_n)$, *we can decide whether* $\sum_{i \in S} p_i C_i \geq p(S)$ *for all* $S \subset \mathcal{N}$, *or find a violated inequality, by the following algorithm:*

1. *Sort the jobs in order of increasing* C_i, *and let* S_i *be the set containing the first* i *jobs in the sorted sequence.*

2. *Among the* n *sets* $S_1, \ldots, S_n$, *select a set* S_k *that maximizes*

$$f(S) = p(S) - \sum_{i \in S} p_i C_i.$$

3. *If* $f(S_k) \leq 0$, *then* $\sum_{i \in S} p_i C_i \geq p(S)$ *for all* $S \subset \mathcal{N}$. *Otherwise, a violated inequality, involving the set* S_k, *has been found.*

Proof. Let S be a set that maximizes the function

$$f(S) = p(S) - \sum_{i \in S} p_i C_i,$$

over all $S \subset \mathcal{N}$. For $j \in S$, we can use the definition of $f(S)$ and $p(S)$ to obtain

$$f(S) = f\bigl(S \setminus \{j\}\bigr) + p_j \sum_{i \in S} p_i - p_j C_j.$$

Since $f\bigl(S \setminus \{j\}\bigr) \leq f(S)$, we obtain that for all $j \in S$,

$$C_j \leq \sum_{i \in S} p_i.$$

For $j \notin S$, we have

$$f\bigl(S \cup \{j\}\bigr) = f(S) + p_j \left(p_j + \sum_{i \in S} p_i - C_j \right).$$

---

[3]Theorem 12.1 can also be proved using the results of Exercise 8.10 on submodular function minimization.

Since $f\big(S \cup \{j\}\big) \le f(S)$, we obtain that for all $j \notin S$,

$$C_j - p_j \ge \sum_{i \in S} p_i.$$

Therefore, if $j \in S$, then $C_j \le \sum_{i \in S} p_i$. If $j \notin S$, then $C_j > \sum_{i \in S} p_i$. Hence, if S maximizes $f(S)$, then $j \in S$ if and only if $C_j \le \sum_{i \in S} p_i$. This implies that if $j \in S$, then for every m such that $C_m < C_j$, we have $m \in S$. Therefore, we may sort the jobs in order of increasing C_k and construct the nested family of sets $S_1, \ldots, S_n$, where S_i contains the first i jobs in the sorted sequence. The optimum subset S may then be found among $S_1, \ldots, S_n$, and the correctness of the algorithm follows. $\qquad\square$

Note that the most time consuming operation is the sorting in Step 1, which can be accomplished in $O(n \log n)$ time; see, e.g. Cormen, Leiserson, and Rivest (1990).

Single machine scheduling problems with release times, deadlines, and precedence constraints

We next show that the separation algorithm provided by Theorem 12.2 leads to an efficient computation of lower bounds for several difficult ($\mathcal{NP}$-hard) variations of the single machine scheduling problem. Suppose that job i must be completed between time r_i and d_i. In addition, there are precedence constraints among jobs that are described by a directed graph $G = (\mathcal{N}, \mathcal{A})$, where

$$\mathcal{A} = \big\{ (i,j) \mid \text{job } i \text{ must be processed before job } j \big\}.$$

The problem of finding a schedule that minimizes $\sum_{i \in \mathcal{N}} w_i C_i$, in the presence of release times, deadlines, and precedence constraints, is known to be $\mathcal{NP}$-hard [Garey and Johnson (1979)]. However, the following linear programming problem provides a lower bound on the optimal objective function value:

$$\text{minimize} \quad \sum_{i=1}^{n} w_i C_i$$

$$\text{subject to} \quad \sum_{i \in S} p_i C_i \ge \frac{1}{2} \sum_{i \in S} p_i^2 + \frac{1}{2} \left(\sum_{i \in S} p_i \right)^2, \quad \forall\, S \subset \mathcal{N}, \qquad (12.3)$$

$$r_i \le C_i \le d_i, \qquad\qquad\qquad \forall\, i \in \mathcal{N},$$

$$C_j \ge C_i + p_j, \qquad\qquad\qquad \forall\, (i,j) \in \mathcal{A}.$$

Because of Theorem 12.2, we can solve the separation problem, i.e., identify a violated constraint if one exists, in polynomial time. This allows us to use the cutting plane algorithm of Section 6.3 to solve problem (12.3). From a theoretical point of view, this also leads to a polynomial time (but impractical) method, based on the ellipsoid algorithm (cf. Section 8.5).

Job	1	2	3	4
p_i	2	6	8	11
d_i	10	28	29	30
w_i	0.5	2	3	4

Table 12.9: Data for the single machine scheduling problem with deadlines.

Example 12.3 We consider the 4-job, single machine problem with deadlines d_i, but without release times (all r_i are equal to p_i) or precedence constraints. The problem data are shown in Table 12.9. In order to solve the linear programming problem (12.3), we start with a small number of constraints. The initial linear programming problem is

$$\text{minimize} \quad 0.5C_1 + 2C_2 + 3C_3 + 4C_4$$
$$\text{subject to} \quad 2C_1 + 6C_2 + 8C_3 + 11C_4 \geq 477$$
$$2 \leq C_1 \leq 10$$
$$6 \leq C_2 \leq 28$$
$$8 \leq C_3 \leq 29$$
$$11 \leq C_4 \leq 30.$$

An optimal solution is $\mathbf{C}^* = \left(C_1^*, C_2^*, C_3^*, C_4^*\right) = \left(10, 28, 8, 20\frac{5}{11}\right)$, with objective function value $166\frac{9}{11}$. However, the vector $\mathbf{C}^*$ does not correspond to a feasible schedule, since $C_1^* < C_4^* < C_1^* + p_4$. We now invoke the separation algorithm. Note that $C_3^* < C_1^* < C_4^* < C_2^*$. Since

$$f\left(\{3\}\right) = 0, \quad f\left(\{1,3\}\right) = 0, \quad f\left(\{1,3,4\}\right) = 6, \quad f\left(\{1,2,3,4\}\right) = 0,$$

the subset maximizing $f(S)$ is $S = \{1, 3, 4\}$. We therefore add the constraint

$$2C_1 + 8C_3 + 11C_4 \geq 315.$$

The new optimal solution is $\mathbf{C}^* = (10, 27, 8, 21)$ with value 167. Since this corresponds to a feasible schedule, it is an optimal solution to the original scheduling problem.

It is possible, however, that the optimal solution to the linear programming problem (12.3) corresponds to an infeasible schedule. In particular, there might be two jobs i and j, such that $C_i \leq C_j < C_i + p_j$. We can then propose a branch and bound algorithm, in which we branch by considering the cases that either job i is processed before job j, and therefore, $C_j \geq C_i + p_j$, or job j is processed before job i, and therefore, $C_i \geq C_j + p_i$. We add the corresponding constraint to the linear programming problem, find an improved lower bound, and continue until a feasible solution is obtained.

Even when the optimal solution to the linear programming problem (12.3) corresponds to an infeasible schedule, a feasible schedule can always be constructed as long as there are no deadlines ($d_i = \infty$). Let C_i^* be an optimal solution to the linear programming problem (12.3). We sort the C_i^*, and we create a feasible schedule by processing the jobs in the same order, inserting idle periods whenever needed to satisfy the constraints $C_i \geq r_i$. Note that the precedence constraints will automatically be satisfied.

Next, we provide evidence that the heuristic provides reasonable solutions by showing that it constitutes a 1-approximation algorithm when both release times and deadlines are absent ($r_i = p_i$, $d_i = \infty$). We assume, without loss of generality, that $C_1^* \leq C_2^* \leq \cdots \leq C_n^*$. In the heuristic solution, the completion time of job j is $\overline{C}_j = \sum_{k=1}^{j} p_k$. Since C_j^* is a feasible solution to the linear programming problem, we obtain

$$C_j^* \sum_{k=1}^{j} p_k \geq \sum_{k=1}^{j} p_k C_k^*$$

$$\geq \frac{1}{2} \sum_{k=1}^{j} p_k^2 + \frac{1}{2} \left(\sum_{k=1}^{j} p_k \right)^2$$

$$\geq \frac{1}{2} \left(\sum_{k=1}^{j} p_k \right)^2,$$

and thus,

$$C_j^* \geq \frac{1}{2} \sum_{k=1}^{j} p_k = \frac{1}{2} \overline{C}_j.$$

Let $Z_{\mathrm{LP}} = \sum_{k \in \mathcal{N}} w_k C_k^*$. Let $Z_{\mathrm{H}} = \sum_{k \in \mathcal{N}} w_k \overline{C}_k$. We have thus shown that

$$Z_{\mathrm{LP}} \leq Z_{\mathrm{H}} \leq 2 Z_{\mathrm{LP}},$$

i.e., the heuristic produces a solution within a factor of two from the optimal in the worst case, which is the best known bound for this $\mathcal{NP}$-hard problem.

Job shop scheduling

We consider the problem of scheduling a set $\mathcal{N}$ of n jobs on m machines. Job $i \in \mathcal{N}$ consists of k stages, each of which must be completed on a particular machine (we assume for simplicity that all jobs have the same number k of stages). The pair (i, j), called *task* (i, j), represents the jth stage of the ith job. The processing time of task (i, j) is p_{ij}. The completion time of job i is the completion time of the last task of job i, i.e., task (i, k). The objective is to find a schedule that minimizes the weighted sum of job completion times, subject to the following restrictions:

(a) The schedule must be nonpreemptive. That is, once a machine begins processing a stage of a job, it must complete that stage before doing anything else.

(b) Each machine may work on at most one task at any given time.

(c) The stages of each job must be completed in order.

In order to formulate the problem, let C_{ij} be the completion time of task (i, j). For each machine r, $r = 1, \ldots, m$, let M_r represent the set of tasks that must be completed on it.

The objective function:
The objective is

$$\text{minimize} \quad \sum_{i=1}^{n} w_i C_{ik}.$$

Constraints:

In order to ensure that the stages of each job are completed in order, we add the constraints

$$C_{ij} \geq C_{i,j-1} + p_{ij}, \qquad \forall\, i, j.$$

These constraints ensure that a stage of a job cannot begin before the previous stage is completed.

In addition, all tasks in the set M_r need to be scheduled on machine r. Therefore, the completion times C_{ij}, for $(i, j) \in M_r$, need to satisfy the constraints (12.1) of the single machine scheduling problem:

$$\sum_{(i,j) \in S} C_{ij} p_{ij} \geq \frac{1}{2} \sum_{(i,j) \in S} p_{ij}^2 + \frac{1}{2} \left(\sum_{(i,j) \in S} p_{ij} \right)^2, \qquad \forall\, S \subset M_r.$$

Therefore, the following linear programming problem provides a lower bound on the optimal objective function value over all feasible schedules:

$$\text{minimize} \quad \sum_{i=1}^{n} w_i C_{ik} \qquad\qquad (12.4)$$

subject to the constraints

$$\sum_{(i,j) \in S} C_{ij} p_{ij} \geq \frac{1}{2} \sum_{(i,j) \in S} p_{ij}^2 + \frac{1}{2} \left(\sum_{(i,j) \in S} p_{ij} \right)^2, \qquad \forall\, S \subset M_r, \ \forall\, r,$$

$$C_{ij} \geq C_{i,j-1} + p_{ij}, \qquad\qquad\qquad\qquad \forall\, i, j.$$

Note that by using the separation algorithm described in Theorem 12.2 for each r, $r = 1, \ldots, m$, we can solve the separation problem (identify violated constraints) in $O(mn \log n)$ time.

As in the single machine case with release times, deadlines, and precedence constraints, an optimal solution to the linear programming problem

(12.4) does not necessarily correspond to a feasible schedule for the job shop scheduling problem. However, a feasible solution can be easily generated by the following heuristic:

Job shop scheduling heuristic

1. Solve the linear programming problem (12.4) by using the cutting plane method and the separation algorithm described in Theorem 12.2.

2. Create a feasible schedule based on the order of the optimal C_{ij}^* as follows. For each machine r, sort the set $\{C_{ij}^* \mid (i,j) \in M_r\}$ from lowest to highest. That will give us an ordering of tasks for each machine.

3. Each machine processes its tasks in order, as soon as the jobs become available.

For example, suppose machine 1 must process tasks $(1,1)$, $(2,1)$, $(3,4)$, and $(4,2)$. Suppose that $C_{11}^* = 13$, $C_{21}^* = 8$, $C_{34}^* = 18$, and $C_{42}^* = 12$. Then, machine 1 will process the tasks in order of increasing completion times, that is, in the order $(2,1)$, $(4,2)$, $(1,1)$, $(3,4)$. Task $(2,1)$ is immediately available, so it will be processed immediately, and the completion time of task $(2,1)$ will be equal to its processing time. Machine 1 will then wait until stage 1 of job 4 has been completed, so that it can begin work on task $(4,2)$. When the machine finishes task $(4,2)$, task $(1,1)$ is immediately available, so it will be processed immediately.

Moreover, a branch and bound algorithm can be devised as follows. After solving the linear programming problem (12.4), we can detect that a schedule is infeasible if there are tasks (i,j) and (k,l) processed on the same machine r, such that

$$C_{ij}^* \leq C_{kl}^* < C_{ij}^* + p_{kl}.$$

As in the single machine scheduling problem, we branch by considering the cases that either task (i,j) is processed before task (k,l) on machine r, and therefore, $C_{kl} \geq C_{ij} + p_{kl}$, or task (k,l) is processed before task (i,j) on machine r, and therefore, $C_{ij} \geq C_{kl} + p_{ij}$. We add the corresponding constraint to the linear programming problem, find an improved lower bound, and continue until a feasible solution is obtained.

Example 12.4 We consider a job shop with 3 machines, 3 jobs, and 3 stages per job. The processing times p_{ij} and the weights w_i are given in Table 12.10.

The sets M_i, $i = 1, 2, 3$ are as follows.

$$M_1 = \{(1,1),\ (2,1),\ (3,3)\},$$
$$M_2 = \{(1,2),\ (2,3),\ (3,1)\},$$
$$M_3 = \{(1,3),\ (2,2),\ (3,2)\}.$$

	stage 1	stage 2	stage 3	w_i
job 1	2	3	2	1
job 2	3	4	1	1
job 3	2	2	2	1

Table 12.10: Processing times for a job shop with 3 machines, 3 jobs, and 3 stages per job.

We solve the linear programming problem (12.4). The solution is given in Table 12.11. The optimal objective function value is 23.67. The ordering of the

	stage 1	stage 2	stage 3
job 1	2.00	5.00	7.00
job 2	5.67	9.67	10.67
job 3	2.00	4.00	6.00

Table 12.11: The job completion times C_{ij}^* provided by the solution to the linear programming problem (12.4).

tasks for each machine is as follows. Machine 1 processes tasks in the order

$$(1,1), \ (2,1), \ (3,3).$$

Machine 2 processes tasks in the order

$$(3,1), \ (1,2), \ (2,3).$$

Machine 3 processes tasks in the order

$$(3,2), \ (1,3), \ (2,2).$$

However, the schedule is not feasible, because for the tasks $(2,1)$ and $(3,3)$ that are processed by machine 1, we have

$$C_{21}^* < C_{33}^* < C_{21}^* + p_{33}.$$

The job shop heuristic then gives the schedule shown in Table 12.12, with objective function value of 26.

If we apply the branch and bound algorithm to the solution to the linear programming problem (12.4), we add the constraint $C_{33} - C_{21} \geq 3$ and find that the objective function value of the new linear programming problem improves

	stage 1	stage 2	stage 3
job 1	2	5	7
job 2	5	11	12
job 3	2	4	7

Table 12.12: The job completion times provided by the job shop heuristic.

to 24.5, but the corresponding schedule is still infeasible. Further branching finds that the optimal objective function value becomes 26 and finds a feasible schedule with objective function value equal to 26. Alternatively, to explore the other half of the branch and bound tree, we add the constraint $C_{21} - C_{33} \geq 2$ to the original linear programming problem (12.4), and we find that the optimal objective function value increases to 26. As we have mentioned, the job scheduling heuristic produces a schedule whose cost is equal to 26. Since this is equal to the lower bound provided by the linear programming problem, the heuristic has produced an optimal schedule.

Computational results suggest that the linear programming problem (12.4) for problems involving up to 20 machines, 20 jobs, and 20 stages per job can be solved in minutes in a SUN SPARC 20 using a cutting plane algorithm and the CPLEX optimization library. The job shop heuristic quickly produces feasible schedules for problems involving up to 20 machines, 20 jobs, and 20 stages per job, that are approximately within a factor of two of the lower bound provided by the linear programming problem (12.4). The branch and bound algorithm routinely solves such problems to within $5\% - 10\%$ from the lower bound in less than an hour. The key to success in this application is:

(a) Although the formulation (12.4) has an exponential number of constraints, it can be solved efficiently, because the separation problem can be solved fast.

(b) It is easy to check whether the solution to the linear programming relaxation is infeasible and to identify violated constraints. This gives a natural and effective way to branch.

12.6   Summary

The availability of workstations, modeling languages, and optimization libraries has advanced optimization capabilities significantly. However, such advances do not imply that users can naively apply this technology to construct effective decision support systems. At the hands of an imaginative analyst the process of modeling, exploiting structure, and fine tuning of optimization algorithms will lead to better solution methods and, therefore, to more informed, insightful, and better decisions.

12.7   Exercises

Exercise 12.1* (The stable matching problem) This problem models how hospitals and residents are matched. There is a set of n hospitals and n medical residents. Each hospital has a strictly ordered list of the n residents and each resident has a strictly ordered list of the n hospitals. A perfect matching M of the hospitals and residents is called unstable if there exist a hospital i and a resident j, who are not matched under M, but prefer each other over their assigned mates under M. A perfect matching is stable if no such pair exists in the matching.

(a) Formulate the problem of deciding whether a stable matching exists as an integer programming problem.

(b) Using linear programming theory prove that a stable matching always exists.

(c) Use linear programming to compute such a stable matching for $n = 9$. The preference order of the hospitals is given in the following table. For example, intern 1 is the second choice of hospital 1.

	I_1	I_2	I_3	I_4	I_5	I_6	I_7	I_8	I_9
H_1	2	8	3	9	6	5	7	1	4
H_2	7	3	2	1	8	5	4	6	9
H_3	7	8	3	9	6	5	2	1	4
H_4	1	3	5	7	4	6	8	9	2
H_5	6	3	1	8	2	5	9	4	7
H_6	2	6	1	4	8	5	7	9	3
H_7	2	7	9	8	3	4	1	5	6
H_8	3	8	4	9	5	6	1	7	2
H_9	4	8	3	9	6	5	7	1	2

Similarly, the preference order of the interns is given in the following table. For example, hospital 1 is the third choice of intern 1.

	H_1	H_2	H_3	H_4	H_5	H_6	H_7	H_8	H_9
I_1	3	7	9	8	2	4	1	5	6
I_2	6	2	3	8	1	4	5	7	9
I_3	6	3	1	8	2	5	9	4	7
I_4	9	8	3	2	5	6	7	1	4
I_5	3	8	2	9	5	6	1	7	4
I_6	2	6	1	4	8	5	7	9	3
I_7	8	2	9	3	6	7	5	1	4
I_8	9	1	5	7	4	6	8	2	3
I_9	9	8	7	6	1	2	4	5	3

Job/Stage	1	2	3	4	5	6	7	8	9	10
1	29	78	9	36	49	11	62	56	44	21
2	43	90	75	11	69	28	46	46	72	30
3	91	85	39	74	90	10	12	89	45	33
4	81	95	71	99	9	52	85	98	22	43
5	14	6	22	61	26	69	21	49	72	53
6	84	2	52	95	48	72	47	65	6	25
7	46	37	61	13	32	21	32	89	30	55
8	31	86	46	74	32	88	19	68	36	79
9	76	69	76	51	85	11	40	89	26	74
10	85	13	61	7	64	76	47	52	90	45

Table 12.13: Processing times for a job shop with 10 machines, 10 jobs, and 10 stages per job. For example $p_{11} = 29$ and $p_{12} = 78$.

Exercise 12.2 (The electric power capacity expansion problem revisited) Solve Example 6.5 in two ways: as a single linear programming problem and using Benders decomposition. Use the following data.

The generator capacity costs in hundreds of thousands of dollars per megawatt (MW) are

$$c_1 = 4.0, \ c_2 = 2.5,$$

the operating costs are

$$f_{11} = 4.3, \ f_{21} = 2.0, \ f_{31} = 0.5, \ f_{12} = 8.7, \ f_{22} = 4.0, \ f_{32} = 1.0,$$

and the unserved demand penalties are

$$g_1 = g_2 = g_3 = 10.0.$$

The minimum generator capacities in MW are

$$b_1 = b_2 = 1000.$$

For every load level i, the demands in MW are

$$d_{i,1} = 900, \ d_{i,2} = 1000, \ d_{i,3} = 1100, \ d_{i,4} = 1200,$$

with probabilities

$$p_{i,1} = 0.15, \ p_{i,2} = 0.45, \ p_{i,3} = 0.25, \ p_{i,4} = 0.15.$$

The availability of generator 1 is

$$a_{1,1} = 1.0, \ a_{1,2} = 0.9, \ a_{1,3} = 0.5, \ a_{1,4} = 0.1,$$

with probabilities

$$q_{1,1} = 0.2, \ q_{1,2} = 0.3, \ q_{1,3} = 0.4, \ q_{1,4} = 0.1.$$

Machine/Job	1	2	3	4	5	6	7	8	9	10
M_1	1	1	2	3	2	7	2	2	1	2
M_2	2	6	1	1	3	2	1	3	2	1
M_3	3	2	4	2	1	1	4	1	5	3
M_4	4	5	3	8	5	4	3	10	3	8
M_5	5	3	10	4	6	9	10	5	9	9
M_6	6	8	6	10	4	3	6	4	4	7
M_7	7	7	8	5	10	8	5	6	7	4
M_8	8	9	7	7	8	10	9	9	8	10
M_9	9	10	5	6	7	5	8	7	10	5
M_{10}	10	4	9	9	9	6	7	8	6	6

Table 12.14: Each row represents the stages from each job that a machine needs to process. For example, machine 1 needs to process tasks $(1, 1), (2, 1), (3, 2), \ldots, (10, 2)$.

The availability of generator 2 is

$$a_{2,1} = 1.0, \ a_{2,2} = 0.9, \ a_{2,3} = 0.7, \ a_{2,4} = 0.1, \ a_{2,5} = 0,$$

with probabilities

$$q_{2,1} = 0.1, \ q_{2,2} = 0.2, \ q_{2,3} = 0.5, \ q_{2,4} = 0.1, \ q_{2,5} = 0.1.$$

Exercise 12.3 Using a modeling language, formulate Exercise 10.4, and solve it using an optimization library.

Exercise 12.4 * (**A large scale job shop scheduling problem**) Solve the job shop scheduling problem with 10 machines, 10 jobs, and 10 stages per job. Table 12.13 depicts the processing times p_{ij}, and Table 12.14 specifies the sets M_r. The weights are $w_i = 1$, so our objective is to minimize the average completion time.

Exercise 12.5 * (**A large scale traveling salesman problem**) Generate 1000 random points in the unit square $[0, 1]^2$. The distance c_{ij} is the Euclidean distance between the points i and j. Solve the linear programming relaxation of the cutset formulation of the traveling salesman problem on these 1000 points. Based on the solution to the linear programming relaxation, develop a branch and cut algorithm to generate near optimal traveling salesman tours. *Hint:* Use Lagrangean relaxation for bounding.

Exercise 12.6 * (**A large scale facility location problem**) Generate 200 random points in the unit square $[0, 1]^2$. The distance c_{ij} is the Euclidean distance between the points i and j. Solve the facility location problem for $K = 10$ facilities, where each facility must be one of the 200 random points.

Player	r_i	a_i	h_i	s_i	d_i
p_1	1	7	5.9	10	10
p_2	2	14	6.0	14	9
p_3	3	12	6.3	19	8
p_4	4	4	6.0	18	6
p_5	5	9	6.2	20	8
p_6	7	6	6.4	21	10
p_7	7	8	6.6	23	10
p_8	4	2	6.4	13	5
p_9	8	2	6.8	17	8
p_{10}	5	5	6.3	25	8
p_{11}	10	6	6.8	20	9
p_{12}	8	8	6.7	30	10
p_{13}	10	2	7.2	24	9
p_{14}	9	5	6.8	15	7
p_{15}	6	3	6.8	17	6
p_{16}	16	2	6.7	3	6
p_{17}	11	1	7.3	27	9
p_{18}	12	5	7.1	26	10
p_{19}	11	1	7.2	21	9
p_{20}	9	1	7.0	14	8

Table 12.15: The rebounding average r_i, assists average a_i, height h_i, scoring average s_i, and overall defense ability d_i for player $i = 1, \ldots, 20$.

Exercise 12.7 Solve Exercise 10.2 using the data of Table 12.15. The desired targets are $r = 7$, $a = 6$, $h = 6.6$, $s = 18$, $d = 8.5$.

Exercise 12.8 * (A large scale fixed charge network design problem) Generate 100 random points in the unit square $[0, 1]^2$. Let G be the complete directed graph on these 100 points. Let b_i be the demand or supply of point i. The demands for the first 99 points are independent and uniformly distributed in the interval $[-100, 100]$. The demand for the 100th point is equal to $-\sum_{i=1}^{99} b_i$. Let the transportation cost c_{ij} be equal to the Euclidean distance between points i and j, and let the construction cost d_{ij} be ten times the Euclidean distance. Solve the fixed charge network design problem on these 100 points (see Exercise 10.9 for the definition of the fixed charge network design problem).

Exercise 12.9 * (The graph coloring problem) Given an undirected graph $G = (\mathcal{N}, \mathcal{E})$, we want to assign a color to every node in $\mathcal{N}$, so that adjacent nodes are assigned different colors, and the total number of colors is minimized. Generate a graph on 100 nodes, so that if you draw it on the plane no two edges intersect. Such graphs are called *planar*. Solve the problem by using a branch and bound approach. *Hint*: We can always color planar graphs using 4 colors. Use this information to assist the bounding process.

12.8   Notes and sources

12.1 For further information on the modeling languages GAMS and AM-PLE, see the corresponding manuals. The *OR/MS Today* journal has frequent surveys of optimization solvers. The journal *Interfaces* contains many successful applications of linear optimization methods to problems arising in telecommunications, finance, transportation, manufacturing, services, etc.

12.2 Table 12.1 has been compiled by Weber (1995), based on experiments by several researchers. The general guidelines for the relative performance of various algorithms are from our experimentation with large scale linear programming problems, and also from the manual of the CPLEX optimization library.

12.3 The model, the solution methodology, and the computational results for the fleet assignment problem are taken from Hane et al. (1995). For further advances and an application of the fleet assignment problem in an industrial context, see Rushmeier and Kontogiorgis (1997).

12.4 The model and the computational results for the flow management problem in the US network are taken from Bertsimas and Stock (1997). The computational results for the European network are from Vranas (1996).

12.5 The formulation of the single machine scheduling problem is from Queyranne (1993). The indexing rule (Theorem 12.1) is from Smith (1956). The job shop scheduling heuristic is motivated by the work of Schultz (1996). A comprehensive review of known formulations and approximation algorithms for machine scheduling problems is given in Hall et al. (1996). The branch and bound algorithm, and the computational results for the job shop scheduling problem are from Bertsimas and Hsu (1997). An alternative cutting plane approach for job shop scheduling problems, in which we are interested in minimizing the maximum completion time, is proposed in Applegate and Cook (1991). For the same problem, a different enumerative but effective approach is proposed in Martin and Shmoys (1996).

12.7 The stable matching problem addressed in Exercise 12.1 was first defined and solved in Gale and Shapley (1962). A linear programming approach to the problem is given in Teo (1996). Exercise 12.2 is almost identical to a problem formulated and solved in Infanger (1993). The data in Exercise 12.4 are from Fisher and Thompson (1963). This is a famous instance of the job shop scheduling problem, and it took decades until a provably optimal solution was obtained.

References

AHUJA, R. K., T. L. MAGNANTI, and J. B. ORLIN. 1993. *Network Flows*, Prentice Hall, Englewood Cliffs, NJ.

ANDERSEN, E., J. GONDZIIO, C. MESZAROS, and X. XU. 1996. Implementation of interior point methods for large scale linear programming, in *Interior point methods in mathematical programming*, T. Terlaky (ed.), Kluwer Academic Publisher, Boston, MA.

APPLEGATE, D., and W. COOK. 1991. A computational study of the job shop scheduling problem, *ORSA Journal on Computing*, **3**, 149-156

BALAS, E., S. CERIA, G. CORNUÉJOLS, and N. NATRAJ. 1995. Gomory cuts revisited, working paper, Carnegie-Mellon University, Pittsburgh, PA.

BALAS, E., S. CERIA, and G. CORNUÉJOLS. 1995. Mixed 0 − 1 programming by lift-and-project in a branch and cut environment, working paper, Carnegie-Mellon University, Pittsburgh, PA.

BARAHONA, F., and É. TARDOS. 1989. Note on Weintraub's minimum cost circulation algorithm, *SIAM Journal on Computing*, **18**, 579-583.

BARNES, E. R. 1986. A variation on Karmarkar's algorithm for solving linear programming problems, *Mathematical Programming*, **36**, 174-182.

BARR, R. S., F. GLOVER, and D. KLINGMAN. 1977. The alternating path basis algorithm for the assignment problem, *Mathematical Programming*, **13**, 1-13.

BARTHOLDI, J. J., J. B. ORLIN, and H. D. RATLIFF. 1980. Cyclic scheduling via integer programs with circular ones, *Operations Research*, **28**, 1074-1085.

BAZARAA, M. S., J. J. JARVIS, and H. D. SHERALI. 1990. *Linear Programming and Network Flows*, 2nd edition, Wiley, New York, NY.

BEALE, E. M. L. 1955. Cycling in the dual simplex algorithm, *Naval Research Logistics Quarterly*, **2**, 269-275.

BELLMAN, R. E. 1958. On a routing problem, *Quarterly of Applied Mathematics*, **16**, 87-90.

BENDERS, J. F. 1962. Partitioning procedures for solving mixed-variables programming problems, *Numerische Mathematik*, **4**, 238-252.

BERTSEKAS, D. P. 1979. A distributed algorithm for the assignment problem, working paper, Laboratory for Information and Decision Systems, M.I.T., Cambridge, MA.

BERTSEKAS, D. P. 1981. A new algorithm for the assignment problem. *Mathematical Programming*, **21**, 152-171.

BERTSEKAS, D. P. 1991. *Linear Network Optimization*, M.I.T. Press, Cambridge, MA.

BERTSEKAS, D. P. 1995a. *Dynamic Programming and Optimal Control*, Athena Scientific, Belmont, MA.

BERTSEKAS, D. P. 1995b. *Nonlinear Programming*, Athena Scientific, Belmont, MA.

BERTSEKAS, D. P., and J. N. TSITSIKLIS. 1989. *Parallel and Distributed Computation: Numerical Methods*, Prentice Hall, Englewood Cliffs, NJ.

BERTSIMAS, D., and L. HSU. 1997. A branch and cut algorithm for the job shop scheduling problem, working paper, Operations Research Center, M.I.T., Cambridge, MA.

BERTSIMAS, D., and X. LUO. 1997. On the worst case complexity of potential reduction algorithms for linear programming, *Mathematical Programming*, to appear.

BERTSIMAS, D., and S. STOCK. 1997. The air traffic flow management problem with enroute capacities, *Operations Research*, to appear.

BLAND, R. G. 1977. New finite pivoting rules for the simplex method, *Mathematics of Operations Research*, **2**, 103-107.

BLAND, R. G., D. GOLDFARB, and M. J. TODD. 1981. The ellipsoid method: a survey, *Operations Research*, **29**, 1039-1091.

BORGWARDT, K.-H. 1982. The average number of pivot steps required by the simplex-method is polynomial, *Zeitschrift für Operations Research*, **26**, 157-177.

BOYD, S., and L. VANDENBERGHE. 1995. *Introduction to convex optimization with engineering applications*, lecture notes, Stanford University, Stanford, CA.

BRADLEY, S. P., A. C. HAX, and T. L. MAGNANTI. 1977. *Applied Mathematical Programming*, Addison-Wesley, Reading, MA.

CARATHÉODORY, C. 1907. Über den Variabilitätsbereich der Koeffizienten von Potenzreihen, die gegebene Werte nicht annehmen, *Mathematische Annalen*, **64**, 95-115.

CERIA, S., C. CORDIER, H. MARCHAND, and L. A. WOLSEY. 1995. Cutting planes for integer programs with general integer variables, working paper, Columbia University, New York, NY.

CHARNES, A. 1952. Optimality and degeneracy in linear programming, *Econometrica*, **20**, 160-170.

CHRISTOFIDES, N. 1975. Worst-case analysis of a new heuristic for the traveling salesman problem, Report 388, Graduate School of Industrial Administration, Carnegie-Mellon University, Pittsburgh, PA.

CHVÁTAL, V. 1983. *Linear Programming*, W. H. Freeman, New York, NY.

CLARK, F. E. 1961. Remark on the constraint sets in linear programming, *American Mathematical Monthly*, **68**, 351-352.

COBHAM, A. 1965. The intrinsic computational difficulty of functions, in *Logic, Methodology and Philosophy of Science*, Y. Bar-Hillel (ed.), North-Holland, Amsterdam, The Netherlands, 24-30.

COOK, S. A. 1971. The complexity of theorem proving procedures, in *Proceedings of the 3rd ACM Symposium on the Theory of Computing*, 151-158.

CORMEN, T. H., C. E. LEISERSON, and R. L. RIVEST. 1990. *Introduction to Algorithms,* McGraw-Hill, New York, NY.

CUNNINGHAM, W. H. 1976. A network simplex method, *Mathematical Programming*, **11**, 105-116.

DAHLEH, M. A., and I. DIAZ-BOBILLO. 1995. *Control of Uncertain Systems: A Linear Programming Approach*, Prentice Hall, Englewood Cliffs, NJ.

DANTZIG, G. B. 1951. Application of the simplex method to a transportation problem, in *Activity Analysis of Production and Allocation*, T. C. Koopmans (ed.), Wiley, New York, NY, 359-373.

DANTZIG, G. B. 1963. *Linear Programming and Extensions*, Princeton University Press, Princeton, NJ.

DANTZIG, G. B. 1992. An ϵ-precise feasible solution to a linear program with a convexity constraint in $1/\epsilon^2$ iterations independent of problem size, working paper, Stanford University, Stanford, CA.

DANTZIG, G. B., A. ORDEN, and P. WOLFE. 1955. The generalized simplex method for minimizing a linear form under linear inequality constraints, *Pacific Journal of Mathematics*, **5**, 183-195.

DANTZIG, G. B., and P. WOLFE. 1960. The decomposition principle for linear programs, *Operations Research*, **8**, 101-111.

DIJKSTRA, E. 1959. A note on two problems in connexion with graphs, *Numerische Mathematik*, **1**, 269-271.

DIKIN, I. I. 1967. Iterative solutions of problems of linear and quadratic programming, *Soviet Mathematics Doklady*, **8**, 674-675.

DIKIN, I. I. 1974. On the convergence of an iterative process, *Upravlyaemye Sistemi*, **12**, 54-60. (In Russian.)

DINES, L. L. 1918. Systems of linear inequalities, *Annals of Mathematics*, **20**, 191-199.

DUDA, R. O., and P. E. HART. 1973. *Pattern Classification and Scene Analysis*, Wiley, New York, NY.

EDMONDS, J. 1965a. Paths, trees, and flowers, *Canadian Journal of Mathematics*, **17**, 449-467.

EDMONDS, J. 1965b. Maximum matching and a polyhedron with $0 - 1$ vertices, *Journal of Research of the National Bureau of Standards*, **69B**, 125-130.

EDMONDS, J. 1971. Matroids and the greedy algorithm, *Mathematical Programming*, **1**, 127-136.

EDMONDS, J., and R. M. KARP. 1972. Theoretical improvements in algorithmic efficiency for network flow problems, *Journal of the ACM*, **19**, 248-264.

ELIAS, P., A. FEINSTEIN, and C. E. SHANNON. 1956. Note on maximum flow through a network, *IRE Transactions on Information Theory*, **2**, 117-119.

FARKAS, G. 1894. On the applications of the mechanical principle of Fourier, *Mathematikai és Természettudományi Értesitö*, **12**, 457-472. (In Hungarian.)

FIACCO, A. V., and G. P. McCORMICK. 1968. *Nonlinear programming: sequential unconstrained minimization techniques*, Wiley, New York, NY.

FEDERGRUEN, A., and H. GROENEVELT. 1986. Preemptive scheduling of uniform machines by ordinary network flow techniques, *Management Science*, **32**, 341-349.

FISHER, H., and G. L. THOMPSON. 1963. Probabilistic learning combinations of local job shop scheduling rules, in *Industrial Scheduling*, J. F. Muth and G. L. Thompson (eds.), Prentice Hall, Englewood Cliffs, NJ, 225-251.

FLOYD, R. W. 1962. Algorithm 97: shortest path. *Communications of ACM*, **5**, 345.

FORD, L. R. 1956. Network flow theory, report P-923, Rand Corp., Santa Monica, CA.

FORD, L. R., and D. R. FULKERSON. 1956a. Maximal flow through a network, *Canadian Journal of Mathematics,* **8**, 399-404.

FORD, L. R., and D. R. FULKERSON. 1956b. Solving the transportation problem, *Management Science*, **3**, 24-32.

FORD, L. R., and D. R. FULKERSON. 1962. *Flows in Networks,* Princeton University Press, Princeton, NJ.

FOURIER. J. B. J. 1827. Analyse des Travaux de l'Académie Royale des Sciences, pendant l'année 1824, Partie mathématique, *Histoire de l'Académie Royale des Sciences de l'Institut de France*, **7**, xlvii-lv.

FREUND, R. M. 1991. Polynomial-time algorithms for linear programming based only on primal affine scaling and projected gradients of a potential function, *Mathematical Programming*, **51**, 203-222.

FREUND, R. M., and B. SHANNAHAN. 1992. Short-run manufacturing problems at DEC, report, Sloan School of Management, M.I.T., Cambridge, MA.

FRISCH, M. R. 1956. La résolution des problèmes de programme linéaire par la méthode du potential logarithmique, *Cahiers du Séminaire D' Econometrie*, **4**, 7-20.

FULKERSON, D. R., and G. B. DANTZIG. 1955. Computation of maximum flow in networks, *Naval Research Logistics Quarterly*, **2**, 277-283.

GALE, D., H. W. KUHN, and A. W. TUCKER. 1951. Linear programming and the theory of games, in *Activity Analysis of Production and Allocation*, T. C. Koopmans (ed.), Wiley, New York, NY, 317-329.

GALE, D., and L. S. SHAPLEY. 1962. College admissions and the stability of marriage, *American Mathematical Monthly*, **69**, 9-15.

GAREY, M. R., and D. S. JOHNSON. 1979. *Computers and Intractability: a Guide to the Theory of NP-completeness*, W. H. Freeman, New York, NY.

GEMAN, S. and D. GEMAN. 1984. Stochastic Relaxation, Gibbs distribution, and the Bayesian restoration of images, *IEEE Transactions on Pattern Analysis and Machine Intelligence*, **6**, 721-741.

GILL, P. E., W. MURRAY, and M. H. WRIGHT. 1981. Practical Optimization, Academic Press, New York, NY.

GILMORE, P. C., and R. E. GOMORY. 1961. A linear programming approach to the cutting stock problem, *Operations Research*, **9**, 849-859.

GILMORE, P. C., and R. E. GOMORY. 1963. A linear programming approach to the cutting stock problem – part II, *Operations Research*, **11**, 863-888.

GOEMANS, M., and D. BERTSIMAS. 1993. Survivable networks, LP relaxations and the parsimonious property, *Mathematical Programming*, **60**, 145-166.

GOEMANS, M., and D. WILLIAMSON. 1993. A new 3/4 approximation algorithm for MAX SAT, in *Proceedings of the 3rd International Conference in Integer Programming and Combinatorial Optimization*, 313-321.

GOLDBERG, A. V., and R. E. TARJAN. 1988. A new approach to the maximum flow problem, *Journal of the ACM*, **35**, 921-940.

GOLDBERG, A. V., and R. E. TARJAN. 1989. Finding minimum-cost circulations by cancelling negative cycles, *Journal of the ACM*, **36**, 873-886.

GOLDFARB, D., and J. K. REID. 1977. A practicable steepest-edge simplex algorithm, *Mathematical Programming*, **12**, 361-371.

GOLUB, G. H., and C. F. VAN LOAN. 1983. *Matrix Computations*, The Johns Hopkins University Press, Baltimore, MD.

GOMORY, R. E. 1958. Outline of an algorithm for integer solutions to linear programs, *Bulletin of the American Mathematical Society*, **64**, 275-278.

GONZAGA, C. 1989. An algorithm for solving linear programming in $O(n^3 L)$ operations, in *Progress in Mathematical Programming*, N. Megiddo (ed.), Springer-Verlag, New York, NY, 1-28.

GONZAGA, C. 1990. Polynomial affine algorithms for linear programming, *Mathematical Programming*, **49**, 7-21.

GRÖTSCHEL, M., L. LOVÁSZ, and A. SCHRIJVER. 1981. The ellipsoid method and its consequences in combinatorial optimization, *Combinatorica*, **1**, 169-197.

GRÖTSCHEL, M., L. LOVÁSZ, and A. SCHRIJVER. 1988. *Geometric Algorithms and Combinatorial Optimization*, Springer-Verlag, New York, NY.

HAIMOVICH, M. 1983. The simplex method is very good! – on the expected number of pivot steps and related properties of random linear programs, preprint.

HAJEK, B. 1988. Cooling schedules for optimal annealing, *Mathematics of Operations Research*, **13**, 311-329.

HALL, L. A., and R. J. VANDERBEI. 1993. Two thirds is sharp for affine scaling, *Operations Research Letters*, **13**, 197-201.

HALL, L. A., A. S. SCHULTZ, D. B. SHMOYS, and J. WEIN. 1996. Scheduling to minimize average completion time; off-line and on-line approximation algorithms, working paper, Johns Hopkins University, Baltimore, MD.

HANE , C. A., C. BARNHART, E. L. JOHNSON, R. E. MARSTEN, G. L. NEMHAUSER, and G. SIGISMONDI. 1995. The fleet assignment problem: solving a large-scale integer program, *Mathematical Programming*, **70**, 211-232.

HARRIS, P. M. J. 1973. Pivot selection methods of the Devex LP code, *Mathematical Programming*, **5**, 1-28.

HAYKIN, S. 1994. *Neural Networks: A Comprehensive Foundation*, McMillan, New York, NY.

HELD, M., and R. M. KARP. 1962. A dynamic programming approach to sequencing problems, *SIAM Journal on Applied Mathematics*, **10**, 196-210.

HELD, M., and R. M. KARP. 1970. The traveling salesman problem and minimum spanning trees, *Operations Research*, **18**, 1138-1162.

HELD, M., and R. M. KARP. 1971. The traveling salesman problem and minimum spanning trees: part II, *Mathematical Programming*, **1**, 6-25.

HELLY, E. 1923. Über Mengen konvexer Körper mit gemeinschaftlichen Punkten, *Jahresbericht Deutsche Mathematische Vereinungen*, **32**, 175-176.

HOCHBAUM, D. (ed.). 1996. *Approximation algorithms for NP-hard problems*, Kluwer Academic Publishers, Boston, MA.

HU, T. C. 1969. *Integer Programming and Network Flows*, Addison-Wesley, Reading, MA.

IBARRA, O. H., and C. E. KIM. 1975. Fast approximation algorithms for the knapsack and sum of subset problems, *Journal of the ACM*, **22**, 463-468.

INFANGER, G. 1993. *Planning under uncertainty: solving large-scale stochastic linear programs*, Boyd & Fraser, Danvers, MA.

JOHNSON, D. S., C. ARAGON, L. MCGEOCH, and C. SCHEVON. 1990. Optimization by simulated annealing: an experimental evaluation, part I: graph partitioning, *Operations Research*, **37**, 865-892.

JOHNSON, D. S., C. ARAGON, L. MCGEOCH, and C. SCHEVON. 1992. Optimization by simulated annealing: an experimental evaluation, part II: graph coloring and number partitioning, *Operations Research*, **39**, 378-406.

KALAI, G., and D. KLEITMAN. 1992. A quasi-polynomial bound for the diameter of graphs of polyhedra, *Bulletin of the American Mathematical Society*, **26**, 315-316.

KALL, P., and S. W. WALLACE. 1994. *Stochastic Programming*, Wiley, New York, NY.

KARMARKAR, N. 1984. A new polynomial-time algorithm for linear programming, *Combinatorica*, **4**, 373-395.

KARP, R. M. 1972. Reducibility among combinatorial problems, in *Complexity of Computer Computations*, R. E. Miller and J. W. Thacher (eds.), Plenum Press, New York, NY, 85-103.

KARP, R. M. 1978. A characterization of the minimum cycle mean in a digraph, *Discrete Mathematics*, **23**, 309-311.

KARP, R. M., and C. H. PAPADIMITRIOU. 1982. On linear characterizations of combinatorial optimization problems, *SIAM Journal on Computing*, **11**, 620-632.

KHACHIAN, L. G. 1979. A polynomial algorithm in linear programming, *Soviet Mathematics Doklady*, **20**, 191-194.

KIRKPATRICK, S., C. D. GELATT, JR., and M. P. VECCHI. 1983. Optimization by simulated annealing, *Science*, **220**, 671-680.

KLEE, V., and G. J. MINTY. 1972. How good is the simplex algorithm?, in *Inequalities – III*, O. Shisha (ed.), Academic Press, New York, NY, 159-175.

KLEE, V., and D. W. WALKUP. 1967. The d-step conjecture for polyhedra of dimension $d < 6$, *Acta Mathematica*, **117**, 53-78.

KLEIN, M. 1967. A primal method for minimal cost flows with application to the assignment and transportation problems, *Management Science*, **14**, 205-220.

KOJIMA, M., S. MIZUNO, and A. YOSHISE. 1989. A primal-dual interior point algorithm for linear programming, in *Progress in Mathematical Programming*, N. Megiddo (ed.), Springer-Verlag, New York, NY, 29-47.

KUHN, H. W. 1955. The Hungarian method for the assignment problem, *Naval Research Logistics Quarterly*, **2**, 83-97.

LAWLER, E. L. 1976. *Combinatorial Optimization: Networks and Matroids,* Holt, Rinehart, and Winston, New York, NY.

LAWLER, E. L., J. K. LENSTRA, A. H. G. RINNOOY KAN, and D. B. SHMOYS (eds.). 1985. *The Traveling Salesman Problem: a Guided Tour of Combinatorial Optimization*, Wiley, New York, NY.

LENSTRA, J. K., A. H. G. RINNOOY KAN, and A. SCHRIJVER (eds.). 1991. *History of Mathematical Programming: A Collection of Personal Reminiscences,* Elsevier, Amsterdam, The Netherlands.

LEVIN, A. Y. 1965. On an algorithm for the minimization of convex functions, *Soviet Mathematics Doklady*, **6**, 286-290.

LEVIN, L. A. 1973. Universal sorting problems, *Problemy Peredachi Informatsii*, **9**, 265-266. (In Russian.)

LEWIS, H. R., and C. H. PAPADIMITRIOU. 1981. *Elements of the Theory of Computation*, Prentice Hall, Englewood Cliffs, NJ.

LUENBERGER, D. G. 1969. *Optimization by Vector Space Methods*, Wiley, New York, NY.

LUENBERGER, D. G. 1984. *Linear and Nonlinear Programming,* 2nd ed., Addison-Wesley, Reading, MA.

LUSTIG, I., R. E. MARSTEN, and D. SHANNO. 1994. Interior point methods: computational state of the art, *ORSA Journal on Computing*, **6**, 1-14.

MAGNANTI, T. L., and L. A. WOLSEY. 1995. Optimal Trees, in *Handbook of Operations Research and Management Science, Volume 6, Network Models*, M. O. Ball, C. L. Monma, T. L. Magnanti and G. L. Nemhauser (eds.), North Holland, Amsterdam, The Netherlands, 503-615.

MARSHALL, K. T., and J. W. SUURBALLE. 1969. A note on cycling in the simplex method, *Naval Research Logistics Quarterly*, **16**, 121-137.

MARTIN, P., and D. B. SHMOYS. 1996. A new approach to computing optimal schedules for the job-shop scheduling problem, in *Proceedings of the 5th International Conference in Integer Programming and Combinatorial Optimization*, 389-403.

MCSHANE, K. A., C. L. MONMA, and D. SHANNO. 1991. An implementation of a primal-dual interior point method for linear programming, *ORSA Journal on Computing*, **1**, 70-83.

MEGIDDO, N. 1989. Pathways to the optimal set in linear programming, in *Progress in Mathematical Programming*, N. Megiddo (ed.), Springer-Verlag, New York, NY, 131-158.

MEGIDDO, N., and SHUB, M. 1989. Boundary behavior of interior point algorithms in linear programming, *Mathematics of Operations Research*, **14**, 97-146.

MINKOWSKI, H. 1896. *Geometrie der Zahlen*, Teubner, Leipzig, Germany.

MIZUNO, S. 1996. Infeasible interior point algorithms, in *Interior Point Algorithms in Mathematical Programming*, T. Terlaky (ed.), Kluwer Academic Publishers, Boston, MA.

MONTEIRO, R. D. C., and I. ADLER. 1989a. Interior path following primal-dual algorithms; part I: linear programming, *Mathematical Programming*, **44**, 27-41.

MONTEIRO, R. D. C., and I. ADLER. 1989b. Interior path following primal-dual algorithms; part II: convex quadratic programming, *Mathematical Programming*, **44**, 43-66.

MOTZKIN, T. S. 1936. *Beiträge zur Theorie der linearen Ungleichungen* (Inaugural Dissertation Basel), Azriel, Jerusalem.

MURTY, K. G. 1983. *Linear Programming*, Wiley, New York, NY.

NEMHAUSER, G. L., and L. A. WOLSEY. 1988. *Integer and Combinatorial Optimization*, Wiley, New York, NY.

NESTEROV, Y., and A. NEMIROVSKII. 1994. *Interior point polynomial algorithms for convex programming*, SIAM, Studies in Applied Mathematics, **13**, Philadelphia, PA.

VON NEUMANN, J. 1947. Discussion of a maximum problem, unpublished working paper, Institute for Advanced Studies, Princeton, NJ.

VON NEUMANN, J. 1953. A certain zero-sum two-person game equivalent to the optimal assignment problem, in *Contributions to the Theory of Games, II*, H. W. Kuhn and A. W. Tucker (eds.), *Annals of Mathematics Studies*, **28**, Princeton University Press, Princeton, NJ, 5-12.

ORDEN, A. 1993. LP from the '40s to the '90s, *Interfaces*, **23**, 2-12.

ORLIN, J. B. 1984. Genuinely polynomial simplex and non-simplex algorithms for the minimum cost flow problem, technical report 1615-84, Sloan School of Management, M.I.T., Cambridge, MA.

PADBERG, M. W., and M. R. RAO. 1980. The Russian method and integer programming, working paper, New York University, New York, NY.

PAPADIMITRIOU, C. H. 1994. *Computational Complexity*, Addison-Wesley, Reading, MA.

PAPADIMITRIOU, C. H., and K. STEIGLITZ. 1982. *Combinatorial Optimization: Algorithms and Complexity*, Prentice Hall, Englewood Cliffs, NJ.

PLOTKIN, S., and É. Tardos. 1990. Improved dual network simplex, in *Proceedings of the First ACM-SIAM Symposium on Discrete Algorithms*, 367-376.

POLJAK, B. T. 1987. *Introduction to Optimization*, Optimization Software Inc., New York, NY.

PRIM, R. C. 1957. Shortest connection networks and some generalizations, *Bell System Technical Journal*, **36**, 1389-1401.

QUEYRANNE, M. 1993. Structure of a simple scheduling polyhedron, *Mathematical Programming*, **58**, 263-285.

RECSKI, A. 1989. *Matroid Theory and its Applications in Electric Network Theory and in Statics*, Springer-Verlag, New York, NY.

RENEGAR, J. 1988. A polynomial time algorithm based on Newton's method for linear programming, *Mathematical Programming*, **40**, 59-93.

ROCKAFELLAR, R. T. 1970. *Convex Analysis*, Princeton University Press, Princeton, NJ.

ROCKAFELLAR, R. T. 1984. *Network Flows and Monotropic Optimization,* Wiley, New York, NY.

ROSS, S. 1976. Risk, return, and arbitrage, in *Risk and Return in Finance*, I. Friend, and J. Bicksler (eds.), Cambridge, Ballinger, England.

ROSS, S. 1978. A simple approach to the valuation of risky streams, *Journal of Business*, **51**, 453-475.

RUDIN, W. 1976. *Real Analysis,* McGraw-Hill, New York, NY.

RUSHMEIER, R. A., and S. A. KONTOGIORGIS. 1997. Advances in the optimization of airline fleet assignment, *Transportation Science*, to appear.

SCHRIJVER, A. 1986. *Theory of Linear and Integer Programming*, Wiley, New York, NY.

SCHULTZ, A. S. 1996. Scheduling to minimize total weighted completion time: performance guarantees of LP-based heuristics and lower bounds, in *Proceedings of the 5th International Conference in Integer Programming and Combinatorial Optimization*, 301-315.

SHOR, N. Z. 1970. Utilization of the operation of space dilation in the minimization of convex functions, *Cybernetics*, **6**, 7-15.

SMALE, S. 1983. On the average number of steps in the simplex method of linear programming, *Mathematical Programming,* **27**, 241-262.

SMITH, W. E. 1956. Various optimizers for single-stage production, *Naval Research Logistics Quarterly*, **3**, 59-66.

STIGLER, G. 1945. The cost of subsistence, *Journal of Farm Economics*, **27**, 303-314.

STOCK, S. 1996. Allocation of NSF graduate fellowships, report, Sloan School of Management, M.I.T., Cambridge, MA.

STONE, R. E., and C. A. TOVEY. 1991. The simplex and projective scaling algorithms as iteratively reweighted least squares, *SIAM Review*, **33**, 220-237.

STRANG, G. 1988. *Linear Algebra and its Applications*, 3rd ed., Academic Press, New York, NY.

TARDOS, É. 1985. A strongly polynomial minimum cost circulation algorithm, *Combinatorica,* **5**, 247-255.

TEO, C. 1996. Constructing approximation algorithms via linear programming relaxations: primal dual and randomized rounding techniques, Ph.D. thesis, Operations Research Center, M.I.T., Cambridge, MA.

TSENG, P. 1989. A simple complexity proof for a polynomial-time linear programming algorithm, *Operations Research Letters*, **8**, 155-159.

TSENG, P., and Z.-Q. LUO. 1992. On the convergence of the affine scaling algorithm, *Mathematical Programming*, **56**, 301-319.

TSUCHIYA, T. 1991. Global convergence of the affine scaling methods for degenerate linear programming problems, *Mathematical Programming*, **52**, 377-404.

TSUCHIYA, T., and M. MURAMATSU. 1995. Global convergence of a long-step affine scaling algorithm for degenerate linear programming problems, *SIAM Journal on Optimization*, **5**, 525-551.

TUCKER, A. W. 1956. Dual systems of homogeneous linear relations, in *Linear Inequalities and Related Systems*, H. W. Kuhn and A. W. Tucker (eds.), Princeton University Press, Princeton, NJ, 3-18.

VANDERBEI, R. J., M. S. MEKETON, and B. A. FREEDMAN. 1986. A modification of Karmarkar's linear programming algorithm, *Algorithmica*, **1**, 395-407.

VANDERBEI, R. J., J. C. LAGARIAS. 1990. I. I. Dikin's convergence result for the affine-scaling algorithm, in *Mathematical Developments Arising from Linear Programming*, J. C. Lagarias and M. J. Todd (eds.), American Mathematical Society, Providence, RI, *Contemporary Mathematics*, **114**, 109-119.

VRANAS, P. 1996. Optimal slot allocation for European air traffic flow management, working paper, German aerospace research establishment, Berlin, Germany.

WAGNER, H. M. 1959. On a class of capacitated transportation problems, *Management Science,* **5**, 304-318.

WARSHALL, S. 1962. A theorem on boolean matrices, *Journal of the ACM*, **23**, 11-12.

WEBER, R. 1995. Personal communication.

WEINTRAUB, A. 1974. A primal algorithm to solve network flow problems with convex costs, *Management Science*, **21**, 87-97.

WILLIAMS, H. P. 1990. *Model Building in Mathematical Programming*, Wiley, New York, NY.

WILLIAMSON, D. 1994. On the design of approximation algorithms for a class of graph problems, Ph.D. thesis, Department of EECS, M.I.T., Cambridge, MA.

YE, Y. 1991. An $O(n^3L)$ potential reduction algorithm for linear programming, *Mathematical Programming*, **50**, 239-258.

YE, Y., M. J. TODD, and S. MIZUNO. 1994. An $O(\sqrt{n}L)$-iteration homogeneous and self-dual linear programming algorithm, *Mathematics of Operations Research*, **19**, 53-67.

YUDIN, D. B., and A. NEMIROVSKII. 1977. Informational complexity and efficient methods for the solution of convex extremal problems, *Matekon*, **13**, 25-45.

ZHANG, Y., and R. A. TAPIA. 1993. A superlinearly convergent polynomial primal-dual interior point algorithm for linear programming, *SIAM Journal on Optimization*, **3**, 118-133.

Index